Astronomy and Astrophysics Olympiad

Volume 3: Problems and Solutions

Astronomy and Astrophysics Olympiad

Volume 3: Problems and Solutions

Mihail Sandu

Romanian Physics Olympiad Committee, Romania

World Scientific

NEW JERSEY • LONDON • SINGAPORE • BEIJING • SHANGHAI • HONG KONG • TAIPEI • CHENNAI • TOKYO

Published by

World Scientific Publishing Europe Ltd.
57 Shelton Street, Covent Garden, London WC2H 9HE
Head office: 5 Toh Tuck Link, Singapore 596224
USA office: 27 Warren Street, Suite 401-402, Hackensack, NJ 07601

British Library Cataloguing-in-Publication Data
A catalogue record for this book is available from the British Library.

Cover image credit: NASA

Translation from Romanian by Daniela Berciu

ASTRONOMY AND ASTROPHYSICS OLYMPIAD
Volume 3: Problems and Solutions

ISBN 978-1-80061-710-0 (hardcover)
ISBN 978-1-80061-696-7 (paperback)
ISBN 978-1-80061-697-4 (ebook for institutions)
ISBN 978-1-80061-698-1 (ebook for individuals)

For any available supplementary material, please visit
https://www.worldscientific.com/worldscibooks/10.1142/Q0500#t=suppl

Desk Editors: Kannan Krishnan/Gabriel Rawlinson/Shi Ying Koe

Typeset by Stallion Press
Email: enquiries@stallionpress.com

Foreword

Astronomy and Astrophysics are among the oldest sciences, yet they continue to undergo rapid development. Over time, the focus has shifted from simple observations of celestial motions to detailed investigations of galaxies, black holes and the cosmic microwave background. Today, progress in these fields is shaped by powerful telescopes, large-scale surveys, and theoretical models that push the limits of our current knowledge.

Such progress depends not only on professional research but also on the cultivation of new generations of scientists. Competitions like the Astronomy Olympiad and the Astronomy and Astrophysics Olympiad play an important role in this process. By challenging high school students to engage with advanced concepts and problem-solving techniques, these events help develop the critical skills and curiosity essential for a career in science.

Despite their educational value, there remains a lack of comprehensive resources tailored specifically to these Olympiads. The present collection of three volumes, containing original problems crafted by Professor Mihail Sandu, addresses this need in an outstanding manner, offering students and teachers alike a wide range of tools critically needed for preparing for such competitions.

Professor Sandu is a highly respected educator with decades of experience at both high school and university levels. His contributions to academic competitions are remarkable. Among other achievements, he prepared all theory problems for the 2014 International Olympiad on Astronomy and Astrophysics, as well as all practical test problems for the 2019 International Astronomy Olympiad, both held in Romania. More recently, he played a key role in the first Junior International Olympiad on Astronomy and Astrophysics in 2022. He has published nearly 100 books in Romanian and English, including textbooks and problem collections in Physics and Astronomy that have guided generations of students.

I have had the privilege of knowing Professor Sandu personally. His dedication, clarity of thought, and genuine enthusiasm for teaching are evident both in his presence at competitions and in his writing. Over more than five decades, he has supported and inspired countless students, exemplifying a rare commitment to education and mentorship. I am confident that the present collection will prove to be an invaluable resource for students preparing for Olympiads, and that it will continue to inspire future generations of astronomers and astrophysicists.

Andrei Constantin
Royal Society Dorothy Hodgkin Fellow,
Department of Physics, University of Oxford,
and Physics & Mathematics Tutor
at Mansfield College Oxford

Contents

Problem 1

A Spaceship to Alpha Centauri

A space shuttle leaves Earth in a straight line with uniform motion toward the α Centauri star with the velocity $\vec{u}$ relative to the Earth, as shown in the drawing in Figure 1.1. The α Centauri star is considered to be at rest relative to the Earth. Immediately after the launch of the space shuttle, a cosmic rocket takes off from onboard the shuttle towards the α Centauri star.

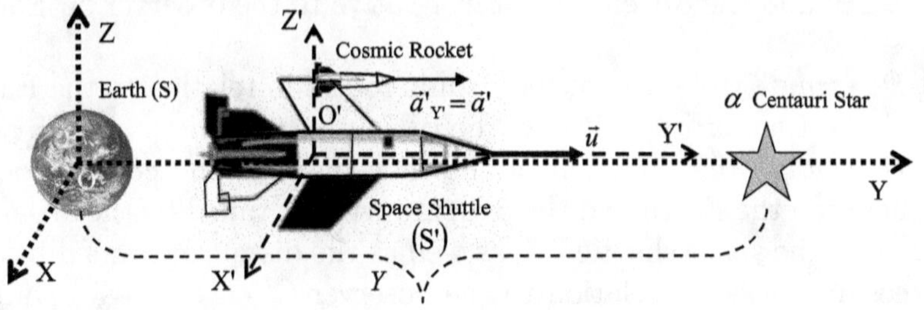

Fig. 1.1

The propulsion force of the cosmic rocket sends it toward the α Centauri star at a constant acceleration, $\vec{a}'_{Y'} = \vec{a}'$, relative to the space shuttle's inertial system, S$'$.

At the time of the launch of the space shuttle, when the origins, O and O$'$, of the two inertial reference systems, S and S$'$, associated with the Earth and the space shuttle, respectively, coincide, the clocks in the two reference systems have been synchronized so that $t = t' = 0$.

The cosmic rocket takes off from the space shuttle from the point corresponding to the origin of the inertial system associated with the space shuttle. The speed of light in a vacuum is c.

a) *Establish* the relationship between the acceleration of the cosmic rocket in relation to the Earth, $a_Y = a$, and the speed of the cosmic rocket in relation to the Earth, $\mathrm{v}_Y = \mathrm{v}$.

b) *Establish* the speed law of the cosmic rocket in relation to the Earth, $\mathrm{v}_Y(t) = \mathrm{v}(t)$.

c) *Establish* the law of acceleration of the cosmic rocket in relation to the Earth, $a_Y(t) = a(t)$.

d) *Establish* the law of the position coordinate of the cosmic rocket in relation to the Earth, $y(t)$. *It is known that:*

$$\int \frac{A + B \cdot x}{C + D \cdot x} \cdot \mathrm{d}x = \frac{1}{D}\left(B \cdot x + \frac{\Delta}{D} \cdot \ln|C + D \cdot x|\right);$$

$$\Delta = AD - BC.$$

e) *Determine* the distance between the Earth and the α Centauri star, Y, if the duration of the cosmic rocket's travel between the Earth and the α Centauri Star, relative to the observer on Earth, is T.

f) *Determine* the speed of the cosmic rocket in relation to the Earth at the time of its arrival at the α Centauri star.

g) *Determine* the duration of the movement of the cosmic rocket between the Earth and the α Centauri star, timed by the observer O′ on the space shuttle, T', as well as the distance traveled by the cosmic rocket in relation to the observer O′ on the space shuttle from the moment the rocket took off from the space shuttle until its arrival at the α Centauri star, Y'.

h) *Particularize* the results from parts **b, c**, and **d** for the case $u \ll c$, knowing that:

$$\ln(1 + x) \approx x - \frac{1}{2}x^2, \quad \text{if } x \ll 1.$$

Solution

a) According to the notation in Figure 1.2, which corresponds to a certain moment in the evolution of the cosmic rocket framed by the

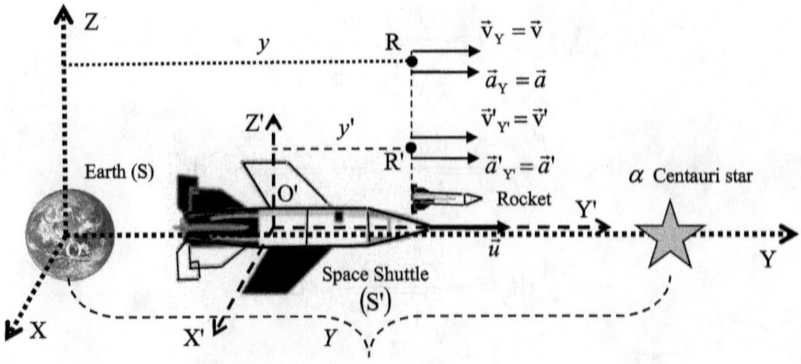

Fig. 1.2

two inertial reference systems, it follows that:

$$\mathrm{R}'(0, y', 0; t'); \quad \mathrm{R}(0, y, 0; t);$$

$$y = \frac{y' + ut'}{\sqrt{1 - \frac{u^2}{c^2}}} > y'; \quad t = \frac{t' + \frac{uy'}{c^2}}{\sqrt{1 - \frac{u^2}{c^2}}} > t';$$

$$\mathrm{v_Y} = \frac{\mathrm{d}y}{\mathrm{d}t} = \frac{\frac{\mathrm{d}y' + u \cdot \mathrm{d}t'}{\sqrt{1-\frac{u^2}{c^2}}}}{\frac{\mathrm{d}t' + \frac{u}{c^2}\mathrm{d}y'}{\sqrt{1-\frac{u^2}{c^2}}}} = \frac{\mathrm{d}y' + u \cdot \mathrm{d}t'}{\mathrm{d}t' + \frac{u}{c^2}\mathrm{d}y'} = \frac{\left(\frac{\mathrm{d}y'}{\mathrm{d}t'} + u\right) \cdot \mathrm{d}t'}{\left(1 + \frac{u}{c^2} \cdot \frac{\mathrm{d}y'}{\mathrm{d}t'}\right) \cdot \mathrm{d}t'};$$

$$\mathrm{v_Y} = \frac{\left(\frac{\mathrm{d}y'}{\mathrm{d}t'} + u\right)}{\left(1 + \frac{u}{c^2} \cdot \frac{\mathrm{d}y'}{\mathrm{d}t'}\right)}; \quad \mathrm{v_Y} = \frac{\mathrm{v}'_{\mathrm{Y}'} + u}{\left(1 + \frac{u}{c^2} \cdot \mathrm{v}'_{\mathrm{Y}'}\right)};$$

$$\mathrm{dv_Y} = \frac{\mathrm{d}\left(\mathrm{v}'_{\mathrm{Y}'} + u\right) \cdot \left(1 + \frac{u}{c^2} \cdot \mathrm{v}'_{\mathrm{Y}'}\right) - \left(\mathrm{v}'_{\mathrm{Y}'} + u\right) \cdot \mathrm{d}\left(1 + \frac{u}{c^2} \cdot \mathrm{v}'_{\mathrm{Y}'}\right)}{\left(1 + \frac{u}{c^2} \cdot \mathrm{v}'_{\mathrm{Y}'}\right)^2};$$

$$\mathrm{dv_Y} = \frac{\mathrm{dv}'_{\mathrm{Y}'} \cdot \left(1 + \frac{u}{c^2} \cdot \mathrm{v}'_{\mathrm{Y}'}\right) - \left(\mathrm{v}'_{\mathrm{Y}'} + u\right) \cdot \frac{u}{c^2}\mathrm{dv}'_{\mathrm{Y}'}}{\left(1 + \frac{u}{c^2} \cdot \mathrm{v}'_{\mathrm{Y}'}\right)^2};$$

$$\mathrm{dv_Y} = \frac{1 - \frac{u^2}{c^2}}{\left(1 + \frac{u}{c^2} \cdot \mathrm{v}'_{\mathrm{Y}'}\right)^2} \cdot \mathrm{dv}'_{\mathrm{Y}'};$$

$$t = \frac{t' + \frac{uy'}{c^2}}{\sqrt{1 - \frac{u^2}{c^2}}};$$

$$\mathrm{d}t = \frac{\mathrm{d}t' + \frac{u}{c^2} \cdot \mathrm{d}y'}{\sqrt{1 - \frac{u^2}{c^2}}} = \frac{1 + \frac{u}{c^2} \cdot \frac{\mathrm{d}y'}{\mathrm{d}t'}}{\sqrt{1 - \frac{u^2}{c^2}}} \cdot \mathrm{d}t';$$

$$\mathrm{d}t = \frac{1 + \frac{u}{c^2} \cdot \mathrm{v}'_{\mathrm{Y}'}}{\sqrt{1 - \frac{u^2}{c^2}}} \cdot \mathrm{d}t';$$

$$a_{\mathrm{Y}} = \frac{\mathrm{d}\mathrm{v}_{\mathrm{Y}}}{\mathrm{d}t}; \quad a'_{\mathrm{Y}'} = \frac{\mathrm{d}\mathrm{v}'_{\mathrm{Y}'}}{\mathrm{d}t'};$$

$$a_{\mathrm{Y}} = \frac{\frac{1-\frac{u^2}{c^2}}{\left(1+\frac{u}{c^2}\cdot \mathrm{v}'_{\mathrm{Y}'}\right)^2} \cdot \mathrm{d}\mathrm{v}'_{\mathrm{Y}'}}{\frac{1+\frac{u}{c^2}\cdot \mathrm{v}'_{\mathrm{Y}'}}{\sqrt{1-\frac{u^2}{c^2}}} \cdot \mathrm{d}t'} = \frac{\frac{1-\frac{u^2}{c^2}}{\left(1+\frac{u}{c^2}\cdot \mathrm{v}'_{\mathrm{Y}'}\right)^2}}{\frac{1+\frac{u}{c^2}\cdot \mathrm{v}'_{\mathrm{Y}'}}{\sqrt{1-\frac{u^2}{c^2}}}} \cdot \frac{\mathrm{d}\mathrm{v}'_{\mathrm{Y}'}}{\mathrm{d}t'};$$

$$a_{\mathrm{Y}} = a'_{\mathrm{Y}'} \cdot \frac{\left(1 - \frac{u^2}{c^2}\right)^{3/2}}{\left(1 + \frac{u}{c^2} \cdot \mathrm{v}'_{\mathrm{Y}'}\right)^3}; \quad \mathrm{v}_{\mathrm{Y}} = \frac{\mathrm{v}'_{\mathrm{Y}'} + u}{\left(1 + \frac{u}{c^2} \cdot \mathrm{v}'_{\mathrm{Y}'}\right)};$$

$$\mathrm{v}'_{\mathrm{Y}'} = \frac{\mathrm{v}_{\mathrm{Y}} - u}{\left(1 - \frac{u}{c^2} \cdot \mathrm{v}_{\mathrm{Y}}\right)};$$

$$a_{\mathrm{Y}} = a'_{\mathrm{Y}'} \cdot \frac{\left(1 - \frac{u^2}{c^2}\right)^{3/2}}{\left(1 + \frac{u}{c^2} \cdot \frac{\mathrm{v}_{\mathrm{Y}}-u}{1-\frac{u}{c^2}\cdot \mathrm{v}_{\mathrm{Y}}}\right)^3};$$

$$a_{\mathrm{Y}} = a'_{\mathrm{Y}'} \cdot \frac{\left(1 - \frac{u^2}{c^2}\right)^{3/2}}{\left(1 + \frac{u}{c^2} \cdot \frac{\mathrm{v}_{\mathrm{Y}}-u}{c^2-u\mathrm{v}_{\mathrm{Y}}} \cdot c^2\right)^3}; \quad a_{\mathrm{Y}} = a'_{\mathrm{Y}'} \cdot \frac{\left(1 - \frac{u^2}{c^2}\right)^{3/2}}{\left(1 + \frac{u\mathrm{v}_{\mathrm{Y}}-u^2}{c^2-u\mathrm{v}_{\mathrm{Y}}}\right)^3};$$

$$a_{\mathrm{Y}} = a'_{\mathrm{Y}'} \cdot \frac{\left(1 - \frac{u^2}{c^2}\right)^{3/2}}{\left(\frac{c^2-u\mathrm{v}_{\mathrm{Y}}+u\mathrm{v}_{\mathrm{Y}}-u^2}{c^2-u\mathrm{v}_{\mathrm{Y}}}\right)^3};$$

$$a_Y = a'_{Y'} \cdot \frac{\left(1 - \frac{u^2}{c^2}\right)^{3/2}}{\left(\frac{c^2 - u^2}{c^2 - u\mathrm{v}_Y}\right)^3}; \quad a_Y = a'_{Y'} \cdot \frac{\left(1 - \frac{u^2}{c^2}\right)^{3/2}}{\left(\frac{1 - \frac{u^2}{c^2}}{1 - \frac{u\mathrm{v}_Y}{c^2}}\right)^3};$$

$$a_Y = a'_{Y'} \cdot \frac{\left(1 - \frac{u\mathrm{v}_Y}{c^2}\right)^3}{\left(1 - \frac{u^2}{c^2}\right)^{3/2}};$$

$$a'_{Y'} = a'; \quad a_Y = a; \quad \mathrm{v}_Y = v; \quad a = a' \cdot \frac{\left(1 - \frac{uv}{c^2}\right)^3}{\left(1 - \frac{u^2}{c^2}\right)^{3/2}}.$$

b)

$$\mathrm{v}_Y = \frac{u + \mathrm{v}'_{Y'}}{1 + \frac{u}{c^2} \cdot \mathrm{v}'_{Y'}};$$

$$\mathrm{v}'_{Y'} = a'_{Y'} \cdot t';$$

$$\mathrm{v}_Y = \frac{u + a'_{Y'} t'}{1 + \frac{u}{c^2} \cdot a'_{Y'} t'};$$

$$t = \frac{t' + \frac{uy'}{c^2}}{\sqrt{1 - \frac{u^2}{c^2}}} > t'; \quad t' = \frac{t - \frac{uy}{c^2}}{\sqrt{1 - \frac{u^2}{c^2}}} < t; y = ut;$$

$$t' = \frac{t - \frac{u}{c^2} ut}{\sqrt{1 - \frac{u^2}{c^2}}} = \frac{t\left(1 - \frac{u^2}{c^2}\right)}{\sqrt{1 - \frac{u^2}{c^2}}};$$

$$t' = t \cdot \sqrt{1 - \frac{u^2}{c^2}};$$

$$\mathrm{v}_Y = \frac{u + a'_{Y'} t'}{1 + \frac{u}{c^2} \cdot a'_{Y'} t'};$$

$$\mathrm{v}_Y = \frac{u + a'_{Y'} \cdot \sqrt{1 - \frac{u^2}{c^2}} \cdot t}{1 + \frac{u}{c^2} \cdot a'_{Y'} \cdot \sqrt{1 - \frac{u^2}{c^2}} \cdot t} = \mathrm{v}_Y(t); \quad a'_{Y'} = a'; \mathrm{v}_Y = \mathrm{v};$$

$$\mathrm{v}_Y = \frac{u + a'_{Y'} \cdot \sqrt{1 - \frac{u^2}{c^2}} \cdot t}{1 + \frac{u}{c^2} \cdot a'_{Y'} \cdot \sqrt{1 - \frac{u^2}{c^2}} \cdot t} = \mathrm{v}_Y(t).$$

c) From the previous equations:

$$a_{\mathrm{Y}} = a'_{\mathrm{Y}'} \cdot \frac{\left(1 - \frac{u\mathrm{v}_{\mathrm{Y}}}{c^2}\right)^3}{\left(1 - \frac{u^2}{c^2}\right)^{3/2}}; \quad a_{\mathrm{Y}} = a'_{\mathrm{Y}'} \cdot \frac{\left(1 - \frac{u^2}{c^2}\right)^{3/2}}{\left(1 + \frac{u}{c^2} \cdot \frac{\mathrm{v}_{\mathrm{Y}} - u}{1 - \frac{u}{c^2} \cdot \mathrm{v}_{\mathrm{Y}}}\right)^3},$$

$$\mathrm{v}_{\mathrm{Y}} = \frac{u + a'_{\mathrm{Y}'} \cdot \sqrt{1 - \frac{u^2}{c^2}} \cdot t}{1 + \frac{u}{c^2} \cdot a'_{\mathrm{Y}'} \cdot \sqrt{1 - \frac{u^2}{c^2}} \cdot t} = \mathrm{v}_{\mathrm{Y}}(t).$$

This results in:

$$\frac{\mathrm{v}_{\mathrm{Y}} - u}{1 - \frac{u}{c^2} \cdot \mathrm{v}_{\mathrm{Y}}} = \frac{\frac{u + a'_{\mathrm{Y}'} \cdot \sqrt{1 - \frac{u^2}{c^2}} \cdot t}{1 + \frac{u}{c^2} \cdot a'_{\mathrm{Y}'} \cdot \sqrt{1 - \frac{u^2}{c^2}} \cdot t} - u}{1 - \frac{u}{c^2} \cdot \frac{u + a'_{\mathrm{Y}'} \cdot \sqrt{1 - \frac{u^2}{c^2}} \cdot t}{1 + \frac{u}{c^2} \cdot a'_{\mathrm{Y}'} \cdot \sqrt{1 - \frac{u^2}{c^2}} \cdot t}};$$

$$\frac{\mathrm{v}_{\mathrm{Y}} - u}{1 - \frac{u}{c^2} \cdot \mathrm{v}_{\mathrm{Y}}} = \frac{\frac{u + a'_{\mathrm{Y}'} \cdot \sqrt{1 - \frac{u^2}{c^2}} \cdot t - u - \frac{u^2}{c^2} \cdot a'_{\mathrm{Y}'} \cdot \sqrt{1 - \frac{u^2}{c^2}} \cdot t}{1 + \frac{u}{c^2} \cdot a'_{\mathrm{Y}'} \cdot \sqrt{1 - \frac{u^2}{c^2}} \cdot t}}{\frac{1 + \frac{u}{c^2} \cdot a'_{\mathrm{Y}'} \cdot \sqrt{1 - \frac{u^2}{c^2}} \cdot t - \frac{u}{c^2}\left(u + a'_{\mathrm{Y}'} \cdot \sqrt{1 - \frac{u^2}{c^2}} \cdot t\right)}{1 + \frac{u}{c^2} \cdot a'_{\mathrm{Y}'} \cdot \sqrt{1 - \frac{u^2}{c^2}} \cdot t}};$$

$$\frac{\mathrm{v}_{\mathrm{Y}} - u}{1 - \frac{u}{c^2} \cdot \mathrm{v}_{\mathrm{Y}}} = \frac{\frac{u + a'_{\mathrm{Y}'} \cdot \sqrt{1 - \frac{u^2}{c^2}} \cdot t - u - \frac{u^2}{c^2} \cdot a'_{\mathrm{Y}'} \cdot \sqrt{1 - \frac{u^2}{c^2}} \cdot t}{1}}{\frac{1 + \frac{u}{c^2} \cdot a'_{\mathrm{Y}'} \cdot \sqrt{1 - \frac{u^2}{c^2}} \cdot t - \frac{u}{c^2}\left(u + a'_{\mathrm{Y}'} \cdot \sqrt{1 - \frac{u^2}{c^2}} \cdot t\right)}{1}};$$

$$\frac{\mathrm{v}_{\mathrm{Y}} - u}{1 - \frac{u}{c^2} \cdot \mathrm{v}_{\mathrm{Y}}} = \frac{\frac{a'_{\mathrm{Y}'} \cdot \sqrt{1 - \frac{u^2}{c^2}} \cdot t \cdot \left(1 - \frac{u^2}{c^2}\right)}{1}}{\frac{1 - \frac{u^2}{c^2} + \frac{u}{c^2} \cdot a'_{\mathrm{Y}'} \cdot \sqrt{1 - \frac{u^2}{c^2}} \cdot t - \frac{u}{c^2}\left(a'_{\mathrm{Y}'} \cdot \sqrt{1 - \frac{u^2}{c^2}} \cdot t\right)}{1}};$$

$$\frac{\mathrm{v}_{\mathrm{Y}} - u}{1 - \frac{u}{c^2} \cdot \mathrm{v}_{\mathrm{Y}}} = \frac{\frac{a'_{\mathrm{Y}'} \cdot \sqrt{1 - \frac{u^2}{c^2}} \cdot t \cdot \left(1 - \frac{u^2}{c^2}\right)}{1}}{\frac{1 - \frac{u^2}{c^2}}{1}};$$

$$\frac{\mathrm{v}_{\mathrm{Y}} - u}{1 - \frac{u}{c^2} \cdot \mathrm{v}_{\mathrm{Y}}} = \frac{\frac{a'_{\mathrm{Y}'} \cdot \sqrt{1 - \frac{u^2}{c^2}} \cdot t}{1}}{1};$$

$$\frac{\mathrm{v}_{\mathrm{Y}} - u}{1 - \frac{u}{c^2} \cdot \mathrm{v}_{\mathrm{Y}}} = a'_{\mathrm{Y}'} \cdot \sqrt{1 - \frac{u^2}{c^2}} \cdot t;$$

$$a_{\mathrm{Y}} = a'_{\mathrm{Y}'} \cdot \frac{\left(1 - \frac{u^2}{c^2}\right)^{3/2}}{\left(1 + \frac{u}{c^2} \cdot \frac{\mathrm{v}_{\mathrm{Y}} - u}{1 - \frac{u}{c^2} \cdot \mathrm{v}_{\mathrm{Y}}}\right)^3};$$

$$a_{\mathrm{Y}} = a'_{\mathrm{Y}'} \cdot \frac{\left(1 - \frac{u^2}{c^2}\right)^{3/2}}{\left(1 + \frac{u}{c^2} \cdot a'_{\mathrm{Y}'} \cdot \sqrt{1 - \frac{u^2}{c^2}} \cdot t\right)^3} = a_{\mathrm{Y}}(t).$$

d) We know that:

$$\mathrm{v}_{\mathrm{Y}} = \frac{u + a'_{\mathrm{Y}'} \cdot \sqrt{1 - \frac{u^2}{c^2}} \cdot t}{1 + \frac{u}{c^2} \cdot a'_{\mathrm{Y}'} \cdot \sqrt{1 - \frac{u^2}{c^2}} \cdot t} = \mathrm{v}_{\mathrm{Y}}(t);$$

$$\mathrm{v}_{\mathrm{Y}} = \frac{\mathrm{d}y}{\mathrm{d}t}.$$

This results in:

$$y = \int \mathrm{v}_{\mathrm{Y}} \mathrm{d}t = \int \frac{u + a'_{\mathrm{Y}'} \cdot \sqrt{1 - \frac{u^2}{c^2}} \cdot t}{1 + \frac{u}{c^2} \cdot a'_{\mathrm{Y}'} \cdot \sqrt{1 - \frac{u^2}{c^2}} \cdot t} \cdot \mathrm{d}t;$$

$$\int \frac{A + B \cdot x}{C + D \cdot x} \cdot \mathrm{d}x = \frac{1}{D}\left(B \cdot x + \frac{\Delta}{D} \cdot \ln|C + D \cdot x|\right);$$

$$\Delta = AD - BC;$$

$$A = u; \quad B = a'_{\mathrm{Y}'} \cdot \sqrt{1 - \frac{u^2}{c^2}}; \quad C = 1;$$

$$D = \frac{u}{c^2} \cdot a'_{\mathrm{Y}'} \cdot \sqrt{1 - \frac{u^2}{c^2}}; \quad x = t;$$

$$\Delta = \frac{u^2}{c^2} \cdot a'_{\mathrm{Y}'} \cdot \sqrt{1 - \frac{u^2}{c^2}} - a'_{\mathrm{Y}'} \cdot \sqrt{1 - \frac{u^2}{c^2}}$$

$$= -a'_{\mathrm{Y}'} \cdot \sqrt{1 - \frac{u^2}{c^2}} \cdot \left(1 - \frac{u^2}{c^2}\right);$$

$$\Delta = -a'_{Y'} \cdot \left(1 - \frac{u^2}{c^2}\right)^{3/2};$$

$$y(t) = \frac{1}{\frac{u}{c^2} \cdot a'_{Y'} \cdot \sqrt{1 - \frac{u^2}{c^2}}} \left(a'_{Y'} \cdot \sqrt{1 - \frac{u^2}{c^2}} \cdot t - \frac{a'_{Y'} \cdot \left(1 - \frac{u^2}{c^2}\right)^{3/2}}{\frac{u}{c^2} \cdot a'_{Y'} \cdot \sqrt{1 - \frac{u^2}{c^2}}} \right.$$
$$\left. \cdot \ln\left|1 + \frac{u}{c^2} \cdot a'_{Y'} \cdot \sqrt{1 - \frac{u^2}{c^2}} \cdot t\right| \right);$$

$$y(t) = \frac{c^2}{u} \cdot \frac{1}{a'_{Y'} \cdot \sqrt{1 - \frac{u^2}{c^2}}} \left(a'_{Y'} \cdot \sqrt{1 - \frac{u^2}{c^2}} \cdot t - \frac{c^2}{u} \cdot \frac{\left(1 - \frac{u^2}{c^2}\right)^{3/2}}{\sqrt{1 - \frac{u^2}{c^2}}} \right.$$
$$\left. \cdot \ln\left|1 + \frac{u}{c^2} \cdot a'_{Y'} \cdot \sqrt{1 - \frac{u^2}{c^2}} \cdot t\right| \right);$$

$$y(t) = \frac{c^2}{u \cdot a'_{Y'}} \left(a'_{Y'} \cdot t - \frac{c^2 \cdot \sqrt{1 - \frac{u^2}{c^2}}}{u} \cdot \ln\left|1 + \frac{u}{c^2} \cdot a'_{Y'} \cdot \sqrt{1 - \frac{u^2}{c^2}} \cdot t\right| \right);$$

$$y(t) = \frac{c^2}{u} \left(t - \frac{c^2 \cdot \sqrt{1 - \frac{u^2}{c^2}}}{u \cdot a'_{Y'}} \cdot \ln\left|1 + \frac{u}{c^2} \cdot a'_{Y'} \cdot \sqrt{1 - \frac{u^2}{c^2}} \cdot t\right| \right).$$

e)
$$t = T; \quad y(t) = y(T) = Y;$$

$$y(t) = \frac{c^2}{u \cdot a'_{Y'}} \left(a'_{Y'} \cdot t - \frac{c^2 \cdot \sqrt{1 - \frac{u^2}{c^2}}}{u} \cdot \ln\left|1 + \frac{u}{c^2} \cdot a'_{Y'} \cdot t \cdot \sqrt{1 - \frac{u^2}{c^2}}\right| \right);$$

$$Y = \frac{c^2}{u \cdot a'_{Y'}} \left(a'_{Y'} \cdot T - \frac{c^2 \cdot \sqrt{1 - \frac{u^2}{c^2}}}{u} \cdot \ln\left|1 + \frac{u}{c^2} \cdot a'_{Y'} \cdot T \cdot \sqrt{1 - \frac{u^2}{c^2}}\right| \right).$$

f)

$$t = T; \quad \mathrm{v_Y}(t) = \mathrm{v_Y}(T) = \mathrm{v_{Y,max}};$$

$$\mathrm{v_Y} = \frac{u + a'_{Y'} \cdot \sqrt{1 - \frac{u^2}{c^2}} \cdot t}{1 + \frac{u}{c^2} \cdot a'_{Y'} \cdot \sqrt{1 - \frac{u^2}{c^2}} \cdot t} = \mathrm{v_Y}(t);$$

$$\mathrm{v_{Y,max}} = \frac{u + a'_{Y'} \cdot T \cdot \sqrt{1 - \frac{u^2}{c^2}}}{1 + \frac{u}{c^2} \cdot a'_{Y'} \cdot T \cdot \sqrt{1 - \frac{u^2}{c^2}}}.$$

g)

$$Y' = \frac{a'_{Y'} T'^2}{2}; \quad Y = \frac{Y' + uT'}{1 + \frac{u\mathrm{v}'_{Y',\mathrm{max}}}{c^2}}; \quad \mathrm{v}'_{Y',\mathrm{max}} = a'_{Y'} T';$$

$$Y = \frac{Y' + uT'}{1 + \frac{ua'_{Y'} T'}{c^2}}; \quad Y = \frac{\frac{a'_{Y'} T'^2}{2} + uT'}{1 + \frac{ua'_{Y'} T'}{c^2}};$$

$$\frac{a'_{Y'} T'^2}{2} + uT' = Y + Y \frac{ua'_{Y'} T'}{c^2};$$

$$a'_{Y'} T'^2 - 2u \left(\frac{Y a'_{Y'}}{c^2} - 1 \right) T' - 2Y = 0;$$

$$T' = \frac{u \left(\frac{Y a'_{Y'}}{c^2} - 1 \right) + \sqrt{u^2 \left(\frac{Y a'_{Y'}}{c^2} - 1 \right)^2 + 2Y a'_{Y'}}}{a'_{Y'}}; \quad Y' = \frac{a'_{Y'} T'^2}{2}.$$

h) If $u \ll c$, then:

Particularizing the results in part b), we have:

$$\mathrm{v_Y} = \frac{u + a'_{Y'} \cdot \sqrt{1 - \frac{u^2}{c^2}} \cdot t}{1 + \frac{u}{c^2} \cdot a'_{Y'} \cdot \sqrt{1 - \frac{u^2}{c^2}} \cdot t} = \mathrm{v_Y}(t);$$

$$u \ll c; \quad \mathrm{v_Y} = u + a'_{Y'} t = u + a_Y t = \mathrm{v_Y}(t);$$

Particularizing the results in part c), we have:

$$a_Y = a'_{Y'} \cdot \frac{\left(1 - \frac{u^2}{c^2}\right)^{3/2}}{\left(1 + \frac{u}{c^2} \cdot \frac{v_Y - u}{1 - \frac{u}{c^2} \cdot v_Y}\right)^3};$$

$$u \ll c; \quad a_Y = a'_{Y'}.$$

Particularizing the results in part d), we have:

$$y(t) = \frac{c^2}{u \cdot a'_{Y'}}\left(a'_{Y'} \cdot t - \frac{c^2 \cdot \sqrt{1 - \frac{u^2}{c^2}}}{u} \cdot \ln\left|1 + \frac{u}{c^2} \cdot a'_{Y'} \cdot \sqrt{1 - \frac{u^2}{c^2}} \cdot t\right|\right);$$

$$y(t) = \frac{c^2}{u} \cdot \left(t - \frac{c^2 \cdot \sqrt{1 - \frac{u^2}{c^2}}}{a'_{Y'} \cdot u} \cdot \ln\left|1 + \frac{u}{c^2} \cdot a'_{Y'} \cdot \sqrt{1 - \frac{u^2}{c^2}} \cdot t\right|\right);$$

$$x = \frac{u}{c^2} \cdot a'_{Y'} \cdot \sqrt{1 - \frac{u^2}{c^2}} \cdot t \ll 1;$$

$$\ln|1 + x| \approx x - \frac{1}{2}x^2;$$

$$y(t) = \frac{c^2}{u} \cdot \left(t - \frac{c^2 \cdot \sqrt{1 - \frac{u^2}{c^2}}}{a'_{Y'} \cdot u} \cdot \left(\frac{u}{c^2} \cdot a'_{Y'} \cdot \sqrt{1 - \frac{u^2}{c^2}} \cdot t \right.\right.$$
$$\left.\left. - \frac{1}{2}\left(\frac{u}{c^2} \cdot a'_{Y'} \cdot \sqrt{1 - \frac{u^2}{c^2}} \cdot t\right)^2\right)\right);$$

$$y(t) = \frac{c^2}{u} \cdot \left(t - \frac{c^2 \cdot \sqrt{1 - \frac{u^2}{c^2}}}{a'_{Y'} \cdot u} \cdot \left(\frac{u}{c^2} \cdot a'_{Y'} \cdot \sqrt{1 - \frac{u^2}{c^2}} \cdot t \right.\right.$$
$$\left.\left. - \frac{1}{2}\left(\frac{u^2}{c^4} \cdot (a'_{Y'})^2 \cdot \left(1 - \frac{u^2}{c^2}\right) \cdot t^2\right)\right)\right);$$

$$y(t) = \frac{c^2}{u} \cdot \left(t - \frac{c^2 \cdot \sqrt{1 - \frac{u^2}{c^2}}}{a'_{Y'} \cdot u} \cdot \left(\frac{u}{c^2} \cdot a'_{Y'} \cdot \sqrt{1 - \frac{u^2}{c^2}} \cdot t \right.\right.$$

$$\left.\left. - \frac{1}{2} \left(\frac{u^2}{c^4} \cdot (a'_{Y'})^2 \cdot \left(1 - \frac{u^2}{c^2}\right) \cdot t^2 \right)\right)\right);$$

$$y(t) = \frac{c^2}{u} \cdot \left(t - \sqrt{1 - \frac{u^2}{c^2}} \cdot \left(\sqrt{1 - \frac{u^2}{c^2}} \cdot t \right.\right.$$

$$\left.\left. - \frac{1}{2} \left(\frac{u}{c^2} \cdot (a'_{Y'}) \cdot \left(1 - \frac{u^2}{c^2}\right) \cdot t^2 \right)\right)\right);$$

$$y(t) = \frac{c^2}{u} \cdot \left(t - \left(\left(1 - \frac{u^2}{c^2}\right) \cdot t - \frac{1}{2} \left(\frac{u}{c^2} \cdot (a'_{Y'}) \cdot \left(1 - \frac{u^2}{c^2}\right)^{3/2} \cdot t^2 \right)\right)\right);$$

$$y(t) = \frac{c^2}{u} \cdot \left(t - t + \frac{u^2}{c^2} \cdot t + \frac{1}{2} \cdot \frac{u}{c^2} \cdot a'_{Y'} \cdot \left(1 - \frac{u^2}{c^2}\right) \cdot t^2 \right);$$

$$y(t) = \frac{c^2}{u} \cdot \left(\frac{u^2}{c^2} \cdot t + \frac{1}{2} \cdot \frac{u}{c^2} \cdot a'_{Y'} \cdot t^2 \right);$$

$$y(t) = \frac{c^2}{u} \cdot \frac{u^2}{c^2} \cdot t + \frac{1}{2} \cdot \frac{c^2}{u} \cdot \frac{u}{c^2} \cdot a'_{Y'} \cdot t^2;$$

$$y(t) = u \cdot t + \frac{1}{2} \cdot a'_{Y'} \cdot t^2; \quad a'_{Y'} = a'; \quad y = u \cdot t + \frac{1}{2} \cdot a' \cdot t^2.$$

Problem 2

Asteroid 2010GD37

Given its trajectory, the asteroid **2010GD37** was expected to be particularly threatening to Earth in December 2019.

As a precautionary measure, specialists planned to launch a projectile from an artificial satellite of Earth, aimed at either destroying the asteroid before it got very close to Earth or diverting the asteroid from the current trajectory to another trajectory that took it away from Earth.

Consider that the transfer of the projectile from the satellite to the asteroid occurs on a single ellipse. The drawing in Figure 2.1 shows, at scale, the points E (the center of the Earth and the focus F_1 of the transfer ellipse), S (the satellite at the launch of projectile P), and A (the asteroid at the time of impact with the projectile). *Given*: $r = 30010.88\,\text{km}$; $\Delta\theta = 46°$.

a) *Determine* the elements of the elliptical transfer orbit of the projectile: **1)** large semi-axis, a; **2)** small semi-axis, b; **3)** eccentricity, e; **4)** minimum distance from Earth, r_{min}; **5)** maximum distance from Earth, r_{max}.

b) *Determine* the projectile's rotation period around the Earth, T, if the projectile were to miss the asteroid.

c) *Determine* the duration of the projectile's motion, $\Delta t = t - t_0$, from point S to point A, knowing: the geometric elements represented at the same scale in Figure 2.1, where $r = 30010.88\,\text{km}$ and $\Delta\theta = 46°$; the mass of the Earth, $M = 5.94 \cdot 10^{24}\,\text{kg}$; and the constant of gravitational attraction, $G = 6.67 \cdot 10^{-11}\,\text{Nm}^2\,\text{kg}^{-2}$.

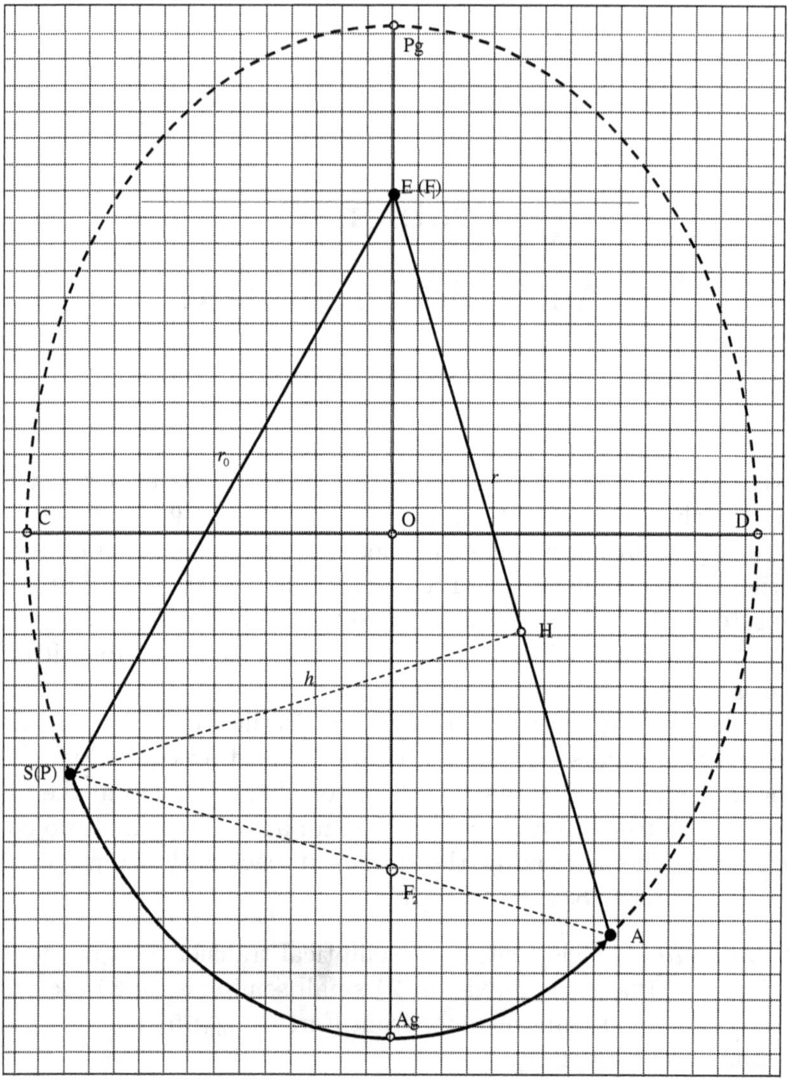

Fig. 2.1

d) *Determine* the distance d_{SA} between points S and A, as well as the distance l_{SA} traveled by the projectile from its launch from satellite S to meeting asteroid A.

e) *Determine* the elements of the velocity vector (orientation and modulus) of the projectile, P, in relation to the Earth, at the time of its launch from the circum-terrestrial satellite S, so that the transfer of the projectile from point S to point A occurs on a single ellipse, $\vec{v}_{\text{ellipse}} = \vec{v}_0$.

f) *Determine* the projectile's velocity, $\vec{v}$, orientation, and modulus on impact with the asteroid, at point A.

g) *Evaluate* the possibility of observing the projectile with the naked eye from the surface of the Earth when the projectile is at the maximum distance from the Earth. We know: the albedo of the full Moon, $\alpha_{\text{M}} = 0.12$; the radius of the Moon, $R_{\text{M}} = 1738\,\text{km}$; the distance from Earth to the Moon, $r_{\text{EM}} = 384\,400\,\text{km}$; and the apparent magnitude of the full Moon, $m_{\text{M}} = -12.7^{\text{m}}$. It is known that the projectile is a metal sphere with a perfectly reflecting surface ($\alpha_{\text{Projectile}} = 1$) and with radius $R_{\text{Projectile}} = 400\,\text{mm}$.

h) *Justify* the location of the focus of the single transfer ellipse represented in the drawing in Figure 2.1, making use of the drawing in Figure 2.2, knowing that the focus is inside the SA segment.

Students may use scissors, thread, a compass, and a graduated ruler.

Solution

a) To determine the elements of the projectile's elliptical orbit (large semi-axis, a; small semi-axis, b; eccentricity, e; minimum distance r_{min}; maximum distance, r_{max}), knowing that

$$r = 30\,010.88\,\text{km} \quad \text{and} \quad r_{\text{measured drawing}} = 153\,\text{mm},$$

it follows that the scale of all linear geometric dimensions in the drawing in Figure 2.1 is

$$S = \frac{r}{r_{\text{measured drawing}}} = \frac{30010.88}{153}\,\frac{\text{km}}{\text{mm}}.$$

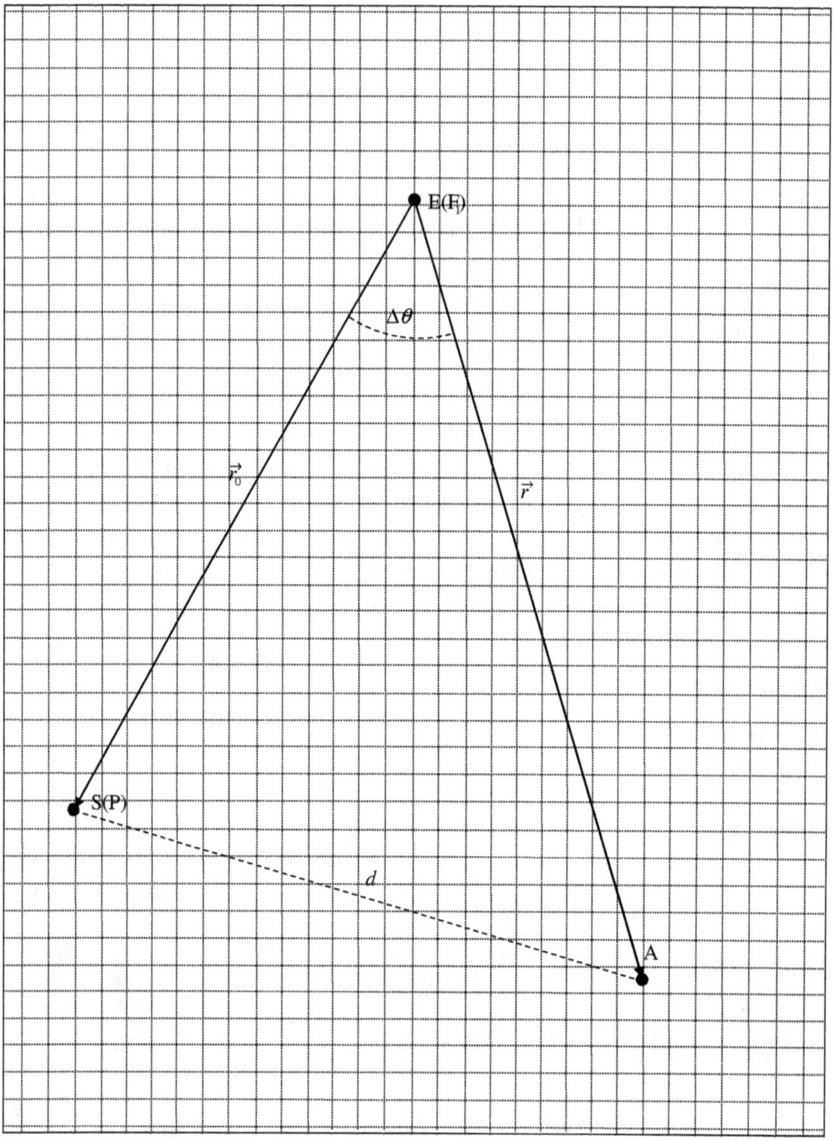

Fig. 2.2

So, we get:

$$r_{0,\,\text{measured}} = 133\,\text{mm}; \quad r_0 = r_{0,\,\text{measured drawing}} \cdot S = 26087.88\,\text{km};$$

$$r_{\text{measured}} = 153\,\text{mm};$$

$$2a_{\text{measured drawing}} = 200\,\text{mm}; \quad a_{\text{measured drawing}} = 100\,\text{mm};$$

$$a = a_{\text{measured drawing}} \cdot S \approx 19614.95\,\text{km};$$

$$2b_{\text{measured drawing}} = 148\,\text{mm}; \quad b_{\text{measured drawing}} = 74\,\text{mm};$$

$$b = b_{\text{measured drawing}} \cdot S \approx 14515.06\,\text{km};$$

$$2c_{\text{measured drawing}} = 134\,\text{mm}; \quad c_{\text{measured drawing}} = 67\,\text{mm};$$

$$c = c_{\text{measured drawing}} \cdot S \approx 13142.01\,\text{km};$$

$$e = \sqrt{1 - \frac{b^2}{a^2}} = \sqrt{1 - \frac{b^2_{\text{measured drawing}}}{a^2_{\text{measured drawing}}}} \approx 0.67;$$

$$r_{\text{min, measured drawing}} = 33\,\text{mm};$$

$$r_{\text{min}} = r_{\text{min, measured drawing}} \cdot S \approx 6472.93\,\text{km}; r_{\text{min}} = a(1 - e);$$

$$r_{\text{max, measured drawing}} = 167\,\text{mm};$$

$$r_{\text{max}} = r_{\text{max, measured}} \cdot S \approx 32756.97\,\text{km}; \quad r_{\text{max}} = a(1 + e).$$

b)

$$T^2 = \frac{4\pi^2}{G(M+m)} \cdot a^3; \quad m \ll M; \quad T^2 = \frac{4\pi^2}{GM} \cdot a^3;$$

$$M = 5.98 \cdot 10^{24}\,\text{kg}; \quad G = 6.67 \cdot 10^{-11}\,\text{Nm}^2\,\text{kg}^{-2};$$

$$a = 19607.84\,\text{km};$$

$$T = 2\pi\sqrt{\frac{a^3}{GM}} = 2 \cdot 3.14 \cdot \sqrt{\frac{19607.84^3 \cdot 10^9}{6.67 \cdot 10^{-11} \cdot 5.98 \cdot 10^{24}}}\,\text{s} \approx 27301.76\,\text{s};$$

$$T \approx 455.02\ \text{min} \approx 7.58\,\text{h}.$$

c) On the transfer ellipse in Figure 2.1, construct the segment SH ⊥ EA, representing the height of the triangle ESA, and measure the length of this segment on the drawing:

$$(\text{SH})_{\text{measured drawing}} = h_{\text{measured drawing}} = 98\,\text{mm};$$

$$\begin{aligned}\Sigma_{\text{ellipse transfer}} &= \pi ab = \pi S a_{\text{measured drawing}} \cdot S b_{\text{measured drawing}} \\ &= \pi S^2 a_{\text{measured drawing}} b_{\text{measured drawing}};\end{aligned}$$

$$\Sigma_{\text{sector ellipse}} = \Sigma_{\Delta(\text{ESA})} + \Sigma_{\text{segment ellipse}};$$

$$\begin{aligned}\Sigma_{\Delta(\text{ESA})} &= \frac{1}{2} rh = \frac{1}{2} S r_{\text{measured drawing}} S h_{\text{measured drawing}} \\ &= \frac{1}{2} S^2 r_{\text{measured drawing}} h_{\text{measured drawing}}.\end{aligned}$$

To calculate $\Sigma_{\text{segment ellipse}}$ by counting, we estimate that there are $n = 100$ small squares, each with a side length of $l_{\text{measured drawing}} = 5\,\text{mm}$. Thus, corresponding to the same scale, S, the result is:

$$\begin{aligned}\Sigma_{\text{segment ellipse transfer}} &= n \cdot S l_{\text{measured drawing}} \cdot S l_{\text{measured drawing}} \\ &= n S^2 l^2_{\text{measured drawing}}.\end{aligned}$$

Under these conditions, it follows that:

$$\Sigma_{\text{sector ellipse transfer}} = \Sigma_{\Delta(\text{ESA})} + \Sigma_{\text{segment ellipse}};$$

$$\begin{aligned}\Sigma_{\text{sector ellipse transfer}} &= \frac{1}{2} S^2 r_{\text{measured drawing}} h_{\text{measured drawing}} \\ &\quad + n S^2 l^2_{\text{measured drawing}}.\end{aligned}$$

According to Kepler's second law (the law of areas), it follows that:

$$T \ldots\ldots\ldots\ldots\ldots\ldots\ldots\ldots \Sigma_{\text{transfer ellipse}};$$

$$\Delta t \ldots\ldots\ldots\ldots\ldots\ldots \Sigma_{\text{sector ellipse transfer}};$$

$$\Delta t = \frac{\Sigma_{\text{sector ellipse transfer}}}{\Sigma_{\text{transfer ellipse}}} \cdot T,$$

representing the duration of projectile P's displacement until it meets asteroid A.

Under these conditions, the results are:

$$\Delta t = \frac{\frac{1}{2}S^2 r_{\text{measured drawing}} h_{\text{measured drawing}} + nS^2 l^2_{\text{measured drawing}}}{\pi S^2 a_{\text{measured drawing}} b_{\text{measured drawing}}} \cdot T;$$

$$\Delta t = \frac{\frac{1}{2} r_{\text{measured drawing}} h_{\text{measured drawing}} + n l^2_{\text{measured drawing}}}{\pi a_{\text{measured drawing}} b_{\text{measured drawing}}} \cdot T;$$

$$r_{\text{measured drawing}} = 155\,\text{mm}; \quad h_{\text{measured drawing}} = 98\,\text{mm};$$

$$l_{\text{measured drawing}} = 5\,\text{mm};$$

$$n = 100; \quad a_{\text{measured drawing}} = 100\,\text{mm}; \quad b_{\text{measured drawing}} = 74\,\text{mm};$$

$$T \approx 454 \text{ min} \approx 7.56\,\text{h};$$

$$\Delta t = \frac{\frac{1}{2}155\,\text{mm} \cdot 98\,\text{mm} + 100 \cdot 25\,\text{mm}^2}{3.14 \cdot 100\,\text{mm} \cdot 74\,\text{mm}} \cdot 7.56\,\text{h};$$

$$\Delta t = \frac{155 \cdot 49 + 100 \cdot 25}{3.14 \cdot 100 \cdot 74} \cdot 7.56\,\text{h};$$

$$\Delta t = 3.28\,\text{h}.$$

d)

$$d_{\text{SA, measured}} = 115\,\text{mm};$$

$$d_{\text{SA}} = d_{\text{SA, measured drawing}} \cdot S \approx 22549.01\,\text{km}.$$

A wire is placed along the sector of the ellipse between points S and A. Measuring the length of this wire results in:

$$l_{\text{SA, measured}} = 135\,\text{mm};$$

$$l_{\text{SA}} = l_{\text{SA, measured}} \cdot S = 135\,\text{mm} \cdot \frac{30010.88\,\text{km}}{153\,\text{mm}} \approx 26480.18\,\text{km}.$$

e) Determining the direction of the initial velocity means determining the direction of the tangent to the ellipse at point S. This is done using the optical properties of the ellipse, according to which the light rays from the focus of an ellipsoidal concave mirror after reflection all pass through the other focus of the mirror, as shown in the drawing in Figure 2.3.

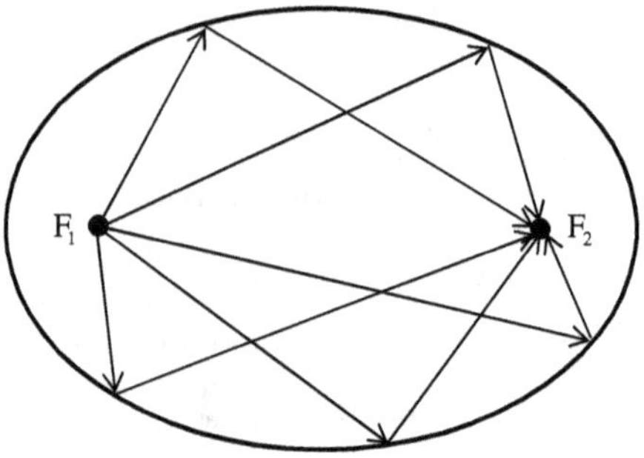

Fig. 2.3

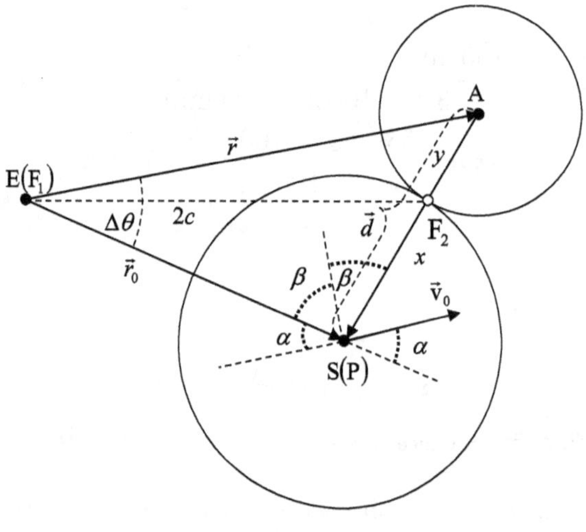

Fig. 2.4

As a result, the direction of the tangent to the ellipse forms angles equal to the vector radii of S from the two foci, as shown in the drawings in Figures 2.3, 2.4, and 2.5. The tangent to the ellipse at point S is perpendicular to the bisector of the angle ASE.

Under these conditions, the direction of $\vec{v}_0$ and the direction of $\vec{r}_0$ form the angle that is measured directly on the drawing with the help of a protractor, considering that the drawing was constructed to respect the numerical values of the known quantities: r_0, r, and $\Delta\theta$.

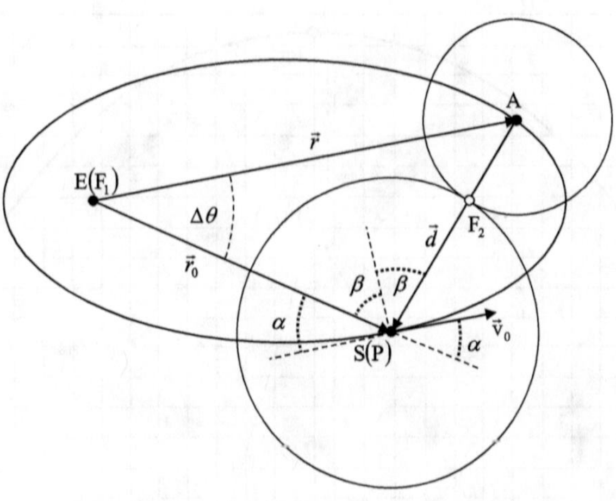

Fig. 2.5

Under these conditions, the direction of $\vec{v}_0$, corresponding to the projectile P launched from point S, and the direction of $\vec{r}_0$ form angle α, which can be measured in the drawing in Figure 2.6: $\alpha \approx 54°$.

If the projectile P launched from the satellite S passes through A, it means that the points S and A are on the same ellipse, whose focus is the Earth, E, as indicated in the drawing in Figure 2.7.

The movement of the projectile on this ellipse occurs in compliance with the laws of conservation of energy and angular momentum.

For those moments when the projectile passes through one of the points B_1 or B_2 (the apogee and perigee of the ellipse), the equalities $E = E_0$ and $L = L_0$ lead to:

$$\frac{m_0 v_{1,2}^2}{2} - G\frac{m_0 M}{r_{1,2}} = \frac{m_0 v_0^2}{2} - G\frac{m_0 M}{r_0},$$

where: m_0 – projectile mass; M – the mass of the Earth; G – gravitational attraction constant. Additionally:

$$\frac{v_{1,2}^2}{2} - \quad G\frac{M}{r_{1,2}} = \frac{v_0^2}{2} - G\frac{M}{r_0};$$

$$m_0 v_{1,2} r_{1,2} = m_0 v_0 r_0 \sin\alpha;$$

$$v_{1,2} r_{1,2} = v_0 r_0 \sin\alpha;$$

$$\left(\frac{v_0^2}{2} - G\frac{M}{r_0}\right) r_{1,2}^2 + GM r_{1,2} - \frac{1}{2} v_0^2 r_0^2 \sin^2\alpha = 0.$$

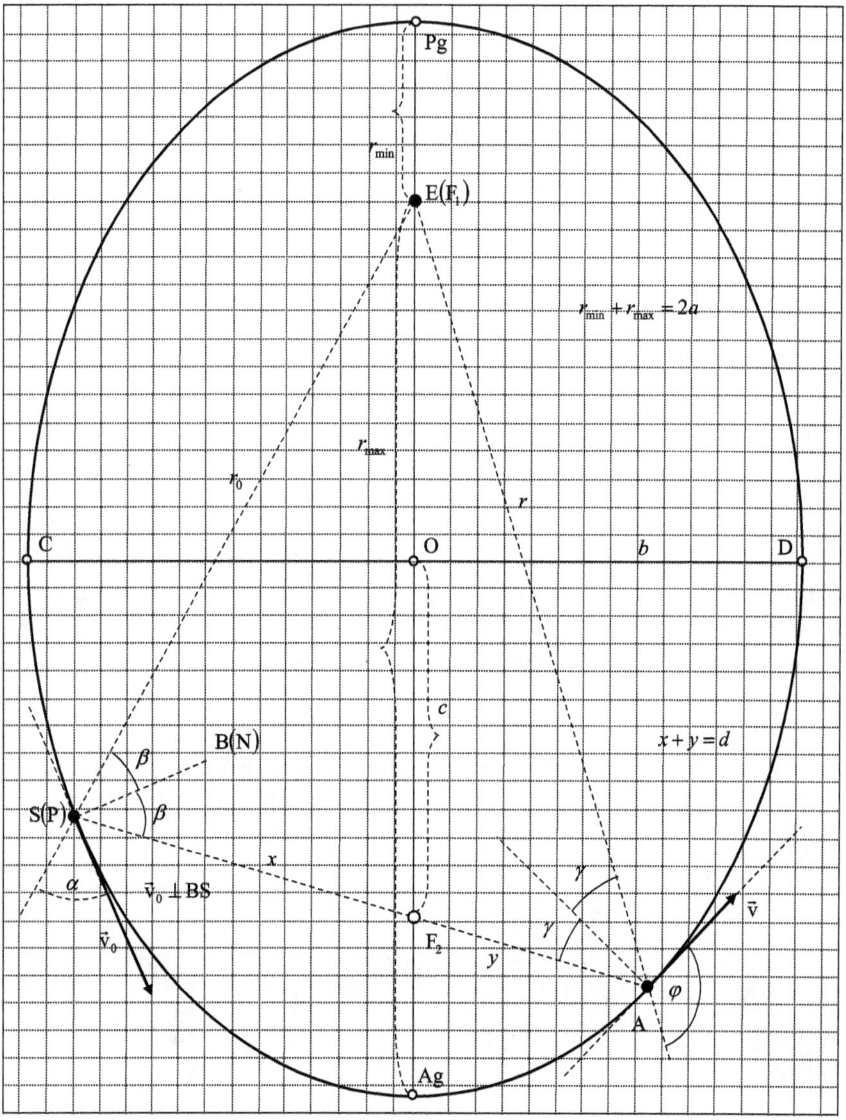

Fig. 2.6

The two roots, r_1 and r_2, of this equation represent the values $r_{1,2}$ at apogee and perigee (r_{min}, r_{max}), so that:

$$a = \frac{1}{2}(r_1 + r_2) = \frac{1}{2}(r_{min} + r_{max}).$$

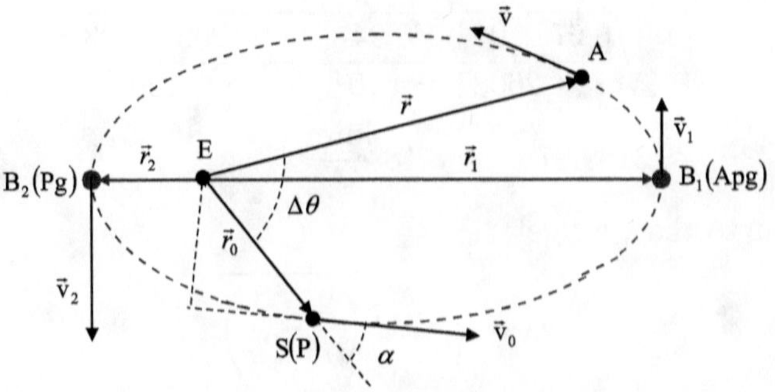

Fig. 2.7

From Viète's relation, it follows that:

$$a = \frac{GMr_0}{2KM - r_0 v_0^2},$$

a relationship independent of α (initial injection velocity orientation, $\vec{v}_0$);

$$v_0 = \sqrt{GM\left(\frac{2}{r_0} - \frac{1}{a}\right)};$$

$$v_0 = \sqrt{GM\frac{2a - r_0}{a\,r_0}} = \sqrt{\frac{GM}{r_0} \cdot \frac{2a - r_0}{a}},$$

representing the speed of projectile P at the time of its launch.

The result is:

$$S = \frac{30000\,\text{km}}{153\,\text{mm};};$$

$$r_0 = 133\,\text{mm} \cdot S;$$

$$r_0 = 133\,\text{mm} \cdot \frac{30010.88\,\text{km}}{153\,\text{mm}} \approx 26087.88\,\text{km};$$

$$M = 5.94 \cdot 10^{24}\,\text{kg}; \quad G = 6.67 \cdot 10^{-11}\,\text{Nm}^2\,\text{kg}^{-2};$$

$$2a = 200\,\text{mm} \cdot S; a = 100\,\text{mm} \cdot S;$$

$$v_0 = \sqrt{\frac{6.67 \cdot 10^{-11}\,\text{Nm}^2\,\text{kg}^{-2} \cdot 5.94 \cdot 10^{24}\,\text{kg}}{26087.88 \cdot 10^3\,\text{m}} \cdot \frac{200 - 133}{100}};$$

$$\mathrm{v}_0 = \sqrt{\frac{6.67 \cdot 10^{-11} \cdot 5.94 \cdot 10^{24}}{26087.88 \cdot 10^3} \cdot \frac{200 - 133}{100}} \, \frac{\mathrm{m}}{\mathrm{s}}$$

$$\approx 3189.87 \, \frac{\mathrm{m}}{\mathrm{s}} = 3.18 \, \frac{\mathrm{km}}{\mathrm{s}}.$$

f) Similar to that, we get:

$$\mathrm{v}_\mathrm{A} = \sqrt{GM\left(\frac{2}{r} - \frac{1}{a}\right)};$$

$$\mathrm{v}_\mathrm{A} = \sqrt{GM\left(\frac{2}{r} - \frac{1}{a}\right)} = \sqrt{GM\frac{2a - r}{ar}}$$

$$= \sqrt{\frac{GM}{r} \cdot \frac{2a_{\text{measured drawing}} \cdot S - r_{\text{measured drawing}} \cdot S}{a_{\text{measured drawing}} \cdot S}};$$

$$\mathrm{v}_\mathrm{A} = \sqrt{\frac{GM}{r} \cdot \frac{2a_{\text{measured drawing}} - r_{\text{measured drawing}}}{a_{\text{measured drawing}}}},$$

representing the projectile's speed at the impact with the asteroid, at point A;

$$r = 30010.88 \text{ km}; r_{\text{measured drawing}} = 153 \, \text{mm};$$

$$\mathrm{v}_\mathrm{A} = \sqrt{\frac{6.67 \cdot 10^{-11} \, \mathrm{Nm^2 \, kg^{-2}} \cdot 5.94 \cdot 10^{24} \, \mathrm{kg}}{30010.88 \cdot 10^3 \, \mathrm{m}} \cdot \frac{200 - 153}{100}};$$

$$\mathrm{v}_\mathrm{A} = \sqrt{\frac{6.67 \cdot 10^{-11} \cdot 5.94 \cdot 10^{24}}{30010.88 \cdot 10^3} \cdot \frac{200 - 153}{100}} \, \frac{\mathrm{m}}{\mathrm{s}}$$

$$\approx 2974.09 \, \frac{\mathrm{m}}{\mathrm{s}} \approx 2.97 \, \frac{\mathrm{km}}{\mathrm{s}}.$$

Under these conditions, the direction of $\vec{\mathrm{v}}$, corresponding to the impact of the projectile with the asteroid at point A, which is highlighted in the drawing in Figure 2.6, and the direction of $\vec{r}$ form the angle φ, whose value can be measured as:

$$\varphi \approx 118^\circ.$$

g) The integral brightness of the Sun, L_S, is the energy of the total radiation emitted by the Sun in one unit of time, over its entire surface, on all wavelengths, in all directions:

$$L_S = \frac{E_{\text{emitted, Sun}}}{t} = 3.86 \cdot 10^{26}\ \text{W},$$

If Σ is the surface of the circumsolar sphere, whose radius represents the instantaneous distance between the center of the Sun and the center of the Earth (center of the Moon), r_{ES}, as shown in the drawing in Figure 2.8, then the energy of the solar radiation passing through the surface Σ is equal to L_S.

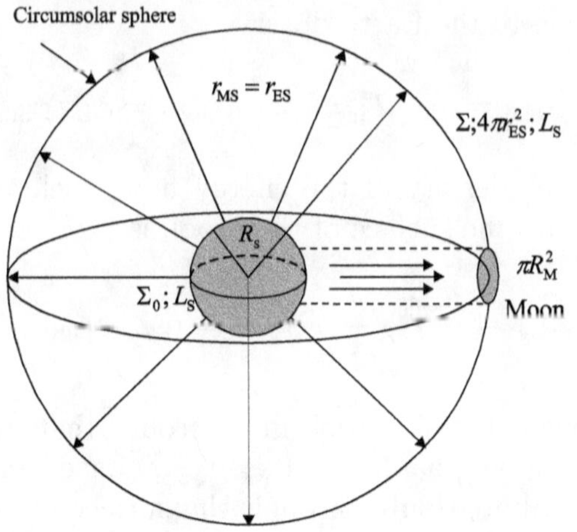

Fig. 2.8

The *density of the Sun's energy flow*, at a distance r_{ES} from the Sun (near the Earth, the Moon and the projectile), is the energy of all the radiation emitted by the Sun that, at that distance, crosses one unit surface area, under normal incidence, in one unit of time, so:

$$\varphi_{\text{Sun}, r_{ES}} = \frac{E_{\text{emitted, Sun}}}{St} = \frac{\frac{E_{\text{emitted, Sun}}}{t}}{S} = \frac{L_S}{S} = \frac{L_S}{4\pi r_{ES}^2} = \text{constant}.$$

The Moon's hemisphere exposed to solar radiation is equivalent to a circular flat disk, having radius R_M and surface area πR_M^2, placed perpendicular to the Moon–Sun direction so that the flow of incident solar radiation at the level of the Moon is

$$F_{\text{incident, full Moon}} = \varphi_{\text{Sun}, r_{\text{ES}}} \cdot \pi R_{\text{M}}^2.$$

If α_{M} is the albedo of the Moon, it follows that:

$$\alpha_{\text{M}} = \frac{F_{\text{reflected, full Moon}}}{F_{\text{incident, full Moon}}},$$

where $F_{\text{reflected, full Moon}}$ is the energy flow of the radiation reflected by the full Moon to the Earth observer;

$$F_{\text{reflected, full Moon}} = \alpha_{\text{M}} \cdot F_{\text{incident, full Moon}} = \alpha_{\text{L}} \cdot \phi_{\text{Sun}, r_{\text{ES}}} \cdot \pi R_{\text{M}}^2.$$

Therefore, the density of the energy flow reaching the observer after reflection on the surface of the Moon is

$$\phi_{\text{Moon, observer}} = \frac{F_{\text{reflected, full Moon}}}{2\pi r_{\text{EM}}^2} = \alpha_{\text{M}} \cdot \phi_{\text{Sun}, r_{\text{ES}}} \cdot \frac{\pi R_{\text{M}}^2}{2\pi r_{\text{PM}}^2}.$$

The previous expression took into account that when the Moon is in the full Moon phase, the density of its energy flow at the observer is distributed only through the surface of the hemisphere with radius r_{EM}.

Similarly, the density of the energy flow reaching the observer after reflection on the surface of the projectile is

$$\phi_{\text{projectile, observer}} = \frac{F_{\text{reflected, projectile}}}{4\pi r_{\text{D, projectile}}^2}$$

$$= \alpha_{\text{projectile}} \cdot \phi_{\text{Sun}, r_{\text{ES}}} \cdot \frac{\pi R_{\text{projectile}}^2}{4\pi r_{\text{D, projectile}}^2}.$$

The previous expression took into account that the density of the energy flow of the projectile at the observer results from the distribution through the surface of the sphere with radius $r_{\text{E, projectile}}$.

Using Pogson's formula, we will compare the apparent visual magnitude of the full Moon with the apparent visual magnitude of the projectile:

$$\log \frac{\phi_{\text{Moon, observer}}}{\phi_{\text{projectile, observer}}} = -0.4\,(m_{\text{full Moon}} - m_{\text{projectile}});$$

$$\log \frac{\phi_{\text{Moon, observer}}}{\phi_{\text{projectile, observer}}} = \log \frac{\alpha_{\text{M}} \cdot \phi_{\text{Sun},r_{\text{ES}}} \cdot \frac{\pi R_{\text{M}}^2}{2\pi r_{\text{EM}}^2}}{\alpha_{\text{projectile}} \cdot \phi_{\text{Sun},r_{\text{ES}}} \cdot \frac{\pi R_{\text{projectile}}^2}{4\pi r_{\text{D, projectile}}^2}}$$

$$= \log \frac{\alpha_{\text{M}} \cdot \frac{R_{\text{M}}^2}{r_{\text{EM}}^2}}{\alpha_{\text{projectile}} \cdot \frac{R_{\text{projectile}}^2}{2r_{\text{D, projectile}}^2}};$$

$$\log \frac{\alpha_{\text{M}} \cdot \frac{R_{\text{M}}^2}{r_{\text{EM}}^2}}{\alpha_{\text{projectile}} \cdot \frac{R_{\text{projectile}}^2}{2r_{\text{D, projectile}}^2}} = -0.4\,(m_{\text{M}} - m_{\text{projectile}});$$

$$\log \frac{\alpha_{\text{M}}}{\alpha_{\text{projectile}}} \cdot \left(\frac{R_{\text{M}}}{R_{\text{projectile}}}\right)^2 \cdot 2 \cdot \left(\frac{r_{\text{D, projectile}}}{r_{\text{EM}}}\right)^2 = -0.4\,(m_{\text{M}} - m_{\text{projectile}});$$

$$\alpha_{\text{M}} = 0.12; \quad \alpha_{\text{projectile}} = 1;$$

$$R_{\text{M}} = 1738\,\text{km}; \quad R_{\text{projectile}} = 400\,\text{mm};$$

$$r_{\text{Earth, projectile}} = r_{\text{max, observer}-\text{projectile}} = r_{\text{max}} = 32745.09\,\text{km};$$

$$r_{\text{Earth, Moon}} = r_{\text{observer, Moon}} = 384400\,\text{km}; \quad m_{\text{M}} = -12.7^{\text{m}};$$

$$\log \frac{\alpha_{\text{M}}}{\alpha_{\text{projectile}}} + 2 \cdot \log \frac{R_{\text{M}}}{R_{\text{projectile}}} + 2 \cdot \log \frac{r_{\text{Earth, projectile}}}{r_{\text{Earth, Moon}}} = -0.4\,(m_{\text{M}} - m_{\text{projectile}});$$

$$\log(0.12) + 2 \cdot \log \frac{1738000\,\text{m}}{0.400\,\text{m}} + 2 \cdot \log \frac{32745.09\,\text{km}}{384400\,\text{km}} = -0.4\,(m_{\text{M}} - m_{\text{projectile}});$$

$$\log(0.12) + 2 \cdot \log \frac{1738000}{0.400} + 2 \cdot \log \frac{32745.09}{384400} = -0.4\,(m_{\text{M}} - m_{\text{projectile}});$$

$$-0.920818754 + 13.27597956 - 2.139274381$$
$$= -0.4\,(m_{\text{M}} - m_{\text{projectile}});$$
$$10.21588643 = -0.4\,(m_{\text{M}} - m_{\text{projectile}});$$
$$m_{\text{M}} - m_{\text{projectile}} = -25.53971606;$$
$$-m_{\text{projectile}} = -25.53971606 - m_{\text{M}};$$
$$m_{\text{projectile}} = 25.53971606 + m_{\text{M}};$$
$$m_{\text{projectile}} = 25.53971606 - 12.7;$$
$$m_{\text{projectile}} = 12.83;$$
$$m_{\text{max}} \approx 6^{m}; \quad m_{\text{projectile}} > m_{\text{max}}.$$

Thus, the projectile was not visible to the naked eye when it was at its peak.

h) Since the problem admits a single solution, it means that the second focus of the ellipse F_2 is inside the SA segment, at the point of tangency of the circles with the centers at points S and A having radii x and y, respectively, as indicated by the drawings in Figures 2.9 and 2.10.

Locating the focus F_2 on the SA segment using known relationships from the geometry of the ellipse, according to the notation in

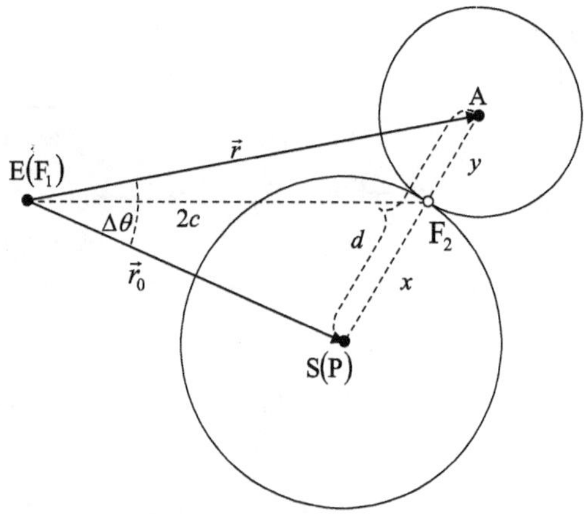

Fig. 2.9

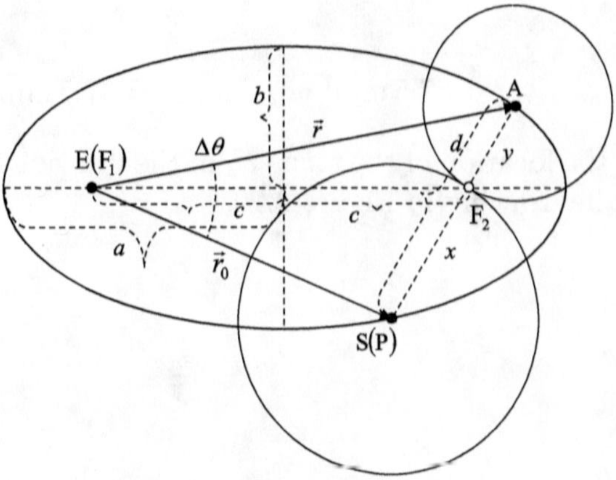

Fig. 2.10

Figures 2.9 and 2.10, results in:

$$\mathrm{ES} + \mathrm{SF}_2 = 2a; \quad \mathrm{EA} + \mathrm{AF}_2 = 2a;$$

$$r_0 + x = 2a; \quad r + y = 2a;$$

$$r_0 + x = r + y;$$

$$x - y = r - r_0 = d_0; \quad x + y = d;$$

$$x - y = d_0; \quad x + y = d;$$

$$x = \frac{1}{2}(d + d_0); \quad y = \frac{1}{2}(d - d_0).$$

From the measurements made on the drawing in Figure 2.1, in the statement of the problem, and from our calculations, the results are:

$$r_{0,\,\text{measured drawing}} = 133\,\text{mm}; \quad r_{\text{measured drawing}} = 153\,\text{mm};$$

$$d_{\text{measured drawing}} = 115\,\text{mm};$$

$$d_{0,\,\text{calculated drawing}} = r_{\text{measured drawing}} - r_{0,\,\text{measured drawing}} = 20\,\text{mm};$$

$$x_{\text{calculated drawing}} = \frac{1}{2}\left(d_{\text{measured drawing}} + d_{0,\,\text{calculated drawing}}\right);$$

$$y_{\text{calculated drawing}} = \frac{1}{2}\left(d_{\text{measured}} - d_{0,\,\text{calculated drawing}}\right);$$

$$x_{\text{calculated drawing}} = 67.5\,\text{mm}; \quad y_{\text{calculated drawing}} = 47.5\,\text{mm}.$$

Thus:

$$x_{\text{measured}} = 67.5\,\text{mm}; \quad y_{\text{measured}} = 47.5\,\text{mm},$$

which allows the location of the focus F_2 in the drawing in Figure 2.2, as shown in the drawing in Figure 2.10.

Problem 3

A Galaxy of Stars Identical to Our Sun!

A science fiction hypothesis proposes the possibility of, beyond the limits of our galaxy, a galaxy whose stars have radii identical and equal to the radius of our Sun.

In addition, observed from Earth, all the stars of this galaxy would have identical apparent magnitudes, equal to the apparent magnitude of our Sun, regardless of the distances at which they would be from Earth.

Establish the relationships between the effective temperatures of the surfaces of the stars in this galaxy and the distances at which they would be from the observer on Earth.

Given: T_{S} – the effective temperature at the surface of the Sun; r_{ES} – the distance between the Earth and the Sun.

Solution

Knowing the relationship between the illumination produced by a star (the energy flux density of the star, $\varphi_{\Sigma,r_{\mathrm{E}\Sigma}}$, at the distance from the star $r_{\mathrm{E}\Sigma}$, i.e., at the observer on Earth), the brightness of the star, L_{Σ}, and the distance between the Earth and the star, $r_{\mathrm{E}\Sigma}$, we obtain:

$$\varphi_{\Sigma,r_{\mathrm{E}\Sigma}} = \frac{L_{\Sigma}}{4\pi r_{\mathrm{E}\Sigma}^2},$$

where the brightness of the star, depending on its temperature and its radius, is given by the expression

$$L_\Sigma = \sigma T_\Sigma^4 4\pi R_\Sigma^2,$$

where σ is the constant from the Stefan–Boltzmann law;

$$\varphi_{\Sigma, r_{E\Sigma}} = \frac{\sigma T_\Sigma^4 R_\Sigma^2}{r_{E\Sigma}^2};$$

$$\log \frac{\varphi_{\Sigma, r_{E\Sigma}}}{\varphi_{\text{Sun}, r_{E,\text{Sun}}}} = -0.4\,(m_\Sigma - m_{\text{Sun}});$$

$$m_\Sigma = m_0;$$

$$\log \frac{\varphi_{\Sigma, r_{E\Sigma}}}{\varphi_{\text{Sun}, r_{E\,\text{Sun}}}} = -0.4\,(m_0 - m_{\text{Sun}}),$$

representing Pogson's formula for the star Σ–Sun ensemble.

Writing the same formula for the ensemble formed by another star Σ' and the Sun:

$$\log \frac{\varphi_{\Sigma', r_{E\Sigma'}}}{\varphi_{\text{Sun}, r_{E,\text{Sun}}}} = -0.4\,(m_{\Sigma'} - m_{\text{Sun}});$$

$$m_{\Sigma'} = m_0;$$

$$\log \frac{\varphi_{\Sigma', r_{E\Sigma'}}}{\varphi_{\text{Sun}, r_{E,\text{Sun}}}} = -0.4\,(m_0 - m_{\text{Sun}});$$

$$\log \frac{\varphi_{\Sigma, r_{E\Sigma}}}{\varphi_{\text{Sun}, r_{E,\text{Sun}}}} = \log \frac{\varphi_{\Sigma', r_{E,\Sigma'}}}{\varphi_{\text{Sun}, r_{E,\text{Sun}}}};$$

$$\frac{\varphi_{\Sigma, r_{E\Sigma}}}{\varphi_{\text{Sun}, r_{E,\text{Sun}}}} = \frac{\varphi_{\Sigma', r_{E\Sigma'}}}{\varphi_{\text{Sun}, r_{E,\text{Sun}}}};$$

$$\varphi_{\Sigma, r_{E\Sigma}} = \varphi_{\Sigma' r_{E\Sigma'}}.$$

This proves that, under the conditions of the statement of the problem:

- The energy flow densities of all stars, at the level of the observer on Earth, are identical, which is why the apparent magnitudes of all stars in the "Galaxy of Exoplanets" are identical, m_0:

$$\varphi_{1,r_{\mathrm{E},1}} = \varphi_{2,r_{\mathrm{E},2}} = \varphi_{3,r_{\mathrm{E},3}} = \cdots\cdots = \varphi_{N,r_{\mathrm{E},N}};$$

$$\frac{\sigma T_1^4 R_1^2}{r_{\mathrm{E},1}^2} = \frac{\sigma T_2^4 R_2^2}{r_{\mathrm{E},2}^2} = \frac{\sigma T_3^4 R_3^2}{r_{\mathrm{E},3}^2} = \cdots\cdots\cdots = \frac{\sigma T_N^4 R_N^2}{r_{\mathrm{E},N}^2}.$$

- The luminosities (absolute luminosities) of the stars must be higher, at greater distances from the Earth, so the apparent magnitudes of all the stars in the "Galaxy of Exoplanets" can remain unchanged, m_0:

$$L_\Sigma = \sigma T_\Sigma^4 4\pi R_\Sigma^2;$$

$$L_1 = \sigma T_1^4 4\pi R_1^2; \quad L_2 = \sigma T_2^4 4\pi R_2^2; \quad L_3 = \sigma T_3^4 4\pi R_3^2; \ldots\ldots\ldots;$$

$$L_N = \sigma T_N^4 4\pi R_N^2;$$

$$L_1 < L_2 < L_3 < \cdots\cdots\cdots < L_N;$$

$$\sigma T_1^4 4\pi R_1^2 < \sigma T_2^4 4\pi R_2^2 < \sigma T_3^4 4\pi R_3^2 < \cdots\cdots\cdots < \sigma T_N^4 4\pi R_N^2;$$

$$T_1^4 R_1^2 < T_2^4 R_2^2 < T_3^4 R_3^2 < \cdots\cdots\cdots < T_N^4 R_N^2.$$

$$R_1 = R_2 = R_3 = \cdots\cdots\cdots = R_N = R_\mathrm{S};$$

$$T_1^4 < T_2^4 < T_3^4 < \cdots\cdots\cdots < T_N^4;$$

$$T_1 < T_2 < T_3 < \cdots\cdots\cdots < T_N.$$

That is, the luminosities of the stars increase when the distances between the Earth and the stars increase because the temperatures of the stars become higher, which can cause the apparent magnitudes of the stars to be constant.

Under these conditions, writing Pogson's formula for each ensemble (star–Sun) results in:

$$\log \frac{\varphi_1}{\varphi_\mathrm{S}} = -0.4\,(m_0 - m_\mathrm{S});$$

$$\varphi_1 = \frac{\sigma T_1^4 R_\mathrm{S}^2}{r_{\mathrm{E},1}^2}; \quad \varphi_{\mathrm{Sun},\, r_{\mathrm{E,Sun}}} = \varphi_\mathrm{S} = \frac{\sigma T_\mathrm{S}^4 R_\mathrm{S}^2}{r_{\mathrm{E,S}}^2};$$

$$\log \frac{\frac{\sigma T_1^4 R_S^2}{r_{E,1}^2}}{\frac{\sigma T_S^4 R_S^2}{r_{E,S}^2}} = 0.4\,(m_S - m_0) = \log\left(\frac{T_1^4}{T_S^4} \cdot \frac{r_{E,S}^2}{r_{E,1}^2}\right);$$

$$m_0 = m_S;$$

$$\frac{T_1^4}{T_S^4} \cdot \frac{r_{E,S}^2}{r_{E,1}^2} = 10^0 = 1; \quad T_1 = T_S \cdot \sqrt{\frac{r_{E,1}}{r_{E,S}}};$$

$$r_{E,1} > r_{E,S}; \quad T_1 > T_S;$$

$$\log \frac{\varphi_2}{\varphi_S} = -0.4\,(m_0 - m_S);$$

$$\varphi_2 = \frac{\sigma T_2^4 R_S^2}{r_{E,2}^2}; \quad \varphi_{\mathrm{Sun},\, r_{\mathrm{E,Sun}}} = \varphi_S = \frac{\sigma T_S^4 R_S^2}{r_{E,S}^2};$$

$$\log \frac{\frac{\sigma T_2^4 R_S^2}{r_{E,2}^2}}{\frac{\sigma T_S^2 R_S^2}{r_{E,S}^2}} = 0.4\,(m_S - m_0) = \log\left(\frac{T_2^4}{T_S^4} \cdot \frac{r_{E,S}^2}{r_{E,2}^2}\right);$$

$$\frac{T_2^4}{T_S^4} \cdot \frac{r_{E,S}^2}{r_{E,2}^2} = 10^0 = 1;$$

$$T_2 = T_S \cdot \sqrt{\frac{r_{E,2}}{r_{E,S}}};$$

$$r_{E,2} > r_{E,S}; \quad T_2 > T_S;$$

$$\log \frac{\varphi_3}{\varphi_S} = -0.4 \cdot (m_0 - m_S);$$

$$\varphi_3 = \frac{\sigma T_3^4 R_S^2}{r_{E,3}^2}; \quad \varphi_{\mathrm{Sun},\, r_{\mathrm{E,Sun}}} = \varphi_S = \frac{\sigma T_S^4 R_S^2}{r_{E,S}^2};$$

$$\log \frac{\frac{\sigma T_3^4 R_S^2}{r_{E,3}^2}}{\frac{\sigma T_S^2 R_S^2}{r_{E,S}^2}} = 0.4 \cdot (m_S - m_0) = \log\left(\frac{T_3^4}{T_S^4} \cdot \frac{r_{E,S}^2}{r_{E,3}^2}\right);$$

$$\frac{T_3^4}{T_S^4} \cdot \frac{r_{E,S}^2}{r_{E,3}^2} = 10^0 = 1;$$

$$T_3 = T_{\rm S} \cdot \sqrt{\frac{r_{\rm E,3}}{r_{\rm E,S}}};$$

$$r_{\rm E,3} > r_{\rm E,S}; \quad T_3 > T_{\rm S};$$

....

$$\log \frac{\varphi_N}{\varphi_{\rm S}} = -0.4 \cdot (m_0 - m_{\rm S}); \quad \varphi_N = \frac{\sigma T_N^4 R_{\rm S}^2}{r_{{\rm E},N}^2};$$

$$\varphi_{{\rm Sun}, r_{\rm E,Sun}} = \varphi_{\rm S} = \frac{\sigma T_{\rm S}^4 R_{\rm S}^2}{r_{\rm E,S}^2};$$

$$\log \frac{\frac{\sigma T_N^4 R_{\rm S}^2}{r_{{\rm E},N}^2}}{\frac{\sigma T_{\rm S}^2 R_{\rm S}^2}{r_{\rm E,S}^2}} = 0.4 \cdot (m_{\rm S} - m_0) = \log \left(\frac{T_N^4}{T_{\rm S}^4} \cdot \frac{r_{\rm E,S}^2}{r_{{\rm E},N}^2} \right);$$

$$\frac{T_N^4}{T_{\rm S}^4} \cdot \frac{r_{\rm E,S}^2}{r_{{\rm E},N}^2} = 10^0 = 1;$$

$$T_N = T_{\rm S} \cdot \sqrt{\frac{r_{{\rm E},N}}{r_{\rm E,S}}};$$

$$r_{{\rm E},N} > r_{\rm E,S}; \quad T_N > T_{\rm S};$$

$$T_1 < T_2 < T_3 < \cdots\cdots\cdots < T_N;$$

$$r_{\rm E,1} < r_{\rm E,2} < r_{\rm E,3} < \cdots\cdots\cdots < r_{{\rm E},N}.$$

Problem 4

Two Astronomical Observatories on an Island

On a small island with a high mountainous relief, there are two astronomical observatories: OA-1, located at the base of the mountain at sea level, and OA-2, located on the top of the mountain at the altitude $H = 500\,\mathrm{m}$, as indicated in the image in Figure 4.1.

Fig. 4.1 (Credit: Kai Lars Scherer; CC BY 3.0)

At both astronomical observatories, simultaneous observations were made of a star, σ, whose equatorial coordinates are: right ascension, $\alpha = 01^{\mathrm{h}}10^{\mathrm{m}}36^{\mathrm{s}}$; declination, $\delta = 12°30'00''$. The geographical coordinates of the island are: north latitude, $\varphi = 43°$; west longitude, $\lambda = 61°$.

The image in Figure 4.2 shows the dependence $m(X_{\mathrm{r}})$ of the apparent magnitude of the star σ, observed in a certain spectral band from the visible range of the electromagnetic spectrum over several hours of one night at the OA-1 astronomical observatory, on X_{r}, "air mass" traversed by the starlight from its entry into the Earth's atmosphere to the astronomical observatory, OA-1. The meaning of "air mass" is specified in the drawing in Figure 4.3.

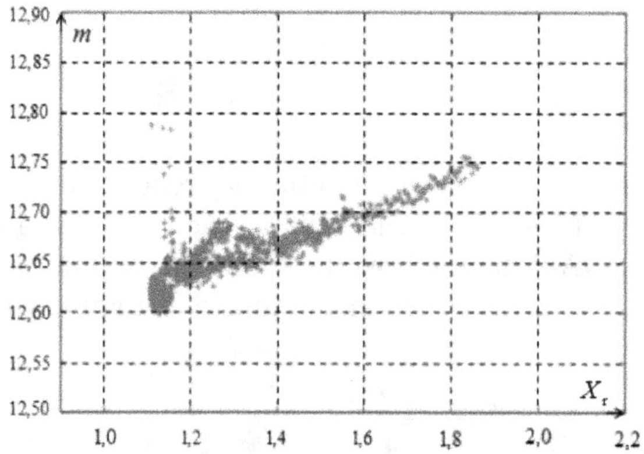

Fig. 4.2

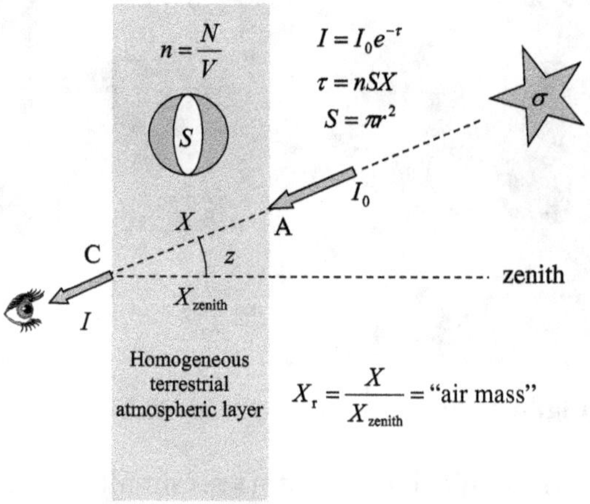

Fig. 4.3

a) *Determine* the zenithal distance, z, of the star at the time of its passage to the meridian of the place.

b) *Determine* what percentage of star σ's light intensity before entering the Earth's atmosphere, I_0, reaches the OA-1 astronomical observatory at sea level, $\eta = I/I_0$, where I is the light intensity after crossing the Earth's atmosphere when it reaches the OA-1 observatory. The refraction of light as it enters the Earth's atmosphere is neglected.

For this problem: the atmospheric layer traversed by the starlight is a homogeneous layer, with flat and parallel faces, and the extinction of starlight in the Earth's atmosphere is determined only by photons absorbed, or reflected, by certain particles in the atmosphere.

We define

$$\kappa = 3.405 \cdot nr^2 X_Z = \text{constant}$$

as a combination of constant quantities (n, r, X_Z), called the "coefficient of the first degree" of the atmospheric extinction, where the meanings of n, r, and X_Z are highlighted in the drawing in Figure 4.3.

The quantity X_Z, also a constant quantity, is the thickness of the homogeneous atmospheric layer with parallel flat faces, equivalent to the real, non-homogeneous atmosphere.

It is known that at the time of its observation in the night sky by the astronomical observatory OA-1, the star σ was at its maximum height above the horizon. The gravitational acceleration at the ground is $g = 9.81\,\text{ms}^{-2}$.

c) *Identify* the spectral band in which the star σ was observed, knowing the values of the "coefficient of the first degree" of the atmospheric extinction, $\kappa(\lambda)$, entered in Table 4.1, where the values of the wavelengths of B, V, G, and R radiation from the electromagnetic spectrum are also visible.

d) *Determine* the apparent magnitude, m_0, of the star if it were observed from outside the atmosphere in the same spectral band.

e) For each of the spectral bands in the visible range specified in Table 4.1, complete the cells in the table by determining the numerical values of the quantity nr^2, corresponding to the absorption of light in each of the specified spectral bands, where: n – the volume concentration of absorbing particles from the Earth's

Table 4.1

Spectral band	U	B	V	G	R	I
λ(nm)		470	550	600	780	
$\kappa(\lambda)$	0.6	0.4	0.2	0.166	0.1	0.08
nr^2						

atmosphere; r – the radius of absorbing particles in the Earth's atmosphere.

For this problem: in the vertical profile of the Earth's atmosphere, the temperature and the gravitational acceleration do not vary with the altitude, h, so the density of the atmospheric air, due only to the action of the terrestrial gravitational forces, is given by the law

$$\rho = \rho_0 e^{-m_1 gh/kT},$$

where: ρ_0 – atmospheric air density at sea level; m_1 – average mass of an "air molecule"; $g = 9.81\,\mathrm{m/s^2}$ – gravitational acceleration; k – Boltzmann's constant; and $T_0 = 273.15\,\mathrm{K}$ – the absolute temperature of the atmosphere.

Given: Boltzmann's constant, $k = 1.38 \cdot 10^{-23}\,\frac{\mathrm{J}}{\mathrm{K}}$; the molar mass of air, $\mu_{\mathrm{air}} = 28.96\,\frac{\mathrm{g}}{\mathrm{mol}}$; the speed of light in a vacuum, $c = 3 \cdot 10^8\,\frac{\mathrm{m}}{\mathrm{s}}$; Planck's constant, $h = 6.625 \cdot 10^{-34}\,\mathrm{Js}$; the temperature at the surface of the star σ, $T = 6000\,\mathrm{K}$; the atomic mass unit, $1\,\mathrm{amu} = 1.66 \cdot 10^{-27}\,kg$; Avogadro's number, $N_\mathrm{A} = 6.023 \cdot 10^{23}\,1/\mathrm{mol}$; and the atmospheric pressure at the base of the homogeneous atmospheric layer, $p_0 = 1.013 \cdot 10^5\,\frac{\mathrm{N}}{\mathrm{m}^2}$.

f) *Draw*, on the same diagram, the graphs of the dependences of the apparent magnitudes, $m(X_\mathrm{r})$, of the star σ, knowing that it was observed from OA-1 in all the visible spectral bands specified in Table 4.1.

It is known that, according to Planck's law, the intensity of radiation emitted by a star (the energy emitted by the star per unit time, per unit area of a surface, at normal incidence, per unit wavelength) is given by the expression

$$I_0(\lambda) = \frac{2hc^2}{\lambda^5}\left(e^{hc/k\lambda T} - 1\right)^{-1}.$$

g) *Determine* the zenithal distance of the star σ for which two of the four visual apparent magnitudes, corresponding to the four visual spectral bands (B, V, G, R), are identical for the OA-1 observer.

h) *Determine* what percentage of star σ's light intensity before entering the Earth's atmosphere, I_0, reaches the OA-2 astronomical observatory from altitude H, $\eta = I/I_0$.

i) Determine the ratio $\eta = I/I_0$ assuming that the Earth's atmosphere is a homogeneous spherical layer, as indicated by the drawing in Figure 4.4. The observations of the star are made at sea level at OA-1. Compare this with the result obtained for part **(b)** and formulate a conclusion.

We know: the radius of the Earth is $R = 6370\,\text{km}$.

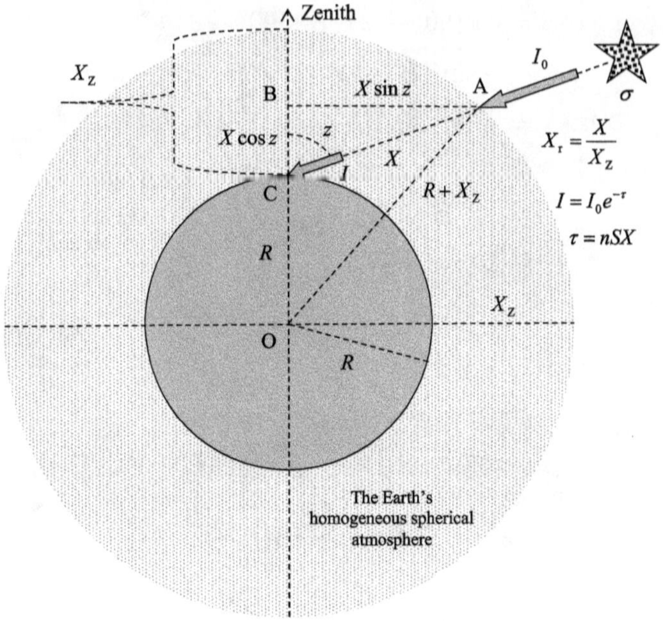

Fig. 4.4

j) *Determine* the ratio $\eta = I/I_0$, assuming that the Earth's atmosphere is an equivalent homogeneous spherical layer, the observations of the star σ being made at the altitude $H = 500\,\text{m}$ above sea level at the astronomical observatory OA-2.

Solution

a) For a star σ, whose apparent position on the celestial sphere is represented in the drawings in Figures 4.5 and 4.6, using one of Gauss's formulas (the second equation of the cosine formulas for the sides) written for the spherical triangle ZPσ (the analog of the standard spherical triangle, ABC), called the *parallactic triangle* or *star position triangle*, we obtain:

$$\cos(\text{arc } Z\sigma) = \cos(\text{arc } ZP) \cdot \cos(\text{arc } P\sigma) + \sin(\text{arc } ZP) \cdot \sin(\text{arc } P\sigma) \cdot \cos H,$$

where H is the hour angle of the star σ;

$$\cos z = \cos(90° - \varphi) \cdot \cos(90° - \delta) + \sin(90° - \varphi) \cdot \sin(90° - \delta) \cdot \cos H;$$

$$\cos z = \sin\varphi \cdot \sin\delta + \cos\varphi \cdot \cos\delta \cdot \cos H.$$

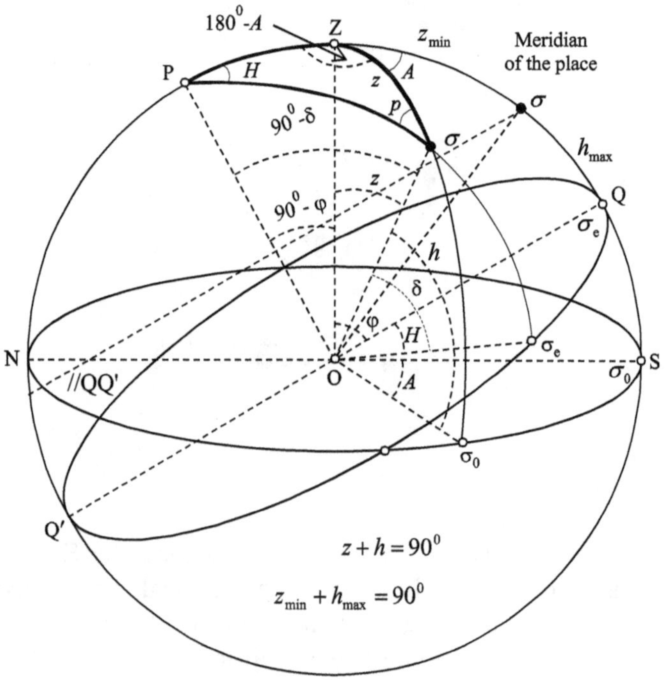

Fig. 4.5

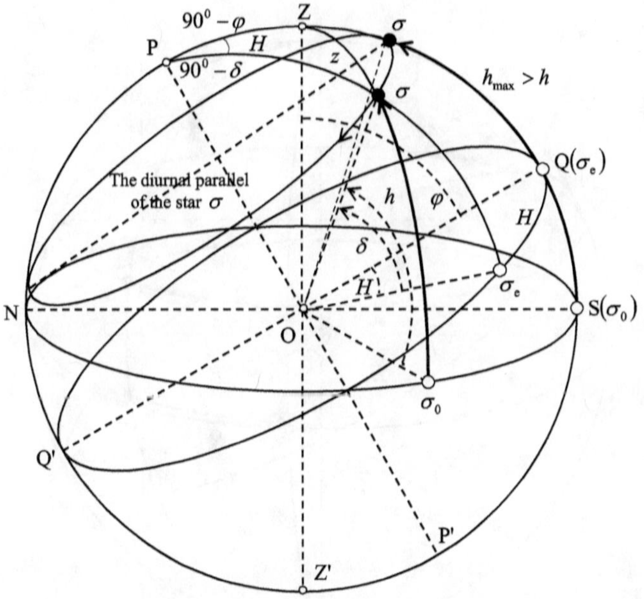

Fig. 4.6

It is known that the vernal point γ, like any point on the ecliptic (drawings in Figures 4.7 and 4.8), is involved in the apparent diurnal movement of the celestial sphere, in a retrograde sense with its celestial (diurnal) parallel identifying with the equator I every day.

At some diurnal moment, the apparent position of the vernal point γ (fictitious, unmarked point on the celestial sphere) is determined by its hour angle, Hγ, measured along the celestial equator, retrograde from the upper meridian of the place, towards the celestial cardinal point west, to the hour circle corresponding to the vernal point γ at that moment of the day.

The *sidereal time* in the place of observation, corresponding to the apparent position of the vernal point γ at a given moment of the day, is the hour angle of the vernal point γ measured along the celestial equator, in a retrograde direction, from the superior meridian of the place to the hour circle of the vernal point γ, expressed in hours:

$$t_s = H_\gamma.$$

In other words, the sidereal time t_s in a certain place (with geographical latitude φ) is the time interval between the passage of the

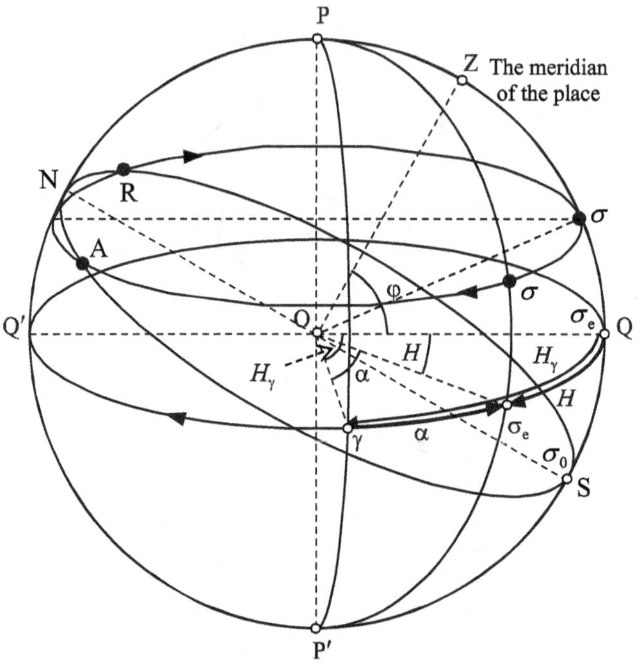

Fig. 4.7

vernal point γ at the superior meridian of the place and a certain diurnal position of the vernal point γ.

The time interval between two consecutive crossings of the vernal point γ at the upper meridian of the place (the time interval between two successive upper culminations of the vernal point γ) is called a *sidereal day.*

Choosing as the origin of the sidereal time ($t_s = 0$) the moment when the vernal point γ passes to the superior meridian of the place, the beginning of the sidereal day, in the considered place, is at midday, when the vernal point γ passes to the superior meridian.

However, there is a major difficulty in determining sidereal time based on the previous definition.

For the vernal point γ, being a fictitious point on the celestial sphere, we cannot observe the transitions to the upper meridian of the place, and its hour angle is impossible to measure directly.

That is why, from the place considered, the passage of a star σ to the upper meridian of the place is observed, and then, at a certain

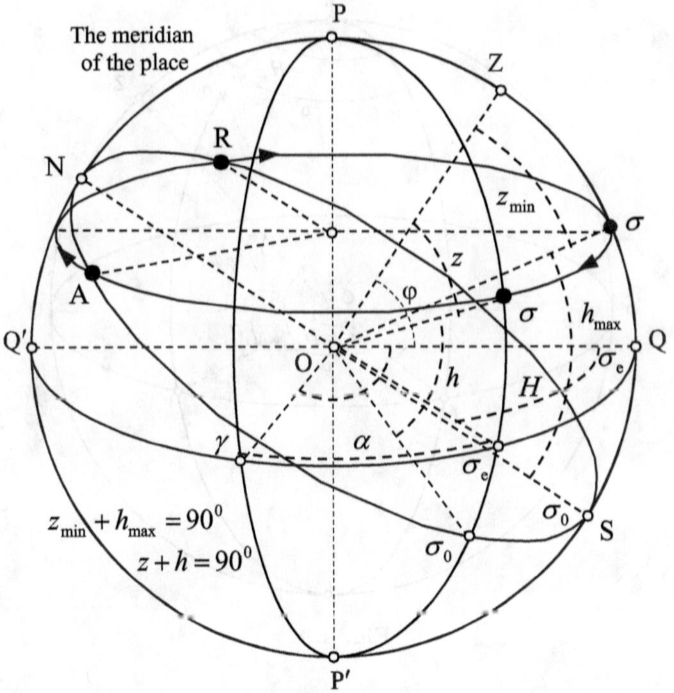

Fig. 4.8

moment of the day, the hour angle H of the star σ is determined, whose right ascension, α, is known, so that we have

$$t_s = H_\gamma = \alpha + H.$$

Corresponding to a diurnal moment of sidereal time, $t_s = H_\gamma$, for a star σ, whose apparent position on the celestial sphere is represented in the drawing in Figure 4.9, the relation

$$H = t_s - \alpha$$

holds, where t_s is the local sidereal time, $t_s = H_\gamma$, and H_γ is the hour angle of the vernal point γ, such that

$$\cos z = \sin\varphi \cdot \sin\delta + \cos\varphi \cdot \cos\delta \cdot \cos(t_s - \alpha).$$

The requirement in the statement of the problem refers to the moment when the star σ passes to the meridian of the place, as

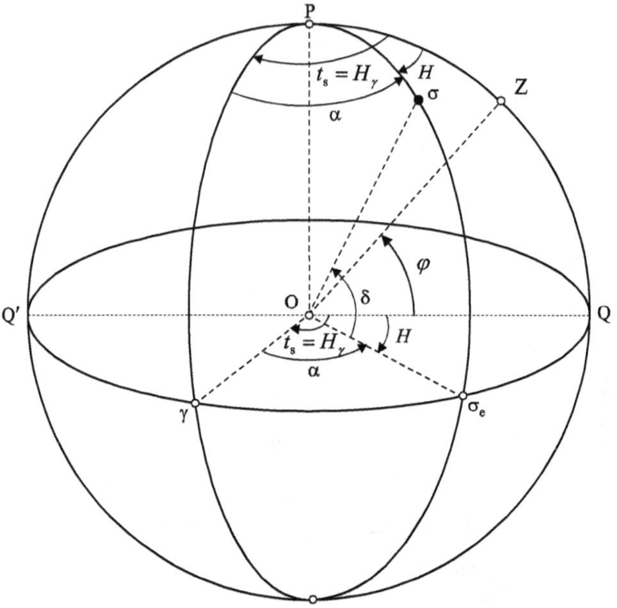

Fig. 4.9

indicated by the drawing in Figure 4.10, when its height above the horizon is maximum, $h_{\max}$. As a result, the local sidereal time of the occurrence of this event is $t_s = 0$, such that:

$$H = t_s - \alpha = -\alpha;$$

$$\cos z = \sin\varphi \cdot \sin\delta + \cos\varphi \cdot \cos\delta \cdot \cos(-\alpha);$$

$$\cos z = \sin\varphi \cdot \sin\delta + \cos\varphi \cdot \cos\delta \cdot \cos\alpha;$$

$$\alpha = 01^{\mathrm{h}}\, 10^{\mathrm{m}}\, 36^{\mathrm{s}} = 17.65°; \quad \delta = 12°30'\,00'' = 12.5°; \quad \varphi = 43°;$$

$$\sin\varphi = 0.681; \quad \cos\varphi = 0.731;$$

$$\sin\delta = 0.216; \quad \cos\delta = 0.976;$$

$$\cos\alpha = 0.952;$$

$$\cos z = 0.681 \cdot 0.216 + 0.731 \cdot 0.976 \cdot 0.952 = 0.826;$$

$$z \approx 34°.$$

b) An effect that must be corrected for when calibrating the instrumental magnitudes of stars is the atmospheric extinction of radiation,

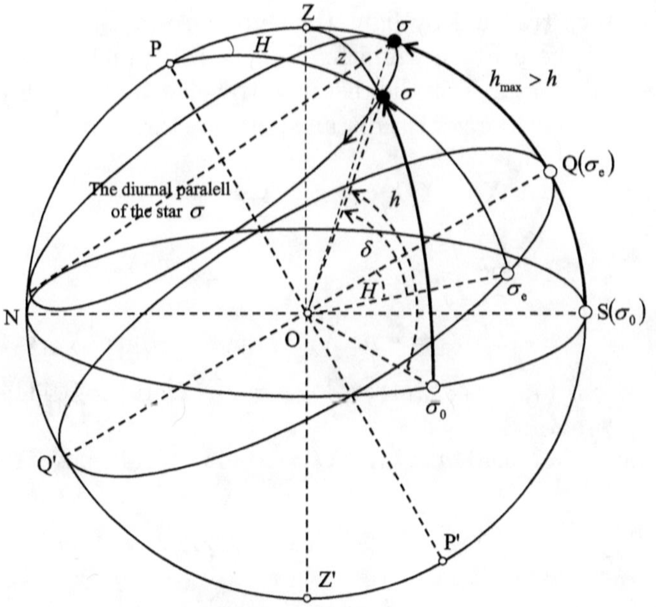

Fig. 4.10

or the diminution of starlight due to passage through the Earth's atmosphere. The longer the path of starlight through the Earth's atmosphere, the greater the extinction of the starlight. As a result, on the same night, from the moment a star rises, being close to the horizon ($z_{\max} = 90°$), until the moment it reaches the zenith ($z = 0$), the distance traveled by the light through the Earth's atmosphere decreases, so that the star becomes brighter (its instrumental magnitude becomes smaller).

For the study of the extinction of stellar radiation due to its selective absorption by particles in the Earth's atmosphere, using the drawing in Figure 4.3 and knowing the empirical formula of the law of absorption, we obtain:

$$I = I_0 \cdot e^{-\tau}; \quad \tau = nSX; \quad n = \frac{N}{V}; \quad S = \pi r^2; \quad X = X_{\mathrm{r}} X_Z;$$

$$X_{\text{zenith}} = X \cos z = X_Z,$$

where r is the radius of absorbing particles in the atmosphere, n is the concentration of absorbing particles in the atmosphere, X_Z

is the distance traveled by light through the atmosphere (thickness of the atmosphere at the zenith, X_Z = constant) when the star is at the zenith, and X is the distance traveled by light through the atmosphere when the zenith distance of the star is z;

$$X = X_{\mathrm{r}} X \cos z; \quad X_{\mathrm{r}} = \frac{1}{\cos z};$$

$$\frac{I}{I_0} = e^{-\tau}; \quad \log\frac{I}{I_0} = \log e^{-nSX} = \log e^{-nSX_Z X_{\mathrm{r}}}$$

$$= -nSX_Z X_{\mathrm{r}} \log e = -n\pi r^2 X_Z X_{\mathrm{r}} \log e;$$

$$\pi = 3.14; \quad e = 2.718; \quad \log e = \log(2.719) = 0.434;$$

$$\log\frac{I}{I_0} = -0.434 n\pi\, r^2 X_Z X_{\mathrm{r}} = -0.434 \cdot 3.14 nr^2 X_Z X_{\mathrm{r}};$$

$$\log\frac{I}{I_0} = -1.362 nr^2 X_Z X_{\mathrm{r}}.$$

On the other hand, according to Pogson's formula, it follows that:

$$\log\frac{I}{I_0} = -0.4(m - m_0); \quad (m - m_0) = -2.5 \cdot \log\frac{I}{I_0},$$

where m_0 is the apparent magnitude of the star, seen from outside the atmosphere (not affected by the phenomenon of atmospheric extinction), and m is the apparent magnitude of the star for the observer (affected by the phenomenon of atmospheric extinction);

$$m - m_0 = -2.5 \cdot \log\frac{I}{I_0} = 2.5 \cdot 1.362 nr^2 X_Z X_{\mathrm{r}};$$

$$m - m_0 = 3.405 \cdot nr^2 X_Z X_{\mathrm{r}};$$

$$\kappa = 3.405 \cdot nr^2 X_Z = \text{constant}.$$

The above is a combination of constant quantities (n, r, X_Z), called the "coefficient of the first degree" of atmospheric extinction, so that:

$$m - m_0 = \kappa X_{\mathrm{r}};$$

$$m = m_0 + \kappa X_{\mathrm{r}}.$$

This proves that the magnitude of the star for the observer on the surface of the Earth, OA-1, after the extinction of the light in the atmosphere, is a function of the parameter

$$X_r = \text{“air mass”},$$

whose physical meaning is that of the “relative” distance traveled by light from entering the Earth's atmosphere to the observer:

$$X_r = \frac{X}{X_{\text{zenith}}},$$

that is, the ratio of the distance traveled by starlight through the atmosphere to the observer, when the star is at some position in the sky, to the distance traveled by starlight through the atmosphere to the observer when the star is at the observer's zenith;

$$X_r \geq 1;$$
$$m(X_r) = m_0 + \kappa X_r.$$

The graph of this dependence is a straight line, as shown in the drawing in Figure 4.11.

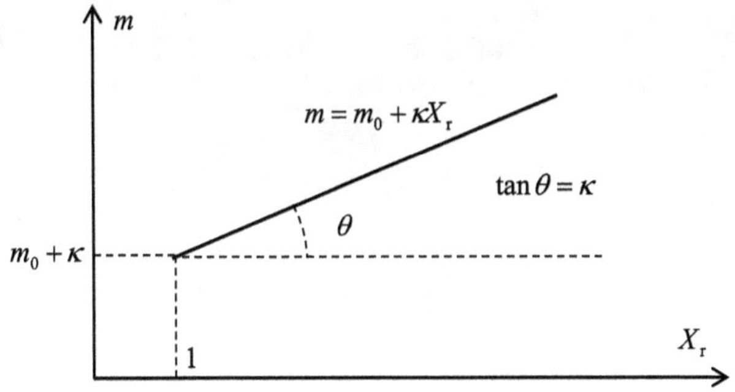

Fig. 4.11

Using the graph represented in the drawing in Figure 4.12, it follows that:

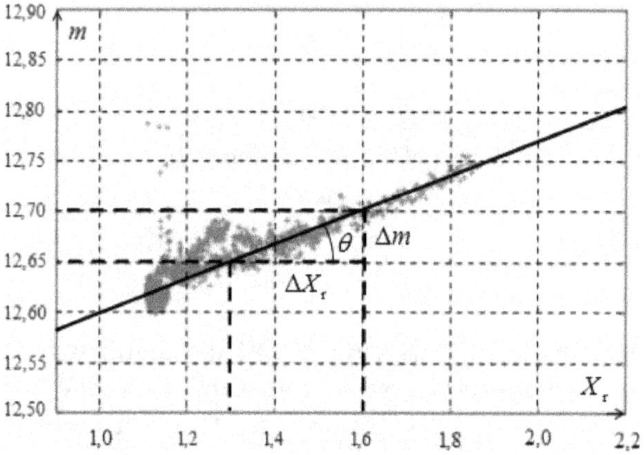

Fig. 4.12

$$\tan\theta = \kappa = \frac{\Delta m}{\Delta X_r} = \frac{0.05}{0.3} \approx 0.166,$$

representing the geometric significance of the "coefficient of the first degree" of atmospheric extinction, $\kappa(\lambda)$;

$$\tan\theta_G = \kappa_G = 0.166;$$

$$0.1 < \kappa_G < 0.2;$$

$$\kappa_R < \kappa_G < \kappa_V;$$

$$\kappa = 3.405nr^2X_Z = \tan\theta = 0.166.$$

Thus:

$$-2.5 \cdot \log\frac{I}{I_0} = 3.405nr^2X_ZX_r = \kappa X_r = 0.166X_r;$$

$$-2.5 \cdot \log\frac{I}{I_0} = 0.166X_r; \quad X_r = \frac{1}{\cos z};$$

$$-2.5 \cdot \log \frac{I}{I_0} = \frac{0.166}{\cos z} = \frac{0.166}{\cos 34°} = \frac{0.166}{0.829};$$

$$\log \frac{I}{I_0} = -\frac{0.166}{0.829 \cdot 2.5} = -0.08;$$

$$\eta = \frac{I}{I_0} = 0.83; \quad I = 0.83 \cdot I_0.$$

c) Locating the value of the coefficient $\kappa = 0.166$ in Table 4.2 that the observation of the star σ was made in the G band, where $\kappa_G = 0.166$. The dependence of the "first degree coefficient" of the atmospheric extinction on the wavelength, $\kappa(\lambda)$, can be found to have higher values for blue radiation (B) than for red radiation (R).

Table 4.2

Spectral band	U	B	V	G	R	I
λ(nm)		470	550	600	780	
$\kappa(\lambda)$	0.6	0.4	0.2	**0.166**	0.1	0.08

d) If the star σ is observed using one of the filters U, B, V, G, R, or I, it follows that:

$$m(X_r; \lambda) = m_0(\lambda) + \kappa(\lambda) X_r(z);$$

$$m(z; \lambda) = m_0(\lambda) + \kappa(\lambda) \cdot X_r.$$

If the star is observed in the G band, when its zenithal distance is the one previously calculated, $z \approx 34°$, then, according to the graph in Figure 4.12:

$$X_r = \frac{1}{\cos z}; \quad z \approx 34°; \quad \cos z = 0.826;$$

$$X_r \approx 1.2; \quad m = 12.63;$$

$$m = m_0 + \kappa X_r;$$

$$X_r = 1.2; \quad m = 12.63;$$

$$m = m_0 + 1.2\kappa;$$

$$m_0 + 1.2\kappa = 12.63; \quad \kappa_G = 0.166;$$

$$m_{0,G} = 12.63 - 1.2\kappa_G = 12.63 - 1.2 \cdot 0.166 = 12.430,$$

representing the magnitude of the star σ, observed outside the Earth's atmosphere, in the spectral band G, when the star's zenith distance is $z \approx 34°$.

e) The general expression of the "first degree coefficient" of atmospheric extinction is

$$\kappa = 3.405nr^2X_Z = \text{constant},$$

where X_Z, also a constant size, is the thickness of the homogeneous atmospheric layer, with parallel flat faces, equivalent to the real, non-homogeneous atmosphere.

For the calculation of the thickness of the homogeneous atmospheric layer, we use the equivalence represented in the drawing in Figure 4.13.

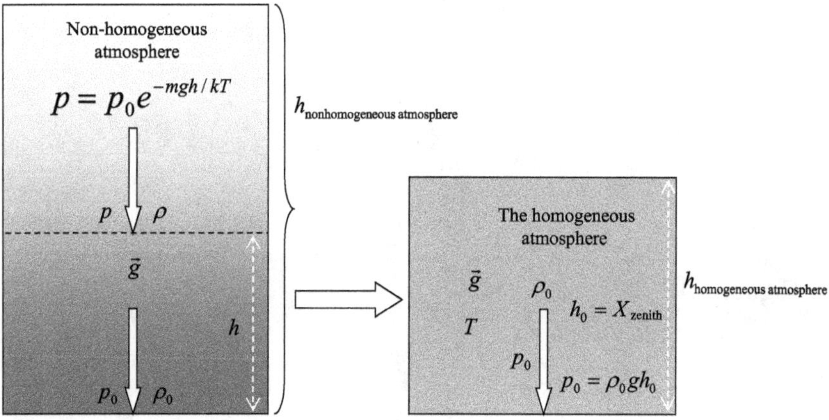

Fig. 4.13

Considering that in the vertical profile of the Earth's atmosphere, the temperature and the gravitational acceleration do not vary with the altitude, h, the density of the atmospheric air, due to the action of the terrestrial gravitational forces, is given by the law

$$\rho = \rho_0 e^{-m_1 gh/kT},$$

where: ρ_0 – atmospheric air density at sea level; m_1 – average mass of an "air molecule"; $g = 9.81\,\mathrm{m/s^2}$ – gravitational acceleration; k – Boltzmann's constant; and $T_0 = 273.15\,\mathrm{K}$ – the absolute temperature of the atmosphere.

If n is the volume concentration of "air molecules", it results that:

$$\rho = \frac{m}{V} = \frac{m_1 N}{V} = m_1 n,$$

where m_1 is the mass of an "air molecule";

$$\rho_0 = \frac{m_0}{V} = \frac{m_1 N_0}{V} = m_1 n_0;$$

$$\rho = \rho_0 e^{-m_1 gh/kT};$$

$$m_1 n = m_1 n_0 e^{-m_1 gh/kT}; \quad n = n_0 e^{-m_1 gh/kT_0};$$

$$p = nkT; \quad p_0 = n_0 kT;$$

$$\frac{p}{kT} = \frac{p_0}{kT} e^{-m_1 gh/kT};$$

$$p = p_0 e^{-m_1 gh/kT},$$

representing the barometric formula for the variation of atmospheric pressure with altitude;

$$p_0 = \rho_0 g h_0; \quad p_0 = 1.013 \cdot 10^5\,\frac{\mathrm{N}}{\mathrm{m^2}};$$

$$\rho_0 = \frac{p_0}{g h_0} = \frac{1.013 \cdot 10^5}{9.81 \cdot 8 \cdot 10^3}\,\frac{\mathrm{kg}}{\mathrm{m^3}} = 1.29\,\frac{\mathrm{kg}}{\mathrm{m^3}},$$

representing the air density in the homogeneous atmosphere equivalent to the real, inhomogeneous atmosphere.

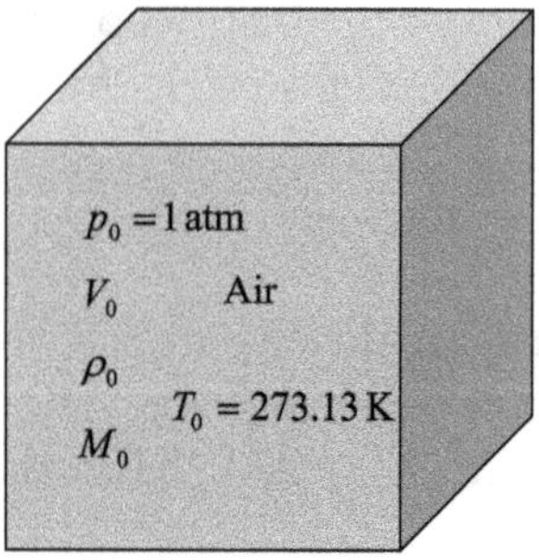

Fig. 4.14

For the air in the container represented in the drawing in Figure 4.14, under normal conditions of pressure and temperature, it follows that:

$$p_0 V_0 = vRT_0 = \frac{N}{N_A} RT_0 = \frac{Nm_1}{N_A m_1} RT_0 = \frac{M_0}{N_A m_1} RT_0;$$

$$\frac{M_0}{V_0} = \rho_0 = \frac{p_0 N_A m_1}{RT_0} = \frac{p_0 m_1}{kT_0},$$

representing the density of the homogeneous atmosphere, equivalent to the inhomogeneous atmosphere;

$$p_0 = \rho_0 g h_0;$$

$$p_0 = \frac{p_0 m_1}{kT_0} g h_0;$$

$$h_0 = \frac{kT_0}{m_1 g},$$

representing the thickness of the homogeneous atmosphere, equivalent to the inhomogeneous atmosphere;

$$k = 1.38 \cdot 10^{-23} \, \frac{\mathrm{J}}{\mathrm{K}};$$

$$\mu = \frac{m}{v} = \frac{m_1 N}{\frac{N}{N_A}} = m_1 N_A;$$

$$m_1 = \frac{\mu_{air}}{N_A} = \frac{28.96 \, \frac{\mathrm{g}}{\mathrm{mol}}}{6.023 \cdot 10^{23} \, \frac{1}{\mathrm{mol}}} = \frac{28.96}{6.023 \cdot 10^{23}} \, \mathrm{g};$$

$$1\,\text{amu} = 1.66 \cdot 10^{-27}\,\text{kg} = 1.66 \cdot 10^{-24}\,\text{g};$$

$$m_1 = \frac{28.96}{6.023 \cdot 10^{23}} \cdot \frac{1}{1.66 \cdot 10^{-24}}\,\text{amu} = \frac{28.96 \cdot 10}{6.023 \cdot 1.66}\,\text{amu} = 28.96\,\text{amu};$$

$$\mu_{\text{air}} = 28.96\,\frac{\text{g}}{\text{mol}}; \quad m_1 = 28.96\,\text{amu} = 28.96 \cdot 1.66 \cdot 10^{-27}\,\text{kg};$$

$$g = 9.81\,\frac{\text{m}}{\text{s}^2};$$

$$t_0 = 0°\text{C}; \quad T_0 = 273.15\,\text{K};$$

$$\rho_0 = \frac{p_0 m_1}{kT} = \frac{1.013 \cdot 10^5 \cdot 28.96 \cdot 1.66 \cdot 10^{-27}}{1.38 \cdot 10^{-23} \cdot 273.15}\,\frac{\text{kg}}{\text{m}^3} \approx 1.3\,\frac{\text{kg}}{\text{m}^3};$$

$$h_0 = \frac{1.38 \cdot 10^{-23} \cdot 273.15}{28.96 \cdot 1.66 \cdot 10^{-27} \cdot 9.81}\,\text{m} \approx 8000\,\text{m} = X_Z;$$

$$h_0 = 8000\,\text{m} = X_Z.$$

Under these conditions, the results are as follows (see Tables 4.3 and 4.4)

$$\kappa(\lambda_{\text{G}}) = \kappa_{\text{G}} = 3.405 \cdot n_{\text{G}} r_{\text{G}}^2 X_Z = 0.166 = \tan\theta_{\text{G}};$$

$$\kappa(\lambda_{\text{R}}) = \kappa_{\text{R}} = 3.405 \cdot n_{\text{R}} r_{\text{R}}^2 X_Z = 0.1 = \tan\theta_{\text{R}};$$

$$\kappa(\lambda_{\text{V}}) = \kappa_{\text{V}} = 3.405 \cdot n_{\text{V}} r_{\text{V}}^2 X_Z = 0.2 = \tan\theta_{\text{V}};$$

$$\kappa(\lambda_{\text{B}}) = \kappa_{\text{B}} = 3.405 \cdot n_{\text{B}} r_{\text{B}}^2 X_Z = 0.4 = \tan\theta_{\text{B}};$$

$$\frac{\kappa_{\text{R}}}{\kappa_{\text{G}}} = \frac{3.405 \cdot n_{\text{R}} r_{\text{R}}^2}{3.405 \cdot n_{\text{G}} r_{\text{G}}^2} = \frac{n_{\text{R}} r_{\text{R}}^2}{n_{\text{G}} r_{\text{G}}^2} = \frac{0.1}{0.166};$$

$$n_{\text{R}} r_{\text{R}}^2 = \frac{0.1}{0.166} \cdot n_{\text{G}} r_{\text{G}}^2;$$

$$n_{\text{G}} r_{\text{G}}^2 = \frac{0.166}{3.405 \cdot X_Z}; \quad X_Z = h_0 = 8000\,\text{m};$$

$$n_{\text{G}} r_{\text{G}}^2 = \frac{0.166}{3.405 \cdot 8} \cdot 10^{-3}\,\text{m}^{-1};$$

$$n_{\text{G}} r_{\text{G}}^2 = 0.00609 \cdot 10^{-3}\,\text{m}^{-1} = 609 \cdot 10^{-8}\,\text{m}^{-1};$$

$$n_{\text{G}} r_{\text{G}}^2 = 609 \cdot 10^{-8}\,\text{m}^{-1};$$

$$n_{\text{R}} r_{\text{R}}^2 = \frac{0.1}{0.166} \cdot 0.00609 \cdot 10^{-3}\,\text{m}^{-1};$$

$$n_{\mathrm{R}} r_{\mathrm{R}}^2 = 0.00366 \cdot 10^{-3}\,\mathrm{m}^{-1} = 366 \cdot 10^{-8}\,\mathrm{m}^{-1};$$

$$n_{\mathrm{R}} r_{\mathrm{R}}^2 = 366 \cdot 10^{-8}\,\mathrm{m}^{-1};$$

$$\frac{\kappa_{\mathrm{V}}}{\kappa_{\mathrm{G}}} = \frac{n_{\mathrm{V}} r_{\mathrm{V}}^2}{n_{\mathrm{G}} r_{\mathrm{G}}^2} = \frac{0.2}{0.166};$$

$$n_{\mathrm{V}} r_{\mathrm{V}}^2 = \frac{0.2}{0.166} \cdot n_{\mathrm{G}} r_{\mathrm{G}}^2;$$

$$n_{\mathrm{V}} r_{\mathrm{V}}^2 = \frac{0.2}{0.166} \cdot 0.00609 \cdot 10^{-3}\,\mathrm{m}^{-1};$$

$$n_{\mathrm{V}} r_{\mathrm{V}}^2 = 0.00733 \cdot 10^{-3}\,\mathrm{m}^{-1} = 733 \cdot 10^{-8}\,\mathrm{m}^{-1};$$

$$n_{\mathrm{V}} r_{\mathrm{V}}^2 = 733 \cdot 10^{-8}\,\mathrm{m}^{-1};$$

$$\frac{\kappa_{\mathrm{B}}}{\kappa_{\mathrm{G}}} = \frac{n_{\mathrm{B}} r_{\mathrm{B}}^2}{n_{\mathrm{G}} r_{\mathrm{G}}^2} = \frac{0.4}{0.166};$$

$$n_{\mathrm{B}} r_{\mathrm{B}}^2 = \frac{0.4}{0.166} \cdot 0.00609 \cdot 10^{-3}\,\mathrm{m}^{-1} = 0.01467 \cdot 10^{-3}\,\mathrm{m}^{-1}$$
$$= 1467 \cdot 10^{-8}\,\mathrm{m}^{-1};$$

$$n_{\mathrm{B}} r_{\mathrm{B}}^2 = 1467 \cdot 10^{-8}\,\mathrm{m}^{-1}.$$

Table 4.3

Spectral band	U	B	V	G	R	I
λ(nm)		470	550	600	780	
$\kappa(\lambda)$	0.6	0.4	0.2	0.166	0.1	0.08

Table 4.4

Spectral band	U	B	V	G	R	I
$\kappa(\lambda)$	0.60	0.40	0.20	0.166	0.10	0.08
$nr^2(10^{-8}\,1/\mathrm{m})$		1467	733	609	366	

f) According to Planck's law, the intensity of the radiation emitted by a star (the energy emitted by a star per unit time, through a unit area of a surface, at normal incidence, per wavelength unit) is given by the expression

$$I_0(\lambda) = \frac{2hc^2}{\lambda^5}\left(e^{hc/k\lambda T} - 1\right)^{-1}, \quad \langle I_0\,(\lambda;T)\rangle_{\mathrm{SI}} = \frac{\mathrm{J}}{\mathrm{s}\cdot\mathrm{m}^2\cdot m}.$$

From this, particularizing for each of the visible spectral bands, it results that (see Table 4.5):

$$I_{0,\mathrm{G}}(\lambda_{\mathrm{G}}) = \frac{2hc^2}{\lambda_{\mathrm{G}}^5}(e^{hc/k\lambda_{\mathrm{G}}T} - 1)^{-1}; \quad \lambda_{\mathrm{G}} = 600\,\mathrm{nm};$$

$$\tan\theta_{\mathrm{G}} = \kappa_{\mathrm{G}} = 0.166;$$

$$k = 1.38 \cdot 10^{-23}\,\frac{\mathrm{J}}{\mathrm{K}}; \quad h = 6.625 \cdot 10^{-34}\,\mathrm{Js}; \quad T = 6000\,\mathrm{K};$$

$$\frac{hc}{k\lambda_{\mathrm{G}}T} = \frac{6.625 \cdot 10^{-34}\,\mathrm{J \cdot s} \cdot 3 \cdot 10^8\,\frac{\mathrm{m}}{\mathrm{s}}}{1.38 \cdot 10^{-23}\,\frac{\mathrm{J}}{\mathrm{K}} \cdot 600 \cdot 10^{-9}\,\mathrm{m} \cdot 6000\,\mathrm{K}} \approx 0.4;$$

$$I_{0,\mathrm{R}}(\lambda_{\mathrm{R}}) = \frac{2hc^2}{\lambda_{\mathrm{R}}^5}(e^{hc/k\lambda_{\mathrm{R}}T} - 1)^{-1}; \quad \lambda_{\mathrm{R}} = 780\,\mathrm{nm};$$

$$\frac{hc}{k\lambda_{\mathrm{R}}T} = \frac{6.625 \cdot 10^{-34}\,\mathrm{J \cdot s} \cdot 3 \cdot 10^8\,\frac{\mathrm{m}}{\mathrm{s}}}{1.38 \cdot 10^{-23}\,\frac{\mathrm{J}}{\mathrm{K}} \cdot 780 \cdot 10^{-9}\,\mathrm{m} \cdot 6000\,\mathrm{K}} \approx 0.3;$$

$$\log\frac{I_{0,\mathrm{R}}}{I_{0,\mathrm{G}}} = -0.4(m_{0,\mathrm{R}} - m_{0,\mathrm{G}});$$

$$\log\left[\left(\frac{\lambda_{\mathrm{G}}}{\lambda_{\mathrm{R}}}\right)^5 \cdot \frac{e^{hc/k\lambda_{\mathrm{G}}T} - 1}{e^{hc\lambda_{\mathrm{R}}T} - 1}\right] = -0.4(m_{0,\mathrm{R}} - m_{0,\mathrm{G}});$$

$$\log\left[\left(\frac{600\,nm}{780\,nm}\right)^5 \cdot \frac{e^{0.4} - 1}{e^{0.3} - 1}\right] = -0.4(m_{0,\mathrm{R}} - m_{0,\mathrm{G}});$$

$$\log\left[\left(\frac{60}{78}\right)^5 \cdot \frac{e^{0,4} - 1}{e^{0,3} - 1}\right] = -0.4(m_{0,\mathrm{R}} - m_{0,\mathrm{G}});$$

$$\log\left[\left(\frac{60}{78}\right)^5 \cdot \frac{1.5 - 1}{1.35 - 1}\right] = -0.4(m_{0,\mathrm{R}} - m_{0,\mathrm{G}});$$

$$\log\left[\left(\frac{60}{78}\right)^5 \cdot \frac{0,5}{0,35}\right] = -0.4(m_{0,\mathrm{R}} - m_{0,\mathrm{G}});$$

$$5 \cdot \log(0.769) + \log(1.428) = -0.4(m_{0,\mathrm{R}} - m_{0,\mathrm{G}});$$

$$m_{0,\mathrm{R}} - m_{0,\mathrm{G}} = -\frac{5 \cdot \log(0.769) + \log(1.428)}{0.4};$$

$$m_{0,\mathrm{R}} - m_{0,\mathrm{G}} = 1.04;$$

$$m_{0,\mathrm{G}} = 12.430;$$

$$m_{0,\mathrm{R}} = 13.470; \kappa_{\mathrm{R}} = 0.1;$$

$$m_{\mathrm{R}} = m_{0,\mathrm{R}} + \kappa_{\mathrm{R}} X_{\mathrm{r}};$$

$$X_{\mathrm{r}} = \frac{X}{X_{\mathrm{zenith}}}; \quad X_{\mathrm{r}} = \frac{1}{\cos z}; \quad z \approx 34^\circ; \quad \cos z = 0.826;$$

$$X_{\mathrm{r}} = \frac{1}{0.826} \approx 1.2;$$

$$X_{\mathrm{r}} \approx 1.2; \kappa_{\mathrm{R}} = 0.1;$$

$$m_{\mathrm{R}} = m_{0,\mathrm{R}} + \kappa_{\mathrm{R}} X_{\mathrm{r}} = 13.470 + 0.1 \cdot 1.2 = 13.590;$$

$$\tan \theta_{\mathrm{R}} = 0.1 = \kappa_{\mathrm{R}};$$

$$I_{0,\mathrm{V}}(\lambda_{\mathrm{V}}) = \frac{2hc^2}{\lambda_{\mathrm{V}}^5}(e^{hc/k\lambda_{\mathrm{V}}T} - 1)^{-1}; \quad \lambda_{\mathrm{V}} = 500\,\mathrm{nm};$$

$$\frac{hc}{k\lambda_{\mathrm{V}}T} = \frac{6.625 \cdot 10^{-34}\,\mathrm{J} \cdot \mathrm{s} \cdot 3 \cdot 10^8\,\frac{\mathrm{m}}{\mathrm{s}}}{1.38 \cdot 10^{-23}\,\frac{\mathrm{J}}{\mathrm{K}} \cdot 500 \cdot 10^{-9}\,\mathrm{m} \cdot 6000\,\mathrm{K}} \approx 0.48;$$

$$\log \frac{I_{0,\mathrm{V}}}{I_{0,\mathrm{G}}} = -0.4(m_{0,\mathrm{V}} - m_{0,\mathrm{G}});$$

$$\log \left[\left(\frac{\lambda_{\mathrm{G}}}{\lambda_{\mathrm{V}}} \right)^5 \cdot \frac{e^{hc/k\lambda_{\mathrm{G}}T} - 1}{e^{hc\lambda_{\mathrm{V}}T} - 1} \right] = -0.4(m_{0,\mathrm{V}} - m_{0,\mathrm{G}});$$

$$\log \left[\left(\frac{600\,\mathrm{nm}}{500\,\mathrm{nm}} \right)^5 \cdot \frac{e^{0.4} - 1}{e^{0.48} - 1} \right] = -0.4(m_{0,\mathrm{V}} - m_{0,\mathrm{G}});$$

$$\log \left[\left(\frac{6}{5} \right)^5 \cdot \frac{1.5 - 1}{1.62 - 1} \right] = -0.4(m_{0,\mathrm{V}} - m_{0,\mathrm{G}});$$

$$\log \left[\left(\frac{6}{5} \right)^5 \cdot \frac{0.5}{0.62} \right] = -0.4(m_{0,\mathrm{V}} - m_{0,\mathrm{G}});$$

$$5 \cdot \log(1.2) + \log(0.806) = -0.4(m_{0,\mathrm{V}} - m_{0,\mathrm{G}});$$

$$m_{0,\mathrm{V}} - m_{0,\mathrm{G}} = -0.755;$$

$$m_{0,\mathrm{G}} = 12.430;$$

$$m_{0,\mathrm{V}} = 11.675; \quad \kappa_\mathrm{V} = 0.2;$$

$$m_\mathrm{V} = m_{0,\mathrm{V}} + \kappa_\mathrm{V} X_\mathrm{r}; \quad X_\mathrm{r} = 1.2;$$

$$m_\mathrm{V} = m_{0,\mathrm{V}} + \kappa_\mathrm{V} X_\mathrm{r} = 11.675 + 0.2 \cdot 1.2 = 11.915;$$

$$\tan\theta_\mathrm{V} = 0.2 = \kappa_\mathrm{V};$$

$$I_{0,\mathrm{B}}(\lambda_\mathrm{B}) = \frac{2hc^2}{\lambda_\mathrm{B}^5}(e^{hc/k\lambda_\mathrm{B}T} - 1)^{-1}; \quad \lambda_\mathrm{B} = 470\,\mathrm{nm};$$

$$\frac{hc}{k\lambda_\mathrm{B}T} = \frac{6.625 \cdot 10^{-34}\,\mathrm{J} \cdot \mathrm{s} \cdot 3 \cdot 10^8\,\frac{\mathrm{m}}{\mathrm{s}}}{1.38 \cdot 10^{-23}\,\frac{\mathrm{J}}{\mathrm{K}} \cdot 470 \cdot 10^{-9}\,\mathrm{m} \cdot 6000\,\mathrm{K}} \approx 0.5;$$

$$\log\frac{I_{0,\mathrm{B}}}{I_{0,\mathrm{G}}} = -0.4(m_{0,\mathrm{B}} - m_{0,\mathrm{G}});$$

$$\log\left[\left(\frac{\lambda_\mathrm{G}}{\lambda_\mathrm{B}}\right)^5 \cdot \frac{e^{hc/k\lambda_\mathrm{G}T} - 1}{e^{hc\lambda_\mathrm{B}T} - 1}\right] = -0.4(m_{0,\mathrm{B}} - m_{0,\mathrm{G}});$$

$$\log\left[\left(\frac{600\,\mathrm{nm}}{470\,\mathrm{nm}}\right)^5 \cdot \frac{e^{0.4} - 1}{e^{0.5} - 1}\right] = -0.4(m_{0,\mathrm{B}} - m_{0,\mathrm{G}});$$

$$\log\left[\left(\frac{60}{47}\right)^5 \cdot \frac{1.5 - 1}{1.65 - 1}\right] = -0.4(m_{0,\mathrm{B}} - m_{0,\mathrm{G}});$$

$$\log\left[\left(\frac{60}{47}\right)^5 \cdot \frac{0.5}{0.65}\right] = -0.4(m_{0,\mathrm{B}} - m_{0,\mathrm{G}});$$

$$\log\left[\left(\frac{60}{47}\right)^5 \cdot \frac{0.5}{0.65}\right] = -0.4(m_{0,\mathrm{B}} - m_{0,\mathrm{G}});$$

$$5 \cdot \log(1.276) + \log(0.769) = -0.4(m_{0,\mathrm{B}} - m_{0,\mathrm{G}});$$

$$m_{0,\mathrm{B}} - m_{0,\mathrm{G}} = -1.037;$$

$$m_{0,\mathrm{G}} = 12.430;$$

$$m_{0,\mathrm{B}} = 11.393;$$

$$m_\mathrm{B} = m_{0,\mathrm{B}} + \kappa_\mathrm{B} X_\mathrm{r}; \quad \kappa_\mathrm{B} = 0.4;$$

$$X_r = 1.2; \quad m_B = m_{0,B} + \kappa_B X_r = 11.393 + 0.4 \cdot 1.2 = 11.873;$$

$$\tan\theta_B = 0.4 = \kappa_B;$$

$$m_{0,G} = 12.430;$$

$$m_G = m_{0,G} + \kappa_G X_r; \quad \kappa_G = 0.166;$$

$$X_r = 1.2; \quad m_G = m_{0,G} + \kappa_G X_r = 12.430 + 0.166 \cdot 1.2 = 12.629;$$

$$\tan\theta_G = 0.166 = \kappa_G.$$

Table 4.5

Spectral band	U	B	V	G	R	I
λ(nm)		470	550	600	780	
$\kappa(\lambda)$	0.60	0.40	0.20	0.166	0.10	0.08
$nr^2(10^{-8}\,1/\text{m})$		1467	733	609	366	

The dependencies of the apparent magnitudes, $m(X_r)$, of the star σ are given by:

$$m_R = m_{0,R} + \kappa_R X_r = 13.470 + 0.1 \cdot X_r;$$

$$m_V = m_{0,V} + \kappa_V X_r = 11.675 + 0.2 \cdot X_r;$$

$$m_B = m_{0,B} + \kappa_B X_r = 11.393 + 0.4 \cdot X_r;$$

$$m_G = m_{0,G} + \kappa_G X_r = 12.430 + 0.166 \cdot X_r.$$

Using the data from Table 4.6, the graphs are represented in Figure 4.15.

Table 4.6

	$X_R = 1$	$X_R = 2$
m_R	13.570	13.670
m_V	11.875	11.915
m_B	11.793	11.873
m_G	12.596	12.629

g) The coordinates of the intersection point of graphs B and V, from Figure 4.15, are:

$$X_r = 1.5; \quad m_B = m_V = 12.00.$$

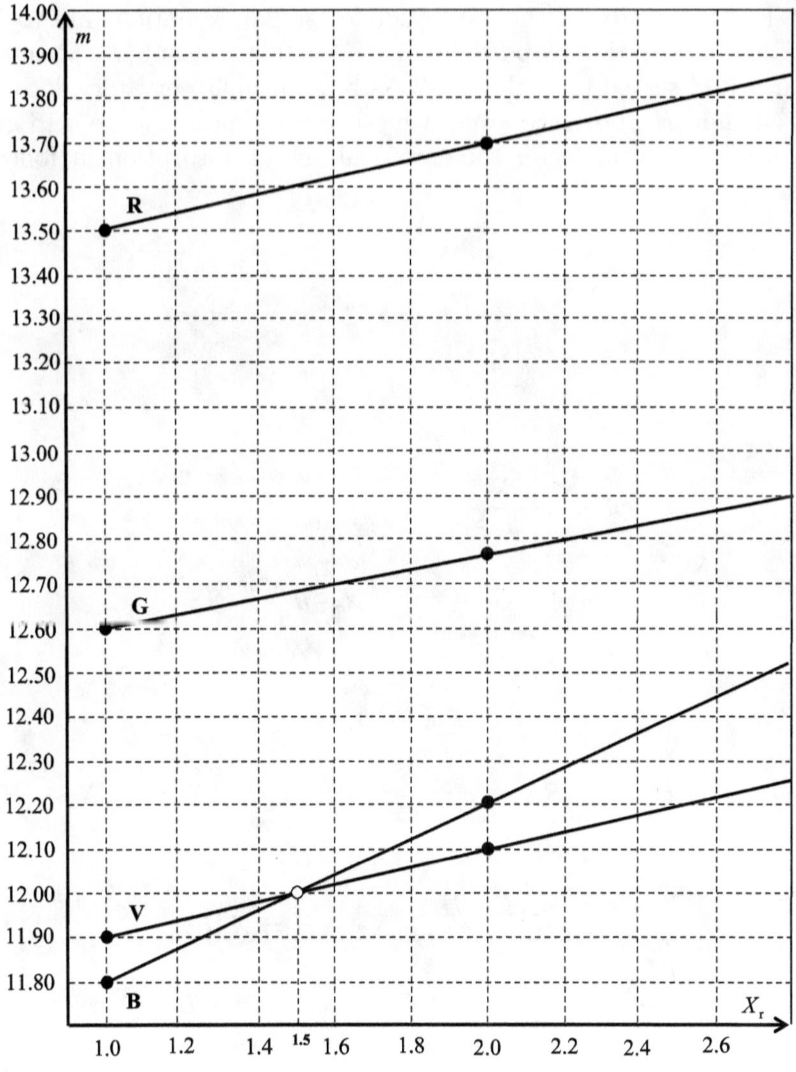

Fig. 4.15

This results in:

$$X_r = \frac{1}{\cos z^*} = 1.5; \quad \cos z^* = 0.66;$$

$$z^* = 37.83^\circ = 37^\circ 49' 48''.$$

h) For the study of the extinction of stellar radiation due to its selective absorption by particles in the Earth's atmosphere, when the star σ is observed from the OA-2 Astronomical Observatory, located at altitude H above sea level, using the drawing in Figure 4.16 and knowing the formula for the empirical law of absorption, it follows that:

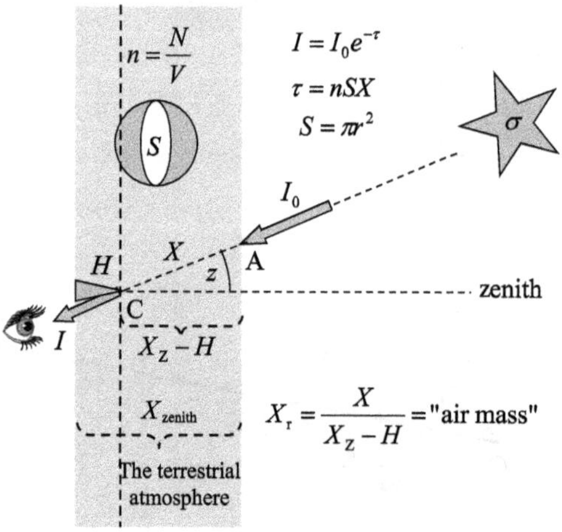

Fig. 4.16

$$I = I_0 \cdot e^{-\tau}; \quad \tau = nSX; \quad n = \frac{N}{V}; \quad S = \pi r^2; \quad X = X_{\mathrm{r}}(X_Z - H);$$

$$\tau = nSX_r(X_Z - H);$$

$$\cos z = \frac{X_Z - H}{X}; \quad X_Z - H = X\cos z;$$

$$X_{\mathrm{r}} = \frac{X}{X_Z - H}; \quad X = X_{\mathrm{r}}(X_Z - H); \quad X_Z - H = X\cos z;$$

$$X_{\mathrm{r}} = \frac{X}{X\cos z} = \frac{1}{\cos z}; \quad X = X_{\mathrm{r}}(X_Z - H);$$

$$\frac{I}{I_0} = e^{-\tau};$$

$$\log\frac{I}{I_0} = \log e^{-nSX} = \log e^{-nSX_r(X_Z - H)}$$

$$= -nSX_r(X_Z - H)\log e = -n\pi r^2 X_{\mathrm{r}}(X_Z - R)\log e;$$

$$\tau = nSX_r(X_Z - H);$$

$$\pi = 3.14; \quad e = 2.718; \quad \log e = \log(2.719) = 0.434;$$

$$\log \frac{I}{I_0} = -0.434 n\pi\, r^2 X_{\mathrm{r}}(X_Z - H) = -0.434 \cdot 3.14 nr^2 X_{\mathrm{r}}(X_Z - H);$$

$$\log \frac{I}{I_0} = -1.362 nr^2 (X_Z - H) X_{\mathrm{r}}.$$

On the other hand, according to Pogson's formula, it follows that:

$$\log \frac{I}{I_0} = -0.4(m - m_0); \quad (m - m_0) = -2.5 \cdot \log \frac{I}{I_0},$$

where m_0 is the apparent magnitude of the star, seen from outside the atmosphere (not affected by the phenomenon of atmospheric extinction) and m is the apparent magnitude of the star for the observer (affected by the phenomenon of atmospheric extinction);

$$m - m_0 = -2.5 \cdot \log \frac{I}{I_0} = 2.5 \cdot 1.362 nr^2 (X_Z - H) X_{\mathrm{r}};$$

$$m - m_0 = 3.405 nr^2 (X_Z - H) X_{\mathrm{r}};$$

$$\kappa_{\text{OA-2}} = 3.405 nr^2 (X_Z - H) = \text{constant}.$$

The above is a combination of constant quantities $(n,\ r,\ X_Z, H)$, called the "coefficient of the first degree" of atmospheric extinction, at the OA-2 Astronomical Observatory, so that:

$$\kappa_{\text{OA-2}} = 3.405 nr^2 X_Z - 3.405 nr^2 H;$$

$$m - m_0 = \kappa_{\text{OA-2}} X_{\mathrm{r}};$$

$$m = m_0 + \kappa_{\text{OA-2}} X_{\mathrm{r}}.$$

This proves that the magnitude of the star for the observer at the altitude H, OA-2, after the extinction of the light in the atmosphere, is a function of the parameter

$$X_{\mathrm{r}} = \text{"air mass"},$$

whose physical meaning is that of the relative distance traveled by light from entering the Earth's atmosphere to the observer:

$$X_{\mathrm{r}} = \frac{X}{X_Z - H},$$

that is, the ratio of the distance traveled by starlight through the atmosphere to the observer when the star is at some position in the sky, to the distance traveled by starlight through the atmosphere to the observer when the star is at the observer's zenith;

$$X_{\mathrm{r}} \geq 1;$$

$$m(X_{\mathrm{r}}) = m_0 + \kappa_{\text{OA-2}} X_{\mathrm{r}}; \quad \tan\theta_{\text{OA-2}} = \kappa_{\text{OA-2}}.$$

This results in:

$$m - m_0 = -2.5 \cdot \log \tfrac{I}{I_0} = 2.5 \cdot 1.362 n r^2 (X_Z - H) X_{\mathrm{r}};$$

$$-2.5 \cdot \log \tfrac{I}{I_0} = 3.405 n r^2 (X_Z - H) X_{\mathrm{r}} = \kappa_{\text{OA-2}} X_{\mathrm{r}};$$

$$-2.5 \cdot \log \tfrac{I}{I_0} = (3.405 n r^2 X_Z - 3.405 n r^2 H) X_{\mathrm{r}} = \kappa_{\text{OA-2}} X_{\mathrm{r}};$$

$$(3.405 n r^2 X_Z - 3.405 n r^2 H) = \kappa_{\text{OA-2}} = \tan\theta_{\text{OA-2}}.$$

Thus, in the band of yellow radiation, we obtain:

$$-2.5 \cdot \log \frac{I}{I_0} = (3.405 n_{\mathrm{G}} r_{\mathrm{G}}^2 X_Z - 3.405 n_{\mathrm{G}} r_{\mathrm{G}}^2 H) X_{\mathrm{r}} = \kappa_{\text{OA-2,G}} X_{\mathrm{r}};$$

$$(3.405 n_{\mathrm{G}} r_{\mathrm{G}}^2 X_Z - 3.405 n_{\mathrm{G}} r_{\mathrm{G}}^2 H) = \kappa_{\text{OA-2,G}},$$

where

$$n_{\mathrm{G}} r_{\mathrm{G}}^2 = 609 \cdot 10^{-8}\,\mathrm{m}^{-1}, \quad X_Z = 8000\,\mathrm{m}, \quad H = 500\,\mathrm{m}.$$

Thus:

$$-2.5 \cdot \log \frac{I}{I_0} = 0.15 \cdot X_{\mathrm{r}} = \kappa_{\text{OA-2,G}} X_{\mathrm{r}};$$

$$\kappa_{\text{OA-2,G}} = 0.15 = \tan\theta_{\text{OA-2,G}};$$

$$-2.5 \cdot \log \frac{I}{I_0} = 0.15 X_{\mathrm{r}};$$

$$-2.5 \cdot \log \frac{I}{I_0} = 0.15 X_{\mathrm{r}}; \quad X_{\mathrm{r}} = \frac{1}{\cos z};$$

$$-2.5 \cdot \log \frac{I}{I_0} = \frac{0.15}{\cos z} = \frac{0.15}{\cos 34^\circ} = \frac{0.15}{0.829};$$

$$\log\frac{I}{I_0} = -\frac{0.15}{0.829\cdot 2.5} = -0.07;$$

$$\eta = \frac{I}{I_0} = 0.85; \quad I = 0.85\cdot I_0.$$

Additionally:

$$(3.405 n_{\mathrm{G}} r_{\mathrm{G}}^2 X_Z - 3.405 n_{\mathrm{G}} r_{\mathrm{G}}^2 H) = \kappa_{\text{OA-2,G}} = \tan\theta_{\text{OA-2,G}};$$

$$3.405 n_{\mathrm{G}} r_{\mathrm{G}}^2 X_Z = \tan\theta_{\text{OA-1,G}} = \tan\theta_{\mathrm{G}} = \kappa_{\mathrm{G}} = 0.166;$$

$$n_{\mathrm{G}} r_{\mathrm{G}}^2 = 609\cdot 10^{-8}\,\mathrm{m}^{-1}; \quad H = 500\,\mathrm{m};$$

$$\tan\theta_{\text{OA-1}} - 3.405 n_{\mathrm{G}} r_{\mathrm{G}}^2 H = \tan\theta_{\text{OA-2,G}};$$

$$\tan\theta_{\text{OA-2,G}} = \tan\theta_{\text{OA-1}} - 3.405 n_{\mathrm{G}} r_{\mathrm{G}}^2 H;$$

$$\tan\theta_{\text{OA-2,G}} < \tan\theta_{\text{OA-1,G}};$$

$$\theta_{\text{OA-2,G}} < \theta_{\text{OA-1}};$$

$$\kappa_{\text{OA-2,G}} = \kappa_{\text{OA-1,G}} - 3.405 n_{\mathrm{G}} r_{\mathrm{G}}^2 H;$$

$$\kappa_{\text{OA-2,G}} < \kappa_{\text{OA-1,G}}.$$

This is indicated by the graphs in Figure 4.17, where:

$$m - m_0 = -2.5\cdot\log\frac{I}{I_0} = 2.5\cdot 1.362 n r^2 (X_Z - H) X_{\mathrm{r}};$$

$$m - m_0 = 2.5\cdot 1.362 n r^2 (X_Z - H) X_{\mathrm{r}};$$

$$m - m_0 = 3.405\cdot n r^2 (X_Z - H) X_{\mathrm{r}};$$

$$m = m_0 + \kappa_{\text{OA-2,G}} X_{\mathrm{r}}.$$

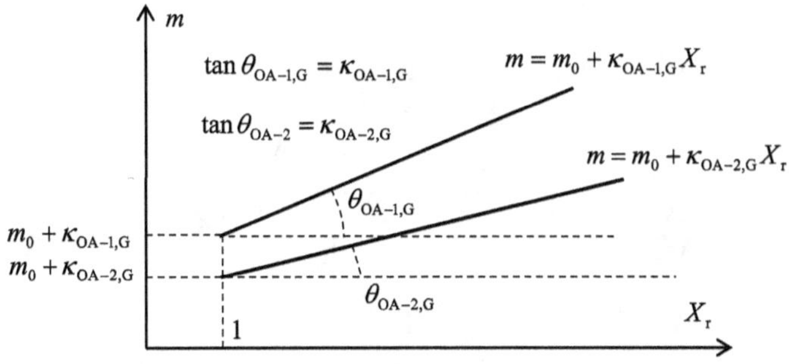

Fig. 4.17

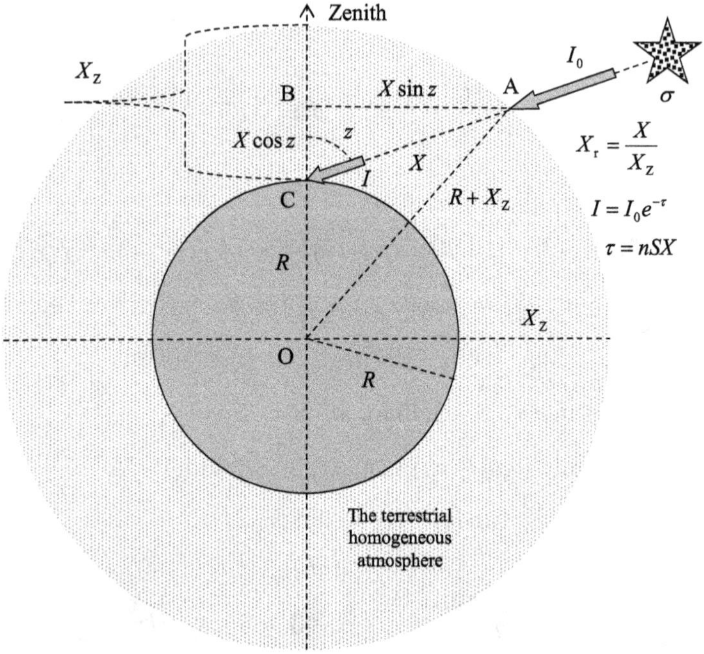

Fig. 4.18

i) In accordance with the notation in Figure 4.18, where the model of the spherical and homogeneous atmospheric layer is presented, from Δ(OAB), it follows that:

$$(R + X \cos z)^2 + (X \sin z)^2 = (R + X_Z)^2;$$

$$R^2 + 2RX \cos z + X^2 \cos^2 z + X^2 \sin^2 z = R^2 + 2RX_Z + X_Z^2;$$

$$2RX \cos z + X^2 = 2RX_Z + X_Z^2;$$

$$X^2 + 2R \cos z \cdot X - X_Z (2R + X_Z) = 0;$$

$$X = \sqrt{R^2 \cos^2 z + X_Z (2R + X_Z)} - R \cos z;$$

$$X_r = \frac{X}{X_Z} = \frac{\sqrt{R^2 \cos^2 z + X_Z (2R + X_Z)} - R \cos z}{X_Z};$$

$$X_{\mathrm{r}} = \frac{\sqrt{R^2\cos^2 z + X_Z\left(2\frac{R^2}{R} + X_Z\frac{R^2}{R^2}\right)} - R\cos z}{X_Z};$$

$$X_{\mathrm{r}} = \frac{\sqrt{R^2\cos^2 z + R^2\left(2\frac{X_Z}{R} + \frac{X_Z^2}{R^2}\right)} - R\cos z}{X_Z};$$

$$X_{\mathrm{r}} = \frac{R\cdot\sqrt{\cos^2 z + \left(2\frac{X_Z}{R} + \frac{X_Z^2}{R^2}\right)} - R\cos z}{X_Z};$$

$$X_{\mathrm{r}} = \frac{R}{X_Z}\cdot\sqrt{\cos^2 z + 2\frac{X_Z}{R} + \left(\frac{X_Z}{R}\right)^2} - \frac{R}{X_Z}\cos z;$$

$$I = I_0\cdot e^{-\tau};\quad \tau = nSX; X_{\mathrm{r}} = \frac{X}{X_Z};\quad X = X_Z X_{\mathrm{r}};$$

$$\frac{I}{I_0} = e^{-\tau};\quad \log\frac{I}{I_0} = \log e^{-nSX} = \log e^{-nSX_Z X_{\mathrm{r}}} = -nSX_Z X_{\mathrm{r}}\log e;$$

$$e = 2.718;$$

$$\log\frac{I}{I_0} = -0.434 n\pi r^2 X_Z X_{\mathrm{r}} = -0.434\cdot 3,14 n r^2 X_Z X_{\mathrm{r}}$$
$$= -1.362 n r^2 X_Z X_{\mathrm{r}};$$

$$\log\frac{I}{I_0} = -0.4(m - m_0);$$

$$m - m_0 = -2.5\cdot\log\frac{I}{I_0} = 2.5\cdot 1.362 n r^2 X_Z X_{\mathrm{r}} = 3.405 n r^2 X_Z X_{\mathrm{r}};$$

$$-2.5\cdot\log\frac{I}{I_0} = 3.405 n r^2 X_Z X_{\mathrm{r}};$$

$$\kappa = 3.405 n r^2 X_Z;\quad -2.5\cdot\log\frac{I}{I_0} = \kappa X_{\mathrm{r}};$$

$$\log\frac{I}{I_0} = -1.362\cdot n r^2 X_Z X_{\mathrm{r}};$$

$$\kappa = 3.405 n r^2 X_Z = \text{constant},$$

being a combination of constant quantities (n, r, X_Z), called the "coefficient of the first degree" of atmospheric extinction.

Using the graph represented in Figure 4.12, the validity of which is maintained in this case as well, it results that:

$$\tan\theta = \kappa = \frac{\Delta m}{\Delta X_{\mathrm{r}}} = \frac{0.05}{0.3} \approx 0.166;$$

$$-2.5\cdot\log\frac{I}{I_0} = \kappa X_{\mathrm{r}}; \quad -2.5\cdot\log\frac{I}{I_0} = 0.166\cdot X_{\mathrm{r}};$$

$$\log\frac{I}{I_0} = -0.0664\cdot X_{\mathrm{r}};$$

$$X_{\mathrm{r}} = \frac{R}{X_Z}\cdot\sqrt{\cos^2 z + 2\frac{X_Z}{R} + \left(\frac{X_Z}{R}\right)^2} - \frac{R}{X_Z}\cos z;$$

$$\log\frac{I}{I_0} = -0.0664\cdot\left[\frac{R}{X_Z}\cdot\sqrt{\cos^2 z + 2\frac{X_Z}{R} + \left(\frac{X_Z}{R}\right)^2} - \frac{R}{X_Z}\cos z\right];$$

$$X_Z = 8000\,\mathrm{m}; \quad R = 6370\,\mathrm{km}; \quad z = 34^\circ; \quad \cos z = 0.829;$$

$$\frac{R}{X_Z} = 796.25; \frac{X_Z}{R} = 0.001255886; 2\frac{X_Z}{R} = 0.002511773;$$

$$\left(\frac{X_Z}{R}\right)^2 = 0.000001577; \quad \cos^2 z = 0.687241;$$

$$\sqrt{\cos^2 z + 2\frac{X_Z}{R} + \left(\frac{X_Z}{R}\right)^2} = 0.830514509;$$

$$\frac{R}{X_Z}\cdot\sqrt{\cos^2 z + 2\frac{X_Z}{R} + \left(\frac{X_Z}{R}\right)^2} = 661.297178;$$

$$\frac{R}{X_Z}\cos z = 660.09125;$$

$$X_{\mathrm{r}} = \left[\frac{R}{X_Z}\cdot\sqrt{\cos^2 z + 2\frac{X_Z}{R} + \left(\frac{X_Z}{R}\right)^2} - \frac{R}{X_Z}\cos z\right] = 1.205928;$$

$$X_r = \frac{R}{X_Z} \cdot \sqrt{\cos^2 z + 2\frac{X_Z}{R} + \left(\frac{X_Z}{R}\right)^2} - \frac{R}{X_Z}\cos z;$$

$$X_r \approx 1.206;$$

$$\log\frac{I}{I_0} = -0.0664 \cdot X_r;$$

$$\log\frac{I}{I_0} = -0.0800784;$$

$$\eta = \frac{I}{I_0} = 0.8316; \quad I = 0.8316 \cdot I_0.$$

j) According to the notation from Figure 4.19, which presents the model of the spherical and homogeneous atmospheric layer, from $\Delta(OAC)$, it results that:

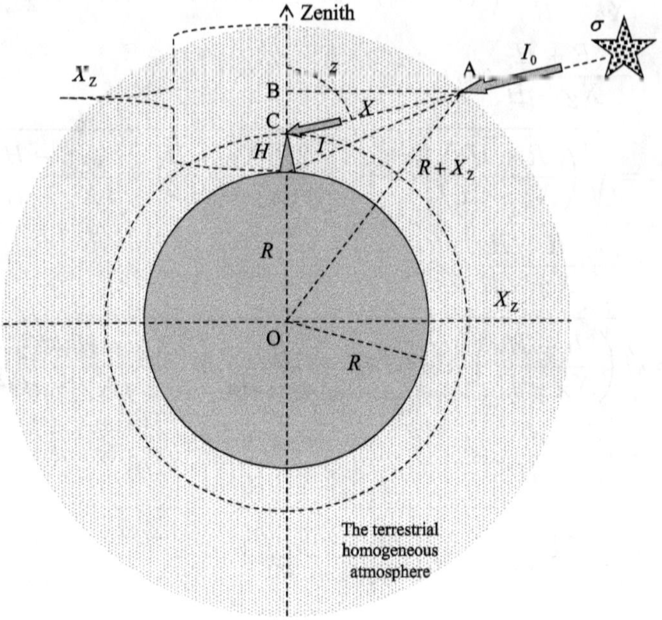

Fig. 4.19

$$(R + X_Z)^2 = (R + H)^2 + X^2 - 2X(R + H)\cos(180 - z);$$

$$\cos(180° - z) = -\cos z;$$

$$(R+X_Z)^2 = (R+H)^2 + X^2 + 2X(R+H)\cos z;$$

$$X^2 + 2(R+H)\cos z \cdot X - 2RX_Z - X_Z^2 + 2RH + H^2 = 0;$$

$$X = -(R+H)\cos z \pm \sqrt{(R+H)^2\cos^2 z + 2RX_Z + X_Z^2 - 2RH - H^2};$$

$$X = -(R+H)\cos z \pm \sqrt{(R+H)^2\cos^2 z + 2R(X_Z - H) + X_Z^2 - H^2};$$

$$X = -(R+H)\cos z + \sqrt{(R+H)^2\cos^2 z + 2R(X_Z - H) + X_Z^2 - H^2};$$

$$X_\mathrm{r} = \frac{X}{X_Z - H};$$

$$X_\mathrm{r} = \frac{\sqrt{(R+H)^2\cos^2 z + 2R(X_Z - H) + X_Z^2 - H^2} - (R+H)\cos z}{X_Z - H};$$

$$X_\mathrm{r} = \frac{1}{X_Z - H}\cdot\sqrt{(R+H)^2\cos^2 z + 2R(X_Z - H) + X_Z^2 - H^2} - \frac{R+H}{X_Z - H}\cos z;$$

$$X_\mathrm{r} = \sqrt{\left(\frac{R+H}{X_Z - H}\right)^2\cos^2 z + \frac{2R(X_Z - H)}{(X_Z - H)^2} + \frac{X_Z^2 - H^2}{(X_Z - H)^2}} - \frac{R+H}{X_Z - H}\cos z;$$

$$X_\mathrm{r} = \sqrt{\left(\frac{R+H}{X_Z - H}\right)^2\cos^2 z + \frac{2R}{(X_Z - H)} + \frac{(X_Z - H)(X_Z + H)}{(X_Z - H)^2}} - \frac{R+H}{X_Z - H}\cos z;$$

$$X_\mathrm{r} = \sqrt{\left(\frac{R+H}{X_Z - H}\right)^2\cos^2 z + \frac{2R}{(X_Z - H)} + \frac{(X_Z + H)}{(X_Z - H)}} - \frac{R+H}{X_Z - H}\cos z;$$

$$X_Z = 8000\,\mathrm{m};\quad R = 6370\,\mathrm{km};\quad z = 34^\circ;\quad \cos z = 0.829;\quad H = 500\,\mathrm{m};$$

$$\frac{R+H}{X_Z - H} = 849.4;\qquad \frac{2R}{X_Z - H} = 1698.666;\qquad \frac{X_Z + H}{X_Z - H} = 1.133;$$

$$X_\mathrm{r} = 1.206950;$$

$$X_\mathrm{r} \approx 1.207;$$

$$\log \frac{I}{I_0} = -0.0664 \cdot X_\mathrm{r};$$

$$\log \frac{I}{I_0} \approx -0.0801448;$$

$$\eta = \frac{I}{I_0} = 0.8315; \quad I = 0.8315 \cdot I_0.$$

Problem 5

Moons of Jupiter

Given the relevant data for Jupiter's four moons (Io, Europa, Ganymede, and Callisto), two astronomers plotted the graphs shown in Figures 5.1 and 5.2, each of which represents the dependence graph $\log|T_{(s)}| = f(\log|a_{(m)}|)$, where: $|T_{(s)}|$ – the numerical value of the period of each month expressed in seconds; $|a_{(m)}|$ – the numerical value of the average distance between Jupiter and any of its moons, expressed in meters.

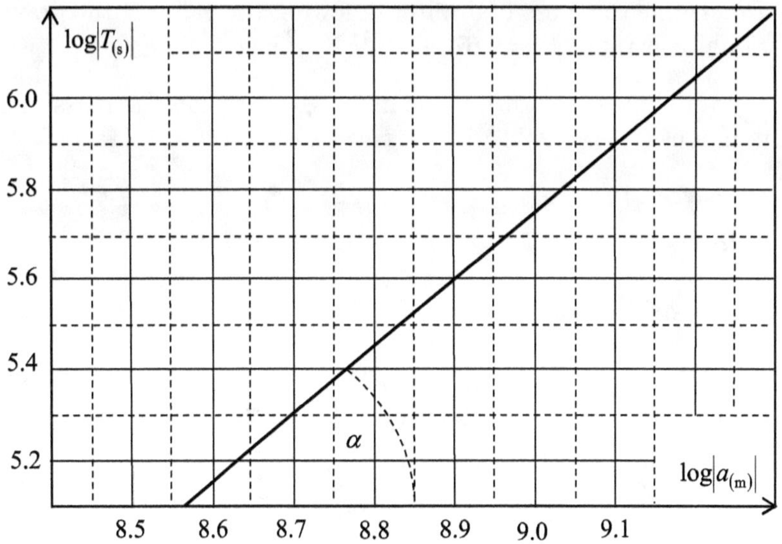

Fig. 5.1

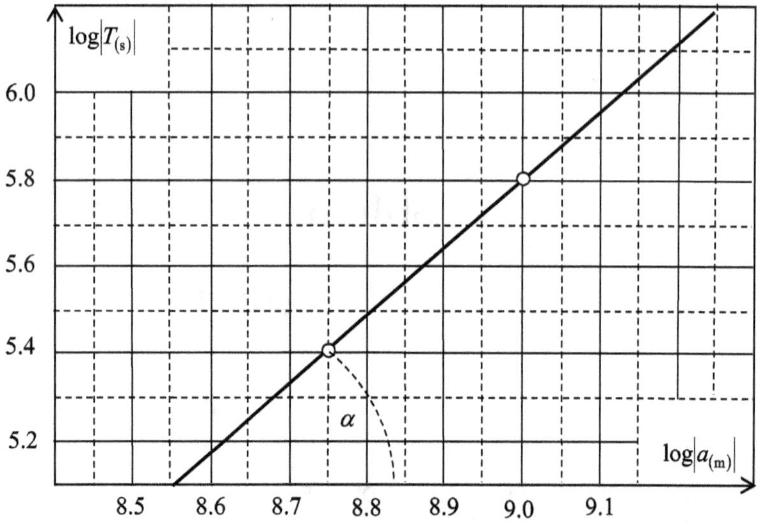

Fig. 5.2

a) Between the graphic variants represented in Figures 5.1 and 5.2, identify the correct version of the dependence $\log|T_{(\mathrm{s})}| = f(\log|a_{(\mathrm{m})}|)$, valid for the four moons of Jupiter: Io, Europa, Ganymede, and Callisto.

b) *Determine* the mass of Jupiter, knowing the value of the gravitational constant, $K = 6.673 \cdot 10^{-11}\,\mathrm{Nm^2\,kg^{-2}}$.

Jupiter's mass is known to be much greater than the mass of any of its moons.

Solution

a) Kepler's third law is written for Jupiter and any of its moons as follows:

$$T^2 = \frac{4\pi^2}{K(M+m)} \cdot a^3.$$

This results in:

$$M \gg m;$$

$$T^2 = \frac{4\pi^2}{KM} \cdot a^3;$$

$$2\log T = \log\frac{4\pi^2}{K} - \log M + 3\log a;$$

$$\log T = \frac{1}{2}\cdot\log\frac{4\pi^2}{K} - \frac{1}{2}\cdot\log M + \frac{3}{2}\cdot\log a;$$

$$\log T = \frac{3}{2}\cdot\log a + \frac{1}{2}\cdot\log\frac{4\pi^2}{K} - \frac{1}{2}\cdot\log M;$$

$$\log T = y; \quad \log a = x;$$

$$m = \frac{3}{2}; \quad \frac{1}{2}\cdot\log\frac{4\pi^2}{K} - \frac{1}{2}\cdot\log M = b;$$

$$y = mx + b,$$

representing the equation of a straight line, where $m = \frac{3}{2} = 1.5$ indicates the slope of the straight line, which is also calculated from each graph. This results in:

$$(\text{Fig. } 5.1)\ m = 1.5;$$

$$(\text{Fig. } 5.2)\ m = 1.6.$$

So, we identify the graphic representation in Figure 5.1 as correct.

b) With the notation and numerical values presented on the system of axes in Figure 5.3, it results that:

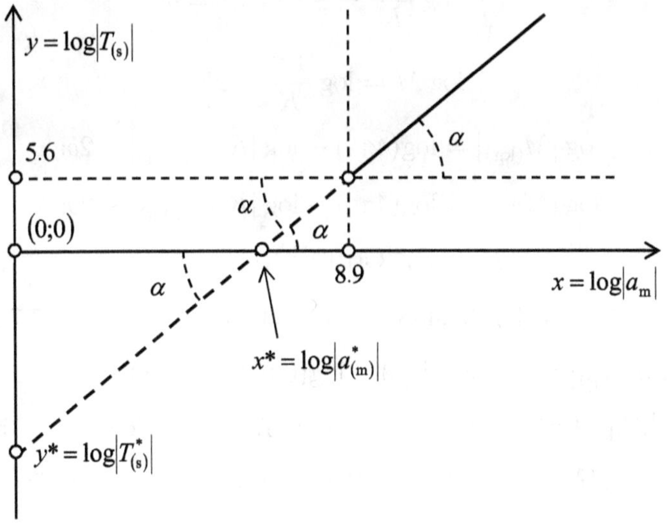

Fig. 5.3

$$\tan\alpha = \frac{5.6}{8.9 - x^*} = m = 1.5;$$

$$\frac{5.6}{8.9 - x^*} = 1.5; \quad x^* = 5.166 = \log(a^*_{(m)});$$

$$\tan\alpha = \frac{5.6 + |y^*|}{8.9} = m = 1.5;$$

$$\frac{5.6 + |y^*|}{8.9} = 1.5; \quad |y^*| = 7.75; y^* = -7.75 = \log|T^*_{(\mathrm{s})}|;$$

$$\tan\alpha = \frac{|y^*|}{x^*} = m = 1.5;$$

$$\frac{x^*}{|y^*|} = 1.5;$$

$$y = mx + b;$$

$$y = 0; \quad x = x^*; \quad 0 = mx^* + b;$$

$$b = -mx^* = -(1.5) \cdot (5.16) = -7.75;$$

$$x = 0; \quad y = y^*; \quad b = y^*;$$

$$b = -mx^* = y^* = -7.75;$$

$$\frac{1}{2} \cdot \log\frac{4\pi^2}{K} - \frac{1}{2} \cdot \log M = b;$$

$$\log M = \log\frac{4\pi^2}{K} - 2b;$$

$$\log|M_{(\mathrm{kg})}| = \log(4\pi^2) - \log|K_{(\mathrm{Nm^2\,kg})}| - 2b;$$

$$\log|M_{(\mathrm{kg})}| = \log(4\pi^2) - \log|K_{(\mathrm{Nm^2\,kg})}| - 2b;$$

$$K = 6.673 \cdot 10^{-11}\,\mathrm{Nm^2\,kg^{-2}};$$

$$\log|M_{(\mathrm{kg})}| = \log(39.4384) - \log(6.673 \cdot 10^{-11}) - 2(-7.75);$$

$$\log|M_{(\mathrm{kg})}| = \log(39.4384) - \log(6.673) - \log(10^{-11}) + 15.5;$$

$$\log|M_{(\mathrm{kg})}| = \log(39.4384) - \log(6.673) + 11 \cdot \log(10) + 15.5;$$

$$\log|M_{(\mathrm{kg})}| = 1.5959 - 0.8243 + 11 + 15.5 = 27.27;$$

$$\log|M_{(\text{kg})}| = 27.27 = \log(10^{27.27}) = \log(10^{27} \cdot 10^{0.27});$$

$$|M_{(\text{kg})}| = 10^{0.27} \cdot 10^{27};$$

$$10^{0.27} = x; \quad \log x = 0.27; \quad x = 1.9;$$

$$|M_{(\text{kg})}| = 1.9 \cdot 10^{27};$$

$$M_{\text{Jupiter}} = 1.9 \cdot 10^{27}\ \text{kg}.$$

Problem 6

A Comet Around the Sun

The rotation period of a comet around the Sun is $T_c = 76$ years, and the minimum distance of the comet from the Sun is $r_{c,min} = 1.8 \cdot 10^8$ km. *Determine* the maximum distance between the comet and the Sun, $r_{c,max}$. *Given*: the radius of the Earth's circular orbit around the Sun, $R_E = 1.5 \cdot 10^8$ km; the period of rotation of the Earth around the Sun, $T_E = 1$ year.

Solution

According to Kepler's third law, it follows that:

$$r_{c,min} + r_{c,max} = 2a_C;$$

$$T_E^2 = \frac{4\pi^2}{KM_S} R_E^3; \quad T_c^2 = \frac{4\pi^2}{KM_S} a_c^3;$$

$$r_{c,max} = 2R_E \cdot \sqrt[3]{\frac{T_c^2}{T_E^2}} - r_{c,min}.$$

Problem 7

Visible Circumpolar Stars

It is commonly believed that the number of stars visible to the naked eye in the entire sky is $N = 6000$ stars. *Estimate* the number of circumpolar stars visible to the naked eye, N_c, if the observer is placed at the angular distances:

a) $\Delta\alpha = 1^\circ$, towards the North Pole;
b) $\Delta\alpha = 1^\circ$, towards the Equator, towards the north.

Solution

a) For an observer located in the center O of the topocentric celestial sphere, at latitude φ and at sea level (zero altitude), all the stars represented in the drawing in Figure 7.1 appear as circumpolar stars. Their diurnal parallels, parallels to the celestial equator, lie above the true horizon of the place (N_0S_0). The star σ_0 is at the limit of circumpolarity because its diurnal parallel touches the true horizon of the place, at the point N_0, but remains above it. Star σ_0 is a *marginally circumpolar star.*

The variant presented does not take into account the refraction of light coming from the star, crossing the Earth's atmosphere.

For this observer, from the isosceles triangle $O\sigma_0N_0$, it results that:

$$\delta_{0,\min} + 90^\circ + (\varphi - \delta_{\min}) = 180^\circ;$$

$$\delta_{0,\min} = 90^\circ - \varphi.$$

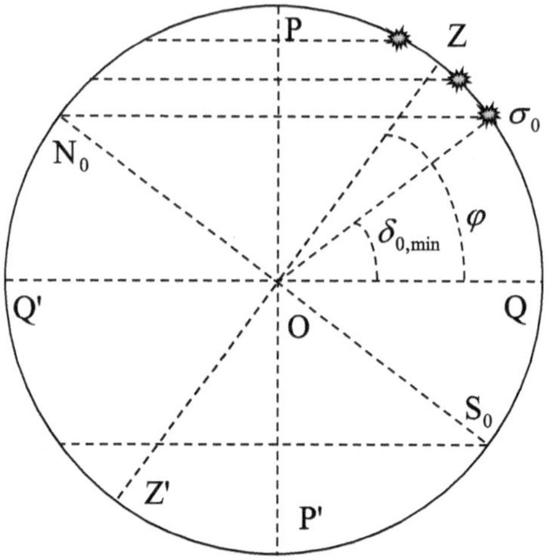

Fig. 7.1

Under the conditions of the problem, if the observer is near the geographic North Pole, as indicated by the drawing in Figure 7.2, the angular distance means that the observer is at an observation point with the latitude $\varphi = 89°$. As a result, for this observer, the star σ_0 with the declination $\delta_{0,\min} = 90° - \varphi = 1°$ is at the limit of circumpolarity. Thus, for this observer, the stars above the celestial equator contained in the equatorial belt of angular width $\Delta\theta = \delta_{0,\min} = 1°$ will not be visible circumpolar stars. They will be rising and setting stars. So will the stars included in the equatorial belt below the equator to the diurnal parallel of S_0. The stars below the diurnal parallel of S_0 are circumpolar stars from the southern celestial hemisphere, invisible to the considered observer.

As a result of these clarifications, for the observer located in the Northern Hemisphere at the latitude $\varphi = 89°$, these stars will appear as circumpolar stars visible to the naked eye. These stars are uniformly distributed on the surface of the spherical dome represented in the drawing in Figure 7.3, where $\delta_{0,\min} = 1°$ and $\theta = 89°$.

We know that the surface area of the spherical dome and the surface area of the sphere are:

$$S_{\text{dome}} = 2\pi Rh = 2\pi R \cdot R(1 - \cos\theta) = 4\pi R^2 \sin^2\frac{\theta}{2};$$

$$S_{\text{sphere}} = 4\pi R^2.$$

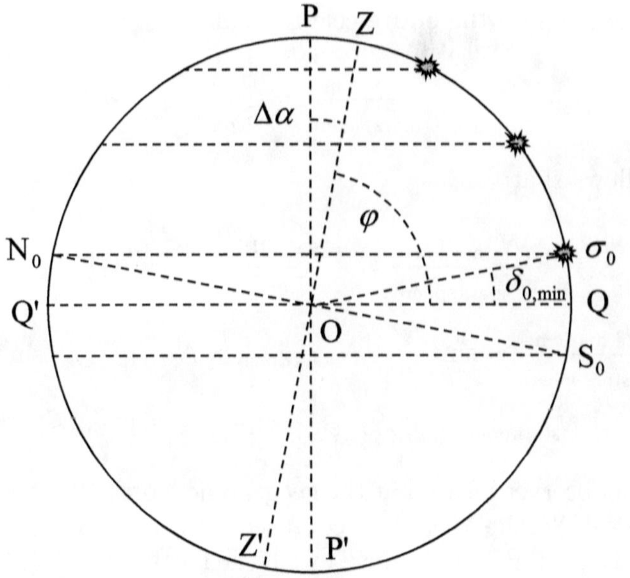

Fig. 7.2

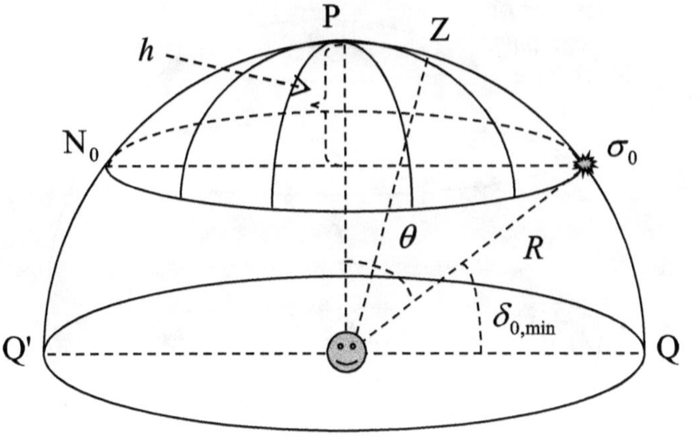

Fig. 7.3

Assuming the uniform distribution of stars on the celestial sphere, it follows that the ratio between the surface area of the dome on the celestial sphere and the surface area of the entire celestial sphere is equal to the ratio between the number of stars on the dome and the number of stars on the entire celestial sphere:

$$\frac{N_{\text{stars dome}}}{N_{\text{stars sphere}}} = \frac{S_{\text{dome}}}{S_{\text{sphere}}}.$$

So, it follows that:

$$\frac{N_{\text{stars dome}}}{N_{\text{stars sphere}}} = \frac{4\pi R^2 \sin^2\frac{\theta}{2}}{4\pi R^2} = \sin^2\frac{\theta}{2};$$

$$\frac{N_{\text{stars dome}}}{N_{\text{stars sphere}}} = \sin^2\frac{\theta}{2}; \quad N_{\text{stars dome}} = N_{\text{stars sphere}} \cdot \sin^2\frac{\theta}{2};$$

$$N_{\text{stars dome}} = 6000 \cdot \sin^2(44.5°) \approx 2947 \text{ stars.}$$

For an observer located at the geographic North Pole ($\varphi = +90°$), the celestial North Pole, P, is confused with the zenith, Z, so that the Earth's axis, PP′, is confused with the local vertical, ZZ′, and the plane of the celestial equator, QQ′, is confused with the plane of the astronomical horizon, NS, as indicated by the drawing in Figure 7.4.

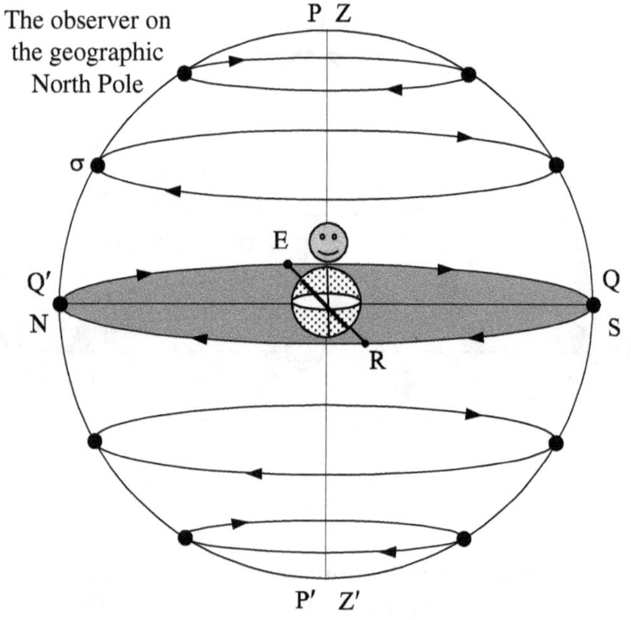

Fig. 7.4

Under these conditions, the observer at the geographic North Pole appreciates that the diurnal celestial parallels of the stars are parallel both to the celestial equator and to the true horizon so that, in relation to the observer, all the stars in the northern celestial hemisphere ($\delta > 0$) are stars without sunset (always visible), and the stars in the southern celestial hemisphere ($\delta < 0$) are stars without sunrise (always invisible).

The number of circumpolar stars (without sunset) visible to the naked eye if the observer were right at the geographic North Pole would be half of the total number (6000) of stars visible in the entire sky to the naked eye, that is, 3000 stars. These are the stars whose declination is $\delta > 0$.

b) For the observer at the latitude $\varphi = \Delta\alpha = 1°$, as indicated in the drawing in Figure 7.5, the star σ_0, at the limit of circumpolarity, is at the angular distance $\Delta\alpha = 1°$ from the celestial North Pole, P.

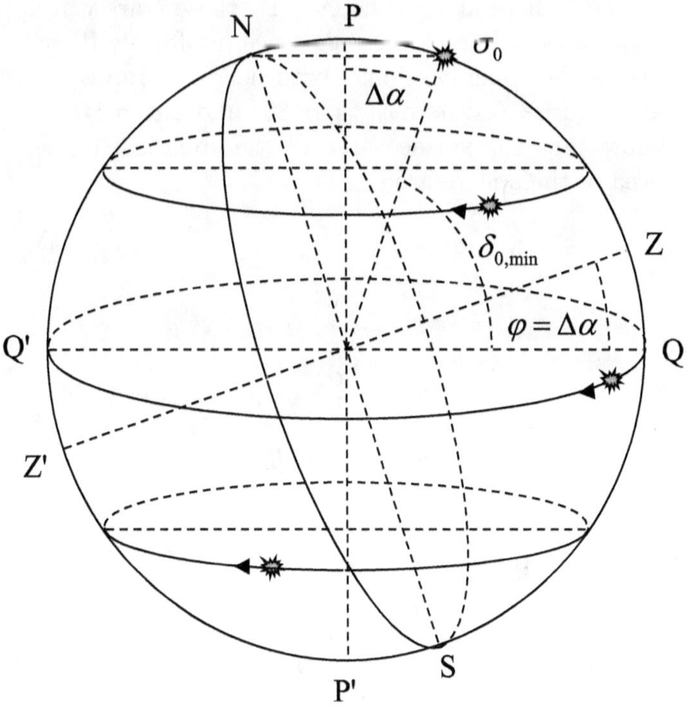

Fig. 7.5

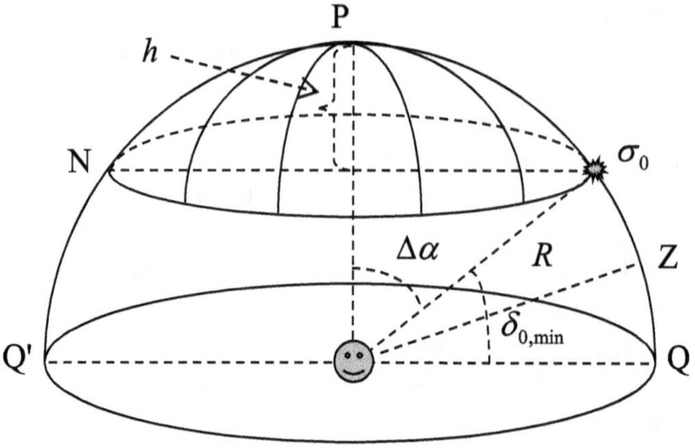

Fig. 7.6

As a result of these clarifications, for the observer located in the Northern Hemisphere at latitude $\varphi = 1°$, these stars will appear as circumpolar stars visible to the naked eye, uniformly distributed on the surface of the spherical dome, with height h, represented in the drawing in Figure 7.6, where $\delta_{0,\min} = 89°$ and $\Delta\alpha = 1°$.

We know that the surface area of the spherical dome and the surface area of the sphere are:

$$S_{\text{dome}} = 2\pi Rh = 2\pi R \cdot R(1 - \cos\Delta\alpha) = 4\pi R^2 \sin^2\frac{\Delta\alpha}{2};$$

$$\sin\Delta\alpha \approx \Delta\alpha;$$

$$S_{\text{dome}} \approx 4\pi R^2 \cdot \frac{(\Delta\alpha)^2}{4} = \pi R^2 \cdot (\Delta\alpha)^2;$$

$$S_{\text{sphere}} = 4\pi R^2.$$

Assuming the uniform distribution of stars on the celestial sphere, it follows that the ratio between the surface area of the dome on the celestial sphere and the surface area of the entire celestial sphere is equal to the ratio between the number of stars on the dome and the number of stars on the entire celestial sphere:

$$\frac{N_{\text{stars dome}}}{N_{\text{stars sphere}}} = \frac{S_{\text{dome}}}{S_{\text{sphere}}}.$$

So, it follows that:

$$\frac{N_{\text{stars dome}}}{N_{\text{stars sphere}}} = \frac{\pi R^2 \cdot (\Delta\alpha)^2}{4\pi R^2} = \frac{1}{4} \cdot (\Delta\alpha)^2;$$

$$N_{\text{stars dome}} = \frac{N_{\text{stars sphere}}}{4} \cdot (\Delta\alpha)^2;$$

$$N_{\text{stars dome}} \approx 0.45,$$

representing the number of circumpolar stars visible to the observer at latitude $\varphi = 1°$.

Being a sub-unit fraction, the result is unacceptable. It means that looking with the naked eye from the specified position, none of the stars in the sky will be appreciated as a visible circumpolar star!

In particular, for an observer located right on the terrestrial Equator ($\varphi = 0$), the north celestial pole, P, is on the horizon, at the north celestial cardinal point, N, and the south celestial pole, P′, is on the horizon at the south celestial cardinal point, S, as indicated by the drawing in Figure 7.7. The plane of the celestial equator is

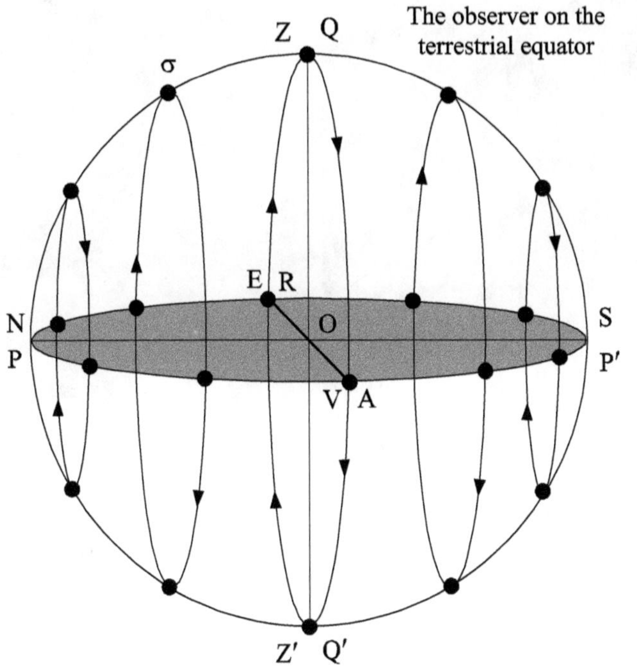

Fig. 7.7

perpendicular to the plane of the true horizon of the place, intersecting it according to the direction of the celestial cardinal points east–west, passing through Z and Z′.

Under these conditions, the observer on the terrestrial Equator appreciates that the diurnal celestial parallels of the stars are circles parallel to the celestial equator, perpendicular to the plane of the true horizon, so that, relative to the observer, all the stars have risen (on the NES sector of the true horizon) and set (on the SWN sector of the true horizon).

Half of the length of the diurnal parallel of each star is above the true horizon, and the other half is below the true horizon, so that the duration of visibility of each star is equal to the duration of its invisibility (12 h). *For this observer there are no visible circumpolar stars.*

Problem 8

Cepheid Period

Cepheids are stars whose volumes are radially variable, through alternate compressions and dilations (Cepheids keep their spherical shapes), with short periods, P, from 1 to 130 days, which causes periodic variations in their brightness, materializing as variations in their apparent magnitudes, which can reach $\Delta m = 2^{\mathrm{m}}$.

During the radial fluctuations of a Cepheid, it remains a homogeneous sphere (with constant density, ρ). In addition, we consider that the temperature and the mass of the Cepheid remain constant, T and μ, respectively.

a) *Determine* the period of the radial variation of the Cepheid's volume, P, knowing the Cepheid's density, ρ, and the gravitational attraction constant, K.

b) *Determine* the apparent magnitude, m, of the Cepheid.

It is known that, for the homogeneous differential equation

$$\frac{\mathrm{d}^2 R}{\mathrm{d}t^2} - q \cdot R = 0,$$

where $R = R(t)$ is the radius of the Cepheid at a given moment, and q is a constant quantity, the general solution is

$$R(t) = a \cdot \cos(\sqrt{q} \cdot t) + b \cdot \sin(\sqrt{q} \cdot t),$$

where a and b are integration constants. For this expression, with P being the period of the radial variation of the Cepheid's volume, it must be true that:

$$\sqrt{q} \cdot t = \sqrt{q} \cdot P = 2\pi.$$

The following constant is known:

$$C = \frac{(\mu \cdot K)^{2/3} \cdot T^4 \cdot P^{4/3} \cdot \Delta_0^2}{(4\pi^2)^{2/3} R_0^2 \cdot T_0^4 \cdot \Delta^2},$$

which includes constants with known values and meanings: μ – Cepheid mass; T – Cepheid surface temperature; P – the period of the Cepheid's radial pulsations; Δ – distance between Earth and the Cepheid; R_0 – radius of the Sun; T_0 – the surface temperature of the Sun; Δ_0 – the distance between the Earth and the Sun; and K – the constant of universal attraction. In addition, the apparent magnitude of the Sun is also known, m_0.

Solution

a) The *luminous intensity* of the Cepheid is:

$$I = \frac{\phi}{\Omega} = \frac{L}{\Omega} = \frac{\frac{W}{t}}{\Omega} = \frac{W}{t \cdot \Omega},$$

i.e., the *energy flux* emitted by the Cepheid per unit solid angle;

$$\Omega = \frac{A}{\Delta^2}; \quad A = \Omega \cdot \Delta^2; \quad \phi = I \cdot \Omega.$$

The *energy illumination* (energy flux density) of the Cepheid, at the observer, is:

$$E = \frac{\phi}{A} = \frac{I \cdot \Omega}{\Omega \cdot \Delta^2};$$

$$E = \frac{I}{\Delta^2};$$

$$E = \frac{\phi}{A} = \frac{\phi}{4\pi\Delta^2} = \frac{\frac{W}{t}}{4\pi\Delta^2} = \frac{L}{4\pi\Delta^2},$$

that is, the energy flux per unit surface area of the Cepheid reaching the observer, located at the distance Δ from the Cepheid, perpendicular to the observer–Cepheid direction.

This results in:

$$L = 4\pi R^2 \cdot \sigma \cdot T^4;$$

$$E = \frac{L}{4\pi\Delta^2}; \quad E = \frac{\phi}{A} = \frac{I \cdot \Omega}{\Omega \cdot \Delta^2}; \quad E = \frac{I}{\Delta^2};$$

$$\frac{L}{4\pi\Delta^2} = \frac{I}{\Delta^2}; \quad L = 4\pi \cdot I; \quad I = \frac{L}{4\pi};$$

$$L = 4\pi R^2 \cdot \sigma \cdot T^4; \quad I = R^2 \cdot \sigma \cdot T^4.$$

These relationships show that a variation in the Cepheid's radius corresponds to a variation in its brightness, and therefore a variation in its apparent magnitude:

$$E = \frac{L}{4\pi\Delta^2}; \quad \mu L = 4\pi R^2 \cdot \sigma \cdot T^4;$$

$$E = \frac{4\pi R^2 \cdot \sigma \cdot T^4}{4\pi\Delta^2};$$

$$E = \frac{R^2 \cdot \sigma \cdot T^4}{\Delta^2}.$$

This represents the illumination energy (energy flux density) of the Cepheid for the observer, a relationship that shows, through the dependence $E = E(R^2)$, that a variation in the Cepheid's radius corresponds to a variation in its brightness and, therefore, a variation in its apparent magnitude.

According to Pogson's formula,

$$\log \frac{E}{E_0} = -0.4 \cdot (m - m_0),$$

where E_0 and m_0 are the illuminance and apparent magnitude of a reference star, respectively.

Corresponding to a moment, t, when the Cepheid is considered a homogeneous sphere with the mass μ, the density ρ, and the radius R, the force acting on a body with mass μ_0 located on the surface of the Cepheid is

$$F = K \cdot \frac{\mu_0 \cdot \mu}{R^2}.$$

Thus, the radial acceleration of the body with mass μ_0 due to the gravitational attraction that the Cepheid exerts on the body when the volume of the Cepheid varies radially is:

$$g = \frac{F}{\mu_0} = \frac{d^2R}{dt^2} = K \cdot \frac{1}{R^2} \cdot \rho \cdot \frac{4\pi}{3} \cdot R^3;$$

$$\frac{d^2R}{dt^2} = \frac{4\pi\rho K}{3} \cdot R;$$

$$q = \frac{4\pi\rho K}{3} = \text{constant};$$

$$\frac{d^2R}{dt^2} = q \cdot R; \quad \frac{d^2R}{dt^2} - q \cdot R = 0.$$

This is a homogeneous differential equation, whose general solution is

$$R(t) = a \cdot \cos\left(\sqrt{q} \cdot t\right) + b \cdot \sin\left(\sqrt{q} \cdot t\right),$$

where a and b are integration constants. For this expression, when $t = P$, where P is the period of the radial variation of the Cepheid's volume, it must be true that

$$\sqrt{q} \cdot t = \sqrt{q} \cdot P = 2\pi.$$

Hence, the period of the alternate contractions and expansions of the Cepheid is:

$$P = \frac{2\pi}{\sqrt{q}}; \quad q = \frac{4\pi\rho K}{3}; \quad P = 2\pi \cdot \sqrt{\frac{3}{4\pi\rho K}}; \quad P = \sqrt{\frac{12\pi^2}{4\pi\rho K}};$$

$$P = \sqrt{\frac{3\pi}{\rho K}};$$

$$\mu = \rho \cdot \frac{4\pi}{3} \cdot R^3; \quad \rho = \frac{3\mu}{4\pi R^3};$$

$$P = \sqrt{\frac{3\pi}{\rho K}}.$$

b)

$$P^2 = \frac{3\pi}{\frac{3\mu}{4\pi R^3} \cdot K} = \frac{4\pi^2}{\mu \cdot K} R^3,$$

a relationship resulting from:

$$R^3 = \frac{\mu \cdot K \cdot P^2}{4\pi^2}; \quad R = \sqrt[3]{\frac{\mu \cdot K \cdot P^2}{4\pi^2}} = \left(\frac{\mu \cdot K \cdot P^2}{4\pi^2}\right)^{1/3};$$

$$R^2 = \left(\frac{\mu \cdot K \cdot P^2}{4\pi^2}\right)^{2/3};$$

$$R^2 = \left(\frac{\mu \cdot K}{4\pi^2}\right)^{2/3} \cdot P^{4/3}.$$

Under these conditions, for the *illumination energy* (energy flux density) of the Cepheid at the observer we obtain:

$$E = \frac{R^2 \cdot \sigma \cdot T^4}{\Delta^2};$$

$$E = \left(\frac{\mu \cdot K}{4\pi^2}\right)^{2/3} \cdot \frac{\sigma \cdot T^4}{\Delta^2} \cdot P^{4/3};$$

$$w = \left(\frac{\mu \cdot K}{4\pi^2}\right)^{2/3} \cdot \sigma \cdot T^4;$$

$$E = w \cdot \frac{P^{4/3}}{\Delta^2};$$

$$E_0 = \frac{R_0^2 \cdot \sigma \cdot T_0^4}{\Delta_0^2};$$

$$\log \frac{E}{E_0} = -0.4 \cdot (m - m_0);$$

$$\log \frac{w \cdot \frac{P^{4/3}}{\Delta^2}}{\frac{R_0^2 \cdot \sigma \cdot T_0^4}{\Delta_0^2}} = -0.4 \cdot (m - m_0);$$

$$\log \frac{w \cdot P^{4/3} \cdot \Delta_0^2}{R_0^2 \cdot \sigma \cdot T_0^4 \cdot \Delta^2} = -0.4 \cdot (m - m_0);$$

$$w = \left(\frac{\mu \cdot K}{4\pi^2}\right)^{2/3} \cdot \sigma \cdot T^4;$$

$$\log \frac{(\mu \cdot K)^{2/3} \cdot \sigma \cdot T^4 \cdot P^{4/3} \cdot \Delta_0^2}{(4\pi^2)^{2/3} R_0^2 \cdot \sigma \cdot T_0^4 \cdot \Delta^2} = -0.4 \cdot (m - m_0);$$

$$\log \frac{(\mu \cdot K)^{2/3} \cdot T^4 \cdot P^{4/3} \cdot \Delta_0^2}{(4\pi^2)^{2/3} R_0^2 \cdot T_0^4 \cdot \Delta^2} = -0.4 \cdot (m - m_0);$$

$$0.4 \cdot m = 0.4 \cdot m_0 - \log \frac{(\mu \cdot K)^{2/3} \cdot T^4 \cdot P^{4/3} \cdot \Delta_0^2}{(4\pi^2)^{2/3} R_0^2 \cdot T_0^4 \cdot \Delta^2};$$

$$m = m_0 - 2.5 \cdot \log \frac{(\mu \cdot K)^{2/3} \cdot T^4 \cdot P^{4/3} \cdot \Delta_0^2}{(4\pi^2)^{2/3} R_0^2 \cdot T_0^4 \cdot \Delta^2}; \quad P = \sqrt{\frac{3\pi}{\rho K}};$$

$$C = \frac{(\mu \cdot K)^{2/3} \cdot T^4 \cdot P^{4/3} \cdot \Delta_0^2}{(4\pi^2)^{2/3} R_0^2 \cdot T_0^4 \cdot \Delta^2},$$

$$m = m_0 - 2.5 \cdot \log C.$$

Problem 9

Satellites with Orbits in Perpendicular Planes

Two artificial satellites of the Earth revolve in circular orbits located in perpendicular planes, one of these planes being the plane of the equator (for the satellite) and the other a circumpolar plane (for the satellite), as shown in the drawing in Figure 9.1. The initial positions of the satellites in the direction of the star σ and the initial position of the observer, O, on the Earth's Equator, indicated in the drawing in Figure 9.1, are: S_{01}, S_{02}, and O_0.

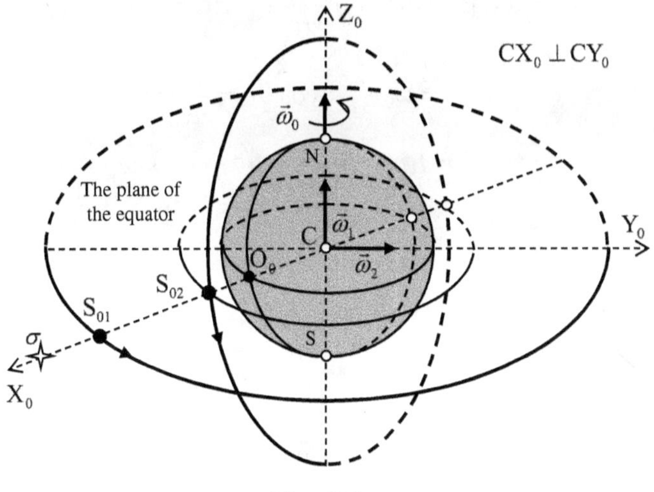

Fig. 9.1

a) *Determine* the duration t_1 of satellite S_1's visibility if the duration of satellite S_2's is t_2. *Given*: the angular velocities of the two satellites, ω_1 and ω_2, and the angular velocity of the Earth's own rotation, ω_0.

b) *Determine* the relationship between the angular velocities of the two satellites, ω_1 and ω_2, and whether the durations of their visibility are equal, $t_1 = t_2 = t$.

c) *Determine* the angle ε between the direction of the observer and the direction of the tangent to the Equator at the point where the observer is located when observing the "disappearance" of the satellite.

d) *Determine* the distance between the two satellites when their mutual visibility disappears. *We know*: the mass of the Earth and the constant of gravitational attraction.

Solution

a)

Visibility of Satellite S_1

According to the notation in Figure 9.2:

$$\alpha_1 = \omega_1 t_1; \quad \omega_1 = \sqrt{\frac{KM}{R_1^3}}; \quad R_1 = \sqrt[3]{\frac{KG}{\omega_1^2}};$$

$$\alpha_{01} = \omega_0 t_1; \quad \cos\beta_1 = \frac{R_E}{R_1};$$

$$\beta_1 = \arccos\left(\frac{R_E}{R_1}\right) = \arccos\left(R_E \cdot \sqrt[3]{\frac{\omega_1^2}{GM}}\right);$$

$$\alpha_1 = \alpha_{01} + \beta_1;$$

$$t_1(\omega_1 - \omega_0) = \beta_1;$$

$$t_1 = \frac{\beta_1}{\omega_1 - \omega_0};$$

$$t_1 = \frac{\arccos\left(R_E \cdot \sqrt[3]{\frac{\omega_1^2}{GM}}\right)}{\omega_1 - \omega_0},$$

representing the duration of satellite S_1's visibility.

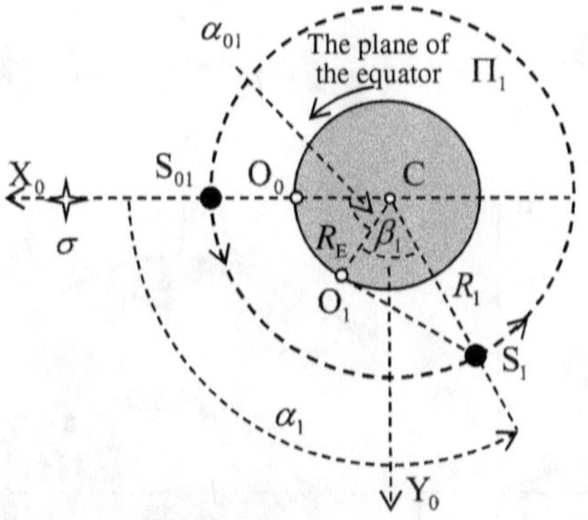

Fig. 9.2

Visibility of Satellite S_2

According to the notation in Figure 9.3, at the initial moment, the observer in position O_0 has a direct line of sight to the satellite in the position S_{02}. From this moment, due to the Earth's rotation, the observer on the Earth's Equator has visual access to space outside the plane Π_E, the plane tangent to the Earth's surface. at the point on the Equator where the observatory is located. If the satellite S_2 is in this space, it will be visible. As the plane Π_E rotates, being fixed in relation to the observer on the Earth's Equator, the satellite "descends" into its orbit in the plane Π_2.

The two planes, Π_E and Π_2, intersect the direction of this intersection (the direction AD in the drawing in Figure 9.3), being permanently parallel to the axis of rotation of the Earth. The dihedral angle between the two planes first decreases from the value 90°, corresponding to the initial moment when the two planes are perpendicular, to the final value 0°, when the two planes become parallel. Then, this angle increases again until the two planes become perpendicular again, and so on.

At some point in its evolution, the satellite disappears from the observer's field of view. This happens when the observer is in position O_2 and the satellite is in position S_2, located on the axis of intersection of the two planes.

At the moment t_2, representing the duration of satellite S_2's visibility, the satellite leaves the field of view of the observer and passes behind the plane Π_E, tangent to the Earth's surface at the point on the Equator where the observer is located, but remains in the plane of its orbit, Π_2.

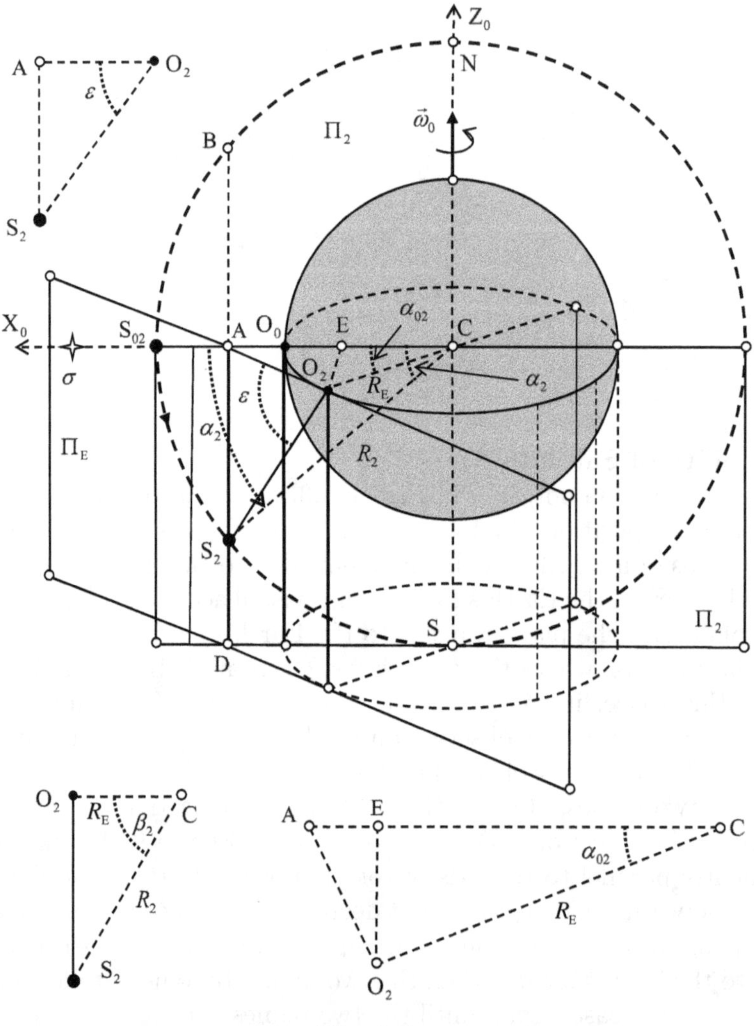

Fig. 9.3

Under these conditions, for the right triangles ACS_2 and ACO_2, it results that:

$$AC = R_2 \cos\alpha_2; \quad AC = \frac{R_E}{\cos\alpha_{02}};$$

$$R_2 \cos\alpha_2 = \frac{R_E}{\cos\alpha_{02}};$$

$$\cos\alpha_2 \cdot \cos\alpha_{02} = \frac{R_E}{R_2}; \quad \alpha_2 = \omega_2 t_2; \quad \alpha_{02} = \omega_0 t_2; \quad \omega_2 = \sqrt{\frac{GM}{R_2^3}};$$

$$R_2 = \sqrt[3]{\frac{GM}{\omega_2^2}};$$

$$\cos\omega_2 t_2 \cdot \cos\omega_0 t_2 = \frac{R_E}{R_2},$$

$$\cos\omega_2 t_2 \cdot \cos\omega_0 t_2 = R_E \cdot \sqrt[3]{\frac{\omega_2^2}{GM}},$$

$$R_E = \sqrt[3]{\frac{GM}{\omega_2^2}} \cdot \cos\omega_2 t_2 \cdot \cos\omega_0 t_2,$$

where t_2 represents the duration of the visibility of satellite S_2.

This results in:

$$t_1 = \frac{\arccos\left(R_E \cdot \sqrt[3]{\frac{\omega_1^2}{GM}}\right)}{\omega_1 - \omega_0};$$

$$t_1 = \frac{\arccos\left(\sqrt[3]{\frac{\omega_1^2}{GM}} \cdot \sqrt[3]{\frac{GM}{\omega_2^2}} \cdot \cos\omega_2 t_2 \cdot \cos\omega_0 t_2\right)}{\omega_1 - \omega_0};$$

$$t_1 = \frac{\arccos\left(\sqrt[3]{\frac{\omega_1^2}{\omega_2^2}} \cdot \cos\omega_2 t_2 \cdot \cos\omega_0 t_2\right)}{\omega_1 - \omega_0}.$$

This represents the duration of the visibility of satellite S_1.

b) If the durations of the visibility of the two satellites are equal,

$$t_1 = t_2 = t,$$

this results in:

$$t = \frac{\arccos\left(\sqrt[3]{\frac{\omega_1^2}{\omega_2^2}} \cdot \cos\omega_2 t \cdot \cos\omega_0 t\right)}{\omega_1 - \omega_0};$$

$$(\omega_1 - \omega_0) \cdot t = \arccos\left(\sqrt[3]{\frac{\omega_1^2}{\omega_2^2}} \cdot \cos\omega_2 t \cdot \cos\omega_0 t_2\right).$$

c) From the right triangles AO_2S_2, CO_2S_2, and ACO_2, shown in the sequences in Figure 9.3, it results that:

$$\cos\varepsilon = \frac{AO_2}{O_2S_2}; \quad \sin\beta_2 = \frac{O_2S_2}{R_2}; \quad \tan\alpha_{02} = \frac{AO_2}{R_E};$$

$$O_2S_2 = R_2\sin\beta_2; \quad AO_2 = R_E\tan\alpha_{02};$$

$$\cos\varepsilon = \frac{AO_2}{O_2S_2};$$

$$\cos\varepsilon = \frac{R_E\tan\alpha_{02}}{R_2\sin\beta_2};$$

$$O_2S_2 = \sqrt{(CS_2)^2 - (CO_2)^2} = \sqrt{R_2^2 - R_E^2} = R_2\sqrt{1 - \left(\frac{R_E}{R_2}\right)^2};$$

$$\sin\beta_2 = \frac{O_2S_2}{R_2}; \quad \sin\beta_2 = \sqrt{1 - \left(\frac{R_E}{R_2}\right)^2}; \quad \alpha_{02} = \omega_0 t_2;$$

$$\cos\varepsilon = \frac{R_E\tan\alpha_{02}}{R_2\sin\beta_2}; \quad \alpha_{02} = \omega_0 t_2;$$

$$\cos\varepsilon = \frac{R_E}{R_2}\cdot\frac{\tan\omega_0 t_2}{\sqrt{1 - \left(\frac{R_E}{R_2}\right)^2}};$$

$$R_E = \sqrt[3]{\frac{GM}{\omega_2^2}}\cdot\cos\omega_2 t_2\cdot\cos\omega_0 t_2;$$

$$\frac{R_E}{\sqrt[3]{GM}} = \frac{1}{\sqrt[3]{\omega_2^2}}\cdot\cos\omega_2 t_2\cdot\cos\omega_0 t_2;$$

$$R_2 = \sqrt[3]{\frac{GM}{\omega_2^2}}; \quad \sqrt[3]{GM} = R_2\cdot\sqrt[3]{\omega_2^2};$$

$$\frac{R_E}{R_2\cdot\sqrt[3]{\omega_2^2}} = \frac{1}{\sqrt[3]{\omega_2^2}}\cdot\cos\omega_2 t_2\cdot\cos\omega_0 t_2;$$

$$\frac{R_E}{R_2} = \cos\omega_2 t_2\cdot\cos\omega_0 t_2;$$

$$\cos\varepsilon = \frac{R_E}{R_2} \cdot \frac{\tan\omega_0 t_2}{\sqrt{1-\left(\frac{R_E}{R_2}\right)^2}};$$

$$\cos\varepsilon = \frac{\cos\omega_2 t_2 \cdot \cos\omega_0 t_2 \cdot \tan\omega_0 t_2}{\sqrt{1-(\cos\omega_2 t_2 \cdot \cos\omega_0 t_2)^2}}.$$

d) The mutual visibility of the two satellites will exist until the line segment joining them is tangent to the surface of the Earth's sphere, at a point T, located below the plane of the Equator, as shown in the drawing in Figure 9.4.

$$d = d_1 + d_2;$$

$$d = \sqrt{R_1^2 - R_E^2} + \sqrt{R_2^2 - R_E^2};$$

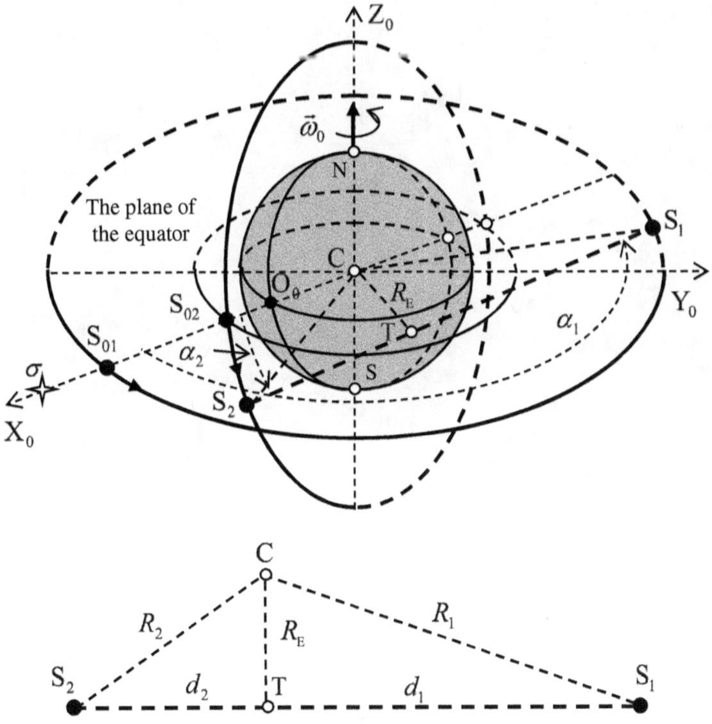

Fig. 9.4

$$R_1 = \sqrt[3]{\frac{GM}{\omega_1^2}}; \quad R_2 = \sqrt[3]{\frac{GM}{\omega_2^2}};$$

$$\frac{R_{\mathrm{E}}}{R_2} = \cos\omega_2 t_2 \cdot \cos\omega_0 t_2; \quad R_{\mathrm{E}} = R_2 \cdot \cos\omega_2 t_2 \cdot \cos\omega_0 t_2;$$

$$d = \sqrt{R_1^2 - R_{\mathrm{E}}^2} + R_2 \cdot \sqrt{1 - \left(\frac{R_{\mathrm{E}}}{R_2}\right)^2};$$

$$d = \sqrt{R_1^2 - R_2^2 (\cos\omega_2 t_2 \cdot \cos\omega_0 t_2)^2} + R_2 \cdot \sqrt{1 - (\cos\omega_2 t_2 \cdot \cos\omega_0 t_2)^2};$$

$$d = \sqrt{\left(\sqrt[3]{\frac{GM}{\omega_1^2}}\right)^2 - \left(\sqrt[3]{\frac{GM}{\omega_2^2}}\right)^2 \cdot (\cos\omega_2 t_2 \cdot \cos\omega_0 t_2)^2}$$
$$+ \sqrt[3]{\frac{GM}{\omega_2^2}} \cdot \sqrt{1 - (\cos\omega_2 t_2 \cdot \cos\omega_0 t_2)^2}.$$

Problem 10

Solar City Tower

The "Solar City Tower" is a construction built on the top of Cotonduba Island in Guanabara Bay (Brazil).

The height of the top of the island is $H = 70\,\text{m}$, and the height of the tower is $h = 105\,\text{m}$. Two seagulls, P_1 and P_2, landed at the base of the island and at the top of the tower, respectively, to watch the sunset.

Determine:

a) the angular diameter of the Sun, θ, as perceived by the two seagulls;
b) the duration of the sunset, τ_1, for the seagull P_1;
c) the descent $\Delta\alpha$ of seagull P_2's horizon below seagull P_1's standard horizon;
d) the delay in the start of the sunset, $\Delta\tau$, for the seagull P_2 versus the seagull P_1;
e) the duration of the sunset, τ_2, for the seagull P_2.

Given: the radius of the Earth, $R = 6380\,\text{km}$; the radius of the Sun, $R_S = 6.96 \cdot 10^5\,\text{km}$; the distance between the Earth and the Sun, $d_{ES} = 15 \cdot 10^7\,\text{km}$; the period of rotation of the Earth around its own axis, $T_E = 24\,\text{h}$; the declination of the Sun on July 26, $\delta = 17°06'39''$; and the latitude of the island of Cotonduba, $\varphi = 22°54'23''$.

Solution

a) Use D_S, the diameter of the Sun, and d_{ES}, the distance between the Earth and the Sun, to calculate the angular diameter of the Sun, θ, seen from Earth, using the drawing in Figure 10.1:

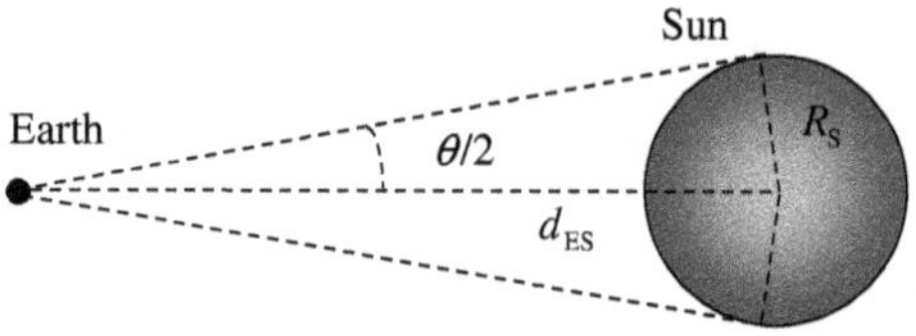

Fig. 10.1

$$\sin\frac{\theta}{2} = \frac{R_S}{d_{ES}} \approx \frac{\theta}{2};$$

$$\theta = \frac{2R_S}{d_{ES}} = \frac{D_S}{d_{ES}} = \frac{2\cdot 6.96\cdot 10^5\ \text{km}}{15\cdot 10^7\ \text{km}} = 0.00928\ \text{rad} \approx 31.9'.$$

b) The drawing in Figure 10.2 shows the evolution of the Sun, moving in retrograde on its diurnal parallel (corresponding to the declination $\delta = 17°06'39''$), as observed by the seagull P_1 at the base of the island, from the moment the sunset begins (when the Sun is above the standard horizon plane, tangent to this plane at the point T_d, and the center of the Sun is on the diurnal parallel, in the position S_d) until the end of the sunset (when the Sun is below the standard horizon, tangent to this plane at the point T_s, and the center of the Sun is on the diurnal parallel, in the position S_s).

During the sunset, τ_1, when the center of the Sun moves along the diurnal parallel from the position S_d to the position S_s, passing through the point A_1, the vector radius of the center of the Sun has rotated in the plane of the diurnal parallel by the angle ϕ, and in the vertical plane it has rotated by an angle equal to the apparent angular diameter of the Sun, θ.

If $2x$ is the distance traveled by the center of the Sun on the diurnal parallel, in a movement considered uniform movement, with speed v, during the sunset (τ_1), and if the right spherical triangle

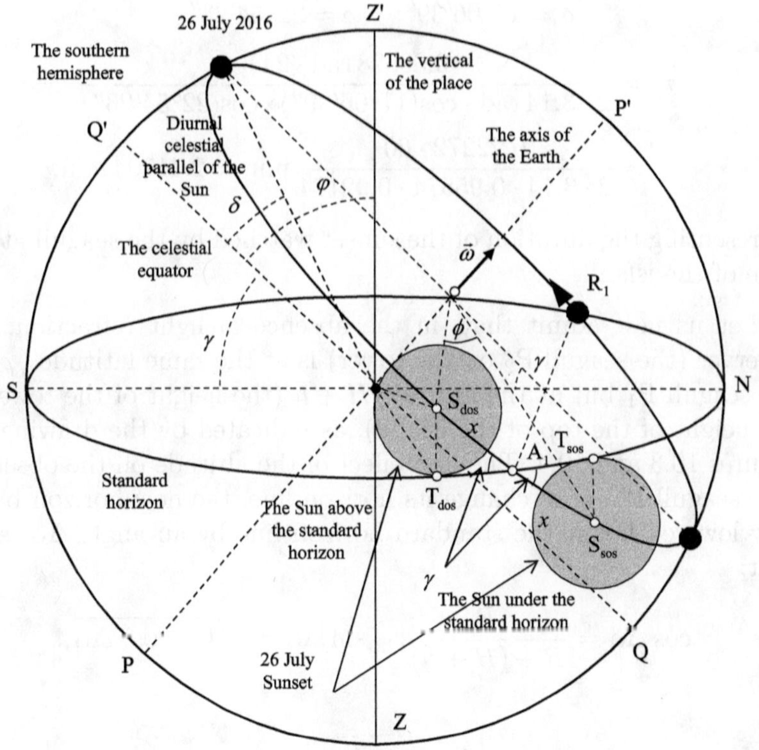

Fig. 10.2

S_dT_dV is accepted to be a plane triangle, it results in:

$$\sin\gamma = \frac{R_S}{x}; \quad x = \frac{R_S}{\sin\gamma}; \quad 2x = \frac{2R_S}{\sin\gamma} = \frac{D_S}{\sin\gamma};$$

$$v = \omega \cdot r_{\text{diurnal parallel}} = \omega \cdot d_{ES} \cdot \cos\delta;$$

$$\tau_1 = \frac{2x}{v} = \frac{2x}{\omega \cdot d_{ES} \cdot \cos\delta} = \frac{\frac{D_S}{\sin\gamma}}{\frac{2\pi}{T_E} \cdot d_{ES} \cdot \cos\delta}$$

$$= \frac{\frac{D_S}{d_{ES}}}{\frac{2\pi}{T_E} \cdot \sin\gamma} = \frac{\theta \cdot T_E}{2\pi \cdot \cos\delta \cdot \sin\gamma};$$

$$\sin\lambda = \sin(90^\circ - \varphi) = \cos\varphi;$$

$$\tau_1 = \frac{\theta \cdot T_E}{2\pi \cdot \cos\delta \cdot \cos\varphi};$$

$$\delta = 17°06'39''; \quad \varphi = 22°54'23'';$$

$$\tau_1 = \frac{0.00928\,\text{rad} \cdot 24\,\text{h}}{2 \cdot 3.14\,\text{rad} \cdot \cos(17°06'39'') \cdot \cos(22°54'23'')}$$
$$= \frac{0.22272 \cdot 60}{2 \cdot 3.14 \cdot 0.95574 \cdot 0.92114}\,\text{min} \approx 2.41704\,\text{min},$$

representing the duration of the sunset watched by the seagull at the base of the island.

c) Let us now admit that, in the absence of light refraction, the observer (the seagull P_2 on the tower) is at the same latitude (φ) as the seagull P_1 but at the altitude $H + h$ (the height of the tower + the height of the top of the island), as indicated by the drawings in Figures 10.3 and 10.4. The first effect of the altitude on the observer (the seagull P_2) is to change its horizon line, the new horizon being now lowered below the standard horizon line by an angle $\Delta\alpha$, such that:

$$\cos\Delta\alpha = \frac{R}{R + (H+h)}; \quad \sin\Delta\alpha = \sqrt{1 - \cos^2\Delta\alpha};$$

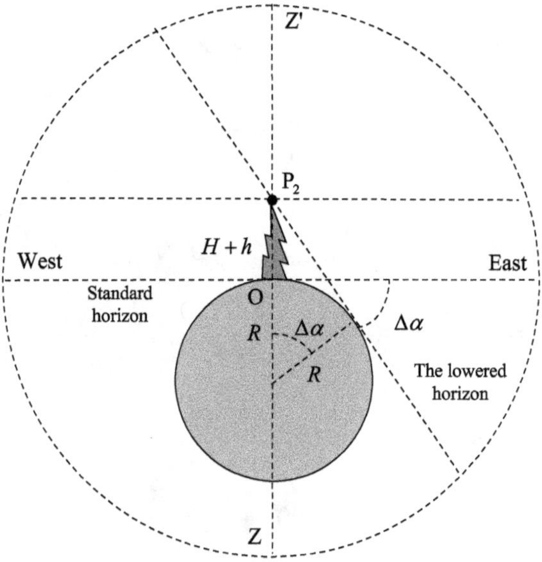

Fig. 10.3

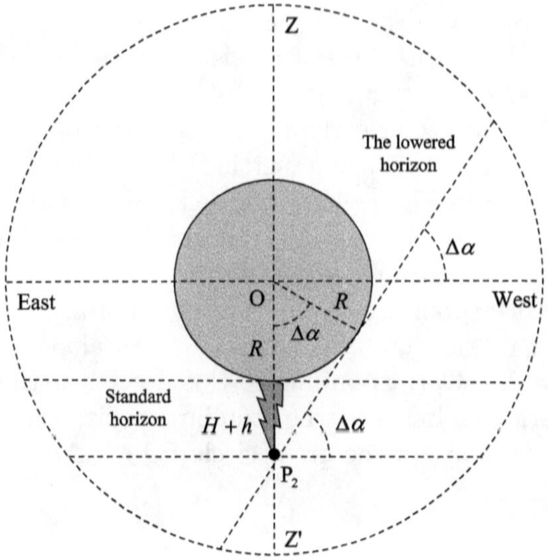

Fig. 10.4

$$\sin \Delta\alpha = \frac{\sqrt{(R + (H+h))^2 - R^2}}{R + (H+h)} = \frac{\sqrt{2R(H+h) + (H+h)^2}}{R + (H+h)}$$

$$\approx \frac{\sqrt{2R(H+h)}}{R} = \sqrt{\frac{2(H+h)}{R}} \approx \Delta\alpha;$$

$$H = 70\,\text{m}; \quad h = 105\,\text{m};$$

$$\Delta\alpha = \sqrt{\frac{2 \cdot 0.175\,\text{km}}{6380\,\text{km}}} \approx 0.00740\,\text{rad} \approx 0.424^\circ \approx 25.5',$$

representing, for the seagull P_2 at the top of the tower, the lowering of its horizon below the standard horizon and the effect of the altitude of the observation point.

The plane of the drawings in Figures 10.3 and 10.4 is the vertical plane of the celestial cardinal points east and west, corresponding to June 26. The intersection of this plane with the celestial sphere is a great circle, which contains the vertical of the place. This great circle does not represent the Sun's apparent diurnal path. The semicircles ZEZ′ and ZWZ′ represent the first vertical and the third vertical, respectively.

d) When the Sun passes below the standard horizon and then sets for the seagull P_1 at the base of the island, the Sun has not yet set for the observer (the seagull P_2) at altitude $H + h$. It will still be seen descending on the celestial sphere, passing below the standard horizon, and then disappearing (setting) below the lowered horizon.

In the drawing in Figure 10.5, the delay of the sunset as an effect of the altitude of the seagull P_2 (the observer) is highlighted, and the movement of the Sun along the apparent diurnal parallel from the position corresponding to the standard horizon, to the position corresponding to the lowered horizon occurs along the arc of the circle $A_1A_2 = \Delta\beta$. Corresponding to this descent is the descent $\Delta\alpha$, along the meridian, between the standard horizon and the lowered horizon, along the arc of the great circle $BA_2 = \Delta\alpha$.

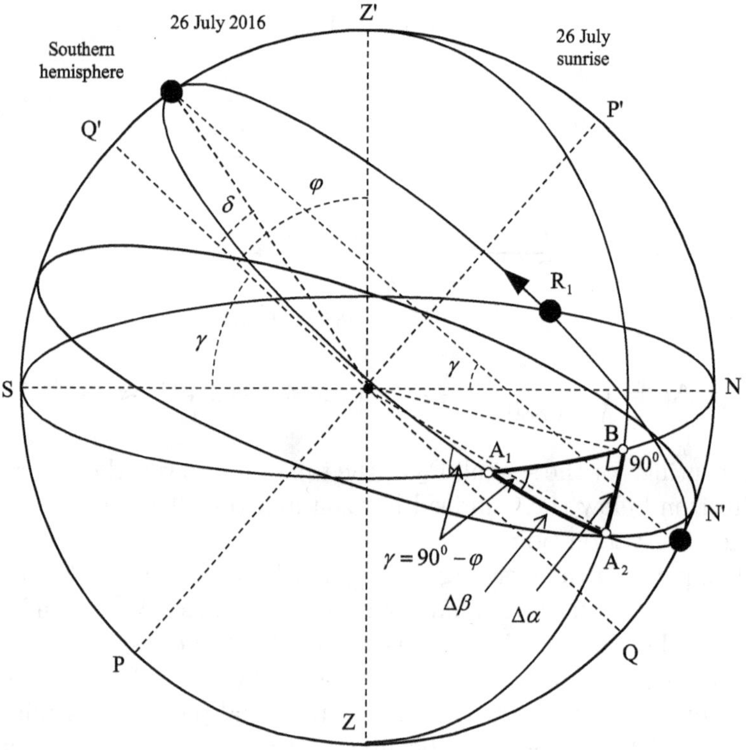

Fig. 10.5

Under these conditions, from the right-angled spherical triangle A_1BA_2, using one of the sine formulas, it follows that:

$$\frac{\sin(90^\circ - \varphi)}{\sin \Delta\alpha} = \frac{\sin 90^\circ}{\sin \Delta\beta};$$

$$\frac{\cos\varphi}{\Delta\alpha} = \frac{1}{\Delta\beta}; \quad \Delta\beta = \frac{\Delta\alpha}{\cos\varphi};$$

$$\Delta\beta = \omega \cdot \Delta\tau = \frac{2\pi}{T_P} \cdot \Delta\tau;$$

$$\Delta\alpha \approx 0.424^\circ; \quad \varphi = 22^\circ 54' 23''; \quad \cos\varphi = 0.92114;$$

$$\Delta\tau = \frac{\Delta\alpha}{\cos\varphi} \cdot \frac{T_P}{2\pi} = \frac{0.424^\circ}{0.92114} \cdot \frac{24 \cdot 60\,\text{min}}{360^\circ} \approx 1.84 \text{ minutes},$$

representing the delay in the onset of the sunset for the seagull P_2 due to the altitude $H + h$ from which the sunset is observed.

e) The second effect of the altitude on the observer (the seagull P_2) is the change in the duration of the sunset. Hence, using the drawing in Figure 10.6, it results that:

$$\sin(\gamma + \Delta\alpha) = \frac{R_S}{y};$$

$$y = \frac{R_S}{\sin(\gamma + \Delta\alpha)}; \quad 2y = \frac{2R_S}{\sin(\gamma + \Delta\alpha)} = \frac{D_S}{\sin(\gamma + \Delta\alpha)};$$

$$\text{v} = \omega \cdot r_{\text{diurnal parallel}} = \omega \cdot d_{ES} \cdot \cos\delta;$$

$$\tau_2 = \frac{2y}{v} = \frac{2y}{\omega \cdot d_{ES} \cdot \cos\delta} = \frac{\frac{D_S}{\sin(\gamma+\Delta\alpha)}}{\frac{2\pi}{T_E} \cdot d_{ES} \cdot \cos\delta}$$

$$= \frac{\frac{D_S}{d_{ES}}}{\frac{2\pi}{T_E} \cdot \cos\delta \cdot \sin(\gamma + \Delta\alpha)} = \frac{\theta \cdot T_E}{2\pi \cdot \cos\delta \cdot \sin(\gamma + \Delta\alpha)};$$

$$\gamma = 90^\circ - \varphi;$$

$$\sin(\gamma + \Delta\alpha) = \sin(90^\circ - \varphi + \Delta\alpha) = \sin[90^\circ - (\varphi - \Delta\alpha)]$$

$$= \cos(\varphi - \Delta\alpha);$$

$$\tau_2 = \frac{\theta \cdot T_E}{2\pi \cdot \cos\delta \cdot \cos(\varphi - \Delta\alpha)};$$

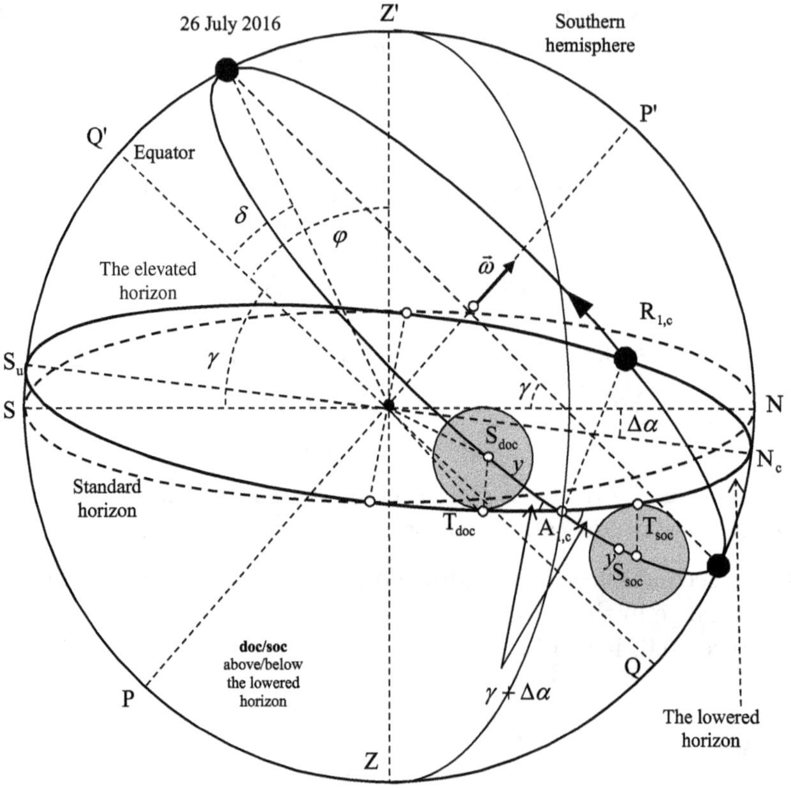

Fig. 10.6

$$\theta = 0.00928\,\text{rad};$$

$$\delta = 17°06'39''; \quad \varphi = 22°54'23''; \quad \Delta\alpha \approx 0.424°;$$

$$\tau_2 = \frac{0.00928\,\text{rad} \cdot 24\,h}{2 \cdot 3.14\,\text{rad} \cdot \cos(17°06'39'') \cdot \cos(22°54'23'' - 0.424°)};$$

$$\tau_2 = \frac{0.22272 \cdot 60}{2 \cdot 3.14 \cdot 0.95574 \cdot 0.92399}\,\text{min} \approx 2.40959\,\text{min},$$

representing the duration of sunset for the seagull P_2, watching the sunset from altitude $H + h$;

$$\tau_1 \approx 2.41704\,\text{min},$$

representing the duration of the sunset watched by the seagull P_1 at the base of the island;

$$\tau_2 < \tau_1,$$

which proves that the duration of the sunset is shorter for the seagull at the top of the tower, P_2, than for the seagull at the base of the island, P_1.

Problem 11

Temperature of Interstellar Space

1) Radiometric measurements by the American astronomer William Coblentz were able to estimate the total radiance of all stars as $Q = 14.5 \cdot 10^{-6} \, \frac{\mathrm{J}}{\mathrm{m^2 s}}$.

a) *Evaluate* the temperature of the interstellar space, T_{INS}, assimilated to a perfect black body, obtained by Coblentz. We know from the Stefan–Boltzmann law that $\sigma = 5.67 \cdot 10^{-8} \, \frac{\mathrm{J}}{\mathrm{m^2 s K^4}}$.

2) A spherical spacecraft of radius r is at a distance Δ from a star of radius R and absolute temperature T, which radiates according to black-body laws.

b) *Determine* the surface temperature of the space probe, Θ, knowing that $R \ll \Delta$.

Planck's law for the intensity of radiation emitted by a star is known:

$$I(\lambda; T) = \frac{2hc^2}{\lambda^5} \cdot \frac{1}{e^{hc/k\lambda T} - 1}.$$

It is known that

$$\int_0^\infty \frac{x^3}{e^x - 1} \cdot \mathrm{d}x = \frac{\pi^2}{15}.$$

c) *Determine* the temperature of the spherical space probe on the surface of the Earth before launch. The following are known: the radius of the Sun, $R = 696392\,\mathrm{km}$; the temperature at the surface of the Sun, $T = 6000\,\mathrm{K}$; and the distance between the Earth and the Sun, $\Delta = 1495 \cdot 10^5\,\mathrm{km}$.

3) A spherical gaseous formation with radius r at the same distance Δ from the star with temperature T cannot be considered a black body because it only absorbs and emits radiation of a certain wavelength, λ.

d) *Determine* the temperature of the gaseous formation. It will be considered that $hc \gg k\lambda T$.

Solution

a)

$$Q = 14.5 \cdot 10^{-6}\,\frac{\mathrm{J}}{\mathrm{m^2 s}};$$

$$Q = \sigma T_{\mathrm{INS}}^4; \quad \sigma = 5.67 \cdot 10^{-8}\,\frac{\mathrm{J}}{\mathrm{m^2 s K^4}};$$

$$\sigma T_{\mathrm{INS}}^4 = 14.5 \cdot 10^{-6}\,\frac{\mathrm{J}}{\mathrm{m^2 s}};$$

$$5.67 \cdot 10^{-8}\,\frac{\mathrm{J}}{\mathrm{m^2 s K^4}} \cdot T_{\mathrm{INS}}^4 = 14.5 \cdot 10^{-6}\,\frac{\mathrm{J}}{\mathrm{m^2 s}};$$

$$5.67 \cdot 10^{-8}\,\frac{1}{\mathrm{K^4}} \cdot T_{\mathrm{INS}}^4 = 14.5 \cdot 10^{-6};$$

$$T_{\mathrm{INS}} \approx 4\,\mathrm{K}.$$

b) The energy emitted by a star, considered a black body, per unit surface area, per unit time, per unit wavelength (i.e., the intensity of the radiation emitted by the star, according to Planck's law) is:

$$I(\lambda; T) = \frac{2hc^2}{\lambda^5} \cdot \frac{1}{e^{hc/k\lambda T} - 1}; \quad \langle I(\lambda; T)\rangle_{\mathrm{SI}} = \frac{\mathrm{J}}{\mathrm{s \cdot m^2 \cdot m}}.$$

I. The energy emitted by the star through its entire surface per unit time, in the range of wavelengths $(\lambda;\ \lambda + d\lambda)$, is:

$$4\pi R^2 \cdot I(\lambda; T) \cdot d\lambda; \langle 4\pi R^2 \cdot I(\lambda; T) \cdot d\lambda\rangle_{\mathrm{SI}} = \frac{\mathrm{J}}{\mathrm{s}}.$$

II. From the energy specified above, the energy that will cross a unit area of a normal surface, located at the distance Δ from the star, is:

$$\frac{4\pi R^2}{4\pi\Delta^2}\cdot I(\lambda;T)\cdot \mathrm{d}\lambda; \quad \left\langle \frac{4\pi R^2}{4\pi\Delta^2}\cdot I(\lambda;T)\cdot \mathrm{d}\lambda \right\rangle_{\mathrm{SI}} = \frac{\mathrm{J}}{\mathrm{s}\cdot \mathrm{m}^2}.$$

III. The spherical space probe with radius r located on the sphere with radius $\Delta \gg r$ is equivalent to a circular disk with a surface area πr^2, such that the energy absorbed by the space probe per unit time is:

$$\pi r^2\cdot\frac{4\pi R^2}{4\pi\Delta^2}\cdot I(\lambda;T)\cdot \mathrm{d}\lambda; \quad \left\langle \pi r^2\cdot\frac{4\pi R^2}{4\pi\Delta^2}\cdot I(\lambda;T)\cdot \mathrm{d}\lambda \right\rangle_{\mathrm{SI}} = \frac{\mathrm{J}}{\mathrm{s}}.$$

IV. Under these conditions, the total energy absorbed by the space probe per unit time, for all wavelengths, is:

$$\begin{aligned} q_{\text{absorbed}} &= \int_0^\infty \pi r^2\cdot\frac{4\pi R^2}{4\pi\Delta^2}\cdot I\left(\lambda;T\right)\cdot \mathrm{d}\lambda \\ &= \pi r^2\cdot\frac{R^2}{\Delta^2}\cdot 2hc^2\cdot\int_0^\infty \frac{1}{\lambda^5}\cdot\frac{1}{e^{hc/k\lambda T}-1}\cdot \mathrm{d}\lambda, \end{aligned}$$

where T is the temperature of the star.

In turn, the space probe, considered a black body, emits radiation so that, corresponding to its absolute temperature, Θ, the energy emitted through its entire surface, $4\pi r^2$, per unit time, is:

$$\begin{aligned} q_{\text{emitted}} &= 4\pi r^2\int_0^\infty I\left(\lambda;\Theta\right)\cdot \mathrm{d}\lambda \\ &= 4\pi r^2\cdot 2hc^2\int_0^\infty \frac{1}{\lambda^5}\cdot\frac{1}{e^{hc/k\lambda\Theta}-1}\cdot \mathrm{d}\lambda. \end{aligned}$$

Corresponding to the moment when the energy absorption–emission process becomes stationary:

$$q_{\text{absorbed}} = q_{\text{emitted}};$$

$$\begin{aligned} \pi r^2\cdot\frac{R^2}{\Delta^2}\cdot 2hc^2\cdot\int_0^\infty \frac{1}{\lambda^5}\cdot\frac{1}{e^{hc/k\lambda T}-1}\cdot \mathrm{d}\lambda \\ = 4\pi r^2\cdot 2hc^2\int_0^\infty \frac{1}{\lambda^5}\cdot\frac{1}{e^{hc/k\lambda\Theta}-1}\cdot \mathrm{d}\lambda; \end{aligned}$$

$$\pi r^2 \cdot \frac{R^2}{\Delta^2} \cdot 2hc^2 \cdot \int_0^\infty \frac{1}{\lambda^5} \cdot \frac{1}{e^{hc/k\lambda T} - 1} \cdot \mathrm{d}\lambda$$

$$= 4\pi r^2 \cdot 2hc^2 \int_0^\infty \frac{1}{\lambda^5} \cdot \frac{1}{e^{hc/k\lambda\Theta} - 1} \cdot \mathrm{d}\lambda;$$

$$\frac{R^2}{\Delta^2} \cdot \int_0^\infty \frac{1}{\lambda^5} \cdot \frac{1}{e^{hc/k\lambda T} - 1} \cdot \mathrm{d}\lambda = 4 \cdot \int_0^\infty \frac{1}{\lambda^5} \cdot \frac{1}{e^{hc/k\lambda\Theta} - 1} \cdot \mathrm{d}\lambda;$$

$$\frac{hc}{k\lambda T} = x;$$

$$\lambda = \frac{hc}{kTx}; \quad \mathrm{d}\lambda = -\frac{hc}{kTx^2} \cdot \mathrm{d}x;$$

$$\int_0^\infty \frac{1}{\lambda^5} \cdot \frac{1}{e^{hc/k\lambda T} - 1} \cdot \mathrm{d}\lambda = -\int_\infty^0 \frac{1}{\left(\frac{hc}{kTx}\right)^5} \cdot \frac{hc}{kTx^2} \cdot \frac{1}{e^x - 1} \cdot \mathrm{d}x$$

$$= \left(\frac{kT}{hc}\right)^5 \frac{hc}{kT} \int_0^\infty x^5 \cdot \frac{1}{x^2} \cdot \frac{1}{e^x - 1} \cdot \mathrm{d}x;$$

$$\int_0^\infty \frac{1}{\lambda^5} e^{-hc/k\lambda T} \mathrm{d}\lambda = \left(\frac{k}{hc}\right)^4 T^4 \int_0^\infty \frac{x^3}{e^x - 1} \cdot \mathrm{d}x;$$

$$\int_0^\infty \frac{x^3}{e^x - 1} \cdot \mathrm{d}x = \frac{\pi^2}{15};$$

$$\int_0^\infty \frac{1}{\lambda^5} e^{-hc/k\lambda T} \mathrm{d}\lambda = \frac{\pi^2}{15} \cdot \left(\frac{k}{hc}\right)^4 \cdot T^4;$$

$$\int_0^\infty \frac{1}{\lambda^5} e^{-hc/k\lambda\Theta} \mathrm{d}\lambda = \frac{\pi^2}{15} \cdot \left(\frac{k}{hc}\right)^4 \cdot \Theta^4;$$

$$\frac{R^2}{\Delta^2} \cdot \int_0^\infty \frac{1}{\lambda^5} \cdot \frac{1}{e^{hc/k\lambda T} - 1} \cdot \mathrm{d}\lambda = 4 \cdot \int_0^\infty \frac{1}{\lambda^5} \cdot \frac{1}{e^{hc/k\lambda\Theta} - 1} \cdot \mathrm{d}\lambda;$$

$$\frac{R^2}{\Delta^2} \cdot \frac{\pi^2}{15} \cdot \left(\frac{k}{hc}\right)^4 \cdot T^4 = 4 \cdot \frac{\pi^2}{15} \cdot \left(\frac{k}{hc}\right)^4 \cdot \Theta^4;$$

$$\frac{R^2}{\Delta^2} \cdot T^4 = 4 \cdot \Theta^4;$$

$$\Theta = T \cdot \sqrt{\frac{R}{2\Delta}}; \quad R \ll \Delta \to \Theta \ll T.$$

That is, at a very large distance from the star, the temperature acquired by the spherical spacecraft is very small compared to the star's temperature, but $\Theta > T_{\text{INS}}$.

c)

$$R = 696392\,\text{km}; \quad T = 6000\,\text{K}; \quad \Delta = 1495 \cdot 10^5\,\text{km};$$

$$\Theta = T \cdot \sqrt{\frac{R}{2\Delta}} = 6000\,\text{K} \cdot \sqrt{\frac{696392\,\text{km}}{2 \cdot 1495 \cdot 10^5\,\text{km}}} \approx 289\,\text{K}.$$

That is, 16°C, that is, the exact temperature value at the Earth's surface obtained from meteorological statistics.

d) Similar reasoning leads to the following results:

I. $4\pi R^2 \cdot I(\lambda; T) \cdot \lambda;$

II. $\dfrac{4\pi R^2}{4\pi \Delta^2} \cdot I(\lambda; T) \cdot \lambda;$

III. $q_{\text{absorbed}} = \pi r^2 \cdot \dfrac{4\pi R^2}{4\pi \Delta^2} \cdot I(\lambda; T) \cdot \lambda;$

IV. $q_{\text{emitted}} = 4\pi r^2 \cdot I(\lambda; \Theta) \cdot \lambda.$

Thus, from the condition of the stationarity of the energy absorption–emission processes, it follows that:

$$q_{\text{absorbed}} = q_{\text{emitted}};$$

$$\frac{R^2}{\Delta^2} \cdot I(\lambda; T) = 4 \cdot I(\lambda; \Theta);$$

$$I(\lambda; T) = \frac{2hc^2}{\lambda^5} \cdot \frac{1}{e^{hc/k\lambda T} - 1}; \quad I(\lambda; \Theta) = \frac{2hc^2}{\lambda^5} \cdot \frac{1}{e^{hc/k\lambda\Theta} - 1};$$

$$\frac{R^2}{\Delta^2} \cdot \frac{2hc^2}{\lambda^5} \cdot \frac{1}{e^{hc/k\lambda T} - 1} = 4 \cdot \frac{2hc^2}{\lambda^5} \cdot \frac{1}{e^{hc/k\lambda\Theta} - 1};$$

$$\frac{R^2}{\Delta^2} \cdot \frac{1}{e^{hc/k\lambda T} - 1} = 4 \cdot \frac{1}{e^{hc/k\lambda\Theta} - 1};$$

$$\frac{R^2}{\Delta^2} \cdot \frac{1}{e^{hc/k\lambda T}(1 - e^{-hc/k\lambda T})} = 4 \cdot \frac{1}{e^{hc/k\lambda\Theta}(1 - e^{-hc/k\lambda\Theta})};$$

$$\frac{R^2}{\Delta^2} \cdot \frac{e^{hc/k\lambda\Theta}}{e^{hc/k\lambda T}} = 4 \cdot \frac{1 - e^{-hc'k\lambda T}}{1 - e^{-hc/k\lambda\Theta}};$$

$$hc \gg k\lambda T; \quad hc \gg k\lambda\Theta;$$

$$1 - e^{-hc/k\lambda T} \approx 1; \quad 1 - e^{-hc/k\lambda\Theta} \approx 1;$$

$$\frac{R^2}{\Delta^2} \cdot \frac{e^{hc/k\lambda\Theta}}{e^{hc/k\lambda T}} = 4;$$

$$e^{hc/k\lambda\Theta - kc/k\lambda T} = \frac{4\Delta^2}{R^2};$$

$$\ln e^{hc/k\lambda\Theta - kc/k\lambda T} = \ln\left(\frac{4\Delta^2}{R^2}\right);$$

$$\frac{hc}{k\lambda\Theta} - \frac{hc}{k\lambda T} = \ln\left(\frac{4\Delta^2}{R^2}\right);$$

$$\frac{1}{\Theta} - \frac{1}{T} = \frac{k\lambda}{hc} \cdot \ln\left(\frac{4\Delta^2}{R^2}\right);$$

$$\Theta = \frac{T}{1 + \frac{k\lambda T}{hc} \cdot \ln\left(\frac{4\Delta^2}{R^2}\right)}.$$

This expression proves that although $\Delta \gg R$, the temperature of the gaseous formation in interstellar space is $\Theta < T$, not $\Theta \ll T$.

Problem 12

Time Integral Mean Values and the Virial Theorem

It is known that the binary star system whose components, σ_1 and σ_2, have the masses m_1 and $m_2 > m_1$ and move around the common center of mass (CM), as indicated by the drawing in Figure 12.1, is equivalent to the system represented in the drawing in Figure 12.2. The body S, whose mass is called the reduced mass of the given star system, $\mu = \frac{m_1 m_2}{m_1 + m_2}$, moves around another body, Σ, with the mass $M = m_1 + m_2$, representing the total mass of the given binary star system. The distance between the two bodies of the equivalent system, r, is at all times the same as the distance between the components of the given binary star system.

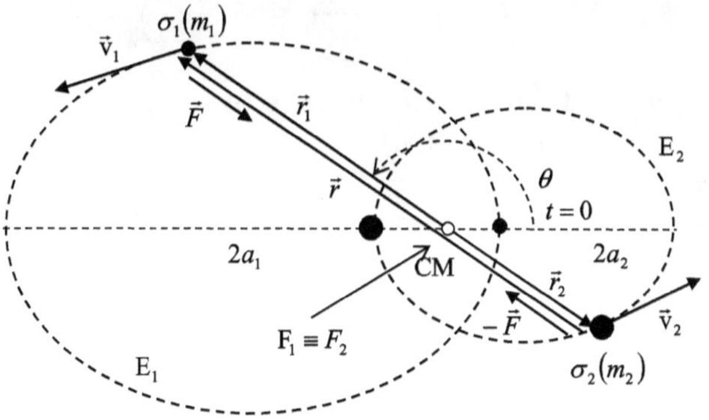

Fig. 12.1

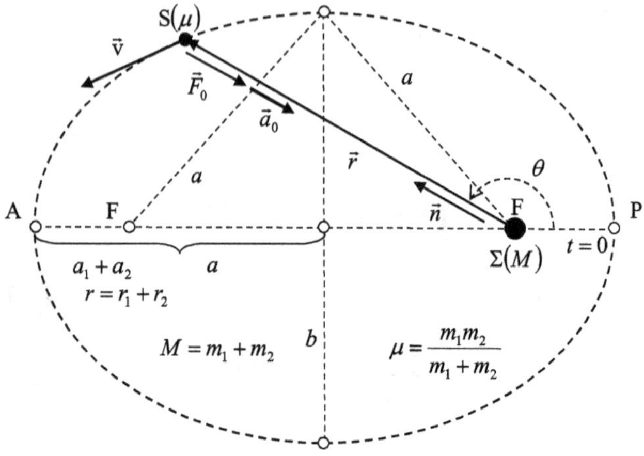

Fig. 12.2

a) *Determine* the temporal integral average of the gravitational potential energy of the equivalent system $\langle E_{\mathrm{p}}(t)\rangle_{\mathrm{t}}$ formed by S and Σ, knowing that, for a continuous function, $f(t)$, the *temporal integral average* for a time interval $\Delta t = t_2 - t_1$ is given by the expression

$$\langle f(t)\rangle = \frac{1}{\Delta t}\int_{t_1}^{t_2} f(t)\cdot \mathrm{d}t.$$

We know that

$$\int_0^{2\pi} \frac{\mathrm{d}\theta}{1 + e\cos\theta} = \frac{2\pi}{\sqrt{1-e^2}}.$$

b) *Determine* the time integral average of the kinetic energy of the equivalent system, $\langle E_{\mathrm{c}}(t)\rangle_{\mathrm{t}}$, formed by S and Σ, using the virial theorem.

c) *Determine* the temporal integral average of the distance between the bodies S and Σ of the equivalent system, $\langle r(t)\rangle_{\mathrm{t}}$.

We know that

$$\int_0^{2\pi} \frac{\mathrm{d}\theta}{(1 + e\cos\theta)^3} = \frac{\pi(2+e^2)}{(1-e^2)^{5/2}}.$$

d) *Determine* the spatial average of the distance between the bodies S and Σ of the equivalent system, $\langle r(t)\rangle_{\mathrm{c}}$, using elements from the geometry of the ellipse combined with symmetry arguments. *Compare* the magnitudes $\langle r(t)\rangle_c$ and $\langle r(t)\rangle_t$.

e) *Determine* the temporal integral average of the square of the velocity of the body S, moving on an ellipse around Σ, $\langle v^2(t)\rangle_t$, and the temporal integral average of the inverse of the distance between the elements of the equivalent system, $\langle \frac{1}{r(t)}\rangle_t$.

Solution

a) If a mobile system is moving on the flat curve represented in the drawing in Figure 12.3, it means that its position vector is $\vec{r} = \vec{r}(t)$, its movement being defined by the parametric equations:

$$r = r(t) \quad \text{and} \quad \theta = \theta(t),$$

where r and θ are plane polar coordinates.

To the given fixed system XOY is attached the mobile system X′OY′ whose axis OX′ has the direction of the vector $\vec{r}$, and OY′⊥$\vec{r}$.

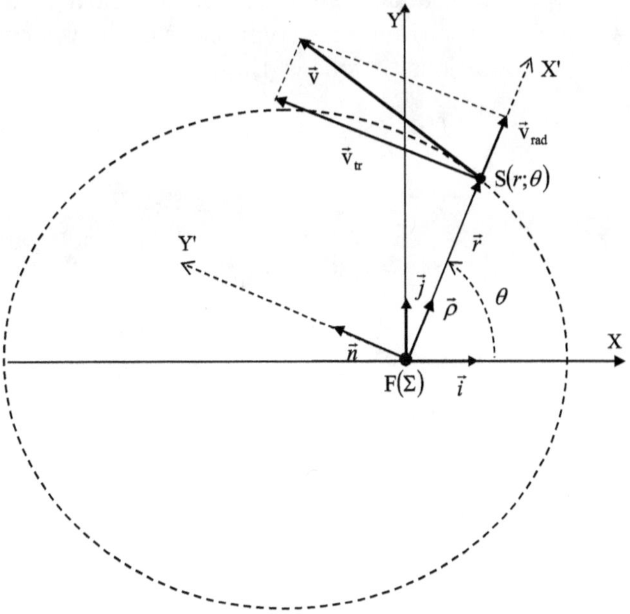

Fig. 12.3

The axes of the new system are given by the expressions:

$$\vec{\rho} = \cos\theta\vec{i} + sin\theta\vec{j};$$
$$\vec{n} = -\sin\theta\vec{i} + cos\theta\vec{j}.$$

It is proved that:

$$\frac{d\vec{\rho}}{dt} = \dot{\vec{\rho}} = \dot{\theta}\,\vec{n}; \quad \frac{d\vec{n}}{dt} = \dot{\vec{n}} = -\dot{\theta}\,\vec{\rho}.$$

From the definition of the instantaneous velocity vector, it follows that:

$$\vec{v} = \frac{d\vec{r}}{dt} = \dot{\vec{r}};$$
$$\vec{r}(t) = r(t)\vec{\rho}(t);$$
$$\vec{v} = \dot{r}\vec{\rho} + r\dot{\vec{\rho}};$$
$$\vec{v} = \dot{r}\vec{\rho} + r\dot{\theta}\,\vec{n},$$

where $\dot{r}\vec{\rho} = \vec{v}_{rad}$ is the radial component of the velocity vector, and $r\dot{\theta}\,\vec{n} = r\frac{d\theta}{dt}\vec{n} = \vec{v}_{tr}$ is the transverse component of the velocity vector.

Under these conditions, it follows that:

$$\bar{L} = \vec{r} \times \mu\vec{v} = \mu(\vec{r} \times \vec{v});$$
$$\vec{r} \times \vec{v} = \frac{\vec{L}}{\mu}; \quad |\vec{r} \times \vec{v}| = \frac{L}{\mu};$$
$$\vec{v} = \vec{v}_{tr} + \vec{v}_{rad};$$
$$\vec{r} \times \vec{v} = \vec{r} \times (\vec{v}_{tr} + \vec{v}_{rad}) = \vec{r} \times \vec{v}_{tr};$$
$$|\vec{r} \times \vec{v}| = |\vec{r} \times \vec{v}_{tr}| = r \cdot v_{tr} \cdot \sin 90^\circ = r \cdot v_{tr};$$
$$v_{tr} = r\dot{\theta} = r \cdot \frac{d\theta}{dt};$$
$$|\vec{r} \times \vec{v}| = r \cdot r \cdot \frac{d\theta}{dt} = r^2 \cdot \frac{d\theta}{dt};$$
$$|\vec{r} \times \vec{v}| = \frac{L}{\mu}; \quad r^2 \cdot \frac{d\theta}{dt} = \frac{L}{\mu}.$$

According to the notation in Figure 12.4, it follows that:

$$\mathrm{d}A = A_{\Sigma \mathrm{SS'}} = A_{\Sigma \mathrm{SD}} + A_{\mathrm{SDS'}};$$

$$\mathrm{d}A = \frac{1}{2} \cdot (r \cdot (r \cdot \mathrm{d}\theta)) + \frac{1}{2} \cdot (dr \cdot (r \cdot \mathrm{d}\theta));$$

$$\mathrm{d}A = \frac{1}{2} \cdot r^2 \cdot \mathrm{d}\theta + \frac{1}{2} \cdot r \cdot dr \cdot \mathrm{d}\theta;$$

$$\mathrm{d}A \approx \frac{1}{2} \cdot r^2 \cdot \mathrm{d}\theta;$$

$$\Omega = \frac{\mathrm{d}A}{\mathrm{d}t} = \frac{1}{2} \cdot r^2 \cdot \frac{\mathrm{d}\theta}{\mathrm{d}t};$$

$$r^2 \frac{\mathrm{d}\theta}{\mathrm{d}t} = \frac{L}{\mu};$$

$$\Omega = \frac{\mathrm{d}A}{\mathrm{d}t} = \frac{1}{2} r^2 \frac{\mathrm{d}\theta}{\mathrm{d}t};$$

$$\Omega = \frac{\mathrm{d}A}{\mathrm{d}t} = \frac{1}{2} \cdot \frac{L}{\mu};$$

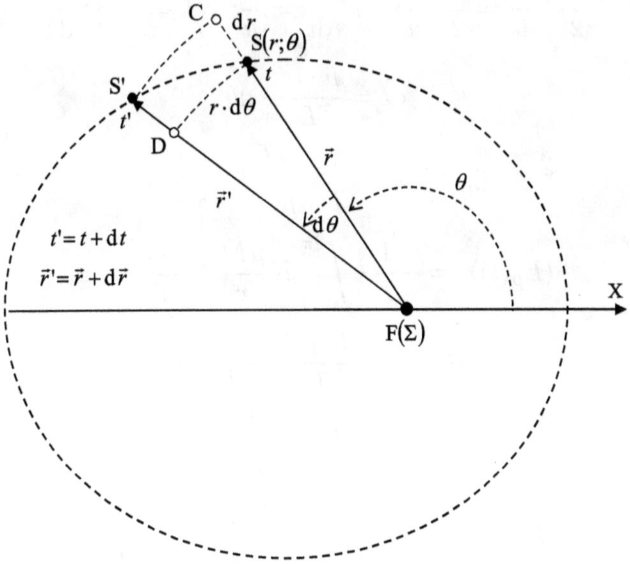

Fig. 12.4

$$\frac{1}{2}r^2\frac{\mathrm{d}\theta}{\mathrm{d}t} = \frac{1}{2}\cdot\frac{L}{\mu}; \quad r^2\frac{\mathrm{d}\theta}{\mathrm{d}t} = \frac{L}{\mu};$$

$$\mathrm{d}t = \frac{\mu\cdot r^2}{L}\cdot\mathrm{d}\theta.$$

The instantaneous gravitational potential energy of the equivalent system $(\mathrm{S};\Sigma)$ being

$$E_{\mathrm{p}}(r) = -K\frac{\mu M}{r} = -K\frac{\mu M}{r(t)} = E_{\mathrm{p}}(t),$$

it follows that the time integral average of the gravitational potential energy of the system during the period T is:

$$\langle E_{\mathrm{p}}(t)\rangle_{\mathrm{t}} = \frac{1}{T}\int_0^T E_{\mathrm{p}}(t)\cdot\mathrm{d}t = -\frac{1}{T}\int_0^T K\frac{\mu M}{r(t)}\cdot\mathrm{d}t;$$

$$\frac{\mathrm{d}A}{\mathrm{d}t} = \frac{1}{2}r^2\frac{\mathrm{d}\theta}{\mathrm{d}t}; \quad \frac{\mathrm{d}A}{\mathrm{d}t} = \frac{1}{2}\cdot\frac{L}{\mu};$$

$$\frac{1}{2}r^2\frac{\mathrm{d}\theta}{\mathrm{d}t} = \frac{1}{2}\cdot\frac{L}{\mu}; \quad r^2\frac{\mathrm{d}\theta}{\mathrm{d}t} = \frac{L}{\mu}; \quad L = \mu\cdot r^2\frac{\mathrm{d}\theta}{\mathrm{d}t};$$

$$\mathrm{d}t = \frac{\mu\cdot r^2}{L}\cdot\mathrm{d}\theta;$$

$$\langle E_{\mathrm{p}}(t)\rangle_{\mathrm{t}} = -\frac{1}{T}\cdot\int_0^T K\frac{\mu M}{r(t)}\cdot\mathrm{d}t;$$

$$\langle E_{\mathrm{p}}(t)\rangle_{\mathrm{t}} = -\frac{1}{T}\cdot\int_0^{2\pi} K\frac{\mu M}{r}\cdot\frac{\mu\cdot r^2}{L}\cdot\mathrm{d}\theta;$$

$$\langle E_{\mathrm{p}}(t)\rangle_{\mathrm{t}} = -\frac{K\mu^2 M}{TL}\cdot\int_0^{2\pi} r\cdot\mathrm{d}\theta;$$

$$r = \frac{a(1-e^2)}{1+e\cos\theta};$$

$$\langle E_{\mathrm{p}}(t)\rangle_{\mathrm{t}} = -\frac{K\mu^2 M}{TL}\cdot\int_0^{2\pi}\frac{a(1-e^2)}{1+e\cos\theta}\cdot\mathrm{d}\theta;$$

$$\langle E_{\mathrm{p}}(t)\rangle_{\mathrm{t}} = -\frac{K\mu^2 Ma(1-e^2)}{TL}\cdot\int_0^{2\pi}\frac{\mathrm{d}\theta}{1+e\cos\theta};$$

$$\int_0^{2\pi} \frac{d\theta}{1 + e\cos\theta} = \frac{2\pi}{\sqrt{1 - e^2}};$$

$$\langle E_p(t)\rangle_t = -\frac{K\mu^2 Ma(1 - e^2)}{TL} \cdot \frac{2\pi}{\sqrt{1 - e^2}};$$

$$\langle E_p(t)\rangle_t = -\frac{2\pi K\mu^2 Ma(1 - e^2)^{1/2}}{TL};$$

$$L = \mu\sqrt{KMa(1 - e^2)};$$

$$T^2 = \frac{4\pi^2}{KM}a^3; \quad T = \frac{2\pi a\sqrt{a}}{\sqrt{KM}};$$

$$\langle E_p(t)\rangle_t = -\frac{2\pi K\mu^2 Ma(1 - e^2)^{1/2}}{\frac{2\pi a\sqrt{a}}{\sqrt{KM}} \cdot \mu \cdot \sqrt{KMa(1 - e^2)}};$$

$$\langle E_p(t)\rangle_t = -K\frac{\mu M}{a}; \quad \mu = \frac{m_1 m_2}{m_1 + m_2}; \quad M = m_1 + m_2;$$

$$\langle E_p(t)\rangle_t = -K\frac{m_1 m_2}{a}.$$

b) The *virial theorem* correlates the temporal averages of the kinetic and potential energies of a physical system with the power q of the distance on which the potential energy of the system depends.

To deduce the relationship between the previously specified elements (to prove the virial theorem), let us recall that, in mathematical analysis, it is proved that if a function of n variables, $f(x_1, x_2, \ldots, x_n)$, is homogeneous of order q, that is,

$$f(\lambda x_1, \lambda x_2, \ldots, \lambda x_n) = \lambda^q \cdot f(x_1, x_2 \ldots x_n),$$

then the following identity is satisfied:

$$x_1\frac{\partial f}{\partial x_1} + x_2\frac{\partial f}{\partial x_2} + \cdots + x_n\frac{\partial f}{\partial x_n} = qf;$$

$$\sum_{k=1}^{n} x_k\frac{\partial f}{\partial x_k} = qf,$$

representing *Euler's theorem* for homogeneous functions of order q.

Indeed, for a system of n material points, since the kinetic energy, *Ec*, is a homogeneous quadratic function (of order $q = 2$), with the components $\vec{v}_1, \vec{v}_2, \ldots, \vec{v}_n$, according to Euler's theorem, stated previously, we have:

$$\vec{v}_1 \frac{\partial E_c}{\partial \vec{v}_1} + \vec{v}_2 \frac{\partial E_c}{\partial \vec{v}_2} + \cdots + \vec{v}_n \frac{\partial E_c}{\partial \vec{v}_n} = 2E_c;$$

$$\sum_{k=1}^{n} \vec{v}_k \frac{\partial E_c}{\partial \vec{v}_k} = 2E_c;$$

$$\frac{\partial E_c}{\partial \vec{v}_k} = \frac{\partial}{\partial \vec{v}_k}\left(\frac{1}{2} m_k \vec{v}_k^2\right) = m_k \vec{v}_k = \vec{p}_k;$$

$$m_k \vec{v}_k \cdot \vec{v}_k = \vec{p}_k \cdot \vec{v}_k = m_k \vec{v}_k^2 = 2 \cdot \frac{1}{2} m_k \vec{v}_k^2;$$

$$\sum_{k=1}^{n} \vec{p}_k \vec{v}_k = 2E_c; \quad \vec{v}_k = \frac{d\vec{r}_k}{dt};$$

$$\sum_{k=1}^{n} \vec{p}_k \frac{d\vec{r}_k}{dt} = 2E_c;$$

$$\frac{d}{dt} \sum_{k=1}^{n} \vec{p}_k \vec{r}_k - \sum_{k=1}^{n} \vec{r}_k \frac{d\vec{p}_k}{dt} = 2E_c;$$

$$\frac{d\vec{p}_k}{dt} = \vec{F}_k = -\nabla_k E_p = -\frac{\partial E_p}{\partial \vec{r}_k} = -\left(\frac{\partial E_p}{\partial x_k}\vec{i} + \frac{\partial E_p}{\partial y_k}\vec{j} + \frac{\partial E_p}{\partial z_k}\vec{k}\right);$$

$$\frac{d\vec{p}_k}{dt} = -\frac{\partial E_p}{\partial \vec{r}_k}; \quad \vec{r}_k \frac{d\vec{p}_k}{dt} = -\vec{r}_k \frac{\partial E_p}{\partial \vec{r}_k};$$

$$\sum_{k=1}^{n} \vec{r}_k \frac{d\vec{p}_k}{dt} = -\sum_{k=1}^{n} \vec{r}_k \frac{\partial E_p}{\partial \vec{r}_k};$$

$$\sum_{k=1}^{n} x_k \frac{\partial f}{\partial x_k} = qf;$$

$$\sum_{k=1}^{n} \vec{r}_k \frac{\partial E_p}{\partial \vec{r}_k} = qE_p;$$

$$E_p = -K\frac{\mu M}{r} = -K\frac{m_1 m_2}{r} = -Km_1 m_2 r^{-1} = -Km_1 m_2 r^q,$$

in agreement with Euler's theorem, if we admit that the potential energy of the system is a homogeneous function of the order $q = -1$;

$$\frac{\mathrm{d}}{\mathrm{d}t}\sum_{k=1}^{n}\vec{p}_k\vec{r}_k - \sum_{k=1}^{n}\vec{r}_k\frac{\mathrm{d}\vec{p}_k}{\mathrm{d}t} = 2E_{\mathrm{c}};$$

$$\sum_{k=1}^{n}\vec{r}_k\frac{\mathrm{d}\vec{p}_k}{\mathrm{d}t} = -qE_{\mathrm{p}}; \quad \sum_{k=1}^{n}\vec{\mathrm{v}}_k\frac{\partial E_{\mathrm{c}}}{\partial\vec{\mathrm{v}}_k} = 2E_{\mathrm{c}};$$

$$\frac{\mathrm{d}}{\mathrm{d}t}\sum_{k=1}^{n}\vec{p}_k\vec{r}_k - \sum_{k=1}^{n}\vec{r}_k\frac{\mathrm{d}\vec{p}_k}{\mathrm{d}t} = 2E_{\mathrm{c}};$$

$$\frac{\mathrm{d}}{\mathrm{d}t}\sum_{k=1}^{n}\vec{p}_k\vec{r}_k + qE_{\mathrm{p}} = 2E_{\mathrm{c}}.$$

In order to calculate the average of this equality in relation to time, we recall that:

- the average value of some function of time, $f(t)$, is the quantity

$$\bar{f} = \lim_{\tau\to\infty}\frac{1}{\tau}\int_0^{\tau} f(t)\mathrm{d}t;$$

- if the function $f(t)$ is derived with respect to the time of a function $F(t)$, then $f(t) = \frac{\mathrm{d}F(t)}{\mathrm{d}t}$, which is bounded (does not have infinite values), and so its average value is zero,

$$\bar{f} = \lim_{\tau\to\infty}\frac{1}{\tau}\int_0^{\tau}\frac{\mathrm{d}F}{\mathrm{d}t}\mathrm{d}t = \lim_{\tau\to\infty}\frac{F(\tau)-F(0)}{\tau} = 0,$$

which is true if the function $F(t)$ refers to a limited domain of space.

Under these conditions, we have:

$$\overline{\frac{\mathrm{d}}{\mathrm{d}t}\sum_{k=1}^{n}\vec{p}_k\vec{r}_k} + q\left\langle E_{\mathrm{p}}\right\rangle_{\mathrm{t}} = 2\left\langle E_{\mathrm{c}}\right\rangle_{\mathrm{t}};$$

$$\overline{\frac{\mathrm{d}}{\mathrm{d}t}\sum_{k=1}^{n}\vec{p}_k\vec{r}_k} = \lim_{\tau\to\infty}\frac{1}{\tau}\int_0^{\tau}\frac{\mathrm{d}}{\mathrm{d}t}\left(\sum_{k=1}^{n}\vec{p}_k\vec{r}_k\right)\mathrm{d}t = 0,$$

because each product $\vec{p}_k\vec{r}_k$ remains finite;

$$2\langle E_\mathrm{c}\rangle_\mathrm{t} = q\langle E_\mathrm{p}\rangle_\mathrm{t}; \quad q = -1;$$
$$2\langle E_\mathrm{c}\rangle_\mathrm{t} = -\langle E_\mathrm{p}\rangle_\mathrm{t};$$
$$2\langle E_\mathrm{c}\rangle_\mathrm{t} + \langle E_\mathrm{p}\rangle_\mathrm{t} = 0.$$

This relation represents the ***virial theorem***, highlighting the connection between the temporal averages of the kinetic and potential energies and the order of homogeneity of the homogeneous function through which the potential energy of the system is expressed.

In point **(a)**, we proved that

$$\langle E_\mathrm{p}(t)\rangle_\mathrm{t} = -K\frac{m_1m_2}{a}.$$

So, it results that:

$$2\langle E_\mathrm{c}\rangle_\mathrm{t} - K\frac{m_1m_2}{a} = 0;$$
$$\langle E_\mathrm{c}(t)\rangle_\mathrm{t} = \frac{1}{2}K\frac{m_1m_2}{a}.$$

c) We now calculate the time integral average of the distance between the bodies S and Σ, equivalent to the given system, $\langle r(t)\rangle_\mathrm{t}$:

$$r = \frac{a(1-e^2)}{1+e\cos\theta}; \quad r = \frac{\frac{a(1-e^2)\mu^2KM}{\mu^2KM}}{1+e\cos\theta}; \quad \mu = \frac{m_1m_2}{m_1+m_2};$$
$$M = m_1 + m_2;$$
$$\langle f(t)\rangle_\mathrm{t} = \frac{1}{T}\int_0^T f(t)\cdot \mathrm{d}t;$$
$$\langle r(t)\rangle_\mathrm{t} = \frac{1}{T}\int_0^T r(t)\cdot \mathrm{d}t; \quad \langle r(t)\rangle_\mathrm{t} = \frac{1}{T}\int_0^T \frac{a(1-e^2)}{1+e\cos\theta}\cdot \mathrm{d}t;$$
$$\langle r(t)\rangle_\mathrm{t} = \frac{a(1-e^2)}{T}\cdot\int_0^T \frac{1}{1+e\cos\theta}\cdot \mathrm{d}t;$$
$$T = 2\pi\sqrt{\frac{a^3}{KM}}; \quad \mathrm{d}t = \frac{\mu\cdot r^2}{L}\cdot \mathrm{d}\theta; \quad r = \frac{a(1-e^2)}{1+e\cos\theta};$$
$$L = \mu\sqrt{KMa(1-e^2)};$$

$$\langle r(t)\rangle_{\mathrm{t}} = \frac{a(1-e^2)}{2\pi\sqrt{\frac{a^3}{KM}}}\int_0^{2\pi}\frac{\frac{\mu\cdot r^2}{L}}{1+e\cos\theta}\cdot \mathrm{d}\theta;$$

$$\langle r(t)\rangle_{\mathrm{t}} = \frac{a(1-e^2)}{2\pi\sqrt{a^3}}\sqrt{KM}\cdot\int_0^{2\pi}\frac{\frac{\mu\cdot r^2}{\mu\sqrt{KMa(1-e^2)}}}{1+e\cos\theta}\cdot \mathrm{d}\theta;$$

$$\langle r(t)\rangle_{\mathrm{t}} = \frac{a(1-e^2)}{2\pi a\sqrt{a}}\cdot\int_0^{2\pi}\frac{\frac{r^2}{\sqrt{a(1-e^2)}}}{1+e\cos\theta}\cdot \mathrm{d}\theta;$$

$$\langle r(t)\rangle_{\mathrm{t}} = \frac{(1-e^2)}{2\pi\sqrt{a}\cdot\sqrt{a}}\cdot\int_0^{2\pi}\frac{\frac{r^2}{\sqrt{(1-e^2)}}}{1+e\cos\theta}\cdot \mathrm{d}\theta;$$

$$\langle r(t)\rangle_{\mathrm{t}} = \frac{(1-e^2)}{2\pi\cdot a}\cdot\int_0^{2\pi}\frac{r^2}{\sqrt{1-e^2}\cdot(1+e\cos\theta)}\cdot \mathrm{d}\theta;$$

$$r = \frac{a(1-e^2)}{1+e\cos\theta};$$

$$\langle r(t)\rangle_{\mathrm{t}} = \frac{(1-e^2)}{2\pi\cdot a}\cdot\int_0^{2\pi}\frac{a^2(1-e^2)^2}{\sqrt{1-e^2}\cdot(1+e\cos\theta)^3}\cdot \mathrm{d}\theta;$$

$$\langle r(t)\rangle_{\mathrm{t}} = a\frac{(1-e^2)^3}{2\pi}\cdot\int_0^{2\pi}\frac{1}{\sqrt{1-e^2}\cdot(1+e\cos\theta)^3}\cdot \mathrm{d}\theta;$$

$$\langle r(t)\rangle_{\mathrm{t}} = a\frac{(1-e^2)^3}{2\pi(1-e^2)^{1/2}}\cdot\int_0^{2\pi}\frac{\mathrm{d}\theta}{(1+e\cos\theta)^3};$$

$$\langle r(t)\rangle_{\mathrm{t}} = a\cdot\frac{(1-e^2)^{5/2}}{2\pi}\cdot\int_0^{2\pi}\frac{\mathrm{d}\theta}{(1+e\cos\theta)^3};$$

$$\int_0^{2\pi}\frac{\mathrm{d}\theta}{(1+e\cos\theta)^3} = \frac{\pi\cdot(2+e^2)}{(1-e^2)^{5/2}};$$

$$\langle r(t)\rangle_{\mathrm{t}} = \frac{3a^2-b^2}{2a};$$

$$a > b;\quad \langle r(t)\rangle_{\mathrm{t}} > a,$$

which proves that the average distance $R = a$, present in the two formulas of Kepler's third law, is not identified with the average temporal distance.

d) Let the points P and P′ be on the contour of an ellipse (curve), symmetrical to the minor axis of the ellipse, as shown in the drawing in Figure 12.5.

It is known that the sum of the distances from some point P on the contour of the ellipse (curve) to the two foci, F and F′, of the ellipse is equal to the major axis of the ellipse:

$$\mathrm{PF} + \mathrm{PF}' = 2a.$$

The average distances from the focus F to all points on the contour of the ellipse (curve) can be calculated by summing the distances from the focus F to all pairs of symmetrical points, that is:

$$\sum_{1}^{n} (\mathrm{FP} + \mathrm{FP}'),$$

where, taking into account the symmetry of the points P and P′ with respect to the minor axis of the ellipse, $\mathrm{FP}' = \mathrm{PF}'$, so that the spatial average of the distance from the focus F to any point P on the ellipse (curve) is

$$\langle \mathrm{FP} \rangle_{\mathrm{c}} = \frac{\sum_1^n (\mathrm{FP} + \mathrm{FP}')}{2n} = \frac{\sum_1^n (\mathrm{PF} + \mathrm{PF}')}{2n} = \frac{2an}{2n} = a = \langle r(t) \rangle_{\mathrm{c}}.$$

This proves that the average distance $R = a$, present in the two formulas of Kepler's third law, is not identified with the average temporal distance:

$$\langle r(t) \rangle_{\mathrm{t}} \neq \langle r(t) \rangle_{\mathrm{c}}.$$

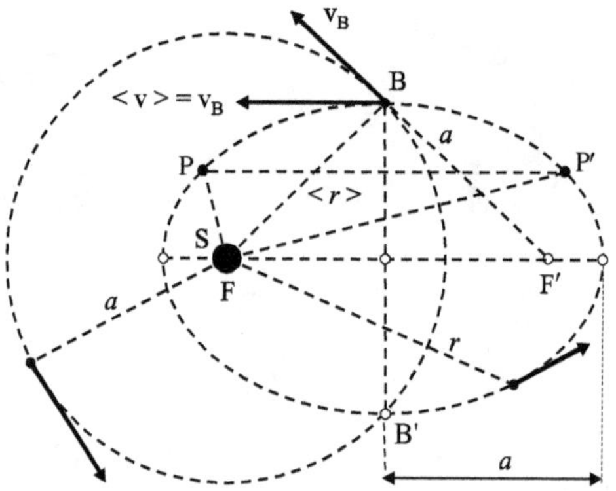

Fig. 12.5

With this result, the distance R from Kepler's third law can be appreciated as an average of the orbit geometry and not as an average of the orbital dynamics.

e)

$$2\langle E_{\mathrm{c}}(t)\rangle_{\mathrm{t}} + \langle E_{\mathrm{p}}(t)\rangle_{\mathrm{t}} = 0;$$

$$\langle E_{\mathrm{c}}(t)\rangle_{\mathrm{t}} = \frac{1}{2}\mu\langle \mathrm{v}^2(t)\rangle_{\mathrm{t}} = \frac{1}{2}\frac{m_1 m_2}{m_1 + m_2}\cdot\langle \mathrm{v}^2(t)\rangle_{\mathrm{t}};$$

$$\langle E_{\mathrm{c}}(t)\rangle_{\mathrm{t}} = \frac{1}{2}K\frac{m_1 m_2}{a};$$

$$\frac{1}{2}\frac{m_1 m_2}{m_1 + m_2}\cdot\langle \mathrm{v}^2(t)\rangle_{\mathrm{t}} = \frac{1}{2}K\frac{m_1 m_2}{a};$$

$$\frac{1}{m_1 + m_2}\cdot\langle \mathrm{v}^2(t)\rangle_{\mathrm{t}} = K\frac{1}{a};$$

$$\langle \mathrm{v}^2(t)\rangle_{\mathrm{t}} = K\frac{m_1 + m_2}{a};$$

$$\langle E_{\mathrm{p}}(t)\rangle_{\mathrm{t}} = -K\mu M\cdot\left\langle\frac{1}{r(t)}\right\rangle_{\mathrm{t}} = -Km_1m_2\cdot\left\langle\frac{1}{r(t)}\right\rangle_{\mathrm{t}};$$

$$2\langle E_{\mathrm{c}}(t)\rangle_{\mathrm{t}} + \langle E_{\mathrm{p}}(t)\rangle_{\mathrm{t}} = 0;$$

$$2\cdot\frac{1}{2}\frac{m_1 m_2}{m_1 + m_2}\cdot\langle \mathrm{v}^2(t)\rangle_{\mathrm{t}} - Km_1m_2\cdot\left\langle\frac{1}{r(t)}\right\rangle_{\mathrm{t}} = 0;$$

$$2\cdot\frac{1}{2}\frac{m_1 m_2}{m_1 + m_2}\cdot\langle \mathrm{v}^2(t)\rangle_{\mathrm{t}} - Km_1m_2\cdot\left\langle\frac{1}{r(t)}\right\rangle_{\mathrm{t}} = 0;$$

$$\frac{m_1 m_2}{m_1 + m_2}\cdot\langle \mathrm{v}^2(t)\rangle_{\mathrm{t}} = Km_1m_2\cdot\left\langle\frac{1}{r(t)}\right\rangle_{\mathrm{t}};$$

$$\frac{1}{m_1 + m_2}\cdot\langle \mathrm{v}^2(t)\rangle_{\mathrm{t}} = K\cdot\left\langle\frac{1}{r(t)}\right\rangle_{\mathrm{t}};$$

$$\langle \mathrm{v}^2(t)\rangle_{\mathrm{t}} = K\cdot(m_1 + m_2)\left\langle\frac{1}{r(t)}\right\rangle_{\mathrm{t}};$$

$$\langle \mathrm{v}^2(t)\rangle_{\mathrm{t}} = K\frac{m_1 + m_2}{a};$$

$$K \cdot (m_1 + m_2) \left\langle \frac{1}{r(t)} \right\rangle_{\mathrm{t}} = K \frac{m_1 + m_2}{a};$$

$$\left\langle \frac{1}{r(t)} \right\rangle_{\mathrm{t}} = \frac{1}{a}.$$

In the historical formulation, Kepler's third law concerning the motion of the planets around the Sun is written as

$$\frac{R_1^3}{T_1^2} = \frac{R_2^3}{T_2^2},$$

where T_1 and T_2 are the periods of the movements of two planets, and R_1 and R_2 are the average distances between the two planets and the Sun, without specifying what kind of average it is.

In the later formulation, given by Newton, Kepler's third law is written as

$$\frac{a_1^3}{T_1^2} = \frac{a_2^3}{T_2^2},$$

where a_1 and a_2 are the semi-major axes of the two ellipses on which the planets move around the Sun.

Problem 13

The Horizontal Diurnal Parallax of a Star, Accurately Determined

The diurnal height parallax of a star, p, is commonly defined, assuming that the Earth is spherical, as the angle at which the Earth's radius, R, corresponding to the observation site, would be seen from the center of the star, as indicated by the drawing in Figure 13.1.

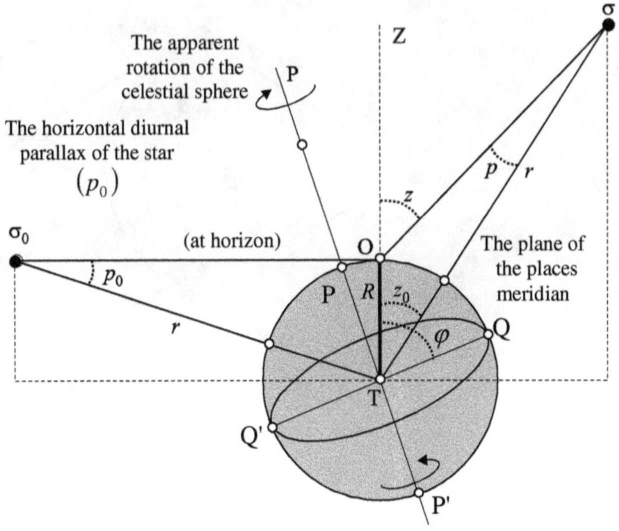

Fig. 13.1

Corresponding to the same observation site, the horizontal diurnal parallax of a star, p_0, highlighted in the drawing in Figure 13.1, is equal to the maximum value of the diurnal height parallax, $p_{\max}$, which occurs when the star is at the observer's horizon, $p_0 = p_{\max}$, so that

$$\sin p_0 \approx p_0 = \frac{R}{r}.$$

In the high-precision determination of the parallaxes of stars, it must be taken into account that the Earth is not spherical. So, in the determination of parallaxes, the R-value, representing the radius of the Earth, must be replaced by the geoid size ρ, highlighted in the drawing in Figure 13.2, which represents the geocentric radius of the geoid, corresponding to the place of observation.

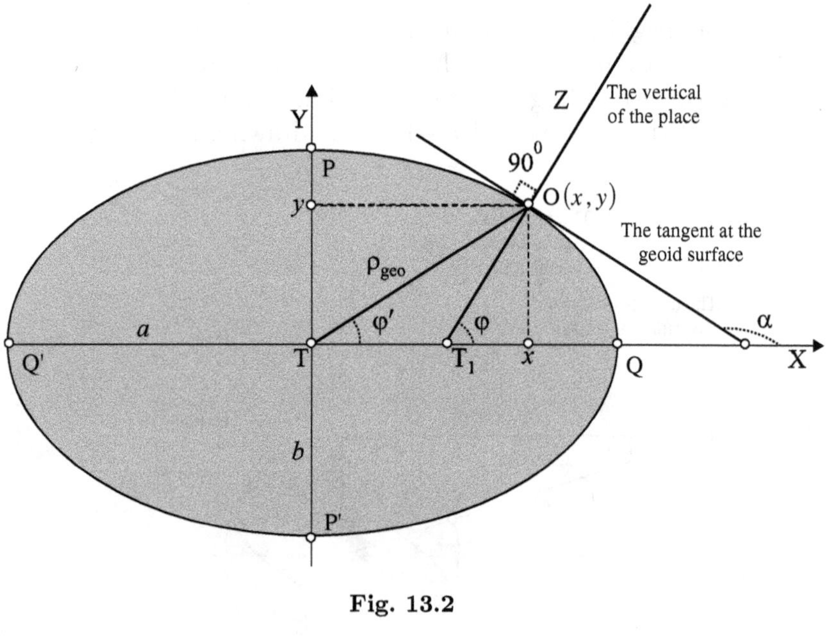

Fig. 13.2

Determine the horizontal parallax, p_0, considering that the Earth is a geoid whose generating ellipse has the semi-minor axis a and the numerical eccentricity e, and the observer is on the surface of the terrestrial geoid at a point with latitude φ. *Particular case*: $\varphi = 0$.

Solution

In this situation, when the Earth has the shape of a geoid (ellipsoid of rotation), as indicated by the drawing in Figure 13.3, let us trace the apparent diurnal motion of the star σ, from the diurnal moment when its diurnal height parallax is p, to the moment when it has reached the position σ_0 on the horizon of the observer and its diurnal height parallax is maximum, $p_{\max}$, a value we mark as the star's horizontal diurnal parallax, $p_0 = p_{\max}$.

Using the drawing in Figure 13.3 and writing the sine theorem for the right triangle O$\mathrm{T}\sigma_0$, the results are:

$$\frac{\sin p_0}{\rho_{\text{geo}}} = \frac{\sin x}{r}; \quad \gamma = 90^0 - (\varphi - \varphi');$$

$$\frac{\sin p_0}{\rho_{\text{geo}}} = \frac{\sin\left[90 - (\varphi - \varphi')\right]}{r};$$

$$\sin\left[90^0 - (\varphi - \varphi')\right] = \cos(\varphi - \varphi');$$

$$\frac{\sin p_0}{\rho_{\text{geo}}} = \frac{\cos(\varphi - \varphi')}{r}; \quad \sin p_0 \approx p_0 = \frac{\rho_{\text{geo}}}{r}\cos(\varphi - \varphi').$$

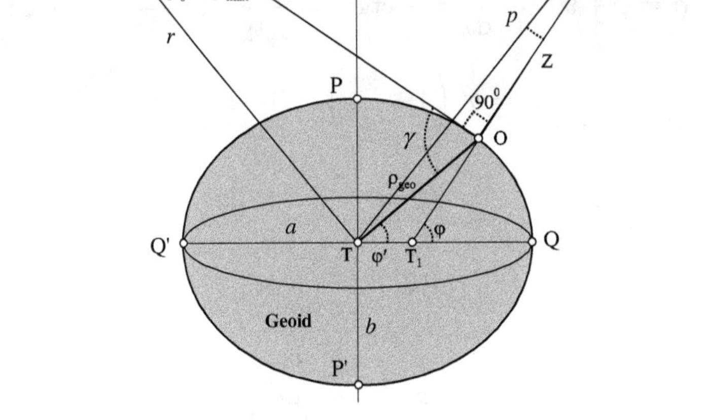

Fig. 13.3

This relationship allows the calculation of the *horizontal diurnal parallax* of a star, p_0, when the Earth has the shape of a geoid (ellipsoid of revolution) if we know: the radius of the geoid corresponding to the place of observation, ρ_{geo}; the geographical (astronomical) latitude of the place of observation, φ; the geocentric latitude of the place of observation, φ', the distance r from the star to the center of the Earth; and the relation between φ and φ'.

In order to establish the relationship between the *geographic latitude* (φ) and the *geocentric latitude* (φ') of place O on the Earth's surface, in the drawing in Figure 13.2 is represented the meridian ellipse of place O, generating the ellipsoid of terrestrial rotation, relative to an orthogonal system of XY axes with the origin at the center T of the Earth. In this system, the position coordinates of place O are $(x,\ y)$, and the equation of the ellipse, in $(x,\ y)$ coordinates, is

$$\frac{x^2}{a^2} + \frac{y^2}{b^2} = 1,$$

where a and b are the major and minor semi-axes of the ellipse (the equatorial and polar axes, respectively, of the ellipsoid).

If α is the angle between the geometric tangent to the ellipse at point O and the TX axis, from the geometric interpretation of the derivative of a function, it follows that:

$$\text{tg}\ \alpha = \frac{\text{d}y}{\text{d}x};$$

$$\alpha = \varphi + 90°; \quad \frac{\text{d}y}{\text{d}x} = -\text{ctg}\ \varphi = -\frac{1}{\text{tg}\ \varphi}; \quad \frac{\text{d}y}{\text{d}x} = -\text{tg}\ \varphi;$$

$$y^2 = b^2\left(1 - \frac{x^2}{a^2}\right); \quad \text{tg}\ \varphi' = \frac{y}{x};$$

$$2y \cdot \text{d}y = -\frac{b^2}{a^2} \cdot 2x \cdot \text{d}x;$$

$$y\,\text{d}y = -\frac{b^2}{a^2}\, x\,\text{d}x;$$

$$\frac{y}{x} = -\frac{b^2}{a^2}\frac{\text{d}x}{\text{d}y};$$

$$\frac{y}{x} = \mathrm{tg}\,\varphi'; \quad \frac{\mathrm{d}y}{\mathrm{d}x} = -\mathrm{tg}\,\varphi;$$

$$\mathrm{tg}\,\varphi' = \frac{b^2}{a^2}\mathrm{tg}\,\varphi;$$

$$e^2 = \frac{a^2 - b^2}{a^2} = 1 - \frac{b^2}{a^2}; \quad \frac{b^2}{a^2} = 1 - e^2;$$

$$\mathrm{tg}\,\varphi' = (1 - e^2)\mathrm{tg}\,\varphi,$$

where e is the numerical eccentricity of the ellipse. Thus, the horizontal diurnal parallax of the star can now be determined:

$$\sin p_0 \approx p_0 = \frac{\rho_{\mathrm{geo}}}{r}\cos(\varphi - \varphi'),$$

where ρ_{geoid} corresponds to the place of observation, whose latitude is φ.

First, the Cartesian coordinates of place O on the surface of the ellipsoid of revolution are determined as follows (depending on the geographic latitude):

$$y = x\,\mathrm{tg}\,\varphi'; \quad y^2 = x^2\frac{b^4}{a^4}\,\mathrm{tg}^2\,\varphi;$$

$$y^2 = b^2\left(1 - \frac{x^2}{a^2}\right);$$

$$b^2\left(1 - \frac{x^2}{a^2}\right) = x^2\frac{b^4}{a^4}\,\mathrm{tg}^2\varphi;$$

$$\frac{x^2}{a^2}\left(1 + \frac{b^2}{a^2}\,\mathrm{tg}^2\,\varphi\right) = 1;$$

$$x^2 = \frac{a^4}{a^2 + b^2\,\mathrm{tg}^2\,\varphi};$$

$$e^2 = \frac{a^2 - b^2}{a^2} = 1 - \frac{b^2}{a^2}; \quad \frac{b^2}{a^2} = 1 - e^2;$$

$$b^2 = a^2(1 - e^2);$$

$$x^2 = \frac{a^2}{1 + (1 - e^2)\,\mathrm{tg}^2\,\varphi};$$

$$x = \frac{a\ \cos\varphi}{\sqrt{1 - e^2 \sin^2\varphi}};$$

$$y = \frac{a\,(1 - e^2)\ \sin\varphi}{\sqrt{1 - e^2 \sin^2\varphi}}.$$

Using the above, we determine the geocentric radius of place O on the Earth's surface:

$$\mathrm{OT} = \sqrt{x^2 + y^2} = \rho_{\mathrm{geo}};$$

$$\mathrm{OT} = a \cdot \sqrt{\frac{1 - 2e^2 \sin^2\varphi + e^4 \sin^2\varphi}{1 - e^2 \sin^2\varphi}} = \rho_{\mathrm{geo}},$$

representing the radius of the geoid at the point corresponding to the latitude φ, knowing the eccentricity of the ellipse, e, and its semi-major axis, a. Thus, we obtain:

$$p_{\mathrm{O}} = \frac{\rho_{\mathrm{geo}}}{r} \cdot \cos\left(\varphi - -\varphi'\right);$$

$$p_{\mathrm{O}} = \frac{a}{r} \cdot \sqrt{\frac{1 - 2e^2 \sin^2\varphi + e^4 \sin^2\varphi}{1 - e^2 \sin^2\varphi}} \cdot \cos\left(\varphi - \varphi'\right).$$

Particular case: $\varphi = 0$

As the drawing in Figure 13.4 indicates, the maximum value of p_{O}, that is, $p_{\mathrm{O,max}}$, is obtained when the star is observed from a point O on the Equator of the terrestrial geoid, where $\rho_{\mathrm{geo}} = a_{\mathrm{e}}$ (equatorial radius of the terrestrial geoid).

The equatorial *horizontal diurnal parallax* is the angle p_{e} at which the equatorial radius of the terrestrial geoid would be seen, if viewed from the center of a star on the horizon of an observation site on the terrestrial Equator.

The equatorial *horizontal diurnal parallax* is equal to the maximum value of the horizontal diurnal parallax of a star viewed from different points on the terrestrial geoid:

$$p_{\mathrm{e}} = p_{\mathrm{O,max}} = \frac{a_{\mathrm{e}}}{r}.$$

This relationship allows the determination of the distance between the center of the Earth and the center of the star if the equatorial

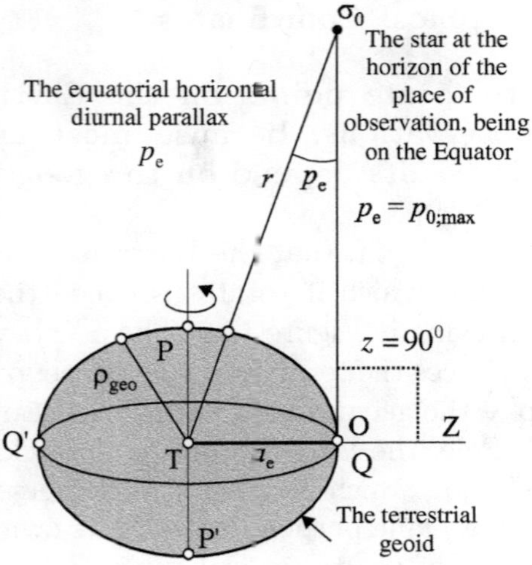

Fig. 13.4

horizontal diurnal parallax of the star is known:

$$r = \frac{a_e}{p_e}.$$

Another observation site, O′, on the same generating ellipse as the observation site O (whose geographic latitude is φ), located at an elementary distance dl measured on the ellipse from the site O(x, y), corresponds to Cartesian coordinates ($x - dx$; $y + dy$) and geographic latitude $\varphi + d\varphi$, so that

$$(dl)^2 = (dx)^2 + (dy).$$

By differentiating the parametric equations of the generating ellipse written previously, depending on the geographic latitude φ, and using the previous relationship, the length of the meridian arc on the generating ellipse between the two places O_1 and O_2, having the geographic latitudes φ_1 and φ_2, respectively, is determined as:

$$l_{12} = \int_{\varphi_1}^{\varphi_2} \sqrt{(dx)^2 + (dy)^2};$$

$$l_{12} = a(1 - e^2) \int_{\varphi_1}^{\varphi_2} \frac{d\varphi}{(1 - e^2 \sin^2 \varphi)^{\frac{3}{2}}},$$

which requires an elliptic integral.

Annex 1. Geographical Coordinates

It is essential to locate points on the Earth's surface for astronomical observations, because most are made from Earth, and their results depend on the geographic position of the observer O.

Assuming, to begin with, that the Earth is spherical, the imaginary axis, pp′, around which it rotates is called the *proper axis*, as indicated by the drawing in Figure 13.5. The points where the proper geographical axis pierces the terrestrial sphere are: p – the geographic North Pole and p′ – the geographic South Pole. Seen from above the geographic North Pole, the Earth rotates counterclockwise.

The great circle qq′, which represents the intersection of the terrestrial sphere with a plane perpendicular to its own axis that passes through the center T of the terrestrial sphere (the plane of the terrestrial Equator), is called the *terrestrial Equator.* It divides the terrestrial sphere into two hemispheres: the Northern (*Boreal*) Hemisphere with the geographic North Pole at the top, and the Southern (*Austral*) Hemisphere with the geographic South Pole at the top.

Small circles on the terrestrial sphere whose planes are parallel to the plane of the terrestrial Equator are called *geographic parallels.* Thus, the parallel bb′ from the Northern Hemisphere located at $23°27'$ from the Equator is called the *Tropic of Cancer*, and the parallel cc′ from the Southern Hemisphere located at $23°27'$ from the Equator is called the *Tropic of Capricorn.* The region on the Earth's surface between the two tropics (including the Equator) is called the *Warm Zone.*

The parallel aa′ located at $23°27'$ from the geographic North Pole is called the *North Polar Circle*, and the parallel dd′ located at $23°27'$ from the geographic South Pole is called the *South Polar Circle.*

The region on Earth's surface between the Tropic of Cancer and the Arctic Circle is the Northern *Temperate Zone*, and the region beyond the Arctic Circle is the Northern *Icecap.* The region on the Earth's surface between the Tropic of Capricorn and the Southern Polar Circle is the Southern *Temperate Zone*, and the region beyond the Southern Polar Circle is the Southern *Icecap.*

The great semicircle passing through the geographic poles of the Earth and through a point O on the Earth's surface is the *geographic meridian of the location* O. The geographic meridian of the

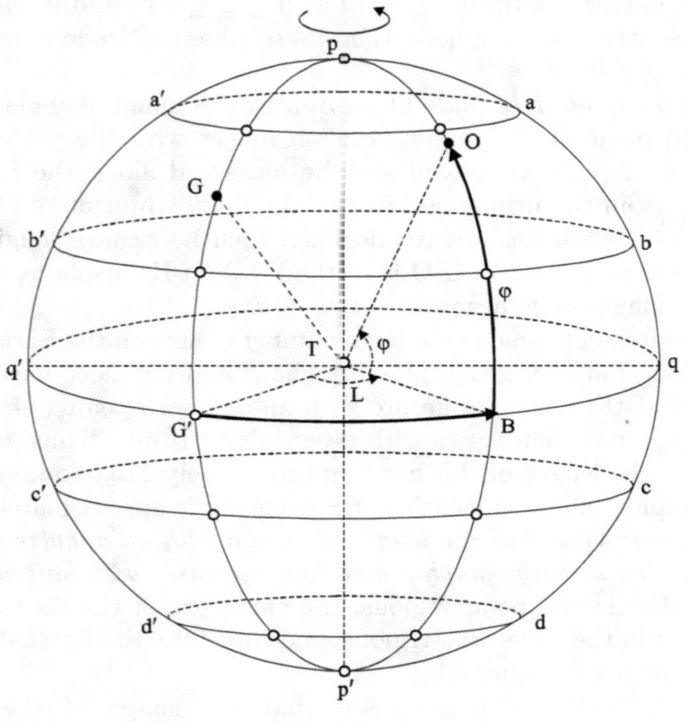

Fig. 13.5

Greenwich Observatory is called the *prime meridian* (origin/zero meridian).

The great circle on the Earth's surface which represents the intersection of the zero meridian plane with the terrestrial sphere divides the Earth's surface into two hemispheres: the Eastern Hemisphere and the Western Hemisphere.

The direction of the segment TO, along which the force of attraction acts in that place due to the Earth, represents the direction of the *geographical vertical* of the place.

The geographic coordinates of the location O on the Earth's surface are the *geographic latitude* (φ) and *geographic longitude* (L).

The *latitude* φ of place O is given by the angle ∍OTB that the vertical of place O makes with the plane of the Equator. It can also be measured along the meridian of place O, starting from the Equator to the vertical of place O. If place O is in the Northern Hemisphere, then its northern latitude is positive, $0 \leq \varphi \leq 90°$, and if place O is in the Southern Hemisphere, then its southern latitude is negative, $-90° \leq \varphi \leq 0$.

The *longitude* L of place O is given by the dihedral angle ρG′TB that the plane of the prime meridian makes with the plane of the meridian of place O. It can also be measured along the Equator, starting from the prime meridian to the meridian of place O. If the place O is in the Eastern Hemisphere, then its eastern longitude is positive, $0 \leq L \leq 180°$. If O is in the Western Hemisphere, then its western longitude is negative, $-180° \leq L \leq 0$.

Measurements made on a large number of arcs on the Earth's surface, along different geographic meridians and parallels, have established that the length of an arc with an angular opening of 1° on a geographic meridian varies with geographic latitude. Thus, near the Equator, the length of this arc is approximately 110.6 km, and near a geographic pole, the length of the same arc is approximately 111.7 km, thus proving that *the length of an arc with an angular opening of 1° on the same geographic meridian increases with latitude.* This means that in the polar regions, the curvature of the Earth is less than that in the equatorial regions, and therefore, the Earth does not have a spherical shape.

Hence, it was first proposed that the shape of the Earth approaches that of an ellipsoid of revolution (spheroid), determined by the rotation movement of the Earth around its own axis. Studies dating back to 1940 established that the minor semi-axis of this ellipsoid (whose direction coincides with the axis of its own rotation) has a length of $b = 6356.86\,\text{km}$, and the major semi-axis located in the equatorial plane has a length of $a = 6378.24\,\text{km}$, leading to a flattening of the ellipsoid of revolution of $\epsilon = \frac{a-b}{a} = \frac{1}{298.3}$.

Subsequent studies on the Earth's Equator proved a flattening of it $\epsilon_e = 1/300$, which corresponds to a difference of 213 m between the maximum and minimum values of the Earth's equatorial radii. In addition, the longitude of the place whose equatorial radius is maximum has the value $L = 15°$ (to the east).

Later, in 1962, measurements made by means of satellites established: the terrestrial equatorial radius has a length of $a = 6375.75\,\text{km}$; the North Polar radius has a length of $b_p = 6355.36\,\text{km}$; the South Polar radius has a length of $b_{p'} = 6355.36\,\text{km}$. The geographic South Pole is 30 m closer to the center of the Earth than the geographic North Pole, so the Earth is a flattened (triaxial) ellipsoid.

This proves that the Earth's real shape differs from that of an ellipsoid of revolution and that it cannot be identified with a simple geometric shape.

Under these conditions, when we refer to the appearance of the Earth, we will no longer think of the real physical form of the Earth's surface, with oceans and continents, with heights and depressions, but we will refer to an imaginary (fictitious) form called the *surface of a geoid*.

A terrestrial surface whose normals, at each of its points, are vertical, is called a *level/equilibrium surface*. So, for example, the free surface of water on a calm ocean is an equilibrium surface (*hydrostatic surface*).

The fictitious extension of the equilibrium surfaces of the seas and oceans under the continents eliminating all physical irregularities, provided that these extensions intersect at right angles the verticals of all places, completes the theoretical surface of the geoid. The vertical of each place is identified with the normal on the surface of the geoid.

The importance of the geoid is that the results of all geodetic measurements on the Earth's surface are reduced (reported) to its level, considered to be the level of the terrestrial sea.

Then, having created the geoid model, using the results of geodetic and gravimetric measurements, a flattened ellipsoid can be reconstructed, which does not differ from the geoid, vertically, by more than 100 m.

The surface of the geoid differs slightly from that of the flattened ellipsoid, passing above the surface of the flattened ellipsoid within the continents and passing below the surface of the flattened ellipsoid within the oceans, as shown in Figure 13.6.

If, in solving most astronomy problems, the Earth is treated as a homogeneous sphere, then when more precise assessments of the shape and dimensions of the Earth are required, we admit that it is an inhomogeneous ellipsoid of revolution (spheroid).

As a consequence of the inhomogeneity, the vertical of any point O on the surface of the Earth, as indicated by the drawing in Figure 13.7, will no longer pass through the center T of the Earth, piercing the plane of the Earth's Equator at a point T1 so that its

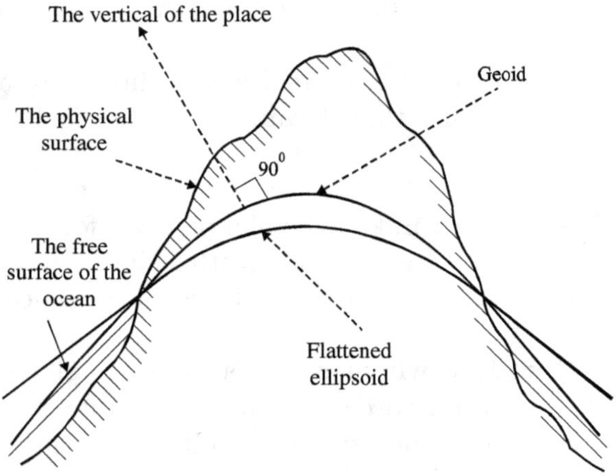

Fig. 13.6

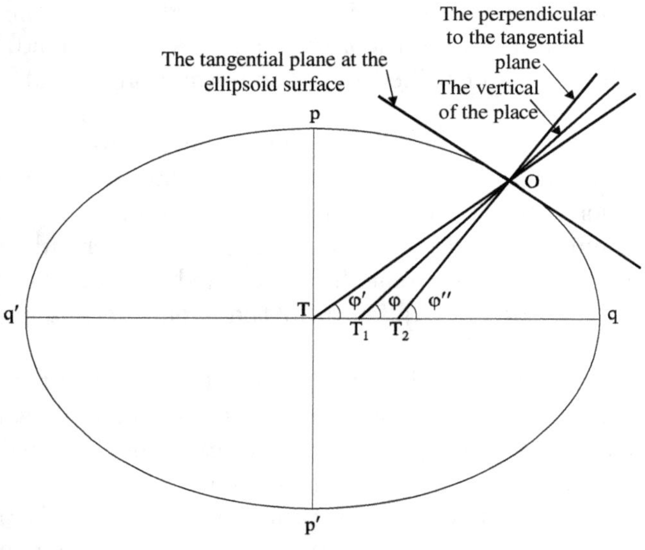

Fig. 13.7

direction, OT_1, deviates from the OT direction towards the center of the Earth.

Also, as a consequence of the inhomogeneity, the direction of the vertical OT_1 is also different from the direction OT_2 of the normal on the plane tangent to the surface of the ellipsoid at point O.

Under these conditions, for point O, the following types of latitudes are defined: *geographical latitude*, $\varphi = \angle OT_1q$, the angle between the vertical of the place and the plane of the terrestrial Equator; the *geocentric latitude*, $\varphi' = \angle OTq$, the angle between the direction towards the center of the Earth and the plane of the terrestrial Equator; the *geodetic latitude*, $\varphi'' = \angle OT_2q$, the angle between the normal on the plane tangent to the surface of the ellipsoid and the plane of the Equator.

Geodetic and gravimetric measurements allowed the determination of the difference $\varphi'' - \varphi$, the deviation of the direction of the plumb line from the normal direction on the surface of the ellipsoid, finding that it does not exceed $3''$, except for the points that represent gravitational anomalies.

Consequently, assuming that $\varphi'' \approx \varphi$, in current astronomy problems, no distinction is made between geographic latitude and geodetic latitude, and we are thus able to consider that the direction of the vertical of a place coincides with the direction of the normal on the surface of the ellipsoid.

The geographic latitude is determined from measurements, and then the geocentric latitude is obtained from calculations.

Continuing to adopt the ellipsoidal form of revolution of the Earth, let us consider that the deviation of the direction of the plumb line from the direction towards the center of the Earth is an effect of the Earth's rotation. As a result, the direction of the vertical of place O is the direction of the resultant between the force of gravitational attraction (oriented towards the center of the Earth, considered homogeneous) and the complementary terrestrial centrifugal force (perpendicular to the axis of rotation), which constitutes the apparent weight

$$\vec{G}_{\mathrm{a}} = \vec{G} + \vec{F}_{\mathrm{cf,c}},$$

whose direction pierces the plane of the Earth's Equator at point T_1, so that the angles φ and φ' define the geographic and geocentric latitudes of the place O, as indicated by the drawing in Figure 13.8.

The upward direction of the vertical OT_1 indicates the zenith, Z, of the topocentric sphere, and the opposite direction indicates the nadir, Z′, of the topocentric sphere, with the center at point O on the Earth's surface.

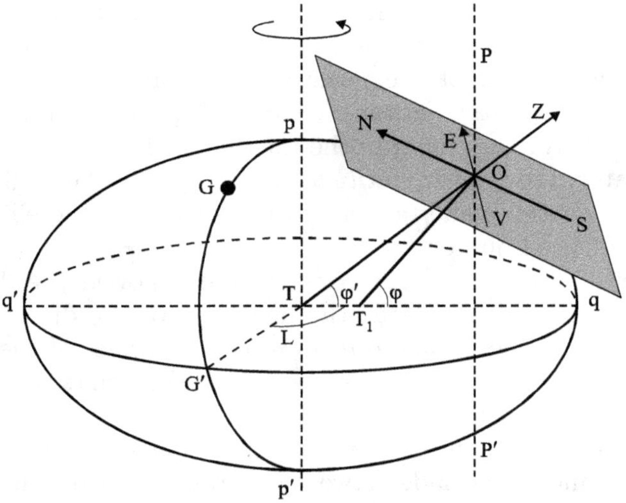

Fig. 13.8

The plane tangent to the terrestrial ellipsoid of revolution at point O represents the *theoretical horizon* of the observer at place O.

The parallel PP′, taken through O to the pp′ line of the terrestrial poles, is the *world axis* of the topocentric celestial sphere corresponding to the place O.

The world axis of place O determines the plane, and the vertical of place O is the *plane of the astronomical meridian* of place O.

The intersection of the plane of the astronomical meridian of place O with the Earth's surface is the generating ellipse of the ellipsoid of revolution.

The intersection of the theoretical horizon of place O with the plane of the astronomical meridian of place O is a straight line, tangent to the meridian ellipse of place O, representing the *meridian* of place O. The extremity of this meridian, oriented towards the North Pole (p) of the Earth, represents the cardinal point north of place O, and the extremity oriented towards the South Pole (p′) of the Earth represents the south cardinal point of place O. In navigation, the meridian of place O is called the *true North–South line* of place O.

The direction perpendicular to the NS meridian of place O, contained in the plane of the theoretical horizon of point O, represents the *true East–West line* of place O, where the east and west extremities indicate the cardinal points east and west of place O.

For place O on the Earth's surface, the following are defined: *geographic latitude,* $\varphi = \angle \mathrm{OT_1q}$; *geocentric latitude,* $\varphi' = \angle \mathrm{OTq}$; *geographic longitude,* $L = \angle \mathrm{G'Tq}$.

Two places on the Earth's surface whose latitudes are equal and of opposite signs and whose longitudes differ by 180° are said to be *antipodes* to each other.

Annex 2. Accurate Horizontal Diurnal Parallax of a Star

An observer at a point O in the Earth's Northern Hemisphere, with latitude $\varphi > 0$, does not perceive the absolute diurnal rotation of the Earth about its axis, relative to a fixed star, σ, whose topocentric angular zenith distance is z and whose distance to the geocentric angular zenith is $z_0 < z$ from the center of the Earth, as indicated by the drawing in Figure 13.9. Still, the observer appreciates the relative diurnal rotation of the star around the Earth's axis (around the world

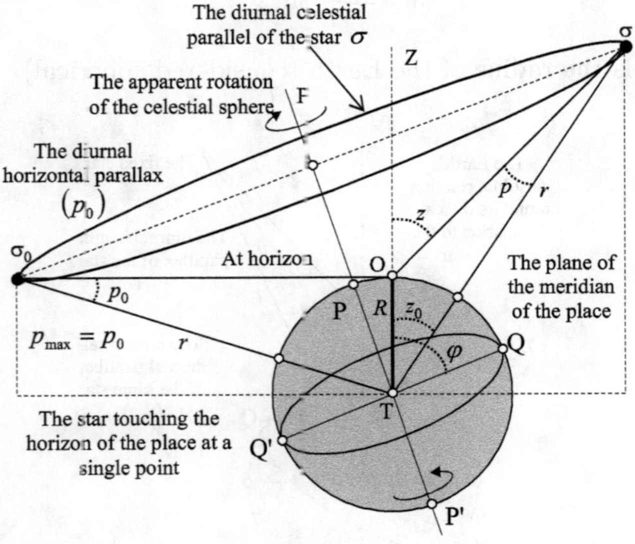

Fig. 13.9

axis) such that it remains, for one day, at the same distance, r, from the center of the Earth.

For simplicity, we have chosen the star σ, as indicated by the drawing in Figure 13.9, so that, in its apparent diurnal motion, it does not pass below the horizon of the place (the plane perpendicular to the vertical of the place, tangent to the surface of the Earth at the point of observation, O), having a single point of contact with the horizon of the place, σ_0, located in the plane of the same meridian of the place.

For the same observer, in the case of the absolute rotation of the Earth around its own axis with respect to the star σ, in the drawing in Figure 13.10, we find the same notation as in Figure 13.9.

The *diurnal height parallax* of the star σ is the angle $p = \angle \mathrm{O}\sigma\mathrm{T}$ under which the radius of the Earth (corresponding to the place of observation) would be seen if viewed from the center of the star.

From $\Delta \mathrm{OT}\sigma$, shown in the drawings in Figures 13.9 and 13.10, in accordance with the theorem of sines, it follows that:

$$\frac{\sin p}{R} = \frac{\sin\left(180^0 - z\right)}{r}; \quad \frac{\sin p}{R} = \frac{\sin z}{r};$$

$$\sin p = \frac{R}{r}\sin z \approx p,$$

where R is the radius of the Earth (considered spherical).

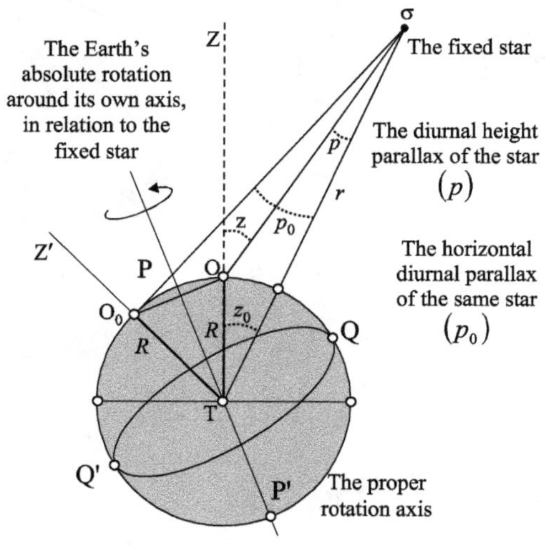

Fig. 13.10

The *diurnal height parallax* of a star depends on the distance between the center of the star and the center of the Earth and the topocentric zenith distance.

The maximum value of the *diurnal height parallax* of a star, $p_{\max} = p_0$, is obtained when, in its apparent motion, the star σ has reached a position σ_0 corresponding to the horizon line, i.e., at its sunset or sunrise, when its topocentric angular zenith distance is $z = 90°$, as shown in the drawing in Figure 13.9.

The case of a star σ', with sunrise and sunset, is indicated by the drawing in Figure 13.11, where σ'_0 is the sunset/rise point of the star.

The *horizontal diurnal parallax* of a star is the angle $p_0 = \angle O\sigma_0 T$ under which the Earth's radius (corresponding to the place of observation) would be seen if viewed from the center of the star when it is on the horizon.

In the position σ_0 of the star relative to the Earth (at the daytime moment when it reaches the horizon plane, the positions σ_0 and σ being symmetrical with respect to the world axis), the distance from the center of the star to the center of the Earth is also r. Thus, from $\Delta OT\sigma_0$, with a right angle at O, represented in the drawings

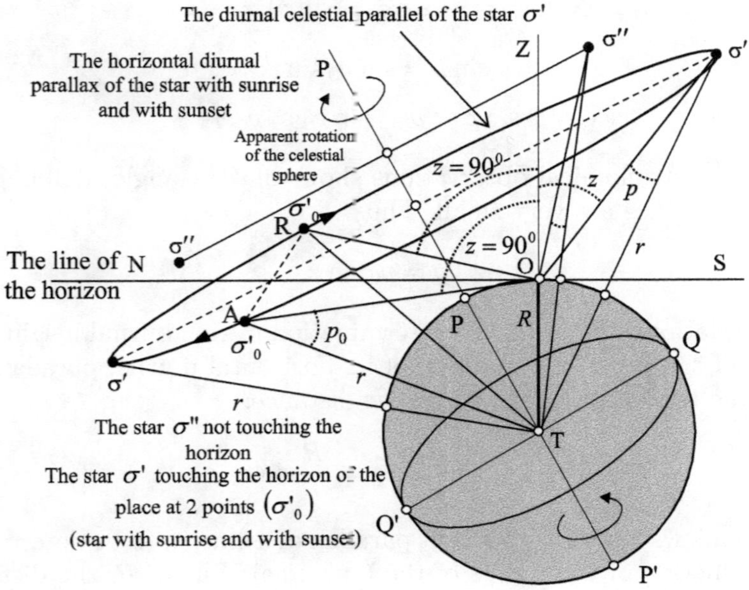

Fig 13.11

in Figures 13.9 and 13.12, we obtain:

$$\sin p_0 = \frac{R}{r}.$$

Moreover, analyzing the absolute diurnal rotation of the Earth around its own axis (which coincides with the direction of the world axis) in relation to the fixed star (drawing in Figure 13.10), it is evident that the distance between the center of the Earth and the center of the star is constant (r). On the other hand, the vertical orientation of the observation site changes due to Earth's rotation, so both the star's topocentric zenith distance, z, and the distance from the observer to the center of the star are variable.

In these conditions, the *diurnal parallax of the star's height* (the angle at which the Earth's radius is seen from the center of the star) is variable, reaching its maximum value when the observer is in position O_0 and sees the star on the horizon of the place ($p_0 = p_{\max}$). *The horizontal diurnal parallax of a star is equal to the maximum value of the diurnal height parallax of the same star.*

Considering the relations that allow the determination of each diurnal parallax of the same star, it follows that:

$$\sin p = \frac{R}{r}\sin z; \quad \sin p_0 = \frac{R}{r};$$

$$\sin p = \sin p_0 \sin z;$$

$$\sin p \approx p; \quad \sin p_0 \approx p_0,$$

because astronomical observations show that the angles defining the two parallaxes are very small. Thus,

$$p = p_0 \sin z.$$

This relationship allows the determination of the diurnal height parallax of a star, p, as a function of its horizontal diurnal parallax, p_0, and the topocentric zenith angular distance:

$$p_0 = \frac{R}{r}; \quad p = \frac{R}{r}\sin z,$$

which allows the diurnal height parallax of a star, p, to be determined as a function of the radius of the (spherical) Earth, R, the distance from the star to the observer on Earth, and the topocentric zenith angular distance, z.

The horizontal diurnal parallax of a star refers to the angle at which the Earth's radius, R, would be seen if it were observed from that star when at the horizon of the observer on Earth, as indicated by the drawing in Figure 13.12. This is under the conditions in which the Earth is considered spherical:

$$\sin p_0 = \frac{R}{r} \approx p_0;$$

$$r = \frac{R}{p_0}.$$

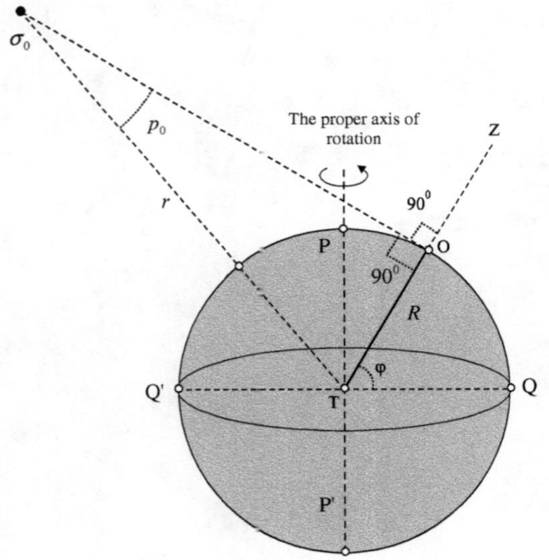

Fig. 13.12

Problem 14

Geostationary Satellite

a) *Determine* the flight parameters (h_0 – altitude; $\vec{v}$ – speed; $\vec{\omega}$ – angular velocity; T – period) of a geostationary satellite, S_{gs}, that revolves around the Earth in a circular orbit in the plane of the Equator, remaining at all times on the vertical of the same point, P, on the Equator, as the drawing in Figure 14.1 indicates.

Knowing: the radius of the Earth, $R = 6370\,\text{km}$; the gravitational acceleration on the ground, $g_0 = 9.81\,\text{m/s}^2$; the period of the Earth's rotation, $T_0 = 24\,\text{h}$.

b) *Specify* the minimum number of such satellites that would ensure the visibility of the entire surface of the Earth, and *determine* the angular and linear distances between the satellites.

c) *Determine* the duration of the mutual visibility between the geostationary satellite, S_{gs}, and another satellite, S, which revolves around the Earth in a higher circular orbit, in the same direction, at the altitude $h > h_0$. At the initial moment, the two satellites are at the minimum distance.

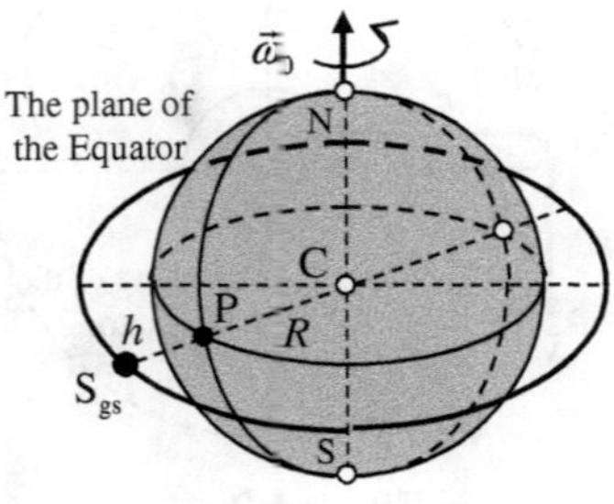

Fig. 14.1

Solution

a) Such a satellite is called a geostationary satellite. Geostationary satellites revolve around the Earth in the plane of the terrestrial Equator. To achieve such a revolution, the satellite is first raised to the altitude of the injection point, h_0, with the help of a carrier rocket, where it is given speed $\vec{v}$ in relation to the center of the Earth, its direction being in the plane of the Equator, perpendicular to the direction passing through the center of the Earth, and the same as the direction of the rotation of the Earth. This is necessary to maintain a circular orbit of radius r around the Earth at the altitude h_0 in such a way that the satellite, S_{gs}, remains permanently above the same point, P, on the Equator.

The stationarity of the flight of this satellite assumes that the angular speed of the satellite, ω_{gs}, is equal to the angular speed of the movement of the Earth's own rotation, ω_0. Thus, according to the notation in Figure 14.2, it follows that:

$$F = K\frac{mM}{r^2} = \frac{m\mathrm{v}^2}{r}; \quad \mathrm{v} = \sqrt{K\frac{M}{r}};$$

$$E = \frac{m\mathrm{v}^2}{2} - K\frac{mM}{r} = -K\frac{mM}{2r} < 0;$$

$$g = K\frac{M}{r^2}; \quad \mathrm{v} = \sqrt{gr}; \quad r = R_\mathrm{E} + h_0;$$

$$g = K\frac{M}{(R_\mathrm{E} + h_0)^2}\frac{R_\mathrm{E}^2}{R_\mathrm{E}^2}; \quad g_0 = K\frac{M}{R_0^2};$$

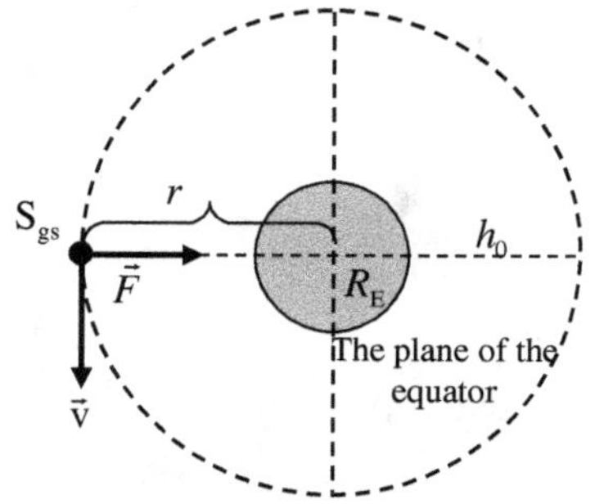

Fig. 14.2

$$g = g_0 \frac{R_{\mathrm{E}}^2}{(R_{\mathrm{E}} + h_0)^2}; \quad \mathrm{v} = R_{\mathrm{E}} \sqrt{\frac{g_0}{R_{\mathrm{E}} + h_0}};$$

$$T_{\mathrm{gs}} = \frac{2\pi r}{\mathrm{v}},$$

where T_{gs} is the time required to perform a complete rotation on the circular orbit (the *sidereal revolution period* of the satellite);

$$T_{\mathrm{gs}} = \frac{2\pi (R_{\mathrm{E}} + h_0)}{R_{\mathrm{E}}} \sqrt{\frac{R_{\mathrm{E}} + h_0}{g_0}},$$

where g_0 is the gravitational acceleration on the ground;

$$T_{\mathrm{gs}} = \frac{2\pi}{\omega_{\mathrm{gs}}}; \quad \omega_{\mathrm{gs}} = \frac{R_{\mathrm{E}}}{R_{\mathrm{E}} + h_0} \sqrt{\frac{g_0}{R_{\mathrm{E}} + h_0}}.$$

The *synodic revolution period* of the satellite, T_{synodic}, is defined as the time between two consecutive passes of the satellite at the zenith of an observer placed on the Equator line:

$$T_{\mathrm{synodic}} = \frac{2\pi}{\omega_{\mathrm{gs}} \pm \omega_0},$$

where ω_0 is the angular speed of the rotation of the Earth;

$$T_{\mathrm{synodic}} = \frac{2\pi}{\frac{R_{\mathrm{E}}}{R_{\mathrm{E}} - h_0} \sqrt{\frac{g_0}{R_{\mathrm{E}} + h_0}} \pm \omega_0},$$

where the sign "+" corresponds to the case when the direction of rotation of the satellite is opposite to the direction of rotation of the Earth, and the sign "−" corresponds to the case when the directions of rotation of the satellite and the Earth are identical.

A particularly interesting case is represented by the satellite that revolves in a circle around the Earth, in the same direction as the direction of the Earth's rotation, at a certain height, so that we have

$$\omega_{\mathrm{gs}} = \frac{R_{\mathrm{E}}}{R_{\mathrm{E}} + h_0} \sqrt{\frac{g_0}{R_{\mathrm{E}} + h_0}} = \omega_0,$$

that is, the satellite's angular speed of sidereal rotation should be equal to the Earth's angular speed of rotation.

Such a satellite is called a *geostationary satellite*, and it appears to be fixed above a point on the Earth's surface.

The period of synodic revolution of the geostationary satellite is $T_{\text{synodic}} \to \infty$.

To be geostationary, the satellite must revolve at the altitude

$$h_0 = \sqrt[3]{\frac{g_0 R_E^2}{\omega_0^2}} - R_E \approx 35800\,\text{km},$$

so its tangential speed must be

$$\text{v} = R_E \sqrt{\frac{g_0}{R_E + h_0}} \approx 3.08\,\text{km/s}.$$

b) To ensure the approximate "visual coverage" of the entire surface of the Earth, three geostationary satellites are needed, distributed at the same altitude, on the same circular orbit, and in the plane of the terrestrial Equator, as indicated by the drawing in Figure 14.3, at the vertices of an equilateral triangle with side length

$$l = 2\,(R_E + h_0)\cos 30^0 \approx 72955\,\text{km} = S_1S_2 = S_2S_3 = S_3S_1.$$

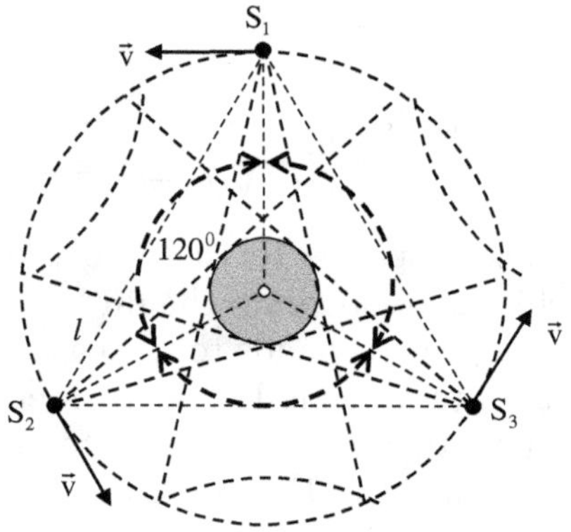

Fig. 14.3

Artificial satellites of the Earth can be launched to revolve in a very large variety of orbits, but they must have the center of the Earth either in the center of their circular orbit or in one of the foci of their ellipse. The directions of the movements of the satellites in these orbits can be direct or retrograde. The planes of these orbits can form different angles with the plane of the Equator. For example, a satellite can revolve in a polar orbit, meaning that the plane of the satellite's orbit is perpendicular to the plane of the Earth's Equator. These satellites fly over the entire surface of the Earth.

c) According to the notation in Figure 14.4, it follows that:

$$\alpha_{\mathrm{sg}} = \omega_0 t; \quad \alpha_{\mathrm{s}} = \omega t;$$

$$\omega_0 = \frac{2\pi}{T_0}; \quad \omega = \frac{2\pi}{T};$$

$$\alpha_{\mathrm{gs}} = \alpha_{\mathrm{s}} + \beta + \gamma; \quad \alpha_{\mathrm{gs}} - \alpha_{\mathrm{s}} = \beta + \gamma;$$

$$\sin\beta = \frac{R_{\mathrm{E}}}{R_{\mathrm{E}} + h}; \quad \beta = \arcsin\left(\frac{R_{\mathrm{E}}}{R_{\mathrm{E}} + h}\right);$$

$$\sin\gamma = \frac{R_{\mathrm{E}}}{R_{\mathrm{E}} + h_0}; \quad \gamma = \arcsin\left(\frac{R_{\mathrm{E}}}{R_{\mathrm{E}} + h_0}\right);$$

$$F = K\frac{mM}{(R_{\mathrm{E}} + h)^2} = m\omega^2 (R_{\mathrm{E}} + h) = m\frac{4\pi^2}{T^2}(R_{\mathrm{E}} + h);$$

$$T^2 = \frac{4\pi^2}{KM}(R_{\mathrm{E}} + h)^3;$$

$$F_0 = K\frac{mM}{(R_{\mathrm{E}} + h_0)^2} = m\omega^2 (R_{\mathrm{E}} + h_0) = m\frac{4\pi^2}{T_0^2}(R_{\mathrm{E}} + h_0);$$

$$T_0^2 = \frac{4\pi^2}{KM}(R_{\mathrm{E}} + h_0)^3; \quad \frac{T^2}{T_0^2} = \frac{(R_{\mathrm{E}} + h)^3}{(R_{\mathrm{E}} + h_0)^3} > 1;$$

$$T^2 = T_0^2\left(\frac{R_{\mathrm{E}} + h}{R_{\mathrm{E}} + h_0}\right)^3; \quad T = T_0\left(\frac{R_{\mathrm{E}} + h}{R_{\mathrm{E}} + h_0}\right)^{3/2};$$

$$\alpha_{\mathrm{gs}} - \alpha_{\mathrm{s}} = \beta + \gamma \quad \omega_0 t - \omega t = \beta + \gamma;$$

$$t = \frac{\beta + \gamma}{\omega_0 - \omega} = \frac{\beta + \gamma}{2\pi\left(\frac{1}{T_0} - \frac{1}{T}\right)} = \frac{\beta + \gamma}{2\pi}\frac{T_0 T}{T - T_0};$$

$$\beta = \arcsin\left(\frac{R_{\mathrm{E}}}{R_{\mathrm{E}} + h}\right); \quad \gamma = \arcsin\left(\frac{R_{\mathrm{E}}}{R_{\mathrm{E}} + h_0}\right);$$

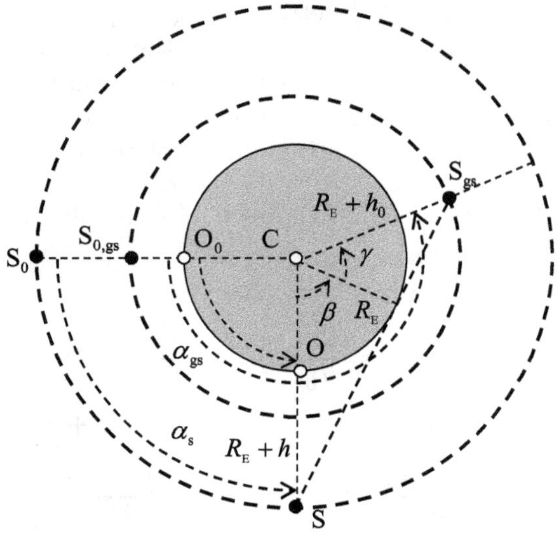

Fig. 14.4

$$T = T_0 \left(\frac{R_E + h}{R_E + h_0} \right)^{3/2};$$

$$t = \frac{\beta + \lambda}{2\pi} T_0 \frac{\left(\frac{R_E + h}{R_E + h_0} \right)^{3/2}}{\left(\frac{R_E + h}{R_E + h_0} \right)^{3/2} - 1}.$$

Problem 15

Limits and Astronomical Spheres

A. The Roche Limit of a Star

Two identical spherical cosmic bodies (1 and 2), each with mass m and radius r, are bound together — behaving as a rigid solid in contact, subject to normal pressure and reaction forces — and revolve around a planet P of mass M and radius r_P. They move along a circular orbit of radius R, maintaining the same angular

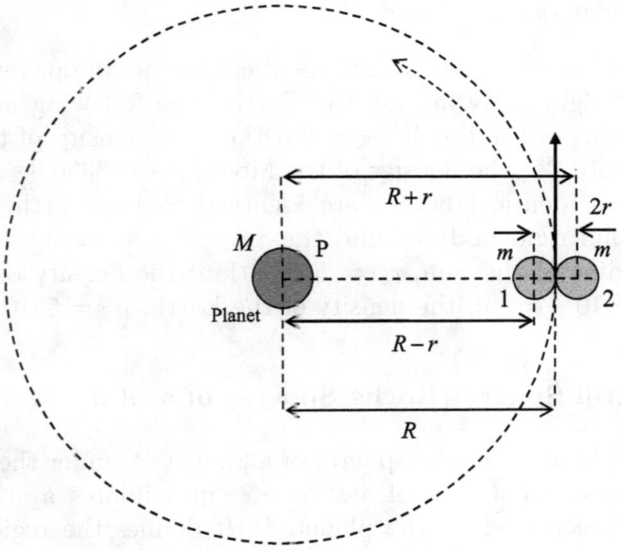

Fig. 15.1

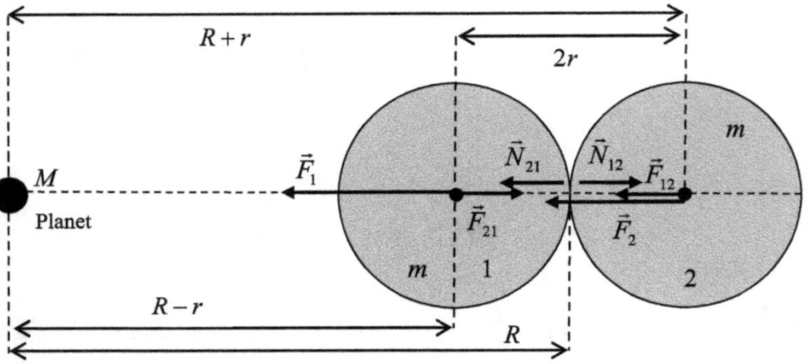

Fig. 15.2

velocity, as depicted in Figure 15.1. This holds true only if their mutual gravitational attraction, materializing in the gravitational forces represented in the drawing in Figure 15.2, is greater than the difference in gravitational forces exerted by the planet on the two bodies, $F_{12} > F_1 - F_2$.

a) *Determine* the minimum value of R, called the *Roche limit*, R_{Roche}, at which the contact between the two bodies ceases. It is known that: $m \ll M$; $r \ll R$; $\sqrt[3]{16} \approx 2.5$.

Particular cases:

1) The two identical bodies are identical to the Moon, revolving as a solid rigid body around the Earth. The following are known: the radius of the Earth, $r_E = 6378\,\text{km}$; the density of the Earth, $\rho_E = 5510\,\frac{\text{kg}}{\text{m}^3}$; the density of the Moon, $\rho_M = 3350\,\frac{\text{kg}}{\text{m}^3}$.

2) The two identical bodies are identical to the Earth, revolving as a solid rigid body around the Sun. The following are known: the radius of the Sun, $r_S = 696000\,\text{km}$; the density of the Sun, $\rho_S = 1410\,\frac{\text{kg}}{\text{m}^3}$; and the density of the Earth, $\rho_E = 5510\,\frac{\text{kg}}{\text{m}^3}$.

B. The Hill Sphere (Roche Sphere) of a Star

The Hill sphere (or Roche sphere) of a planet, P, under the influence of the gravitational field of a star, σ, approximates a sphere with radius r_{Hill} centered on the planet, P. It defines the region within which a moon or satellite, S, with the mass μ, of the planet can orbit the star, σ, in a circle, with the same angular speed, ω, as the planet, but remaining permanently under the gravitational influence of the planet, in the "full moon" position, without the orbit of the satellite being disturbed by the presence of the star.

A planet, P, of mass m, orbits a star, σ, of mass M, on a circle of radius R, with angular velocity ω. At the same time, a satellite (moon) of the planet, S, orbits the same star, σ, on a circle with the radius $R + r_{\text{Hill}}$, at the same angular speed ω. But, it remains permanently under the gravitational influence of the planet, P, in the "full moon" position, as indicated by the drawing in Figure 15.3.

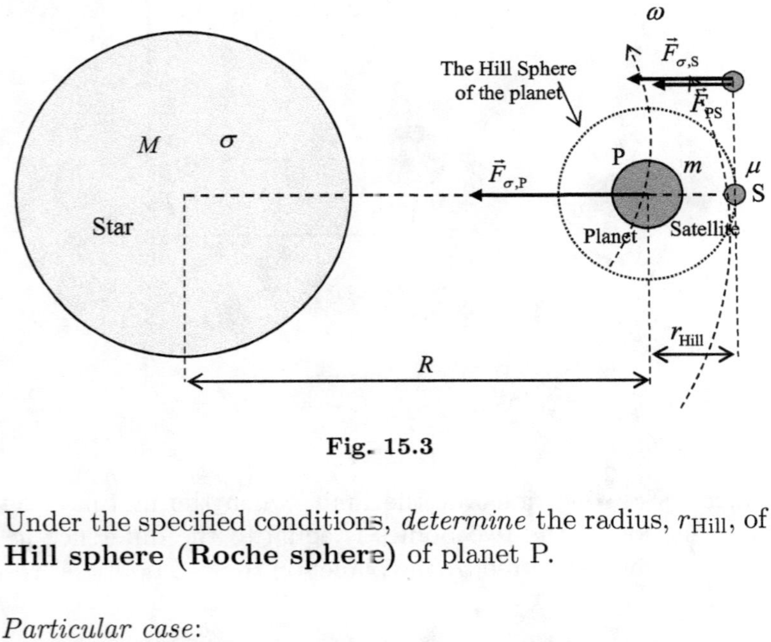

Fig. 15.3

b) Under the specified conditions, *determine* the radius, r_{Hill}, of **the Hill sphere (Roche sphere)** of planet P.

Particular case:

Determine the radius of the Hill sphere (Roche sphere) of the Earth under the influence of the gravitational field of the Sun. This means the sphere in the center of which the Earth is located when the Moon orbits the Sun in a circle with the same angular speed as the Earth, but remains permanently under the gravitational influence of the Earth, in the "full moon" position, without the Moon's orbit being disturbed by the presence of the Sun.

Knowing: $m_{\text{Earth}} = 5.97 \cdot 10^{24}$ kg; $M_{\text{Sun}} = 2 \cdot 10^{30}$ kg; $R_{\text{Sun-Earth}} = 15 \cdot 10^{7}\,\text{km} = 1\text{AU}$.

Solution

a) The Roche limit of a certain celestial body is the minimum distance from this celestial body at which two identical cosmic bodies remain together, without exerting mutual normal pressure, orbiting around the celestial body with the same angular velocity, ω, as indicated by the drawing in Figure 15.4.

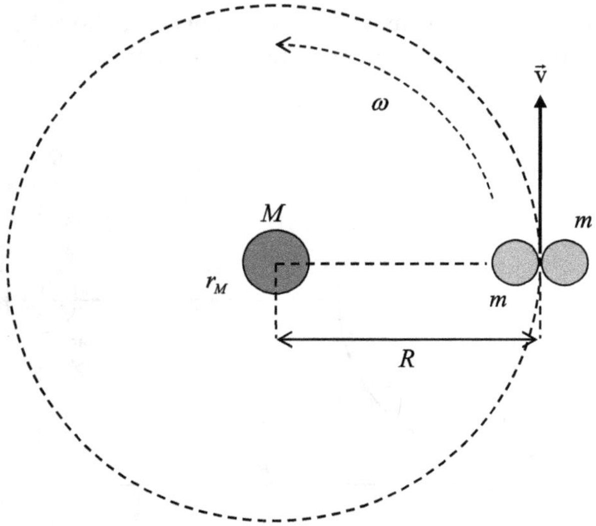

Fig. 15.4

Under these conditions, at the limit, when the mutual gravitational attraction of the two bodies is equal to the difference in the gravitational forces exerted by the planet on the two bodies, it results that:

$$\Delta F = F_1 - F_2 = K\frac{mM}{(R-r)^2} - K\frac{mM}{(R+r)^2};$$

$$\Delta F = K\frac{mM}{R^2\left(1-\frac{r}{R}\right)^2} - K\frac{mM}{R^2\left(1+\frac{r}{R}\right)^2};$$

$$m \ll M; \quad r \ll R;$$

$$\Delta F = K\frac{mM}{R^2}\left(1-\frac{r}{R}\right)^{-2} - K\frac{mM}{R^2}\left(1+\frac{r}{R}\right)^{-2};$$

$$\Delta F \approx K\frac{mM}{R^2}\left(1+2\frac{r}{R}\right) - K\frac{mM}{R^2}\left(1-2\frac{r}{R}\right);$$

$$\Delta F = 4K\frac{mMr}{R^3};$$

$$F_{12} = K\frac{mm}{(2r)^2},$$

$$\Delta F = F_{12};$$

$$4K\frac{mMr}{R^3} = K\frac{m^2}{4r^2};$$

$$R = r\cdot\sqrt[3]{16\frac{M}{m}} = R_{\text{Roche}};$$

$$\sqrt[3]{16} \approx 2.5; \quad R_{\text{Roche}} \approx 2.5\cdot r\cdot\sqrt[3]{\frac{M}{m}};$$

$$m = \rho_m\cdot\frac{4\pi r^3}{3}; \quad M = \rho_M\cdot\frac{4\pi r_M^3}{3};$$

$$R_{\text{Roche}} = r\cdot\sqrt[3]{16\frac{\rho_M r_M^3}{\rho_m r^3}} = r_M\cdot\sqrt[3]{16\frac{\rho_M}{\rho_m}} \approx 2.5\cdot r_M\cdot\sqrt[3]{\frac{\rho_M}{\rho_m}}.$$

Particular cases:

1)

$$r_M = r_{\text{E}}; \quad \rho_M = \rho_{\text{E}}; \quad \rho_m = \rho_{\text{M}};$$

Earth	Radius r_{E} 6378 km	Density ρ $\rho_{\text{E}} = 5510$ kg/m^3		
Moon		$\rho_{\text{M}} = 3350$ kg/m^3	Roche limit R_{Roche} 18970 km	Orbit radius R 384400 km

2)

$$r_M = r_{\text{S}}; \quad \rho_M = \rho_{\text{S}}; \quad \rho_m = \rho_{\text{Earth}};$$

Sun	Radius r_M 696000 km	Density ρ $\rho_S = 1410$ kg/m^3		
Earth		$\rho_E = 5510\,\text{kg/m}^3$	Roche limit R_{Roche} 1113000 km	Orbit radius R 149600000 km

b) Under the above conditions, it results that:

$$m\omega^2 R = G\frac{mM}{R^2}; \quad \omega^2 = \frac{GM}{R^3};$$

$$\mu\omega^2(R + r_{\text{Hill}}) = G\frac{\mu M}{(R + r_{\text{Hill}})^2} + G\frac{\mu m}{r_{\text{Hill}}^2};$$

$$\omega^2(R + r_{\text{Hill}}) = G\frac{M}{(R + r_{\text{Hill}})^2} + G\frac{m}{r_{\text{Hill}}^2};$$

$$\frac{GM}{R^3}\cdot(R + r_{\text{Hill}}) = G\frac{M}{(R + r_{\text{Hill}})^2} + G\frac{m}{r_{\text{Hill}}^2};$$

$$\frac{M}{R^3}\cdot(R + r_{\text{Hill}}) = \frac{M}{(R + r_{\text{Hill}})^2} + \frac{m}{r_{\text{Hill}}^2};$$

$$M(R + r_{\text{Hill}})^3 r_{\text{Hill}}^2 = MR^3 r_{\text{Hill}}^2 + mR^3(R + r_{\text{Hill}})^2;$$

$$mR^3(R + r_{\text{Hill}})^2 = Mr^2(R + r_{\text{Hill}})^3 - MR^3 r_{\text{Hill}}^2;$$

$$mR^3(R + r_{\text{Hill}})^2 = Mr_{\text{Hill}}^2(R^3 + 3R^2 r_{\text{Hill}} + 3Rr_{\text{Hill}}^2 + r_{\text{Hill}}^3) - MR^3 r_{\text{Hill}}^2;$$

$$mR^3(R + r_{\text{Hill}})^2 = MR^3 r_{\text{Hill}}^2 + Mr_{\text{Hill}}^2(3R^2 r_{\text{Hill}} + 3Rr_{\text{Hill}}^2 + r_{\text{Hill}}^3) - MR^3 r_{\text{Hill}}^2;$$

$$mR^3(R + r_{\text{Hill}})^2 = Mr_{\text{Hill}}^3(3R^2 + 3Rr_{\text{Hill}} + r_{\text{Hill}}^2);$$

$$r_{\text{Hill}} \ll R; \quad (R + r_{\text{Hill}})^2 \approx R^2; \quad 3Rr_{\text{Hill}} + r_{\text{Hill}}^2 \approx 0;$$

$$mR^5 = 3MR^2 r_{\text{Hill}}^3;$$

$$mR^3 = 3Mr_{\text{Hill}}^3;$$

$$r_{\text{Hill}} = R\cdot\sqrt[3]{\frac{m}{3M}} = r_{\text{Roche}},$$

representing the Hill sphere radius (Roche sphere radius) for planet P.

If the evolution of the planet P around the star σ occurs on an ellipse with semi-major axis a and eccentricity e, then the radius of the Hill sphere of the planet is given by the expression

$$r_{\text{Hill}} \approx a\,(1-e)\cdot\sqrt[3]{\frac{m}{3M}}.$$

The Hill sphere radius of a planet is the maximum distance from the planet at which a satellite can orbit without another cosmic body, much more massive than the planet, being able to disturb it and remove it from the planet's orbit.

The Hill sphere of a cosmic body is the region in which the cosmic body dominates the attraction forces acting on its satellites. To be gravitationally restrained by a planet, a satellite orbiting said planet must lie inside that planet's Hill sphere, as the drawing in Figure 15.5 indicates.

The Hill sphere of a cosmic body represents (approximates) the sphere of its gravitational influence on a small cosmic body in the face of gravitational perturbations (influences) due to another massive cosmic body. The Hill sphere is also called the Roche sphere and should not be confused with the Roche limit of the considered cosmic body.

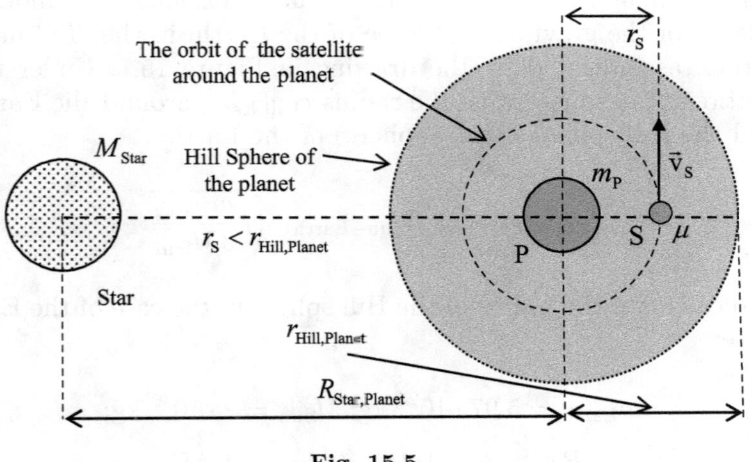

Fig. 15.5

The Hill sphere lies between the Lagrange points, L_1 and L_2, and the two cosmic bodies, along the line of their centers, as indicated by the drawing in Figure 15.6.

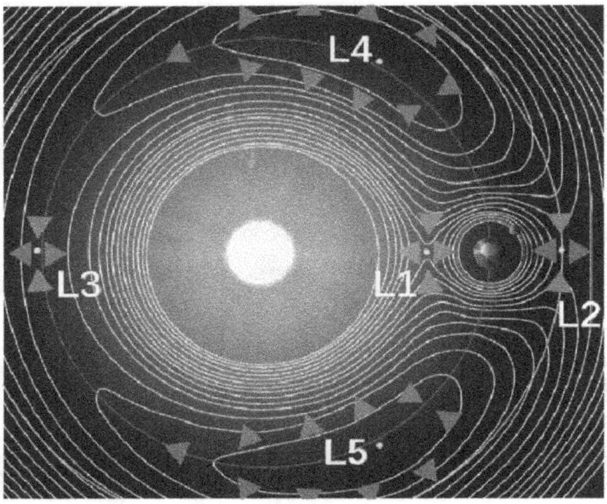

Fig. 15.6

The planet Earth, E, with mass m_E, orbits the Sun, S, with mass M_S, on a circle with the radius $R_{Sun-Earth}$, with the angular velocity ω. At the same time, suppose that the Moon, M, with mass μ_M, orbits the Sun on a circle with the radius $R_{Sun-Earth} + r_{Hill}$, with the same angular velocity ω. But, it remains permanently under the influence of the gravitational force of the Earth, in the "full moon" position, as indicated by the drawing in Figure 15.7. Under these conditions, the sphere with the radius $r_{Hill,Earth}$ around the Earth is called the Hill sphere (Roche sphere) of the Earth:

$$r_{Roche,Earth} = R_{Sun-Earth} \cdot \sqrt[3]{\frac{m_{Earth}}{3M_{Sun}}}.$$

To calculate the radius of the Hill sphere in the case of the Earth, we use:

$$m_{Earth} = 5.97 \cdot 10^{24}\ \text{kg};\ M_{Sun} = 2 \cdot 10^{30}\ \text{kg};$$

$$R_{Sun-Earth} = 15 \cdot 10^7\,\text{km} = 1\ \text{AU}.$$

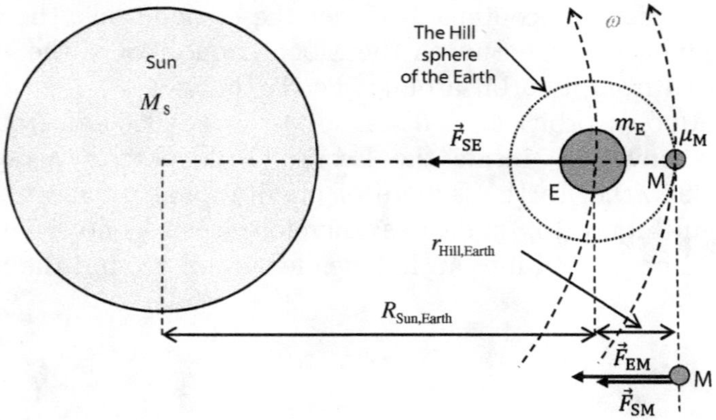

Fig. 15.7

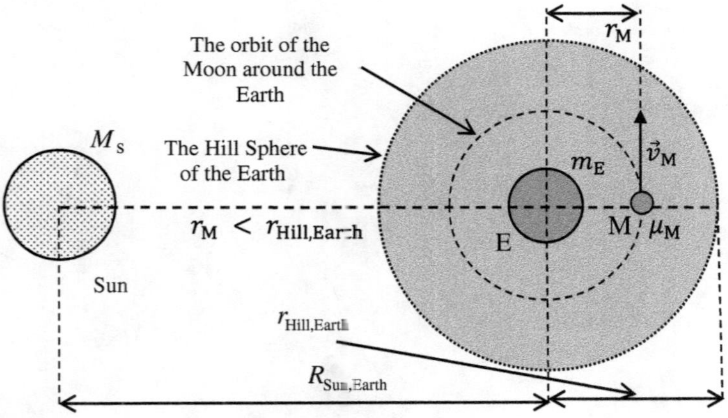

Fig. 15.8

Thus, we obtain:

$$r_{\text{Roche,Earth}} = R_{\text{Sun-Earth}} \cdot \sqrt[3]{\frac{m_{\text{Earth}}}{3M_{\text{Sun}}}}$$

$$= r_{\text{Hill-Earth}} = 1.5 \cdot 10^6\ \text{km} = 0.01\ \text{AU}.$$

The Hill sphere (Roche sphere) of the Earth, located in the gravitational field of the Sun, as indicated by Figure 15.8, represents the sphere, centered on the Earth, within which the Moon's orbit around the Earth is contained. Under these conditions, the gravitational influence of the Sun on the Moon cannot cause the Moon to be removed from its orbit around the Earth.

The Moon's orbit, at a distance $r_{\mathrm{M}} = 384000\,\mathrm{km}$ around the Earth, is obviously inside the Earth's Hill sphere, $r_{\mathrm{Hill-Earth}} = 1.5 \cdot 10^6\,\mathrm{km}$ (the Earth's sphere of gravitational influence), as the drawing in Figure 15.8 indicates; therefore, there is no risk that the Moon will be pushed into an independent orbit around the Sun.

Problem 16

Sunrise

Specify where and when the sunrise with the longest duration can be observed on Earth. *Estimate* this duration.

Solution

For a star σ, whose apparent position on the celestial sphere is represented in the drawing in Figure 16.1, we indicate the horizontal

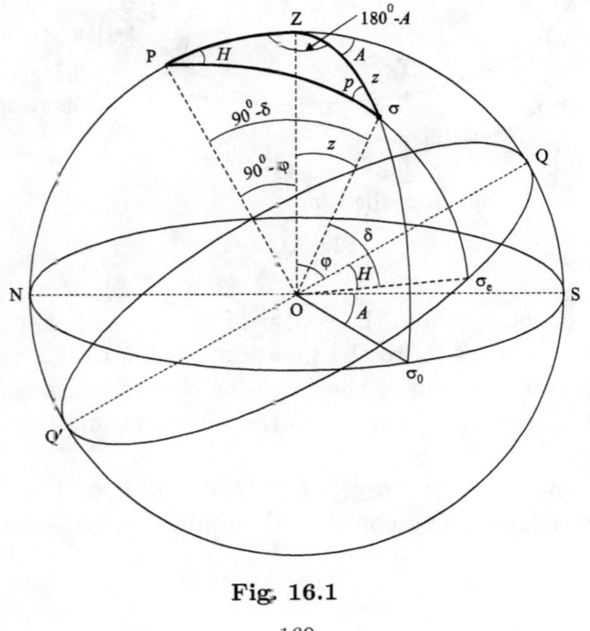

Fig. 16.1

and hourly celestial coordinates, (A; z) and (H; δ), and highlight the spherical triangle Z$P\sigma$, called the *parallactic* or *star position triangle.* The star's parallactic angle, p, is the angle between the great circle representing the star's vertical and the star's hour circle.

For an observer located in a place with the latitude φ, Figure 16.2 shows the revolution of the Sun, moving along the Equator on the days of the equinoxes, from the moment the sunset begins (when the Sun is above the horizon plane, tangent to this plane at the point T_d, and the center of the Sun is on the Equator, in the position S_d) until the end of the sunset (when the Sun is below the horizon, tangent to this plane at the point T_s, and the center of the Sun is on the Equator, in the position S_s).

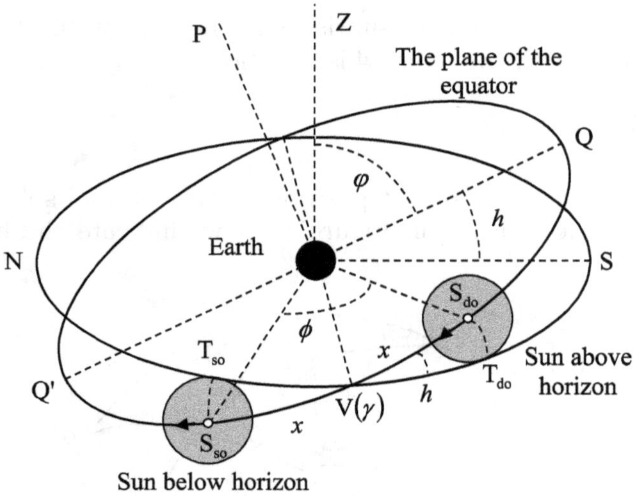

Fig. 16.2

During sunset, τ, when the center of the Sun moves on the Equator from the position S_d to the position S_s, the radius vector of the Sun rotates in the plane of the Equator by the angle ϕ, and in the vertical plane by an angle equal to the apparent angular diameter of the Sun, θ.

If $2x$ is the distance traveled by the center of the Sun on the Equator, in a movement considered uniform, with speed v, during sunset, τ, and if the right spherical triangle $S_d T_d V$ is accepted to be a plane triangle, it follows that:

$$\sin\ h = \frac{R_S}{x}; \quad x = \frac{R_S}{\sin h}; \quad 2x = \frac{2R_S}{\sin h} = \frac{D_S}{\sin h};$$

$$\tau = \frac{2x}{v} = \frac{2x}{\omega \cdot d_{ES}} = \frac{\frac{D_S}{\sin h}}{\frac{2\pi}{T_E} \cdot d_{ES}} = \frac{\frac{D_S}{d_{ES}}}{\frac{2\pi}{T_E} \cdot \sin\ h} = \frac{\theta \cdot T_E}{2\pi \cdot \sin h};$$

$$h = 90° - \varphi;$$

$$\tau = \frac{\theta \cdot T_E}{2\pi \cdot \cos \varphi},$$

representing the duration of sunset/sunrise on the day of the equinox for an observer located at latitude φ;

$$\theta = 31'\ 59.3'' = 31.98';$$

$$\tau = \frac{\frac{31.98'}{360 \cdot 60'} \cdot 24 \cdot 3600\ \text{s}}{\cos \varphi} = \frac{127.92}{\cos \varphi}\ \text{s} = \frac{2.132}{\cos \varphi}\ \text{min} \approx \frac{2\ \text{m}\ 8\ \text{s}}{\cos \varphi}.$$

This proves that the durations of the two events increase as one moves away from the Equator towards places with increasingly higher latitudes.

In particular, on the days of the equinoxes, if the observer is right on the Equator ($\varphi = 0$), as indicated by the drawing in Figure 16.3, when the parallactic angle of the Sun is 90°, the duration of the sunset/sunrise has the minimum value

$$\tau_{\text{min}} = 2\ \text{m}\ 8\ \text{s}.$$

For an observer located in a place with the latitude φ, Figure 16.4 shows the evolution of the Sun moving along the diurnal parallel circle with the center at point C on the axis PP′, having the declination $\delta = \varepsilon$, on the days of the solstices, from the moment the sunset begins (when the Sun is above the horizon, tangent to this plane, and the center of the Sun is on the diurnal parallel) until the end of the sunset (when the Sun is below the horizon, tangent to this plane, and the center of the Sun is on the diurnal parallel).

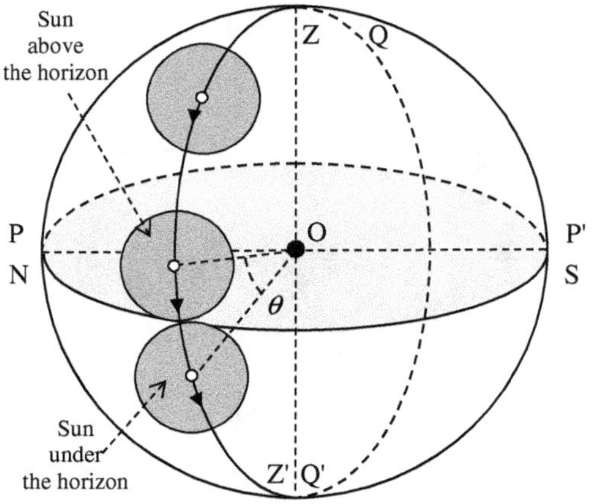

Fig. 16.3

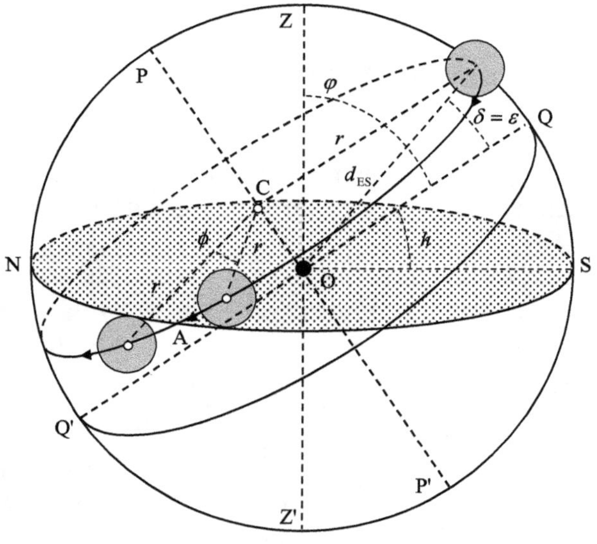

Fig. 16.4

Using the details from Figure 16.5, it follows that:

$$\sin\ h = \frac{R_\text{S}}{x}; \quad x = \frac{R_\text{S}}{\sin h}; \quad 2x = \frac{2R_\text{S}}{\sin h} = \frac{D_\text{S}}{\sin h};$$

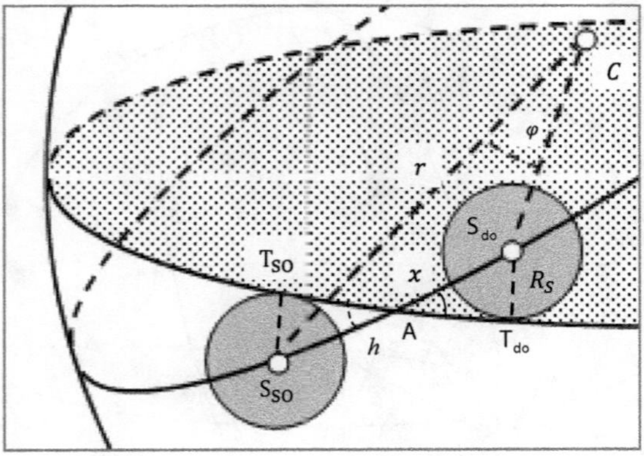

Fig. 16.5

$$\tau = \frac{2x}{v} = \frac{2x}{\omega \cdot r} = \frac{\frac{D_S}{\sin h}}{\frac{2\tau}{T_E} \cdot d_{ES} \cdot \cos\delta}$$

$$= \frac{\frac{D_S}{d_{ES}}}{\frac{2\pi}{T_E} \cdot \sin\ h \cdot \cos\delta} = \frac{\theta \cdot T_E}{2\pi \cdot \sin h \cdot \cos\delta};$$

$$\tau = \frac{\theta \cdot T_E}{2\pi \cdot \sin(90^0 - \varphi) \cdot \cos\delta} = \frac{\theta \cdot T_E}{2\pi \cdot \cos\varphi \cdot \cos\delta},$$

representing the duration of sunset/sunrise on the day of the solstice for an observer located at latitude φ.

If, on the days of the solstices, the observer is right on the corresponding parallel of latitude $\varphi = \delta = \varepsilon = 23°27'$, as indicated by the drawing in Figure 16.6, when the parallactic angle of the Sun is 90°, the duration of the sunset/sunrise has its maximum value:

$$h = 90° - \varphi; \quad \delta = \varepsilon = 23.45°;$$

$$\tau_{\max} = \frac{\frac{\theta \cdot T_E}{2\pi}}{\cos\varphi \cdot \cos\varepsilon} = \frac{\frac{31.98'}{360 \cdot 60'} \cdot 24 \cdot 3600\text{ s}}{\cos^2\varepsilon} = \frac{\tau_{\min}}{\cos^2\varepsilon};$$

$$\tau_{\max} = \frac{2.132\text{ min}}{\cos^2 23.45°} = \frac{2.132}{0.84}\text{ min} \approx 2.54\text{ min} = 2\text{ m }32.4\text{ s}.$$

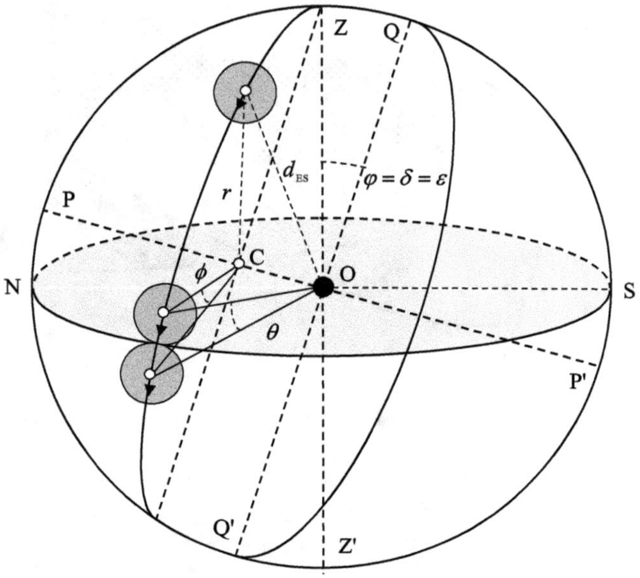

Fig. 16.6

Problem 17

Atmospheric Extinction

At an astronomical observatory, observations are made on a star whose equatorial coordinates are: right ascension, $\alpha = 01^{\mathrm{h}}10^{\mathrm{m}}36^{\mathrm{s}}$; declination, $\delta = 12^\circ 30' 00''$. The geographic coordinates of the astronomical observatory are: north latitude, $\varphi = 43^\circ$; west longitude, $\lambda = 78^\circ$.

In the image in Figure 17.1, the dependence $m(X_{\mathrm{r}})$ of the apparent magnitude of the star σ is represented over several hours of one night at the astronomical observatory.

Notation: X_{r} = "mass of air" traversed by the starlight from its entry into the Earth's atmosphere until it reaches the astronomical observatory.

It will be admitted that: the atmospheric layer traversed by the starlight is a homogeneous layer, with flat and parallel faces, as indicated by the drawing in Figure 17.2; the extinction of the starlight in the Earth's atmosphere is determined only by photons absorbed, or reflected, by very fine particles in the atmosphere, considered identical spheres.

Determine what percentage of the intensity of the star σ's light reaches the observer, $\eta = I/I_0$, after crossing the Earth's atmosphere, when, in the night sky of the astronomical observatory, at the time of its observation, the star σ is at its maximum height above the horizon.

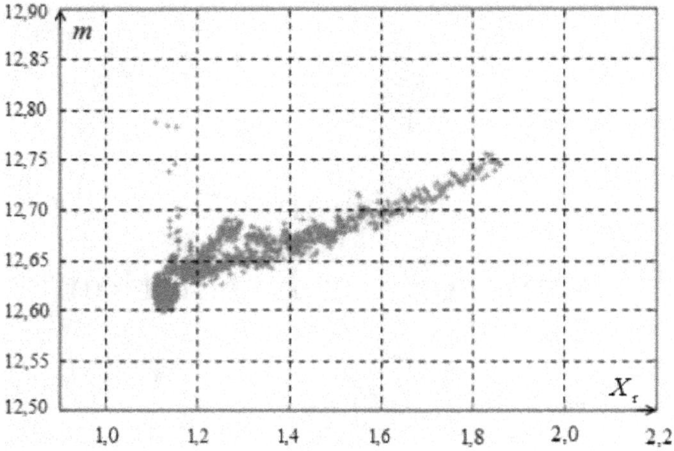

Fig. 17.1

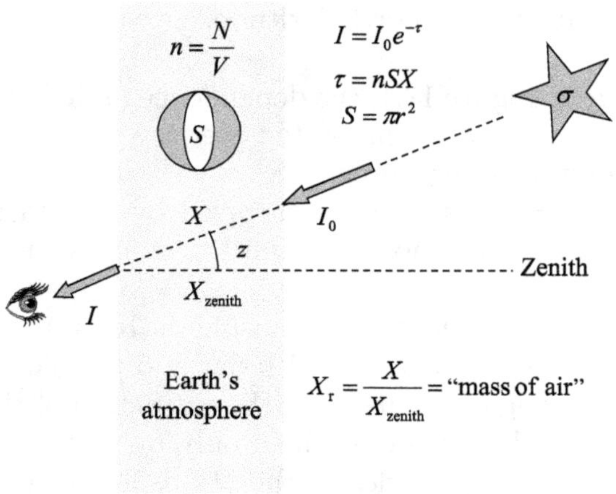

Fig. 17.2

Solution

For a star σ, whose apparent position on the celestial sphere is represented in the drawing in Figure 17.3, using one of Gauss's formulas (the second equation of the cosine formulas for the sides) written for the spherical triangle ZPσ (the analog of the standard spherical triangle, ABC), called the *parallactic triangle* or *position triangle* of

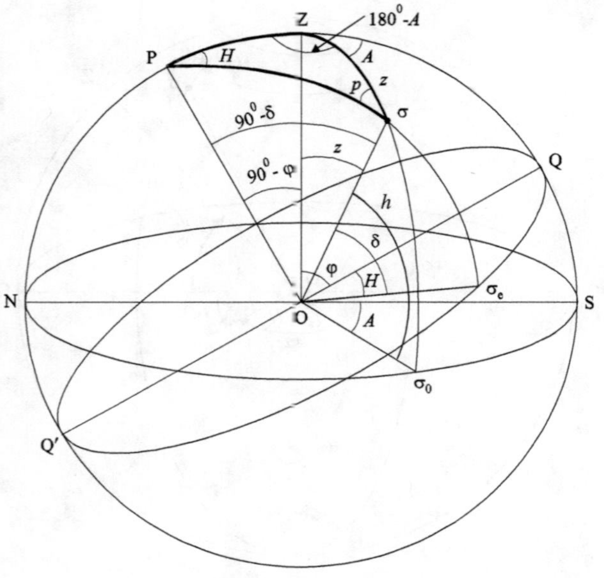

Fig. 17.3

the star, the results are:

$$\cos(\text{arc Z}\sigma) = \cos(\text{arc ZP}) \cdot \cos(\text{arc P}\sigma) + \sin(\text{arc ZP}) \cdot \sin(\text{arc P}\sigma) \cdot \cos H,$$

where H is the hour angle of the star σ;

$$\cos z = \cos(90^\circ - \varphi) \cdot \cos(90^\circ - \delta) + \sin(90^\circ - \varphi) \cdot \sin(90^\circ - \delta) \cdot \cos H;$$

$$\cos z = \sin\varphi \cdot \sin\delta + \cos\varphi \cdot \cos\delta \cdot \cos H.$$

Corresponding to a diurnal moment of sidereal time, $t_{\text{s}} = H_\gamma$, for a star σ, whose apparent position on the celestial sphere is represented in the drawing in Figure 17.4, there exists the relation

$$H = t_{\text{s}} - \alpha,$$

where t_{s} is the local sidereal time, $t_{\text{s}} = H_\gamma$, and H_γ is the hour angle of the vernal point γ, such that

$$\cos z = \sin\varphi \cdot \sin\delta + \cos\varphi \cdot \cos\delta \cdot \cos(t_{\text{s}} - \alpha).$$

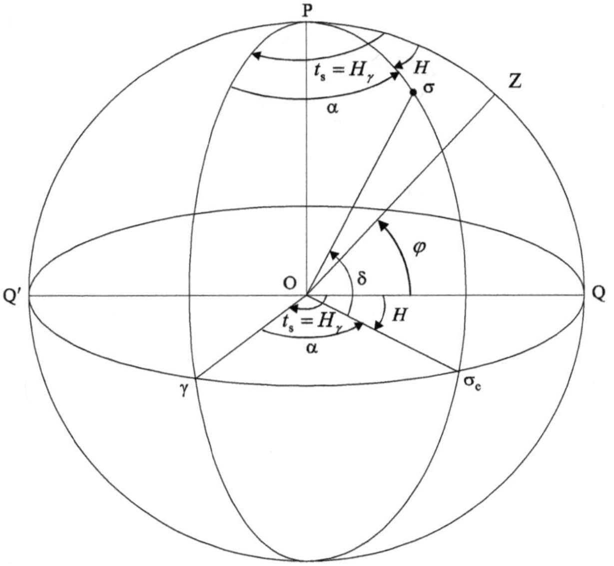

Fig. 17.4

The requirement in the statement of the problem refers to the moment when the star passes to the meridian of the place, as indicated by the drawing in Figure 17.5, when its height above the horizon is maximum, $h_{\max}$. As a result, the local sidereal time of the occurrence of this event is $t_s = 0$, and it follows that:

$$H = t_s - \alpha = -\alpha;$$

$$\cos z = \sin\varphi \cdot \sin\delta + \cos\varphi \cdot \cos\delta \cdot \cos(-\alpha);$$

$$\cos z = \sin\varphi \cdot \sin\delta + \cos\varphi \cdot \cos\delta \cdot \cos\alpha;$$

$$\alpha = 01^h 10^m 36^s = 17.65°; \quad \delta = 12°30'\,00'' = 12.5°; \quad \varphi = 43°;$$

$$\sin\varphi = 0.681; \quad \cos\varphi = 0.731;$$

$$\sin\delta = 0.216; \quad \cos\delta = 0.976;$$

$$\cos\alpha = 0.952;$$

$$\cos z = 0.681 \cdot 0.216 + 0.731 \cdot 0.976 \cdot 0.952 = 0.826;$$

$$z \approx 34°.$$

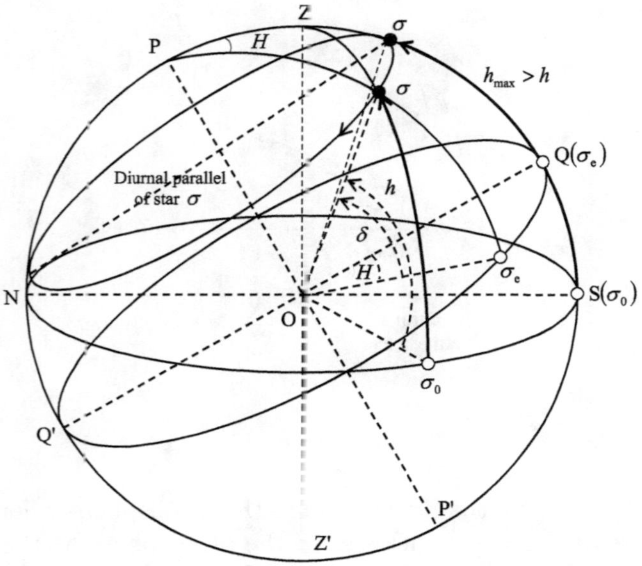

Fig. 17.5

One effect that must be corrected for when calibrating instrumental magnitudes is the atmospheric extinction of radiation (the diminution of starlight due to passage through the Earth's atmosphere). The longer the path of starlight through the Earth's atmosphere, the greater the extinction of the starlight. As a result, from the moment a star rises one night, being close to the horizon ($z = 90°$), until the moment it reaches the zenith ($z = 0$), the distance traveled by the light through the Earth's atmosphere decreases, so that the star gets brighter (its instrumental magnitude becomes smaller).

Studying the extinction of stellar radiation due to its absorption by particles in the Earth's atmosphere, using the drawing in Figure 17.6 and knowing the empirical formula of the law of absorption, we obtain:

$$I = I_0 \cdot e^{-\tau}; \quad \tau = nS\,X; \quad n = \frac{N}{V}; \quad S = \pi r^2; \quad X = X_{\mathrm{r}} X_{\mathrm{z}};$$

$$X_{\mathrm{zenith}} = X \cos z,$$

where r is the radius of absorbing particles in the atmosphere, n is the concentration of absorbing particles in the atmosphere, X_{z} is the

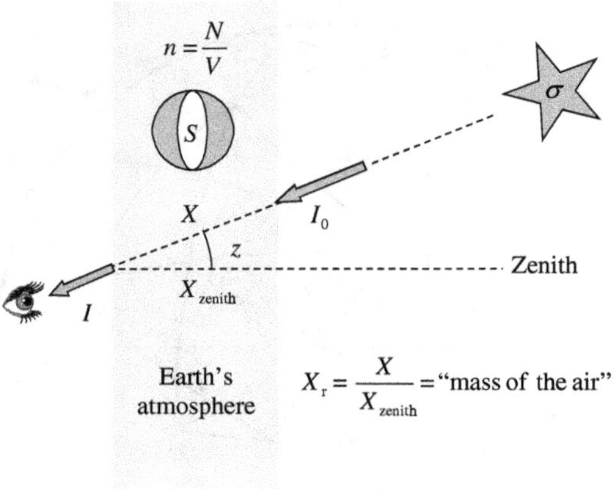

Fig. 17.6

distance traveled by the light through the atmosphere when the star is at the zenith, $z = 0$ (thickness of the atmosphere at the zenith = constant), and X is the distance traveled by the light through the atmosphere when the zenith distance of the star is z;

$$X = X_r X \cos z; \quad X_r = \frac{1}{\cos z};$$

$$\frac{I}{I_0} = e^{-\tau}; \quad \log\frac{I}{I_0} = \log e^{-nSX} = \log e^{-nSX_z X_r} = -nSX_z X_r \log e;$$

$$\log\frac{I}{I_0} = -0.434 n\pi\, r^2 X_z X_r = -0.434 \cdot 3.14 n r^2 X_z X_r$$

$$= -1.362 n r^2 X_z X_r.$$

On the other hand, according to Pogson's formula, it follows that:

$$\log\frac{I}{I_0} = -0,4\,(m - m_0),$$

where m_0 is the apparent magnitude of the star as seen from outside the atmosphere (not affected by the phenomenon of atmospheric extinction), and m is the apparent magnitude of the star to the observer (affected by the phenomenon of atmospheric extinction);

$$m - m_0 = -2.5 \cdot \log\frac{I}{I_0} = 2.5 \cdot 1.362 n r^2 X_z X_r = 3.405 n r^2 X_z X_r;$$

$$\kappa = 3.405 n r^2 X_z = \text{constant}.$$

The above is a combination of constant quantities (n, r, X_z), called the "coefficient of the first degree" of atmospheric extinction. Thus:

$$m - m_0 = \kappa X_r;$$

$$m = m_0 + \kappa X_r.$$

This proves that the magnitude of the star for the observer on the surface of the Earth, after the extinction of the light in the atmosphere, is a function of the parameter

$$X_r = \text{"air mass"},$$

whose physical meaning is that of the relative distance traveled by light from entering the Earth's atmosphere to the observer:

$$X_r = \frac{X}{X_{\text{zenith}}},$$

that is, the ratio of the distance traveled by starlight through the atmosphere to the observer, when the star is in a certain position in the sky, to the distance traveled by starlight through the atmosphere to the observer if the star were at the observer's zenith;

$$X_r \geq 1;$$

$$m(X_r) = m_0 + \kappa X_r.$$

The graph of this dependence is a straight line, as shown in the drawing in Figure 17.7.

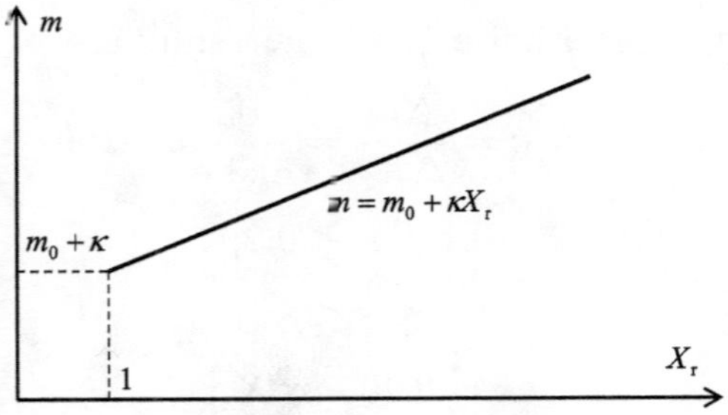

Fig. 17.7

If the observation is made using a filter (U, B, V, G, R, or I), it follows that:

$$m(X_{\mathrm{r}}; \lambda) = m_0(\lambda) + \kappa(\lambda) X_{\mathrm{r}}(z).$$

The extinction coefficient depends on the wavelength, having higher values for blue radiation (B) than for red radiation (R), as indicated by the data in the adjacent table.

Spectral band	U	B	V	R	I
$k(\lambda)$	0.6	0.4	0.2	0.1	0.08

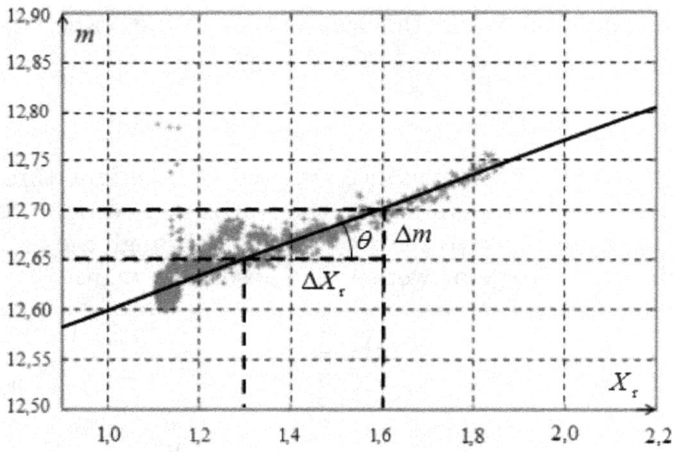

Fig. 17.8

Using the graph in Figure 17.8, the results are:

$$\tan\theta = \kappa = \frac{\Delta m}{\Delta X_{\mathrm{r}}} = \frac{0.05}{0.3} \approx 0.166;$$

$$0.1 < \kappa < 0.2;$$

$$\kappa_{\mathrm{R}} < \kappa < \kappa_{\mathrm{V}};$$

$$\kappa = 3.405 n r^2 X_{\mathrm{z}};$$

$$-2.5 \cdot \log\frac{I}{I_0} = 3.405 n r^2 X_{\mathrm{z}} X_{\mathrm{r}} = \kappa X_{\mathrm{r}} = 0.166 X_{\mathrm{r}};$$

$$-2.5 \cdot \log \frac{I}{I_0} = 0.166 X_{\mathrm{r}}; \quad X_{\mathrm{r}} = \frac{1}{\cos z};$$

$$-2.5 \cdot \log \frac{I}{I_0} = \frac{0.166}{\cos z} = \frac{0.166}{\cos 34^\circ} = \frac{0.166}{0.829};$$

$$\log \frac{I}{I_0} = -\frac{0.166}{0.829 \cdot 2.5} = -0.08;$$

$$\frac{I}{I_0} = 0.83; \quad I = 0.83 \cdot I_0.$$

Problem 18

Geostationary Satellite in the Plane of the Equator

The circular orbit of a geostationary satellite lies in the plane of the Equator. As a result of putting into operation, for a very short time, one of the reactive engines of the satellite, its speed modulus decreases by a value Δv, to a value much lower than the speed of the geostationary satellite without the orientation of the speed vector changing.

Determine:

a) the new rotation period of the satellite, T;
b) the maximum admissible value of Δv so that the satellite does not fall to the Earth's surface.

Given: T_0 – the period of the geostationary satellite; g_0 – the gravitational acceleration on the ground; R – the radius of the Earth. *It is known that*: $(1+x)^n \approx 1+nx$, if $x \ll 1$.

Solution

a) The geostationary evolution of the satellite on the orbit with radius r, highlighted in the drawing in Figure 18.1, occurs in such a way that the angular velocity of the satellite is equal to the angular velocity of the proper rotation of the Earth (the period of the satellite's rotation is equal to the period of the proper rotation of the Earth). The force of gravitational attraction exerted by the Earth on

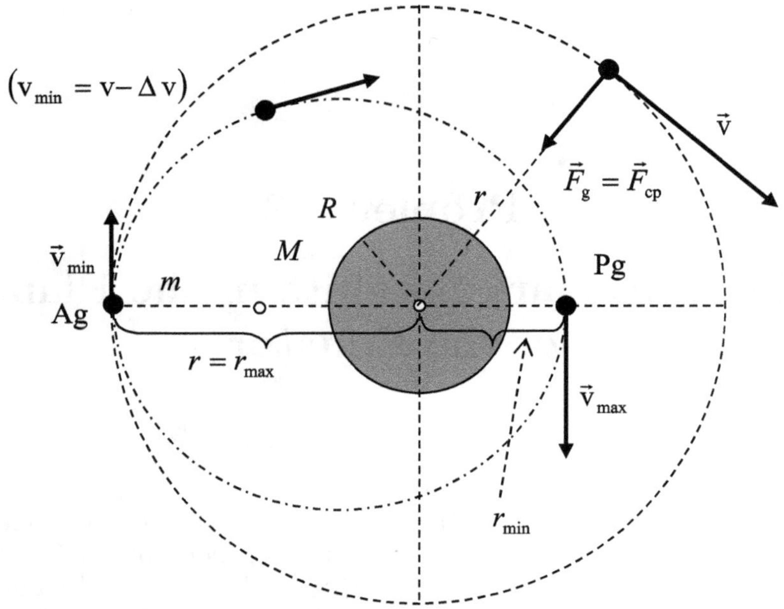

Fig. 18.1

the satellite, being a centripetal force, results in:

$$K\frac{mM}{r^2} = \frac{m\mathrm{v}^2}{r}; \quad K\frac{M}{r} = \mathrm{v}^2;$$

$$g_0 = K\frac{M}{R^2}; \quad T_0 = \frac{2\pi r}{\mathrm{v}}; \quad \frac{g_0 R^2}{r} = \frac{4\pi^2 r^2}{T_0^2};$$

$$r = \sqrt[3]{\frac{g_0 R^2 T_0^2}{4\pi^2}}; \quad \mathrm{v} = \frac{2\pi}{T_0}r; \quad \mathrm{v} = \sqrt[3]{\frac{2\pi g_0 R^2}{T_0}}.$$

After reducing the speed vector modulus by the amount $\Delta\mathrm{v} \ll \mathrm{v}$, the satellite will evolve on an ellipse-shaped orbit, the point where the speed correction occurred representing the apogee of the new elliptical orbit, in whose remote focus is the center of the Earth.

In accordance with the laws of conservation of angular momentum and mechanical energy, it follows that:

$$\mathrm{v}_{\min} r_{\max} = \mathrm{v}_{\max} r_{\min};$$
$$(\mathrm{v} - \Delta\mathrm{v})r = \mathrm{v}_{\max} r_{\min};$$

$$-K\frac{mM}{r_{\max}}+\frac{m\mathrm{v}_{\min}^2}{2}=-K\frac{mM}{r_{\min}}+\frac{m\mathrm{v}_{\max}^2}{2};$$

$$-K\frac{M}{r}+\frac{(\mathrm{v}-\Delta\mathrm{v})^2}{2}=-K\frac{M}{r_{\min}}+\frac{\mathrm{v}_{\max}^2}{2};$$

$$r+r_{\min}=2a;$$

$$a=\frac{r+r_{\min}}{2},$$

representing the semi-major axis of the ellipse.

According to Kepler's third law, if T is the period of the satellite's rotation in the new orbit, it follows that:

$$T_0^2=\frac{4\pi^2}{KM}r^3;\quad T^2=\frac{4\pi^2}{KM}a^3;$$

$$\frac{T^2}{T_0^2}=\frac{a^3}{r^3};\quad \frac{T^2}{T_0^2}=\frac{(r+r_{\min})^3}{(2r)^3};$$

$$-K\frac{M}{r}+\frac{(\mathrm{v}-\Delta\mathrm{v})^2}{2}=-K\frac{M}{r_{\min}}+\frac{\mathrm{v}_{\max}^2}{2};\quad K\frac{M}{r}=\mathrm{v}^2;$$

$$-\mathrm{v}^2+\frac{(\mathrm{v}-\Delta\mathrm{v})^2}{2}=-K\frac{M}{r_{\min}}+\frac{\mathrm{v}_{\max}^2}{2};$$

$$-\mathrm{v}^2+\frac{(\mathrm{v}-\Delta\mathrm{v})^2}{2}=-K\frac{M}{r}\frac{r}{r_{\min}}+\frac{\mathrm{v}_{\max}^2}{2};$$

$$-\mathrm{v}^2+\frac{(\mathrm{v}-\Delta\mathrm{v})^2}{2}=-\mathrm{v}^2\frac{r}{r_{\min}}+\frac{\mathrm{v}_{\max}^2}{2};$$

$$-\mathrm{v}^2+\frac{(\mathrm{v}-\Delta\mathrm{v})^2}{2}=-\mathrm{v}^2\frac{r}{r_{\min}}+\frac{\mathrm{v}_{\max}^2}{2};$$

$$(\mathrm{v}-\Delta\mathrm{v})r=\mathrm{v}_{\max}r_{\min};$$

$$(\mathrm{v}-\Delta\mathrm{v})\frac{r}{r_{\min}}=\mathrm{v}_{\max};$$

$$-\mathrm{v}^2+\frac{(\mathrm{v}-\Delta\mathrm{v})^2}{2}=-\mathrm{v}^2\frac{r}{r_{\min}}+\frac{1}{2}(\mathrm{v}-\Delta\mathrm{v})^2\frac{r^2}{r_{\min}^2};$$

$$\mathrm{v}^2\left(\frac{r}{r_{\min}}-1\right)=-\frac{(\mathrm{v}-\Delta\mathrm{v})^2}{2}+\frac{1}{2}(\mathrm{v}-\Delta\mathrm{v})^2\frac{r^2}{r_{\min}^2};$$

$$\mathrm{v}^2\left(\frac{r}{r_{\min}}-1\right)=\frac{1}{2}(\mathrm{v}-\Delta\mathrm{v})^2\left(\frac{r^2}{r_{\min}^2}-1\right);$$

$$\mathrm{v}^2=\frac{1}{2}(\mathrm{v}-\Delta\mathrm{v})^2\left(\frac{r}{r_{\min}}+1\right);$$

$$\frac{r+r_{\min}}{2r_{\min}}=\frac{\mathrm{v}^2}{(\mathrm{v}-\Delta\mathrm{v})^2};$$

$$\frac{r+r_{\min}}{2}=\frac{\mathrm{v}^2}{(\mathrm{v}-\Delta\mathrm{v})^2}r_{\min};$$

$$\frac{r+r_{\min}}{2r}=\frac{\mathrm{v}^2}{(\mathrm{v}-\Delta\mathrm{v})^2}\frac{r_{\min}}{r};$$

$$\frac{T^2}{T_0^2}=\left(\frac{r+r_{\min}}{2r}\right)^3;$$

$$-K\frac{M}{r}+\frac{(\mathrm{v}-\Delta\mathrm{v})^2}{2}=-K\frac{M}{r_{\min}}+\frac{\mathrm{v}_{\max}^2}{2};$$

$$-K\frac{M}{R^2}\frac{R^2}{r}+\frac{(\mathrm{v}-\Delta\mathrm{v})^2}{2}=-K\frac{M}{R^2}\frac{R^2}{r_{\min}}+\frac{\mathrm{v}_{\max}^2}{2};$$

$$-g_0\frac{R^2}{r}+\frac{(\mathrm{v}-\Delta\mathrm{v})^2}{2}=-g_0\frac{R^2}{r_{\min}}+\frac{\mathrm{v}_{\max}^2}{2};$$

$$(\mathrm{v}-\Delta\mathrm{v})\frac{r}{r_{\min}}=\mathrm{v}_{\max};$$

$$-g_0\frac{R^2}{r}+\frac{(\mathrm{v}-\Delta\mathrm{v})^2}{2}=-g_0\frac{R^2}{r_{\min}}+\frac{1}{2}(\mathrm{v}-\Delta\mathrm{v})^2\frac{r^2}{r_{\min}^2};$$

$$g_0R^2\left(\frac{1}{r_{\min}}-\frac{1}{r}\right)=\frac{1}{2}(\mathrm{v}-\Delta\mathrm{v})^2\left(\frac{r^2}{r_{\min}^2}-1\right);$$

$$g_0R^2\frac{r-r_{\min}}{rr_{\min}}=\frac{1}{2}(\mathrm{v}-\Delta\mathrm{v})^2\frac{r^2-r_{\min}^2}{r_{\min}^2};$$

$$g_0R^2\frac{1}{r}=\frac{1}{2}(\mathrm{v}-\Delta\mathrm{v})^2\frac{r+r_{\min}}{r_{\min}};$$

$$g_0R^2\frac{1}{r}=\frac{1}{2}(\mathrm{v}-\Delta\mathrm{v})^2\left(\frac{r}{r_{\min}}+1\right);$$

$$\frac{r}{r_{\min}} + 1 = \frac{2g_0 R^2 \frac{1}{r}}{(\mathrm{v} - \Delta\mathrm{v})^2};$$

$$\mathrm{v}^2 = K\frac{M}{r} = K\frac{M}{R^2}\frac{R^2}{r} = g_0\frac{R^2}{r};$$

$$\frac{r}{r_{\min}} + 1 = \frac{2\mathrm{v}^2}{(\mathrm{v} - \Delta\mathrm{v})^2};$$

$$\frac{r}{r_{\min}} = \frac{2\mathrm{v}^2}{(\mathrm{v} - \Delta\mathrm{v})^2} - 1;$$

$$\frac{r}{r_{\min}} = \frac{2\mathrm{v}^2 - \mathrm{v}^2 + 2\mathrm{v}\Delta\mathrm{v} - (\Delta\mathrm{v})^2}{(\mathrm{v} - \Delta\mathrm{v})^2} = \frac{\mathrm{v}^2 + 2\mathrm{v}\Delta\mathrm{v} - (\Delta\mathrm{v})^2}{(\mathrm{v} - \Delta\mathrm{v})^2};$$

$$\Delta\mathrm{v} \ll \mathrm{v};$$

$$\frac{r}{r_{\min}} \approx \frac{\mathrm{v}^2 + 2\mathrm{v}\Delta\mathrm{v}}{(\mathrm{v} - \Delta\mathrm{v})^2} = \frac{\mathrm{v}^2(1 + 2\frac{\Delta\mathrm{v}}{\mathrm{v}})}{(\mathrm{v} - \Delta\mathrm{v})^2};$$

$$\frac{r_{\min}}{r} = \frac{(\mathrm{v} - \Delta\mathrm{v})^2}{\mathrm{v}^2\left(1 + 2\frac{\Delta\mathrm{v}}{\mathrm{v}}\right)};$$

$$\frac{r + r_{\min}}{2r} = \frac{\mathrm{v}^2}{(\mathrm{v} - \Delta\mathrm{v})^2}\frac{r_{\min}}{r};$$

$$\frac{r + r_{\min}}{2r} = \frac{\mathrm{v}^2}{(\mathrm{v} - \Delta\mathrm{v})^2}\frac{(\mathrm{v} - \Delta\mathrm{v})^2}{\mathrm{v}^2\left(1 + 2\frac{\Delta\mathrm{v}}{\mathrm{v}}\right)};$$

$$\frac{r + r_{\min}}{2r} = \frac{1}{1 + 2\frac{\Delta\mathrm{v}}{\mathrm{v}}} = \left(1 + 2\frac{\Delta\mathrm{v}}{\mathrm{v}}\right)^{-1};$$

$$\frac{r + r_{\min}}{2r} \approx 1 - 2\frac{\Delta\mathrm{v}}{\mathrm{v}};$$

$$\frac{T^2}{T_0^2} = \left(\frac{r + r_{\min}}{2r}\right)^3;$$

$$\frac{T^2}{T_0^2} = \left(1 - 2\frac{\Delta\mathrm{v}}{\mathrm{v}}\right)^3; \quad T^2 = T_0^2\left(1 - 2\frac{\Delta\mathrm{v}}{\mathrm{v}}\right)^3;$$

$$T = T_0\sqrt{\left(1 - 2\frac{\Delta\mathrm{v}}{\mathrm{v}}\right)^3} = T_0\left(1 - 2\frac{\Delta\mathrm{v}}{\mathrm{v}}\right)^{3/2};$$

$$T \approx T_0\left(1 - 3\frac{\Delta \mathrm{v}}{\mathrm{v}}\right);$$

$$v = \sqrt[3]{\frac{2\pi g_0 R^2}{T_0}};$$

$$T = T_0\left(1 - \sqrt[3]{\frac{T_0}{2\pi g_0 R^2}}3 \cdot \Delta \mathrm{v}\right).$$

b) The accepted limit situation being the one represented in Figure 18.2, when $r_{\min} = R$, in accordance with the laws of conservation of angular momentum and mechanical energy, it results that:

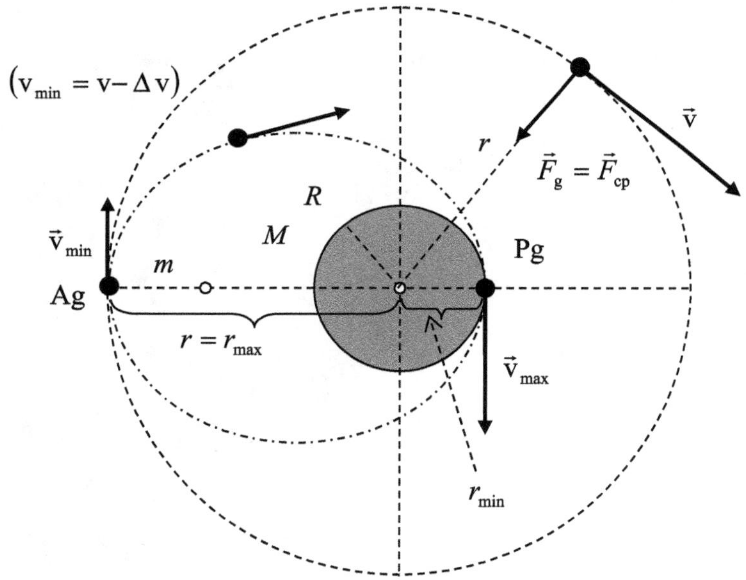

Fig. 18.2

$$(\mathrm{v} - \Delta \mathrm{v})r = \mathrm{v}_{\max} R;$$

$$-K\frac{M}{r} + \frac{(\mathrm{v} - \Delta \mathrm{v})^2}{2} = -K\frac{M}{R} + \frac{\mathrm{v}_{\max}^2}{2};$$

$$-K\frac{M}{R^2}\frac{R^2}{r} + \frac{(\mathrm{v} - \Delta \mathrm{v})^2}{2} = -K\frac{M}{R^2}R + \frac{\mathrm{v}_{\max}^2}{2};$$

$$-g_0\frac{R^2}{r}+\frac{(\mathrm{v}-\Delta\mathrm{v})^2}{2}=-g_0R+\frac{\mathrm{v}_{\max}^2}{2};$$

$$\mathrm{v}_{\max}=(\mathrm{v}-\Delta\mathrm{v})\frac{r}{R};$$

$$g_0R\left(1-\frac{R}{r}\right)=\frac{1}{2}(\mathrm{v}-\Delta\mathrm{v})^2\left(\frac{r^2}{R^2}-1\right);$$

$$2g_0R\left(\frac{r-R}{r}\right)=(\mathrm{v}-\Delta\mathrm{v})^2\left(\frac{r^2-R^2}{R^2}\right);$$

$$(\mathrm{v}-\Delta\mathrm{v})^2=\frac{2g_0R^3}{r\,(r+R)};\quad \Delta\mathrm{v}=\mathrm{v}-R\sqrt{\frac{2g_0R}{r\,(r+R)}}.$$

Problem 19

Special Maneuvers of a Geostationary Satellite

The most common maneuvers performed in orbit by spacecraft consist of variations in speed along the flight direction (namely, accelerations to reach higher orbits, or braking to initiate atmospheric re-entry). In this problem, however, we study how the orbit of a spaceship changes when the pushing action of its rocket engine is applied in the radial direction.

1) Let us consider a geostationary communications satellite whose period of revolution is T_0, having mass m, and moving in the equatorial plane on a circular orbit (with an unknown radius, r_0). This satellite has a "peak engine" that, in normal operation, must ensure the tangential action of the jet necessary to reach the final orbit.

a) *Determine* the analytical expressions of the radius of the orbit, r_0 (depending on g, R_T and T_0), and the speed of the satellite, v_0 (depending on g, R_T and r_0), and *calculate* their numerical values.

b) *Determine* the expressions of the satellite's angular momentum (L_0) and its total mechanical energy (E_0) as a function of v_0, m, g, and R_T.

2) After the geostationary satellite has been placed in the desired location, in the circular geostationary orbit (Figure 19.1), and is ready for operation, an error in the ground control causes the

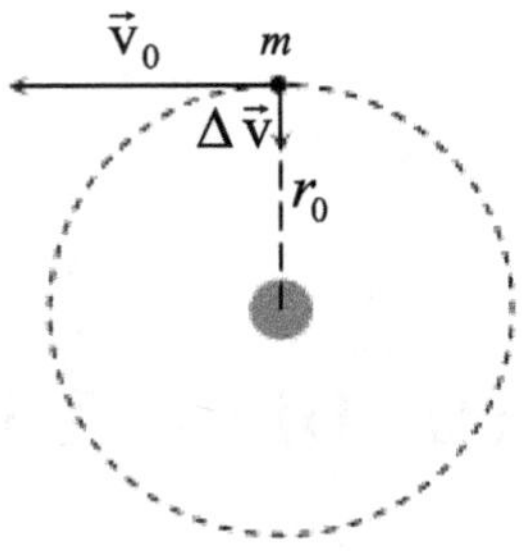

Fig. 19.1

re-ignition of the "apex engine". The action of the engine jet (the reaction of the jet on the satellite) is directed towards Earth, and although the flight control team on Earth immediately shuts down the engine, an unwanted velocity variation is imparted to the satellite. This mechanical shock can be characterized with the parameter $\beta = \Delta v/v_0$.

The duration of the accidental operation of the rocket engine is very small compared to any other duration that characterizes its movement in its orbit, so this duration is negligible.
We assume that $\beta < 1$.

c) *Determine* the characteristics of the new orbit of the satellite: the orbit parameter (p) and the eccentricity of the orbit (ε), depending on r_0 and β. For this, the information in the Annex can be used.

d) *Calculate* the angle α between the major axis of the satellite's new orbit and the satellite's position vector at the moment of accidental engine ignition.

e) *Determine* the analytical expression of the perigee $r_{\min}$ and apogee $r_{\max}$, distances measured from the center of the Earth as functions of r_0 and β, and *calculate* the corresponding numerical values for $\beta = 1/4$.

f) *Determine* the period of the new orbit T, depending on T_0 and β, and *calculate* its numerical value for $\beta = 1/4$.

We assume that the satellite escapes the attraction of the Earth.

g) *Calculate* the minimum value of the parameter β_{ev} necessary for the satellite to escape the attraction of the Earth.

h) *Determine*, in this case, the minimum distance of the satellite on its new trajectory from the center of the Earth as a function of r_0.

We assume that $\beta > \beta_{ev}$.

i) *Determine* the speed of the satellite at infinity v_∞, depending on v_0 and β.

j) *Obtain* the expression of the "shock parameter", b, for the asymptotic escape direction, depending on r_0 and β (see the drawing in Figure 19.2).

k) *Determine* the angle ϕ of the direction of the escape asymptote as a function of β. *Calculate* its numerical value for $\beta = \frac{3}{2}\beta_{ev}$.

For the calculation of numerical values, the following data will be used: radius of the Earth, $R_T = 6.37 \cdot 10^6$ m; gravitational acceleration at the Earth's surface, $g = 9.81\,\text{m/s}^2$; duration of a sidereal day, $T_0 = 24.0$ h

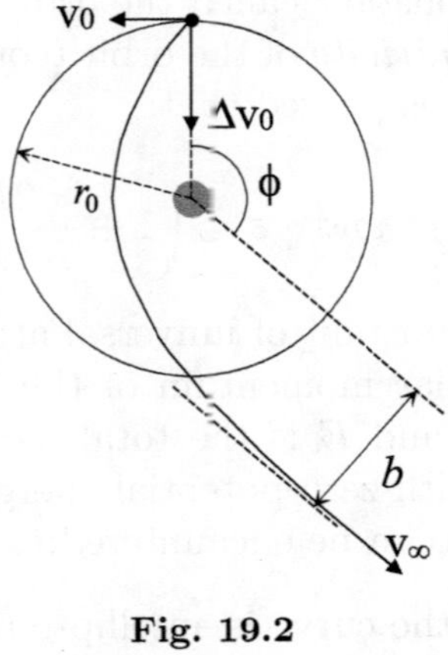

Fig. 19.2

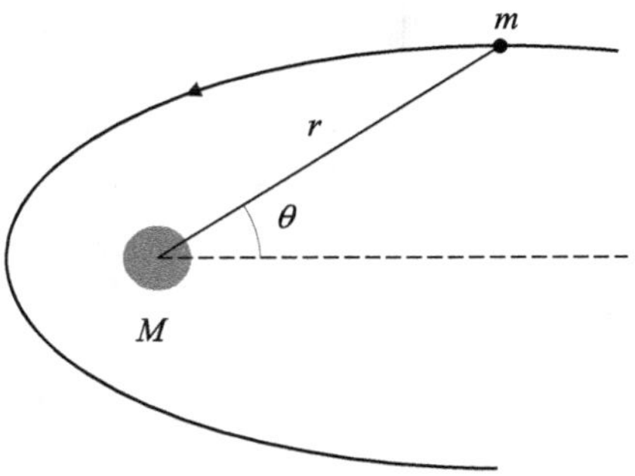

Fig. 19.3

Annex

Under the action of central forces in accordance with the law of inverse squares, bodies describe elliptical, parabolic, or hyperbolic trajectories. In the approximation $m \ll M$, a body with gravitational mass M is located in one of the foci of the trajectory (conic). Placing the origin of the coordinates in this focus, the general equation of these curves can be written in polar coordinates as follows (see Figure 19.3):

$$r(\theta) = \frac{p}{1 - \varepsilon \cos\theta},$$

where p is a positive constant called the orbit (conic) *parameter* and ε is the numerical *eccentricity* of the orbit (conic). Depending on the constants of motion, it is proved that:

$$p = \frac{L^2}{KMm^2} \quad \text{and} \quad \varepsilon = \left(1 + \frac{2EL^2}{K^2M^2m^3}\right)^{1/2},$$

where K is Newton's constant of universal attraction, L is the absolute value of the angular momentum of the body moving in orbit, relative to the origin, and E is the total mechanical energy of the body–Earth system, with zero potential energy at infinity.

The following cases can be encountered:

i. if $0 \leq \varepsilon < 1$, then the curve is an ellipse (circular for $\varepsilon = 0$);
ii. if $\varepsilon = 1$, then the curve is a parabola;
iii. if $\varepsilon > 1$, then the curve is a hyperbola.

Solution

a) In the circular and uniform motion of the satellite around the Earth, the Earth's gravitational attraction force is a centripetal force, so we can write that:

$$K\frac{M_{\mathrm{T}}m}{r_0^2} = \frac{m\mathrm{v}_0^2}{r_0}; \quad \mathrm{v}_0 = \frac{2\pi r_0}{T_0}; \quad g = K\frac{M_{\mathrm{T}}}{R_{\mathrm{T}}^2};$$

$$r_0 = \left(\frac{gR_{\mathrm{T}}^2T_0^2}{4\pi^2}\right)^{1/3} = 4.22\cdot 10^7\mathrm{m};$$

$$\mathrm{v}_0 = R_{\mathrm{T}}\sqrt{\frac{g}{r_0}} = 3.07\cdot 10^3\ \mathrm{m/s}.$$

b)

$$\vec{L}_0 = \vec{r}_0\times m\vec{\mathrm{v}}_0; \quad L_0 = r_0m\mathrm{v}_0 = \frac{gR_{\mathrm{T}}^2}{\mathrm{v}_0^2}m\mathrm{v}_0 = \frac{mgR_{\mathrm{T}}^2}{\mathrm{v}_0};$$

$$E_0 = \frac{1}{2}m\mathrm{v}_0^2 - K\frac{M_{\mathrm{T}}m}{r_0} = \frac{1}{2}m\mathrm{v}_0^2 - \frac{g\,R_{\mathrm{T}}^2\,m}{r_0} = \frac{1}{2}m\mathrm{v}_0^2 - m\mathrm{v}_0^2;$$

$$E_0 = -\frac{1}{2}m\mathrm{v}_0^2.$$

c) The accidental operation time of the rocket engine being very short, the passage of the satellite into the new orbit will occur without its angular momentum in relation to the center of the Earth changing. Using the information in the Annex, we determine the characteristics of the new orbit (orbit parameter and orbital eccentricity) as follows:

$$p = \frac{L_0^2}{KM_{\mathrm{T}}m^2}; \quad KM_{\mathrm{T}} = gR_{\mathrm{T}}^2;$$

$$p = \frac{m^2g^2R_{\mathrm{T}}^4}{\mathrm{v}_0^2}\frac{1}{g\,R_{\mathrm{T}}^2\,m^2} = \frac{g\,R_{\mathrm{T}}^2}{\mathrm{v}_0^2}; \quad \mathrm{v}_0^2 = R_{\mathrm{T}}^2\frac{g}{r_0}; \quad p = r_0;$$

$$\varepsilon = \left(1 + \frac{2EL_0^2}{K^2M_{\mathrm{T}}^2m^3}\right)^{1/2},$$

where E is the total mechanical energy of the satellite–Earth system in the new state;

$$E = \frac{1}{2}m\left[v_0^2 + (\Delta v)^2\right] - K\frac{mM_T}{r_0};$$

$$E = \frac{1}{2}m(\Delta v)^2 + E_0 = \frac{1}{2}m(\Delta v)^2 - \frac{1}{2}mv_0^2;$$

$$E = \frac{1}{2}mv_0^2\left[\frac{(\Delta v)^2}{v_0^2} - 1\right] = \frac{1}{2}mv_0^2(\beta^2 - 1);$$

$$\varepsilon^2 = 1 + \frac{2\frac{1}{2}mv_0^2(\beta^2-1)\left(\frac{mgR_T^2}{v_0}\right)^2}{K^2M_T^2m^3}; \quad KM_T = gR_T^2;$$

$$\varepsilon^2 = \beta^2; \quad \varepsilon = \beta < 1.$$

This proves that the new trajectory of the satellite, acquired as a result of the accidental ignition of the apogee engine, is an ellipse, with the center of the Earth in one of its foci.

d) The initial circular orbit and the final elliptical orbit of the satellite intersect at a point P, where the accidental ignition of the apogee engine occurrs, as shown in the drawing in Figure 19.4. It is also highlighted that the velocity vectors corresponding to each orbit are tangent to the orbits at this point.

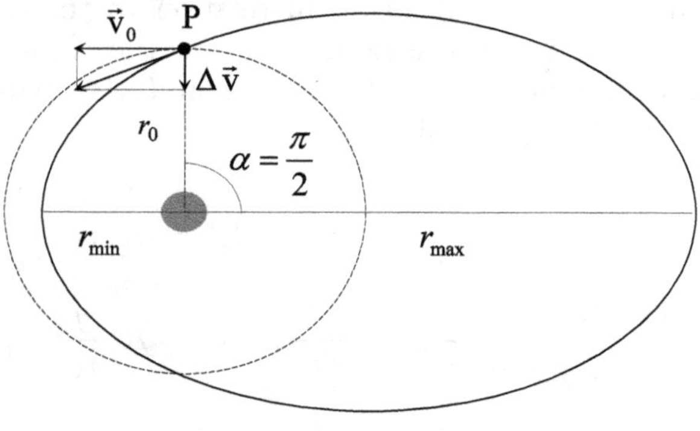

Fig. 19.4

Corresponding to point P, using the information in the Annex as well as the previous results it follows that:

$$r(\theta) = \frac{p}{1 - \varepsilon\cos\theta}; \quad p = r_0; \ \varepsilon = \beta;$$

$$r_P = r(\theta = \alpha) = r_C = \frac{r_0}{1 - \beta\cos\alpha}; \ \alpha = \frac{\pi}{2}.$$

e) The passage of the satellite through the apogee and perigee, when the distances to the center of the Earth are maximum and minimum, corresponds to the values $\theta = 0^0$ and $\theta = 180°$, respectively. Under these conditions, using the information in the Annex and the previous results, for $\beta = 1/4$, we get:

$$r_{\max} = \frac{p}{1-\varepsilon} = \frac{r_0}{1-\beta} = 5.63 \cdot 10^7\,\text{m};$$

$$r_{\min} = \frac{p}{1+\varepsilon} = \frac{r_0}{1+\beta} = 3.38 \cdot 10^7\,\text{m}.$$

The same results must be reached if, using the laws of conservation of mechanical energy and angular momentum, we take into account that in the evolution of the satellite on the elliptical orbit, during its passage through the apogee and perigee, $\vec{v}$ and $\vec{r}$ are perpendicular. Under these conditions, it follows that:

$$E = \frac{1}{2}m\mathrm{v}_0^2(\beta^2 - 1) = \frac{1}{2}m\mathrm{v}^2 - K\frac{mM_\mathrm{T}}{r};$$

$$KM_\mathrm{T} = gR_\mathrm{T}^2;$$

$$E = \frac{1}{2}m\mathrm{v}_0^2(\beta^2 - 1) = \frac{1}{2}m\mathrm{v}^2 - \frac{mgR_\mathrm{T}^2}{r};$$

$$L_0 = \frac{mgR_\mathrm{T}^2}{\mathrm{v}_0} = m\,\mathrm{v}\,r; \quad \mathrm{v} = \frac{gR_\mathrm{T}^2}{r\mathrm{v}_0};$$

$$\mathrm{v}_0^2(\beta^2 - 1) = \mathrm{v}^2 - 2\frac{gR_\mathrm{T}^2}{r}; \quad \mathrm{v}_0^2 = \frac{gR_\mathrm{T}^2}{r_0};$$

$$(\beta^2 - 1)r^2 + 2r_0 r - r_0^2 = \text{o};$$

$$r_{1,2} = \frac{-r_0 \pm \beta r_0}{\beta^2 - 1};$$

$$r_1 = \frac{r_0}{1-\beta} = r_{\max}; \quad r_2 = \frac{r_0}{1+\beta} = r_{\min}.$$

f) According to Kepler's third law, if T is the period of the satellite's evolution on the elliptical orbit, it follows that:

$$\frac{T^2}{a^3} = \frac{T_0^2}{r_0^3},$$

where a is the semi-major axis of the ellipse on which the satellite evolves;

$$a = \frac{r_{\max} + r_{\min}}{2} = \frac{r_0}{1-\beta^2};$$

$$T = T_0(1-\beta^2)^{-3/2}.$$

g) The satellite will escape from the terrestrial gravitational field only if its evolution occurs on an open trajectory (parabola or hyperbola), whose numerical eccentricity must be $\varepsilon \geq 1$. The minimum value of the parameter that characterizes the mechanical shock of the accidental ignition of the apogee engine will be that corresponding to the transfer of the satellite to a parabolic orbit, that is:

$$\varepsilon = 1; \quad \varepsilon = \beta; \quad \beta_{\mathrm{ev}} = 1.$$

The same result can be obtained from energetic considerations, knowing that, in the evolution of the satellite on a parabolic trajectory, when it has reached infinity, the total mechanical energy of the Earth–satellite system is zero, and there the satellite is at rest with respect to the Earth:

$$E = \frac{1}{2}mv_0^2(\beta_{\mathrm{ev}}^2 - 1) = 0; \quad \beta_{\mathrm{ev}} = 1.$$

The result is the same if it is the consequence of the conditions

$$T \to \infty \quad \text{and} \quad r_{\max} \to \infty.$$

h) Under the conditions of escape on a parabolic trajectory, when $\varepsilon = \beta_{\text{ev}} = 1$, the equation of the parabola is

$$r = \frac{p}{1 - \cos\theta},$$

where $p = r_0$. The minimum distance between the satellite and the center of the Earth, corresponding to $\theta = \pi$, will be

$$r'_{\text{min}} = \frac{r_0}{2}.$$

The same result must be reached if the problem is approached, in accordance with the laws of conservation of mechanical energy and angular momentum, recognizing that, at the point corresponding to the minimum distance, the vectors $\vec{\text{v}}_{\text{max}}$ and $\vec{r}'_{\text{min}}$ are perpendicular, and the total energy in the parabolic evolution is $E = 0$:

$$\frac{1}{2}m\text{v}^2_{\text{max}} - K\frac{mM_{\text{T}}}{r'_{\text{min}}} = 0; \quad r_0\text{v}_0 = r'_{\text{min}}\text{v}_{\text{max}};$$

$$\frac{1}{2}\frac{r_0^2\text{v}_0^2}{r'_{\text{min}}} = KM_{\text{T}} = gR_{\text{T}}^2; \quad r'_{\text{min}} = \frac{r_0}{2}.$$

i) If the satellite escapes from the Earth's gravitational field such that at infinity it has speed v_∞ relative to the Earth, then:

$$E = \frac{1}{2}m\text{v}_0^2(\beta^2 - 1) = \frac{1}{2}m\text{v}^2_\infty;$$

$$\text{v}_\infty = \text{v}_0(\beta^2 - 1)^{1/2},$$

the escape occurring on a hyperbolic trajectory.

j) Since $\varepsilon = \beta > \beta_{\text{ev}} = 1$, the escape trajectory of the satellite will be a hyperbola.

From the law of conservation of angular momentum written for the peak engine misfire point and for the point at infinity, using the drawing in Figure 19.5, it follows that:

$$m\,\text{v}_0 r_0 = m\,\text{v}_\infty b;$$

$$b = r_0\frac{\text{v}_0}{\text{v}_\infty}; \quad b = r_0(\beta^2 - 1)^{-1/2}.$$

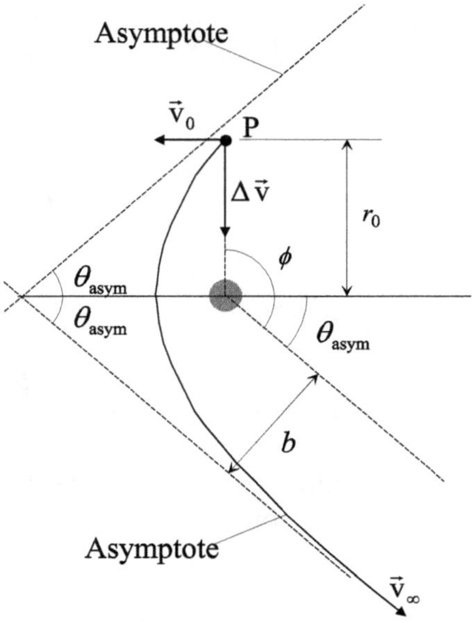

Fig. 19.5

k) The angle between each asymptote and the axis of symmetry of the hyperbola ($\theta_{\max}$) is the angle that appears in the trajectory equation, in the limiting case $r \to \infty$:

$$\frac{1}{r(\theta)} = \frac{1 - \varepsilon \cos\theta}{p}; \quad \lim_{r\to\infty} \frac{1}{r(\theta)} = 0;$$

$$1 - \varepsilon \cos\theta_{\max} = 0; \quad \varepsilon = \beta;$$

$$1 - \beta \cos\theta_{\max} = 0; \quad \theta_{\max} = \cos^{-1}\left(\frac{1}{\beta}\right).$$

This results in:

$$\phi = \frac{\pi}{2} + \theta_{\max}; \quad \phi = \frac{\pi}{2} + \cos^{-1}\left(\frac{1}{\beta}\right); \quad \beta = \frac{3}{2}\beta_{\rm ev} = \frac{3}{2}.$$

Problem 20

Precession of the World Axis

By relating them to short time intervals, the equatorial and ecliptic coordinates of the stars can be considered constant, thus revealing the constancy of the orientations of the planes of the celestial equator and the ecliptic in relation to the "fixed" stars.

By relating them to long time intervals, the equatorial and ecliptic coordinates of the stars resulting from recorded determinations appear to be variable, showing a variation in the orientations of the equatorial and ecliptic planes relative to the "fixes".

a) If the location on the celestial sphere of a star σ, using the equatorial and ecliptic coordinate systems, is the one represented in the drawing in Figure 20.1, then, using Gauss's formulas for the spherical triangle $P\Pi\sigma$ (the analog of the conventional spherical triangle ABC), *establish* the relations between the coordinates of the star according to the two systems, $(\alpha;\ \delta)$ and $(\lambda;\ \beta)$. The angle ε between the plane of the celestial equator and the plane of the ecliptic is known.

b) Considering that the orientation of the plane of the ecliptic is constant but that the vernal point moves on the ecliptic to meet the Sun, the orientation of the plane of the celestial equator is variable, without the angle between the two planes varying. The consequence of this phenomenon, called the precession of the equinox line $(\gamma \leftrightarrow \omega)$ in the ecliptic plane, is the variation of the equatorial coordinates of the stars.

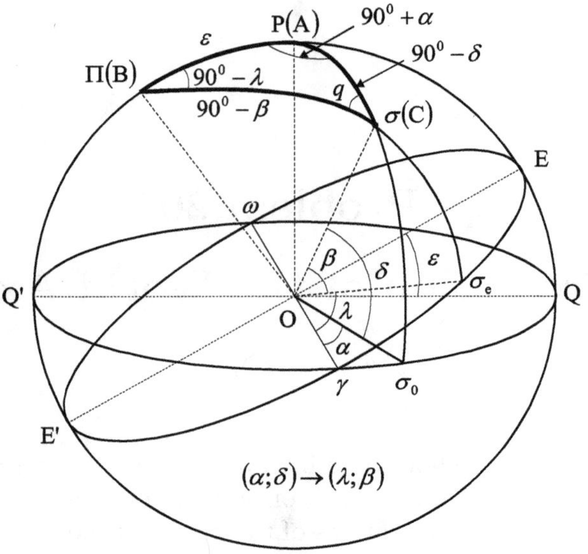

Fig. 20.1

If at some moment, t, the equatorial coordinates of a star σ are α and δ, *determine* their variations, $\Delta\alpha$ and $\Delta\delta$, corresponding to a time interval Δt, caused by the precession of the line of equinoxes in the plane of the ecliptic.

c) *Demonstrate* that the analyzed precession has as its only cause the non-sphericity of the Earth in its gravitational interaction with the Sun, which causes a retrograde movement (from east to west) of the vernal point γ, with the angular velocity $\Omega_\gamma = 50.26''/\text{year}$ and the period $T_\gamma = 26000$ years, thus increasing (*by* $\Delta\alpha$, $\Delta\delta$ and $\Delta\lambda$) the coordinates α, δ and λ.

Solution

a) Using Gauss' formulae, we obtain:

$$\sin a \cdot \sin B = \sin b \cdot \sin A;$$

$$\cos a = \cos b \cdot \cos c + \sin b \cdot \sin c \cdot \cos A;$$

$$\cos b = \cos a \cdot \cos c + \sin a \cdot \sin c \cdot \cos B;$$

$$\sin(90^\circ - \beta) \cdot \sin(90^\circ - \lambda) = \sin(90^\circ - \delta) \cdot \sin(90^\circ + \alpha);$$

$$\cos(90^\circ - \beta) = \cos(90^\circ - \delta) \cdot \cos\varepsilon + \sin(90^\circ - \delta) \cdot \sin\varepsilon \cdot \cos(90^\circ + \alpha);$$

$$\cos(90^\circ - \delta) = \cos(90^\circ - \beta) \cdot \cos\varepsilon + \sin(90^\circ - \beta) \cdot \sin\varepsilon \cdot \cos(90^\circ - \lambda);$$

$$\cos\beta \cdot \cos\lambda = \cos\delta \cdot \cos\alpha;$$

$$\sin\beta = \sin\delta \cdot \cos\varepsilon - \cos\delta \cdot \sin\varepsilon \cdot \sin\alpha;$$

$$\sin\delta = \sin\beta \cdot \cos\varepsilon + \cos\beta \cdot \sin\varepsilon \cdot \sin\lambda,$$

representing the relations between the coordinates of the star according to the two systems, (α; δ) and (λ; β).

b) The phenomenon of the retrograde movement (slipping) (from east to west) of the vernal point γ on the ecliptic, meeting the Sun, is called "precession" (discovered by Hipparchus, with the term deriving from the Latin *praecedere* = to precede).

Current measurements give for the angular velocity of the precession of the vernal point γ the value $\Omega_\gamma = 50.27''$/year and for the period of precession on the ecliptic of the vernal point γ the approximate value $T_\gamma = 26000$ years.

Of course, the reported phenomenon is general: the ecliptic longitudes of all stars increase by $50.27''$ in a year.

Since the movement of the vernal point γ on the ecliptic is retrograde, the presented phenomenon is also called the *retrograde of the equinoxes.*

But what happens, due to the precession of the vernal point γ, to the orientations of the two fundamental planes: the plane of the ecliptic and the plane of the celestial equator?

From the study of the movement of the two bodies, the Earth and the Sun, under the action of the central forces of gravitational attraction, it is known that the plane of their movements (the plane of the ecliptic) remains unchanged (keeps its orientation).

Under these conditions, if the ecliptic is fixed and the vernal point γ slides retrogradely along it with a period of 26000 years, being one of the points of intersection of the ecliptic with the celestial equator, then the celestial equator (the plane of the celestial equator) moves with the same period, changing its orientation, so that the axis of the

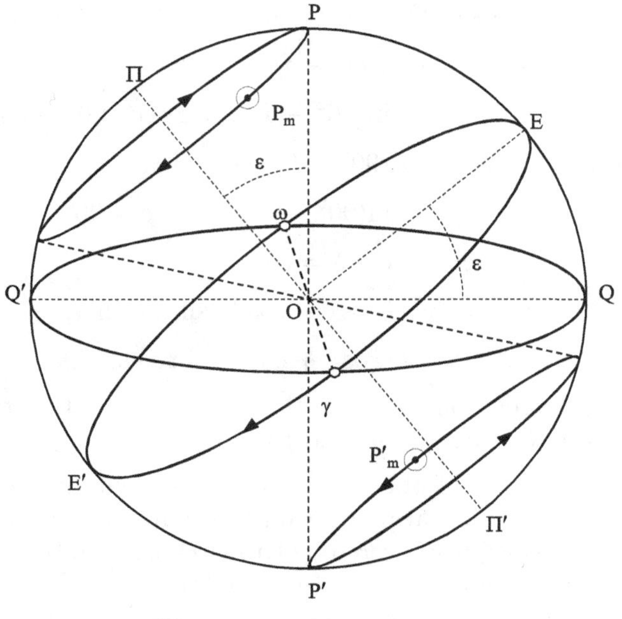

Fig. 20.2

world, PP′, permanently perpendicular to the plane of the celestial equator, rotates around the axis of the ecliptic, ΠΠ′, describing a double-cone surface. The common apex is at the center of the celestial sphere, with the angular opening 2ε and the period 26000 years, and the celestial poles P and P′ describe small circles parallel to the plane of the ecliptic (Fig. 20.2), having the angular radius ε and the rotation period 26000 years.

The movements of the two celestial poles, as well as the movement of the world axis, are called *precession movements*. The two celestial poles, in their precessional motions, are called the mean celestial poles (P_m; P'_m).

Figure 20.3 shows, in planar projection, the small circle on the celestial sphere, with the center at the pole Π of the ecliptic and parallel to the plane of the ecliptic, which describes, in a retrograde direction relative to the fixed stars, the celestial north pole in its precessional movement, when the ecliptic is fixed and the angle between the ecliptic plane and the celestial equatorial plane is constant, $\varepsilon = 23°27'$.

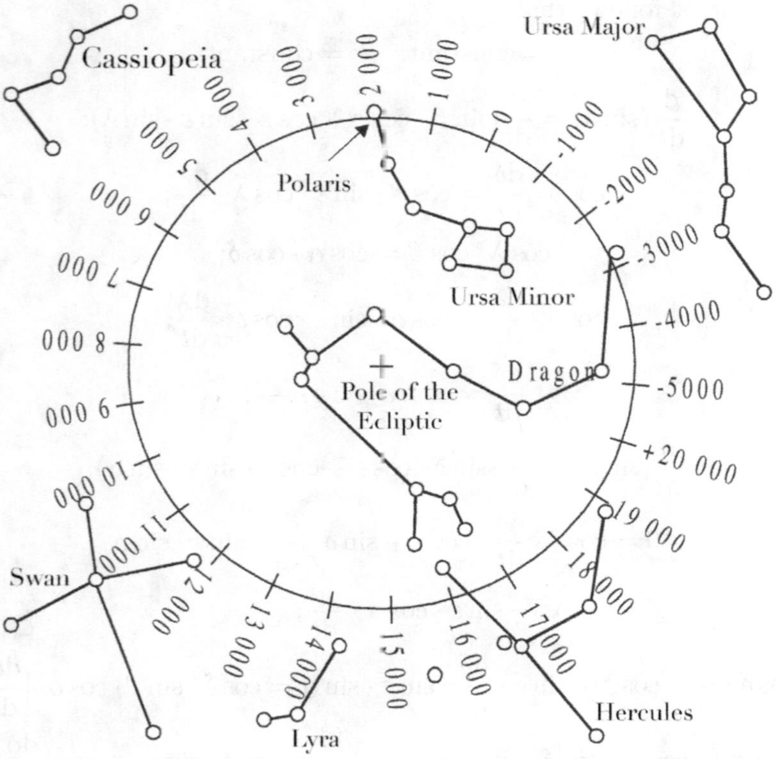

Fig. 20.3

The drawing shows that, at present, the star closest to the north celestial pole (P) is Polaris (α Ursae Minoris) in the constellation Ursa Minor (the Little Dipper). Polaris is currently less than 1° away from the north celestial pole and is gradually moving even closer. The minimum angular distance, approximately $27'$, will be reached around the year 2100. Then, the north celestial pole will travel around the ecliptic pole in search of its other pole star, which it will find in about 12000 years namely the α star (Vega) in the constellation Lyra. 4000 years ago, the closest star (angular distance) to the north celestial pole (the pole star at the time of the construction of the pyramids) was the star α Draconis in the constellation Draco.

Under these conditions, when the coordinates α, δ and λ are variable due to precession, and the coordinate β and the angle ε are constant, it follows that:

$$\beta = \text{constant}; \quad \varepsilon = \text{constant};$$

$$\frac{\mathrm{d}}{\mathrm{d}t}(\sin\delta) = \frac{\mathrm{d}}{\mathrm{d}t}(\sin\beta\cdot\cos\varepsilon + \cos\beta\cdot\sin\varepsilon\cdot\sin\lambda);$$

$$\cos\delta\cdot\frac{\mathrm{d}\delta}{\mathrm{d}t} = \cos\beta\cdot\sin\varepsilon\cdot\cos\lambda\cdot\frac{\mathrm{d}\lambda}{\mathrm{d}t};$$

$$\cos\lambda\cdot\cos\beta = \cos\alpha\cdot\cos\delta;$$

$$\cos\delta\cdot\frac{\mathrm{d}\delta}{\mathrm{d}t} = \cos\alpha\cdot\sin\varepsilon\cdot\cos\delta\cdot\frac{\mathrm{d}\lambda}{\mathrm{d}t};$$

$$\frac{\mathrm{d}\delta}{\mathrm{d}t} = \cos\alpha\cdot\sin\varepsilon\cdot\frac{\mathrm{d}\lambda}{\mathrm{d}t};$$

$$\frac{\mathrm{d}}{\mathrm{d}t}(\sin\beta) = \frac{\mathrm{d}}{\mathrm{d}t}(\sin\delta\cdot\cos\varepsilon - \cos\delta\cdot\sin\varepsilon\cdot\sin\alpha);$$

$$0 = \cos\delta\cdot\frac{\mathrm{d}\delta}{\mathrm{d}t}\cdot\cos\varepsilon + \sin\delta\cdot\frac{\mathrm{d}\delta}{\mathrm{d}t}\cdot\sin\varepsilon\cdot\sin\alpha - \cos\delta\cdot\sin\varepsilon\cdot\cos\alpha\cdot\frac{\mathrm{d}\alpha}{\mathrm{d}t};$$

$$\cos\delta\cdot\frac{\mathrm{d}\delta}{\mathrm{d}t}\cdot\cos\varepsilon + \sin\delta\cdot\frac{\mathrm{d}\delta}{\mathrm{d}t}\cdot\sin\varepsilon\cdot\sin\alpha = \cos\delta\cdot\sin\varepsilon\cdot\cos\alpha\cdot\frac{\mathrm{d}\alpha}{\mathrm{d}t};$$

$$(\cos\delta\cdot\cos\varepsilon + \sin\delta\cdot\sin\varepsilon\cdot\sin\alpha)\cdot\frac{\mathrm{d}\delta}{\mathrm{d}t} = \cos\delta\cdot\sin\varepsilon\cdot\cos\alpha\cdot\frac{\mathrm{d}\alpha}{\mathrm{d}t};$$

$$(\cos\delta\cdot\cos\varepsilon + \sin\delta\cdot\sin\varepsilon\cdot\sin\alpha)\cdot\cos\alpha\cdot\sin\varepsilon\cdot\frac{\mathrm{d}\lambda}{\mathrm{d}t} = \cos\delta\cdot\sin\varepsilon\cdot\cos\alpha\cdot\frac{\mathrm{d}\alpha}{\mathrm{d}t};$$

$$(\cos\delta\cdot\cos\varepsilon + \sin\delta\cdot\sin\varepsilon\cdot\sin\alpha)\cdot\frac{\mathrm{d}\lambda}{\mathrm{d}t} = \cos\delta\cdot\frac{\mathrm{d}\alpha}{\mathrm{d}t};$$

$$\frac{\mathrm{d}\alpha}{\mathrm{d}t} = (\cos\varepsilon + \tan\delta\cdot\sin\varepsilon\cdot\sin\alpha)\cdot\frac{\mathrm{d}\lambda}{\mathrm{d}t};$$

$$\frac{\mathrm{d}\delta}{\mathrm{d}t} = \cos\alpha\cdot\sin\varepsilon\cdot\frac{\mathrm{d}\lambda}{\mathrm{d}t};$$

$$\mathrm{d}t \to \Delta t; \quad \Rightarrow \quad \mathrm{d}\alpha \to \Delta\alpha; \quad \mathrm{d}\delta \to \Delta\delta; \quad \mathrm{d}\lambda \to \Delta\lambda;$$

$$\Delta\delta = \Delta\lambda\cdot\cos\alpha\cdot\sin\varepsilon;$$

$$\Delta\alpha = \Delta\lambda\cdot(\cos\varepsilon + \tan\delta\cdot\sin\varepsilon\cdot\sin\alpha).$$

The above represents the relations between the equatorial coordinates, α and δ, of the star σ at a certain moment, t, and their variations, $\Delta\alpha$ and $\Delta\delta$, as well as the variation of its ecliptic longitude, $\Delta\lambda$, corresponding to a time interval Δt, caused by the precession of the equinox line in the ecliptic plane. Thus, the equatorial coordinates of the star σ at the moment $t + \Delta t$ are $\alpha + \Delta\alpha$ and $\delta + \Delta\delta$, where

$$\Delta\lambda = \Omega_\gamma \cdot \Delta t = \frac{2\pi}{T_\gamma} \cdot \Delta t.$$

c) The physical interpretation of the precession of the world axis and the precession of the celestial poles is given by celestial mechanics, which accepts that they are determined by the precession of the Earth's rotation axis.

Indeed, if the Earth were a homogeneous sphere, or if it consisted of homogeneous spherical layers, the force of gravitational attraction exerted on it would have as its point of application the center of the Earth and would not cause an additional moment of rotation. Then, the axis of rotation of the Earth would maintain its constant inclination to the plane of the actual orbit around the Sun (the plane of the ecliptic), and the phenomenon of the precession of its axis would not occur.

In reality, the Earth is neither spherical nor homogeneous, which results in an additional spin moment.

In order to establish the orientation of this additional moment ($\vec{M}$) as well as its effect on the Earth's own rotational angular momentum ($\vec{J}_{\text{rot}}$), let us accept that the Earth is a homogeneous ellipsoid of revolution (about its axis, pp′), as indicated in Figure 20.4, which moves on an ellipse around the Sun, so that the axis of its rotation is inclined to the plane of the ellipse (plane of the ecliptic) by the angle $90° - \varepsilon$.

Under these conditions, the resultant force that the Sun exerts on the Earth is

$$\vec{F} = \vec{F}_0 + \vec{F}_1 + \vec{F}_2,$$

where the three forces have the meanings indicated in the drawing, which also represents their resultant moment, $\vec{M}$, relative to the center of the Earth.

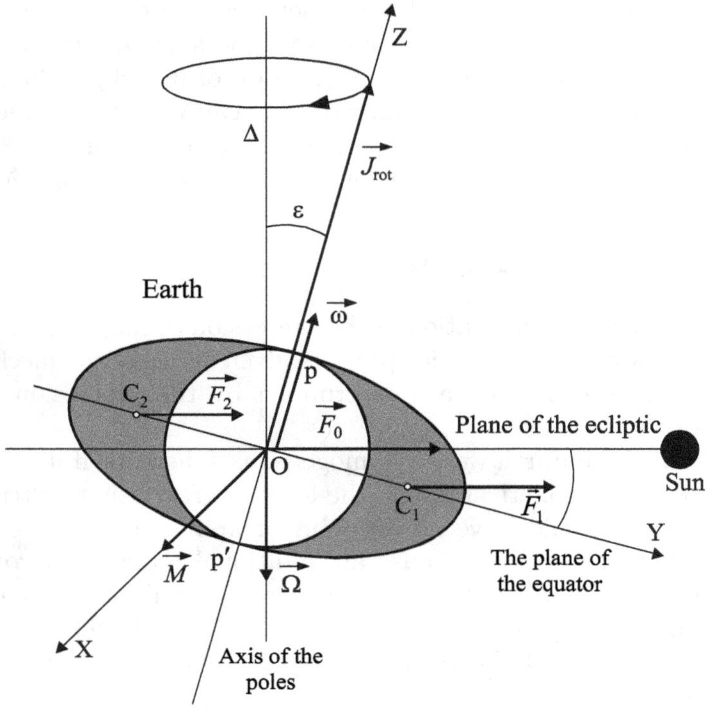

Fig. 20.4

The moment of these forces, $\vec{M}$, will cause a variation in the Earth's rotational angular momentum ($\vec{J}_{\rm rot}$) so that, according to the angular momentum variation theorem, we have

$$\frac{\mathrm{d}\vec{J}_{\rm rot}}{\mathrm{d}t} = \vec{M}.$$

Of course, the angular momentum of the Earth ($\vec{J}_{\rm rot}$) becomes variable as a result of the action of the resultant moment $\vec{M}$, changing only its orientation in space, which, according to Poisson's formula,

$$\frac{\mathrm{d}\vec{J}_{\rm rot}}{\mathrm{d}t} = \dot{\vec{J}}_{\rm rot} = \vec{\Omega} \times \vec{J}_{\rm rot},$$

involves the rotation of the vector $\vec{J}_{\rm rot}$, with the angular velocity $\vec{\Omega}$ (called the angular velocity of precession), around the line (Δ) perpendicular to the plane of the ecliptic.

As the direction of the vector $\vec{J}_{\text{rot}}$ represents the direction of the proper axis pp′ of the Earth, the rotation of the vector $\vec{J}_{\text{rot}}$ indicates the rotation (precession) of the proper axis pp′ of the Earth (in the direction indicated by the orientation of the vector $\vec{\Omega}$, i.e., retrograde), and therefore ultimately represents the precession of the world axis and the poles.

We consider that the analyzed precession has as its only cause the non-sphericity of the Earth, in its gravitational interaction with the Sun, which causes a retrograde slide (from east to west) of the vernal point γ, with the angular velocity $\Omega_\gamma = 50.26''/\text{year}$, which causes increases in the coordinates α, δ and λ.

Problem 21

The Magnitudes of Stars

For a group of 21 stars, the values included in the columns of Table 21.1 are known. The stars are arranged in ascending order according to their apparent visual magnitudes.

Table 21.1

No.	Star	Annual parallax $p_{an}('')$	Apparent magnitude m	Distance between the Sun and the star Δ (parsecs)	Absolute magnitude M
1	α CMa	0.376	−1.46		
2	α Car	0.018	−0.72		
3	α Cen	0.751	−0.27		
4	α Boo	0.009	−0.04		
5	α Lyr	0.123	+0.03		
6	α Aur	0.073	+0.08		
7	β Ori	0.003	+0.12		
8	α Cmi	0.288	+0.38		
9	α Eri	0.032	+0.46		
10	α Ori	0.005	+0.50		
11	β Cen	0.016	+0.61		
12	α Aql	0.198	+0.77		
13	α Tau	0.048	+0.85		

(*Continued*)

Table 21.1 (*Continued*)

No.	Star	Annual parallax $p_{\text{an}}('')$	Apparent magnitude m	Distance between the Sun and the star Δ (parsecs)	Absolute magnitude M
14	α Cru	0.008	+0.87		
15	α Sco	0.019	+0.96		
16	α Vir	0.021	+0.98		
17	β Cyg	0.093	+1.14		
18	α PsA	0.144	+1.16		
19	α Cyg	0.004	+1.25		
20	β Cru	0.007	+1.25		
21	α Leo	0.039	+1.35		

Determine:

a) the distance Δ from the Sun to each star, expressed in parsecs;
b) the absolute magnitude, M, for each star, writing the names of the stars in a table in ascending order of absolute magnitude.
c) among the 21 stars, the star that occupies the same place both in the ranking of apparent visual magnitudes and in the ranking of absolute magnitudes.

Solution

The annual parallax of a star σ, located outside our Solar System, is the angle p_{an} under which the average radius of the Earth's orbit around the Sun, viewed from the center of the star, would be seen at the time of the year when the direction Earth–star (Eσ) is perpendicular to the direction Sun–Earth (SE), as indicated by the drawing in Figure 21.1. From this, it follows that:

$$\sin p_{\text{an}} = \frac{r_{\text{ES}}}{\Delta} \approx p_{\text{an}};$$

$$\Delta = \frac{r_{\text{ES}}}{p_{\text{an}}}; \quad \log|\Delta| = \log\left|\frac{r_{\text{ES}}}{p_{\text{an}}}\right| = \log|r_{\text{ES}}| - \log|p_{\text{an}}|;$$

$$\Delta = \frac{1\ \text{AU}}{p_{\text{an}('')}} = \frac{\frac{1}{206265}\ \text{pc}}{\left|p_{\text{an}('')}\right| \cdot 1''} = \frac{\frac{1}{206265}}{\left|p_{\text{an}('')}\right| \cdot \frac{3.14}{180\cdot60\cdot60}\ \text{rad}}\ \text{pc};$$

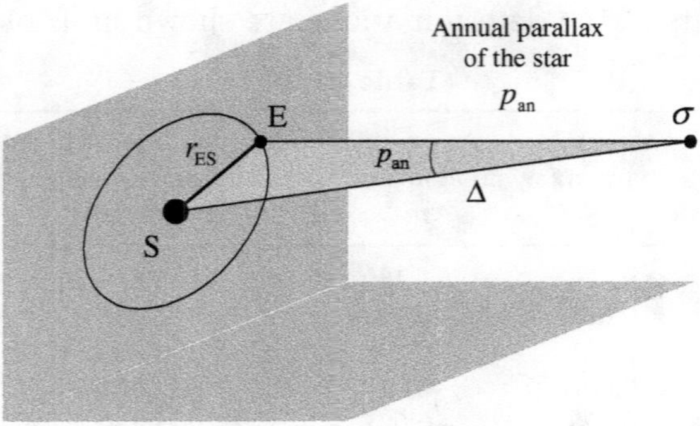

Fig. 21.1

$$\Delta = \frac{1}{\left|p_{\mathrm{an}('')}\right|} \cdot \frac{180 \cdot 60 \cdot 60}{3.14} \cdot \frac{1}{206265}\ \mathrm{pc};$$

$$\Delta = \frac{1}{\left|p_{\mathrm{an}('')}\right|} \cdot \frac{180 \cdot 60 \cdot 60}{3.14} \cdot \frac{1}{206265}\ \mathrm{pc}$$

$$= \frac{1}{\left|p_{\mathrm{an}('')}\right|} \cdot \frac{\frac{180 \cdot 60 \cdot 60}{206265}}{3.14}\ \mathrm{pc} = \frac{1}{\left|p_{\mathrm{an}('')}\right|} \cdot \frac{3.14}{3.14}\ \mathrm{pc};$$

$$\Delta = \frac{1}{\left|p_{\mathrm{an}('')}\right|}\ \mathrm{pc},$$

where $\left|p_{\mathrm{an}('')}\right|$ is the numerical value of p_{an} expressed in seconds.

Using the relationship between the apparent and absolute magnitudes of the star, it follows that:

$$M = m + 5^{\mathrm{m}} - 5^{\mathrm{m}} \log |\Delta|,$$

where $|\Delta|$ is the numerical value of the distance Δ, expressed in parsecs;

$$\log |\Delta| = \log \left(\frac{1}{\left|p_{\mathrm{an}('')}\right|} \right) = -\log \left|p_{\mathrm{an}('')}\right|;$$

$$M = m + 5^{\mathrm{m}} - 5^{\mathrm{m}} \log |\Delta|,$$

$$M = m + 5^{\mathrm{m}} + 5^{\mathrm{m}} \log \left|p_{\mathrm{an}('')}\right|.$$

The results of the determinations are shown in Table 21.2.

Table 21.2

No.	Star	Annual parallax $p_{\text{an}}('')$	Apparent magnitude m	Distance between the Sun and the star Δ (parsecs)	Absolute magnitude M
1	α Cma	0.376	−1.46	2.659	1.41
2	α Car	0.018	−0.72	55.555	−4.44
3	α Cen	0.751	−0.27	1.331	4.10
4	α Boo	0.009	−0.04	111.111	−5.26
5	α Lyr	0.123	+0.03	8.130	0.47
6	α Aur	0.073	+0.08	13.698	−0.60
7	β Ori	0.003	+0.12	333.333	−7.49
8	α Cmi	0.288	+0.38	3.472	2.68
9	α Eri	0.032	+0.46	31.250	−2.01
10	α Ori	0.005	+0.50	200.000	−6.01
11	β Cen	0.016	+0.61	62.500	−3.37
12	α Aql	0.198	+0.77	5.050	2.25
13	α Tau	0.048	+0.85	20.833	−0.74
14	α Cru	0.008	+0.87	125.000	−4.61
15	α Sco	0.019	+0.96	52.631	−2.65
16	α Vir	0.021	+0.98	47.619	−2.41
17	β Cyg	0.093	+1.14	10.752	0.98
18	α Psa	0.144	+1.16	6.944	1.95
19	α Cyg	0.004	+1.25	250.000	−5.74
20	β Cru	0.007	+1.25	142.857	−4.52
21	α Leo	0.039	+1.35	25.641	−0.69

Table 21.3 presents the ranking of the 21 stars in ascending order of their absolute magnitudes. In the parentheses in the first column, the place occupied by the respective star in the ranking according to apparent visual magnitude is indicated. The only star that occupies the same place in both rankings is the star αPsa.

Table 21.3

No.	Star	Distance between the Sun and the star Δ (parsecs)	Absolute magnitude M
1 (7)	β Ori	333.333	−7.49
2 (10)	α Ori	200.000	−6.01
3 (19)	α Cyg	250.000	−5.74
4 (4)	α Boo	111.111	−5.26
5 (14)	α Cru	125.000	−4.61
6 (20)	β Cru	142.857	−4.52
7 (2)	α Car	55.555	−4.44
8 (11)	β Cen	62.500	−3.37
9 (15)	α Sco	52.631	−2.65
10 (16)	α Vir	47.619	−2.41
11 (9)	α Eri	31.250	−2.01
12 (13)	α Tau	20.833	−0.74
13 (21)	α Leo	25.641	−0.69
14 (6)	α Aur	13.698	−0.60
15 (5)	α Lyr	8.130	0.47
16 (17)	β Cyg	10.752	0.98
17 (1)	α Cma	2.659	1.41
18 (18)	α Psa	6.944	1.95
19 (12)	α Aql	5.050	2.25
20 (8)	α Cmi	3.472	2.68
21 (3)	α Cen	1.331	4.10

Problem 22

Bielliptic Gravitational Transfer

An artificial satellite of Earth must be transferred from a low circular orbit of altitude h to a high circular orbit of altitude $H > h$. The transfer of the satellite is achieved by a minimum number of successive activations of very short durations of its jet engines, which result in the arrival of the satellite on two consecutive semi-elliptical transfer trajectories and, finally, its arrival on the high circular orbit.

Identify the two semi-elliptical trajectories, *specify* the minimum number of satellite speed corrections, *determine* the points on these trajectories where the necessary corrections are made and *calculate* the variation of the satellite speed modulus corresponding to each correction.

Knowing: $2a_1 - R - h = 2a_2 - R - H = r_0$, where a_1 and a_2 are the major (unknown) semi-axes of the two semi-ellipses; M – mass of the Earth; R – radius of the Earth; K – constant of gravitational attraction; r_0 – constant whose meaning must be specified.

Solution

The first of the mandatory satellite speed corrections must be performed upon exiting the initial circular orbit, and the last correction must be performed upon entering the final circular orbit. Obviously, for the transfer from one circular orbit to the other circular orbit to be possible with a minimum number of corrections, we must admit that only one more correction is needed, so the minimum total number of corrections must be 3.

As a result, the semi-elliptical transfer trajectories (semi-ellipses I and II) must be chosen as shown in the drawing in Figure 22.1, which also indicates their characteristics and the points where the satellite speed corrections must be performed. The two semi-ellipses have a common focus, F, in which the center of the Earth is located. They have the same apogee ($A_1 \equiv A_2 \equiv A$), located at a distance r_0 from the center of the Earth, and the distance between the perigees (P_I and P_{II}) is equal to the difference in the altitudes of the two circular orbits (circles 1 and 2).

The expressions of the satellite's velocities on circular and elliptical trajectories are known:

$$v = \sqrt{\frac{KM}{r}}; \quad v = \sqrt{KM\left(\frac{2}{r} - \frac{1}{a}\right)},$$

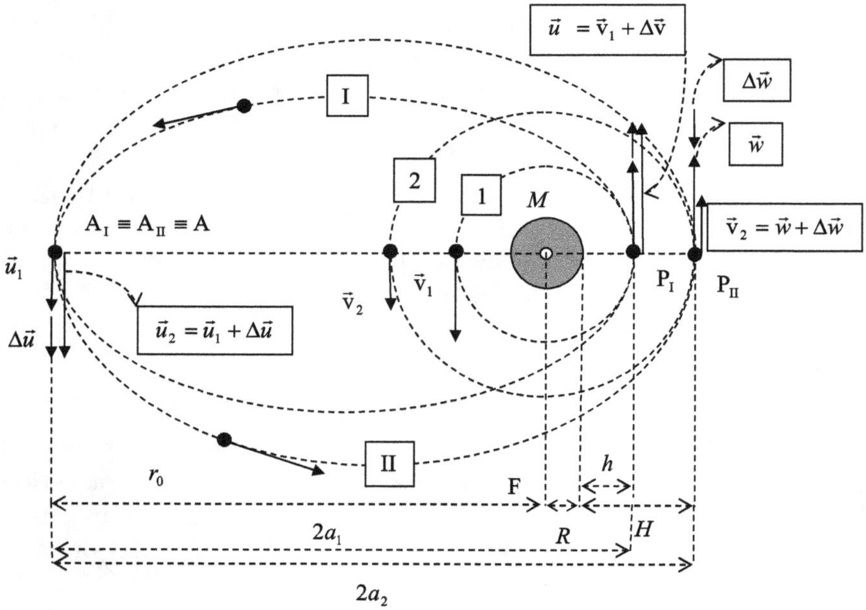

Fig. 22.1

where r is the radius of the circle or the distance from the satellite to the focus of the ellipse, and a is the semi-major axis of the ellipse.

Under these conditions, it follows that:

$$\mathrm{v}_1 = \sqrt{\frac{KM}{R+h}}; \quad u = \sqrt{KM\left(\frac{2}{R+h} - \frac{1}{a_1}\right)}; \quad a_1 = \frac{r_0 + R + h}{2};$$

$$\Delta \mathrm{v} = u - \mathrm{v}_1;$$

$$\Delta \mathrm{v} = \sqrt{KM\left(\frac{2}{R+h} - \frac{1}{a_1}\right)} - \sqrt{\frac{KM}{R+h}} > 0,$$

representing the first correction of the satellite's speed, made at point $\mathrm{P_I}$ for the transfer of the satellite from circle 1 to ellipse I;

$$u_1 = \sqrt{KM\left(\frac{2}{r_0} - \frac{1}{a_1}\right)},$$

representing the speed of the satellite on ellipse I at its apogee, $\mathrm{A_I}$;

$$u_2 = \sqrt{KM\left(\frac{2}{r_0} - \frac{1}{a_2}\right)},$$

representing the required speed of the satellite so that, from the same point, $\mathrm{A_I} \equiv \mathrm{A_{II}} \equiv \mathrm{A}$, the satellite is transferred to ellipse II;

$$a_2 = \frac{r_0 + R + H}{2};$$

$$\Delta u = u_2 - u_1;$$

$$\Delta u = \sqrt{KM\left(\frac{2}{r_0} - \frac{1}{a_2}\right)} - \sqrt{KM\left(\frac{1}{r_2} - \frac{1}{a_1}\right)} > 0,$$

representing the second correction of the satellite's speed, made at point A, for the transfer of the satellite from ellipse I to ellipse II;

$$w = \sqrt{KM\left(\frac{2}{R+H} - \frac{1}{a_2}\right)},$$

representing the speed of the satellite on ellipse II at its perigee, P_{II};

$$v_2 = \sqrt{\frac{KM}{R+H}};$$

$$\Delta w = v_2 - w;$$

$$\Delta w = \sqrt{\frac{KM}{R+H}} - \sqrt{KM\left(\frac{2}{R+H} - \frac{1}{a_2}\right)} < 0,$$

representing the third correction of the satellite's speed, made at point P_{II}, for the transfer of the satellite from ellipse II to circle 2.

Problem 23

Photograph of Jupiter

On a photograph of Jupiter, taken on October 19, 2009, one of Jupiter's satellites (a Galilean moon) and its shadow on the planet's disk can be seen, as indicated by the drawing in Figure 23.1. At that time Jupiter was near the middle of the Capricorn constellation. *Determine* the distance from the moon to the surface of the planet Jupiter. *Specify* the name of the moon. The solution must be illustrated with drawings.

Fig. 23.1

The following values are known:

$$\frac{d_{\rm J,Io}}{R_{\rm J}} = 5.9; \quad \frac{d_{\rm J,Europa}}{R_{\rm J}} = 9.39; \quad \frac{d_{\rm J,Ganimede}}{R_{\rm J}} = 14.97;$$

$$\frac{d_{\rm J,Callisto}}{R_{\rm J}} = 26.33.$$

Solution

The following notation is used in Figure 23.2: S – the Sun; J – Jupiter; L – the moon of Jupiter; U – the shadow of the moon on the surface of Jupiter; $d_{\rm JL}$ – the distance between Jupiter and its moon; a – the projection of the J–L distance in the XX' direction; b – the projection of the J–U distance in the direction of the XX' axis; the angle between the J–S direction and the J–P direction; β – the angle between the directions U–L and U–B; $\alpha \approx \beta$.

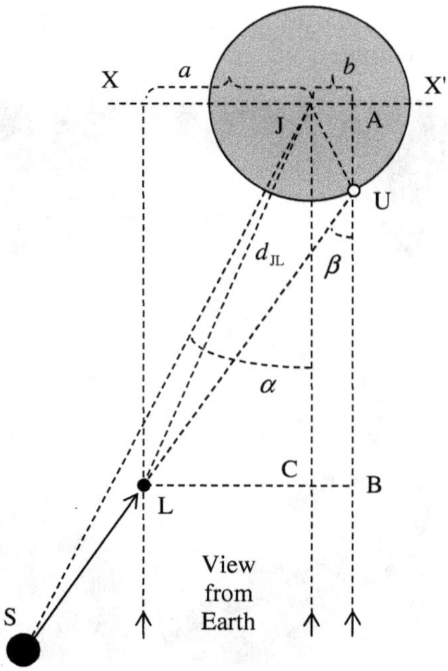

Fig. 23.2

The results are:

$$\Delta(\mathrm{ULB});$$

$$\tan\beta = \frac{a+b}{d_{\mathrm{UB}}}; \quad d_{\mathrm{UB}} = \frac{a+b}{\tan\beta}; \quad \beta \approx \alpha; \quad d_{\mathrm{UB}} = \frac{a+b}{\tan\alpha};$$

$$\Delta(\mathrm{JLC});$$

$$d_{\mathrm{JL}}^2 = d_{\mathrm{JC}}^2 + d_{\mathrm{LC}}^2 = d_{\mathrm{AB}}^2 + d_{\mathrm{LC}}^2 = (d_{\mathrm{AU}} + d_{\mathrm{UB}})^2 + d_{\mathrm{LC}}^2;$$

$$d_{\mathrm{AU}} \approx R_{\mathrm{J}}; \quad d_{\mathrm{LC}} = a;$$

$$d_{\mathrm{JL}}^2 = \left(R_{\mathrm{J}} + \frac{a+b}{\tan\alpha}\right)^2 + a^2;$$

$$\frac{d_{\mathrm{JL}}}{R_{\mathrm{J}}} = \sqrt{\left(1 + \frac{a+b}{R_{\mathrm{J}}\tan\alpha}\right)^2 + \left(\frac{a}{R_{\mathrm{J}}}\right)^2},$$

where the quantities under the radical (a, b, R_{J}) are measured with a ruler, as indicated by the drawing in Figure 23.3, and expressed in the same unit of measure. (The scale at which the photograph was taken is not important at this stage, because the measured quantities

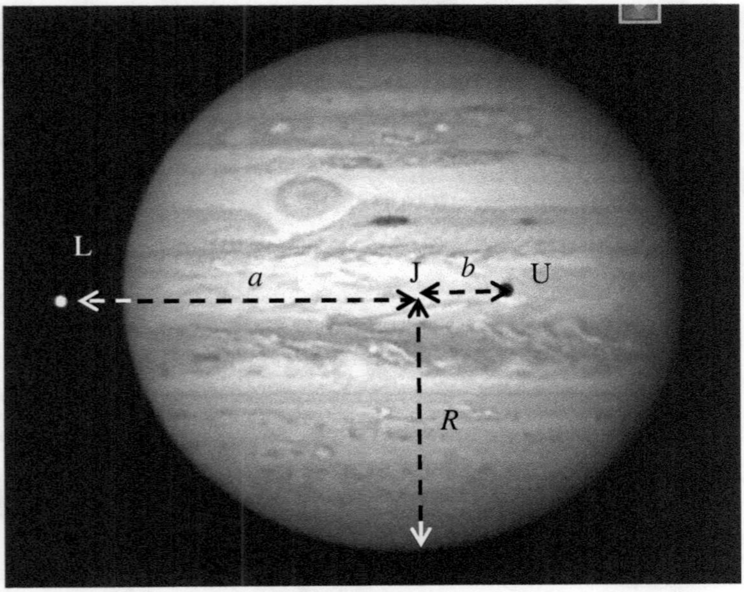

Fig. 23.3

appear in the form of a ratio.) To determine the angle α, we will further analyze all existing possibilities.

Let us recall, from the statement of the problem, that on October 19, 2009, the planet Jupiter was close to the center of the Capricorn constellation (drawing in Figure 23.4). The Sun also passes through the same approximate area, between the end of January and the beginning of February. The approximate value of the angle between the positions of the Sun on the ecliptic, on the geocentric celestial sphere, for October 19 and February 3, a period of 3.6 months, is $\varphi \approx 108°$.

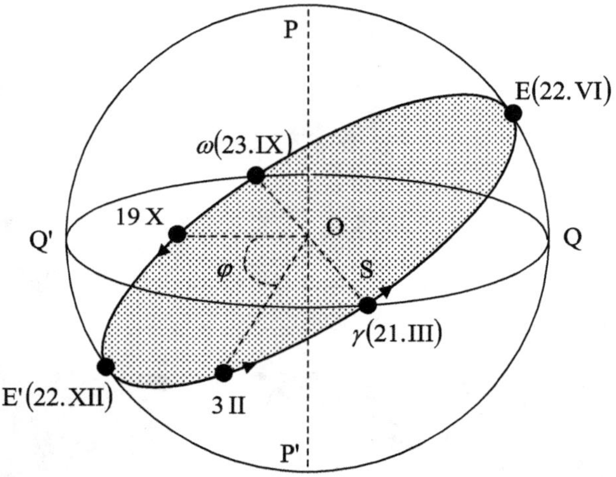

Fig. 23.4

Corresponding to the notation in Figure 23.5, it follows that:

$$d_{\mathrm{JS}'} = d_{\mathrm{SP}'};$$

$$d_{\mathrm{SJ}} \sin\alpha = d_{\mathrm{SP}} \sin\varphi;$$

$$\sin\alpha = \frac{d_{\mathrm{SP}}}{d_{\mathrm{SJ}}} \sin\varphi = \frac{1\ \mathrm{AU}}{5.2\ \mathrm{AU}} \sin(108°) \approx 0.183;$$

$$\alpha \approx 10.5°.$$

Under these conditions, it follows that:

$$\frac{d_{\mathrm{JL}}}{R_{\mathrm{J}}} = \sqrt{\left(1 + \frac{a+b}{R_{\mathrm{J}} \tan\alpha}\right)^2 + \left(\frac{a}{R_{\mathrm{J}}}\right)^2} \approx 9.64.$$

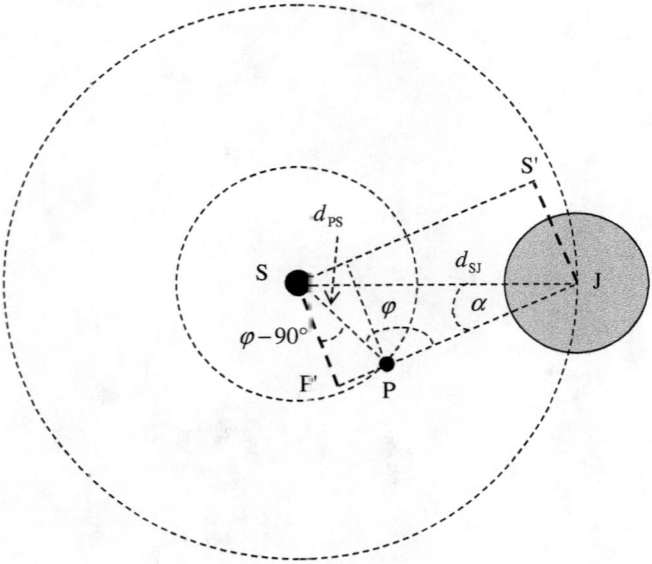

Fig. 23.5

We know:

$$\frac{d_{\mathrm{J,Io}}}{R_{\mathrm{J}}} = 5.9; \quad \frac{d_{\mathrm{J,Europa}}}{R_{\mathrm{J}}} = 9.39;$$

$$\frac{d_{\mathrm{J,Ganimede}}}{R_{\mathrm{J}}} = 14.97; \quad \frac{d_{\mathrm{J,Callisto}}}{R_{\mathrm{J}}} = 26.33.$$

Comparing with the previous result, it follows that:

$$\frac{d_{\mathrm{JL}}}{R_{\mathrm{J}}} = 9.64; \quad \frac{d_{\mathrm{J,Europa}}}{R_{\mathrm{J}}} = 9.39,$$

which confirms that the moon of Jupiter captured in the photo is Europa.

Problem 24

The Mass Function of a Visual Binary Star System

For a given visual binary star system, consisting of stars σ_1 and σ_2, the mass function is defined as

$$f(M_1; M_2; i) = \frac{M_2^3 \sin^3 i}{(M_1 + M_2)^2},$$

where M_1 and M_2 are the masses of the stars σ_1 and σ_2, and i is the angle between the plane of the relative orbit and the plane of the apparent orbit (the angle between the line of sight and the normal on the plane of the relative orbit).

a) *Determine* the masses of the two stars, if they move in concentric circles around their center of mass. *We know*: the period of the system, T; the ratio of the luminosities of the two stars in the system, $k = L_2/L_1 > 1$; the constant of universal attraction, K; the speed of the star σ_1 in relation to the center of mass of the system, v_1. *It is also known that* the luminosity of a star is $L = q \cdot M^4$, where q is a constant, and the center of mass of the system is at rest with respect to the observer.

b) Knowing the numerical value of the mass function of the given system, M_0, *determine* the value of the angle i between the plane of the relative orbit and the plane of the apparent orbit.

Solution

a) In the drawing in Figure 24.1, a binary star system is represented, and the CM of the system is also indicated. The velocities of the two stars, relative to the observer, when their orientations are exactly in the direction of the line of sight, as well as the velocity of the CM relative to the observer on Earth, are denoted as $\vec{v}_1$ and $\vec{v}_2$.

If the stars σ_1 and σ_2, which represent a visual binary star system, move in concentric circles around the common center of mass (CM) and are observed as indicated by the drawing in Figure 24.1, where the plane of the orbits forms an angle of 90° with the plane perpendicular to the direction of observation ($i = 90°$), it results that:

$$a = a_1 + a_2;$$

$$v_1 = \frac{2\pi a_1}{T}; \quad v_2 = \frac{2\pi a_2}{T},$$

where T is the period of rotations of the two stars in relation to the CM;

$$a_1 = \frac{v_1 T}{2\pi}; \quad a_2 = \frac{v_2 T}{2\pi};$$

$$a_1 + a_2 = \frac{T}{2\pi}(v_1 + v_2),$$

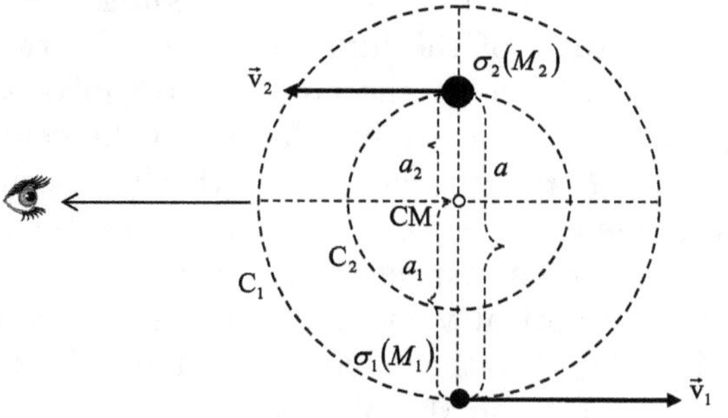

Fig. 24.1

so that, in the reference system of the centre of mass, the distance between the two stars is constant;

$$a = a_1 + a_2; \quad a = \frac{T}{2\pi}(\mathrm{v}_1 + \mathrm{v}_2);$$

$$\frac{T^2}{a^3} = \frac{4\pi^2}{K(M_1 + M_2)};$$

$$\frac{T^2}{\frac{T^3}{(2\pi)^3}(\mathrm{v}_1 + \mathrm{v}_2)^3} = \frac{(2\pi)^2}{K(M_1 + M_2)};$$

$$M_1 + M_2 = \frac{T}{2\pi K}(\mathrm{v}_1 + \mathrm{v}_2)^3.$$

If the observation of the two stars is carried out as shown in the drawing in Figure 24.2, when the plane of the orbits forms an angle $i < 90°$ with the plane perpendicular to the direction of observation, it results in:

$$\mathrm{v}_{1\mathrm{rad,max}} = \mathrm{v}_1 \cdot \cos(90° - i) = \mathrm{v}_1 \cdot \sin i;$$

$$\mathrm{v}_1 = \frac{\mathrm{v}_{1\mathrm{rad,max}}}{\sin i};$$

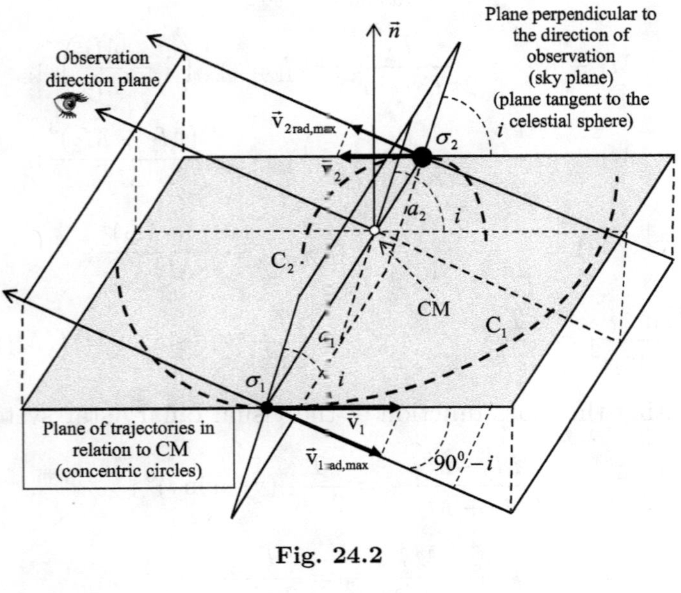

Fig. 24.2

$$\mathrm{v}_{2\mathrm{rad,max}} = \mathrm{v}_2 \cdot \cos(90^\circ - i) = \mathrm{v}_2 \cdot \sin i;$$

$$\mathrm{v}_2 = \frac{\mathrm{v}_{2\mathrm{rad,max}}}{\sin i};$$

$$M_1 + M_2 = \frac{T}{2\pi K}(\mathrm{v}_1 + \mathrm{v}_2)^3;$$

$$M_1 + M_2 = \frac{T}{2\pi K}\left(\frac{\mathrm{v}_{1\mathrm{rad,max}}}{\sin i} + \frac{\mathrm{v}_{2\mathrm{rad,max}}}{\sin i}\right)^3;$$

$$M_1 + M_2 = \frac{T}{2\pi K \cdot \sin^3 i} \cdot \mathrm{v}^3_{1\mathrm{rad,max}}\left(1 + \frac{\mathrm{v}_{2\mathrm{rad,max}}}{\mathrm{v}_{1\mathrm{rad,max}}}\right)^3;$$

$$\vec{H}_{\mathrm{CM}} = \vec{H}_1 + \vec{H}_2 = M_1\vec{\mathrm{v}}_1 + M_2\vec{\mathrm{v}}_2 = 0;$$

$$(M_1 + M_2)\,\mathrm{v}_{\mathrm{CM}} = M_1\mathrm{v}_1 - M_2\mathrm{v}_2 = 0;$$

$$M_1\mathrm{v}_1 = M_2\mathrm{v}_2;$$

$$\mathrm{v}_1 = \frac{\mathrm{v}_{1\mathrm{rad,max}}}{\sin i}; \quad \mathrm{v}_2 = \frac{\mathrm{v}_{2\mathrm{rad,max}}}{\sin i};$$

$$M_1\mathrm{v}_{1\mathrm{rad,max}} = M_2\mathrm{v}_{2\mathrm{rad,max}};$$

$$\frac{\mathrm{v}_{2\mathrm{rad,max}}}{\mathrm{v}_{1\mathrm{rad,max}}} = \frac{M_1}{M_2};$$

$$M_1 + M_2 = \frac{T}{2\pi K \cdot \sin^3 i} \cdot \mathrm{v}^3_{1\mathrm{rad,max}}\left(1 + \frac{M_1}{M_2}\right)^3;$$

$$M_1 + M_2 = \frac{T}{2\pi K \cdot \sin^3 i} \cdot \mathrm{v}^3_{1\mathrm{rad,max}}\frac{(M_1 + M_2)^3}{M_2^3};$$

$$1 = \frac{T}{2\pi K \cdot \sin^3 i} \cdot \mathrm{v}^3_{1\mathrm{rad,max}}\frac{(M_1 + M_2)^2}{M_2^3};$$

$$\frac{M_2^3 \sin^3 i}{(M_1 + M_2)^2} = \frac{T}{2\pi K} \cdot \mathrm{v}^3_{1\mathrm{rad,max}} = \frac{T}{2\pi K}(\mathrm{v}_1 \cdot \sin i)^3 = f(M_1; M_2),$$

representing the mass function of the visual binary star system;

$$\frac{M_2^3 \sin^3 i}{(M_1 + M_2)^2} = \frac{T}{2\pi K}\left(\mathrm{v}_1 \cdot \sin i\right)^3;$$

$$\frac{M_2^3}{(M_1 + M_2)^2} = \frac{T}{2\pi K} \cdot \mathrm{v}_1^3;$$

$$L_1 = qM_1^4; \quad L_2 = qM_2^4;$$

$$\frac{L_2}{L_1} = k = \left(\frac{M_2}{M_1}\right)^4; \quad \frac{M_2}{M_1} = \sqrt[4]{k}; \quad M_2 = \sqrt[4]{k} \cdot M_1;$$

$$\frac{k^{3/4} \cdot M_1^3}{M_1^2 \left(1 + \sqrt[4]{k}\right)^2} = \frac{T}{2\pi K} \cdot \mathrm{v}_1^3;$$

$$M_1 = \frac{T}{2\pi K} \cdot \frac{\left(1 + k^{1/4}\right)^2}{k^{3/4}} \cdot \mathrm{v}_1^3;$$

$$M_2 = \sqrt[4]{k} \cdot M_1;$$

$$M_2 = \sqrt[4]{k} \cdot \frac{T}{2\pi K} \cdot \frac{\left(1 + k^{1/4}\right)^2}{k^{3/4}} \cdot \mathrm{v}_1^3;$$

$$M_2 = \frac{T}{2\pi K} \cdot \frac{\left(1 + k^{1/4}\right)^2}{k^{1/2}} \cdot \mathrm{v}_1^3.$$

b)

$$f\left(M_1; M_2\right) = \frac{M_2^3 \sin^3 i}{\left(M_1 + M_2\right)^2} = M_0;$$

$$\sin i = \sqrt[3]{\frac{M_0 \left(M_1 + M_2\right)^2}{M_2^3}} = \frac{\sqrt[3]{M_0 \left(M_1 + M_2\right)^2}}{M_2}.$$

Problem 25

Length of a Day on Mars

The length of a (sidereal) day on Mars is $\eta = 2.5\%$ longer than the length of a (sidereal) day on Earth. The period of Mars' orbital motion around the Sun (1 Martian tropical year) is $T_{\mathrm{MS}} = 687$ Martian mean solar days. *Determine*, approximately, the difference between the length of a sidereal day and the length of an average solar day on the planet Mars.

Solution

Due to its own rotation, Mars gradually exposes its entire surface to the Sun so that, for an observer on the surface of the planet Mars, the day/night alternation has a different duration than that of the day/night alternation on Earth.

If T_{M} is the duration of the rotation of Mars around its own axis (the duration of a sidereal day on the planet Mars), then, from the statement of the problem, we know that

$$T_{\mathrm{M}} = T_{\mathrm{E}} + \eta T_{\mathrm{E}} = 1.025 \text{ Martian days.}$$

In the drawing in Figure 25.1, the Sun–Mars system is represented, at the moments t_0 and t, when, for the observer at rest on the surface of Mars, the Martian night begins (when the observer enters the dark sector, at sunset, in position A_0) and ends (when the observer leaves the dark sector and enters the light sector, at sunrise, in position A). The positions of Mars in relation to the Sun at the two considered moments are indicated.

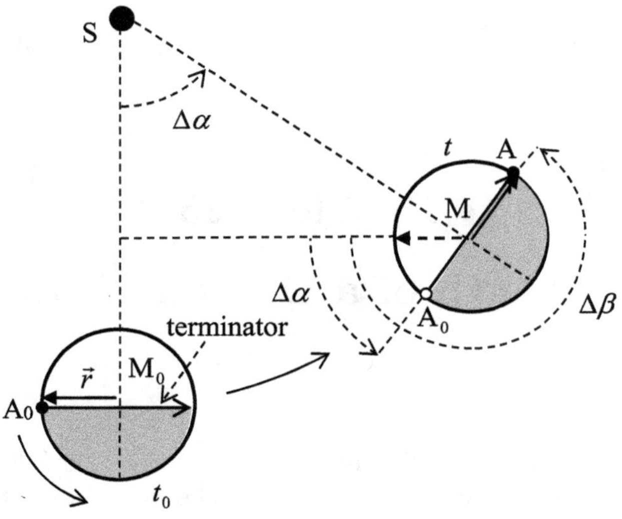

Fig. 25.1

In the time interval $\Delta t = t - t_0$, the Sun–Mars direction rotates by the angle $\Delta\alpha = \omega_{\mathrm{MS}}\Delta t$, where ω_{MS} is the angular velocity of Mars in its circular motion around the Sun, and the vector radius of the observer, $\vec{r}$, relative to the center of Mars, rotates by the angle $\Delta\beta = \omega_{\mathrm{M}}\Delta t$, where ω_{M} is the angular velocity of the rotation of Mars. Obviously, the angle by which the dividing line (the terminator) between the two areas (lit and dark, respectively) on the surface of Mars rotates, in the same time interval, Δt, is $\Delta\alpha$.

The observer will exit the Martian night when $\Delta\beta - \Delta\alpha = \pi$. Under these conditions, it follows that:

$$\omega_{\mathrm{M}}\Delta t - \omega_{\mathrm{MS}}\Delta t = \pi;$$

$$\Delta t = \frac{\pi}{\omega_{\mathrm{M}} - \omega_{\mathrm{MS}}} = \frac{\pi}{\frac{2\pi}{T_{\mathrm{M}}} - \frac{2\pi}{T_{\mathrm{MS}}}} = \frac{T_{\mathrm{M}}T_{\mathrm{MS}}}{2\left(T_{\mathrm{MS}} - T_{\mathrm{M}}\right)}$$

$$\approx 0.513 \text{ terrestrial days.}$$

In the drawing in Figure 25.2, the Sun–Mars system is represented, at the moments t_0 and t, when, for the observer at rest on the surface of Mars, the Martian day begins (entering the lit sector, at sunrise, in position A_0) and ends (leaving the lit sector and entering

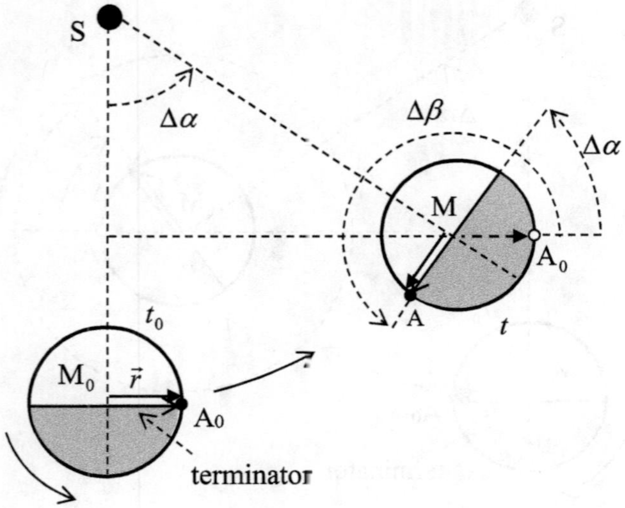

Fig. 25.2

the dark sector, at sunset, in position A). The positions of Mars in relation to the Sun at the two considered moments are indicated.

In the time interval $\Delta t = t - t_0$, the Sun–Mars direction rotates by the angle $\Delta\alpha = \omega_{\mathrm{MS}}\Delta t$, where ω_{MS} is the angular velocity of Mars in its circular motion around the Sun, and the vector radius of the observer, $\vec{r}$, relative to the center of Mars, rotates by the angle $\Delta\beta = \omega_{\mathrm{M}}\Delta t$, where ω_{M} is the angular velocity of the rotation of Mars. The angle by which the dividing line (the terminator) between the two areas (lit and dark, respectively) on the surface of Mars rotates, in the same time interval Δt, is $\Delta\alpha$.

The observer will exit the Martian day when $\Delta\beta - \Delta\alpha = \pi$.

Under these conditions, it results that:

$$\omega_{\mathrm{M}}\Delta t - \omega_{\mathrm{MS}}\Delta t = \pi;$$

$$\Delta t = \frac{\pi}{\omega_{\mathrm{M}} - \omega_{\mathrm{MS}}} = \frac{\pi}{\frac{2\pi}{T_{\mathrm{M}}} - \frac{2\pi}{T_{\mathrm{MS}}}} = \frac{T_{\mathrm{M}}T_{\mathrm{MS}}}{2\left(T_{\mathrm{MS}} - T_{\mathrm{M}}\right)}$$

$$\approx 0.513 \text{ terrestrial days.}$$

In the drawing in Figure 25.3, the Sun–Mars system is represented at the moments t_0 and t, when, for the observer at rest on the surface of Mars, the Martian day begins (entering the lit sector,

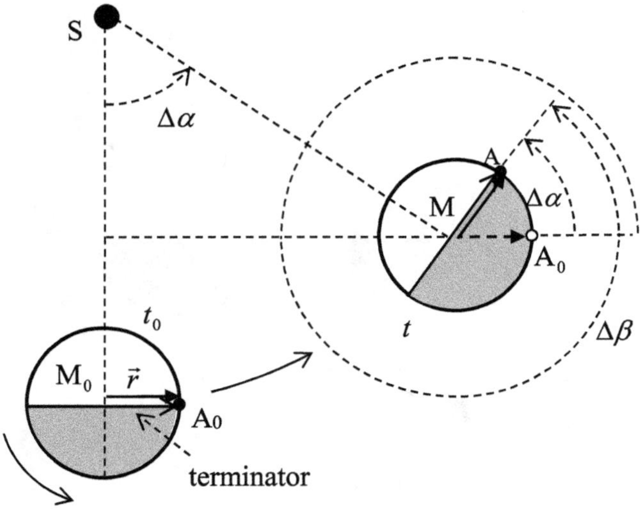

Fig. 25.3

at the first sunrise, in position A_0) and ends (leaving the dark sector and re-entering the lit sector, at the second sunrise, in position A). The positions of Mars in relation to the Sun at the two considered moments are indicated.

In the time interval $\Delta t = t - t_0$, the Sun–Mars direction rotates by the angle $\Delta\alpha = \omega_{\mathrm{MS}}\Delta t$, where ω_{MS} is the angular velocity of Mars in its circular motion around the Sun, and the vector radius of the observer, $\vec{r}$, relative to the center of Mars, rotates by the angle $\Delta\beta = \omega_{\mathrm{M}}\Delta t$, where ω_{M} is the angular velocity of the rotation of Mars. Obviously, the angle by which the dividing line (the terminator) between the two areas (lit and dark, respectively) on the surface of Mars rotates, in the same time interval, Δt, is $\Delta\alpha$.

The observer will re-enter the Martian day when $\Delta\beta - \Delta\alpha = 2\pi$.

Under these conditions, it results that:

$$\omega_{\mathrm{M}}\Delta t - \omega_{\mathrm{MS}}\Delta t = 2\pi;$$

$$\Delta t = \frac{2\pi}{\omega_{\mathrm{M}} - \omega_{\mathrm{MS}}} = \frac{2\pi}{\frac{2\pi}{T_{\mathrm{M}}} - \frac{2\pi}{T_{\mathrm{MS}}}} = \frac{T_{\mathrm{M}}T_{\mathrm{MS}}}{(T_{\mathrm{MS}} - T_{\mathrm{M}})} \approx 1.026 \text{ terrestrial days;}$$

$$\Delta t = 1.026 \cdot 24\ \mathrm{h} = 24.6\ \mathrm{h} = 24\ \mathrm{h}\ 36\ \mathrm{min}\,.$$

This represents the length of the sidereal day on Mars (the duration of one complete rotation of Mars around its axis):

$$1 \text{ Mars sidereal day} = 24 \text{ h } 36 \text{ min.}$$

The Earth/Mars *tropical year* is the time interval, measured from Earth/Mars, between two consecutive passages of the Sun, in its apparent annual motion on the ecliptic, through the vernal point γ, or, equivalently, the time interval required by Earth/Mars, in its rotational motion around the Sun, to return to the same equinox.

For the observer on Earth:

$$\begin{aligned} 1 \text{ tropical year on Earth} &= 365.2422 \text{ average terrestrial solar days} \\ &= 366.2422 \text{ terrestrial sidereal days.} \end{aligned}$$

For the observer on Mars:

$$1 \text{ tropical year on Mars} = 687 \text{ Martian solar days} = 688 \text{ Martian sidereal days.}$$

This means that, on both Earth and Mars, the number of sidereal days in a tropical year is one more than the number of mean solar days:

$$1 \text{ tropical year on Earth} \neq 1 \text{ tropical year on Mars;}$$

$$687 \cdot 1 \text{ average solar day on Mars} = 688 \cdot 1 \text{ sidereal day on Mars;}$$

$$1 \text{ average solar day on Mars} = \frac{688}{687} \cdot 1 \text{ sidereal day on Mars;}$$

$$\begin{aligned} 1 \text{ average solar day on Mars} &= \frac{688}{687} \cdot 24.6 \text{ h} \approx 24.635 \text{ h} \\ &= 24 \text{ h } 38 \text{ min.} \end{aligned}$$

Thus:

$$1 \text{ average solar day on Mars} > 1 \text{ sidereal day on Mars.}$$

Conclusion:

1 average solar day on Mars – 1 sidereal day on Mars = 24 h 38 min – 24 h 36 min = 2 min.

Problem 26

The Temperature on the Surface of the Sun

Estimate the average value of the temperature on the surface of the Sun, if the average value of the temperature on the surface of the Earth is $t_{\mathrm{E}} = 20^0\mathrm{C}$, and the radius of the Sun is approximately $\eta = 0.00464$ of the average Sun–Earth distance, $R_{\mathrm{S}} = \eta d_{\mathrm{S-E}}$.

Solution

Corresponding to the temperature of its outer surface, the energy (heat) released by a body, per unit time, through a unit of its surface area, is directly proportional to the fourth power of the absolute temperature of the body's surface (Stefan–Boltzmann law):

$$q = \frac{Q}{tS} = \sigma T^4,$$

where σ is a proportionality constant (Stefan–Boltzmann constant), the same for any body.

Under these conditions, for the energies released by the Sun and the Earth, per unit time, through a unit of their surface area, we have:

$$q_{\text{Sun}} = \sigma T_{\text{Sun}}^4 = \frac{Q_{\text{emitted by Sun}}}{tS_{\text{Sun}}};$$

$$q_{\text{Earth}} = \sigma T_{\text{Earth}}^4 = \frac{Q_{\text{emitted by Earth}}}{tS_{\text{Earth}}};$$

$$w_{\text{Sun}} = \frac{Q_{\text{emitted by Sun}}}{t} = \sigma T_{\text{Sun}}^4 S_{\text{Sun}} = \sigma T_{\text{Sun}}^4 4\pi R_{\text{Sun}}^2;$$

$$w_{\text{Earth}} = \frac{Q_{\text{emitted by Earth}}}{t} = \sigma T_{\text{Earth}}^4 S_{\text{Earth}} = \sigma T_{\text{Earth}}^4 4\pi R_{\text{Earth}}^2.$$

Fortunately for us, not all of the energy emitted by the Sun is absorbed by the Earth. We can consider that the percentage p of the energy emitted by the Sun that is absorbed by the Earth, per unit time,

$$\frac{Q_{\text{absorbed by Earth}}}{t} = p\frac{Q_{\text{emitted by Sun}}}{t},$$

is approximately equal to the percentage represented by the area of the Earth's surface at the distance of the radius of its orbit, in relation to the area of the spherical surface with a radius equal to the radius of the Earth's orbit:

$$\pi R_{\text{Earth}}^2 \approx p 4\pi d_{\text{Sun–Earth}}^2.$$

This results in:

$$\frac{\frac{Q_{\text{absorbed by Earth}}}{t}}{\frac{Q_{\text{emitted by Sun}}}{t}} = \frac{\pi R_{\text{Earth}}^2}{4\pi d_{\text{Sun–Earth}}^2}.$$

Given the formula of the Earth's energy balance,

$$\frac{Q_{\text{absorbed by Earth}}}{t} = \frac{Q_{\text{emitted by Earth}}}{t},$$

we get:

$$\frac{\frac{Q_{\text{emitted by Earth}}}{t}}{\frac{Q_{\text{emitted by Sun}}}{t}} = \frac{\pi R_{\text{Earth}}^2}{4\pi d_{\text{Sun–Earth}}^2} = \frac{\sigma T_{\text{Earth}}^4 4\pi R_{\text{Earth}}^2}{\sigma T_{\text{Sun}}^4 4\pi R_{\text{Sun}}^2};$$

$$\left(\frac{T_{\text{Earth}}}{T_{\text{Sun}}}\right)^4 = \frac{R_{\text{Sun}}^2}{4d_{\text{Sun–Earth}}^2}; \quad R_{\text{Sun}} = \eta d_{\text{Sun–Earth}};$$

$$\left(\frac{T_{\text{Earth}}}{T_{\text{Sun}}}\right)^4 = \frac{\eta^2}{4};$$

$$T_{\text{Sun}} = T_{\text{Earth}}\sqrt{\frac{2}{\eta}} \approx 6.083 \text{ K}.$$

Problem 27

The Proper Motions of the Stars

By comparing observations of the same stars at very long time intervals, the astronomer Edmond Halley discovered important differences between the coordinates of the same star, thus highlighting that the stars are not "fixed" on the celestial sphere.

As a result, as the drawing in Figure 27.1 indicates, in a time interval Δt, the displacement of a star σ on the celestial sphere is

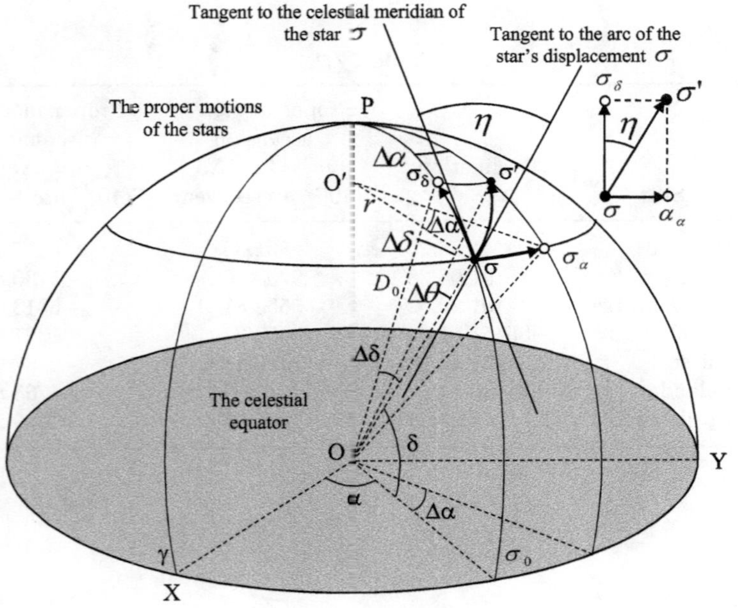

Fig. 27.1

represented by the arc of the great circle $\sigma\sigma'$ so that, corresponding to the two positions, the equatorial coordinates of the star are:

$$\sigma(\alpha, \delta); \quad \sigma'(\alpha + \Delta\alpha, \delta + \Delta\delta).$$

Using the information presented in Tables 27.1 and 27.2, relating to a group of seven stars, *determine*, for each star, the values of the quantities specified in Tables 27.3 and 27.4:

a) the proper motion, μ, expressed in (10^{-3} arcsec/year);
b) the tangent of the angle between the geometric tangent to the displacement of the star in the plane of the sky and the geometric tangent to the celestial meridian of the star, $\tan\eta$;
c) the distance from the Earth to the star, D_0;
d) the transverse velocity of the star, v_{tr};
e) the spatial velocity of the star, v;
f) the brightness of the star, L.
Knowing: $1\,\text{rad} = 206265$ arcsec $= 206265''$; $1\,\text{pc} = 206265\,\text{AU}$.

Specification: for all quantities whose values must be determined, you must apply and demonstrate mathematical expressions.

Table 27.1

No.	Star	Declination Δ (° ′ ″)	Proper motion in ascension $\mu_\alpha = \Delta t/\Delta\alpha$ (10^{-3} arcsec/year)	Proper motion in declination $\mu_\delta = \Delta t/\Delta\delta$ (10^{-3} arcsec/year)
1	Barnard	+04°41′36.20″	−801.30	10327.12
2	Kapteyn	−45°01′06.28″	9203.56	−5730.84
3	Groombridge	+44°01′22.62″	5568.81	−5813.62
4	Lacaille	−35°51′11.04″	8350.64	1327.52
5	Gliese 1	−37°21′26.50″	7089.43	−2337.71
6	Lalande	+35°58′11.56″	−717.00	−4765.85
7	Epsilon Indi	−56°47′09.52″	7231.93	−2539.23

Table 27.2

No.	Star	Radial velocity v_{rad} (km/s)	Parallax p (10^{-3} arcsec)	Apparent magnitude m ($\ldots^{\mathrm{m}}$)
1	Barnard	−110.51	548.31	9.51
2	Kapteyn	+245.19	255.66	8.85
3	Groombridge	−98.35	109.99	6.44
4	Lacaille	+8.81	305.26	7.34
5	Gliese 1	+25.38	230.42	8.57
6	Lalande	−84.69	392.64	7.52
7	Epsilon Indi	−40.00	276.06	4.83

Table 27.3

No.	Star	Proper motion $\mu = \Delta\theta/\Delta t$ (10^{-3} arcsec/year)	The tangent of the angle between the tangent to the displacement of the star in the plane of the sky and the tangent to the celestial meridian of the star tg η	Distance D_0(pc)
1	Barnard			
2	Kapteyn			
3	Groombridge			
4	Lacaille			
5	Gliese 1			
6	Lalande			
7	Epsilon Indi			

Table 27.4

No.	Star	Transversal velocity v_{tr} (km/s)	Spatial velocity v (km/s)	Luminosity $L\,(10^{-4}L_{\mathrm{Sun}})$
1	Barnard			
2	Kapteyn			
3	Groombridge			
4	Lacaille			
5	Gliese 1			
6	Lalande			
7	Epsilon Indi			

Solution

a) The total displacement $\sigma\sigma'$ is the result of the composition of an upward displacement (the arc of the small circle $\sigma\sigma_\alpha$, with its center at O′ and the radius $D_0 \cos\delta$) with a displacement in declination (the arc of the great circle $\sigma\sigma_\delta$).

Considering that the total displacement of the star is very small, using the drawings in Figures 27.2, 27.3 and 27.4, it follows that

$$L_{\text{arc}\,\sigma\sigma'} = \sqrt{(L_{\text{arc}\sigma\sigma_\alpha})^2 + (L_{\text{arc}\,\sigma\sigma_\delta})^2}.$$

In order to compare the displacements of the stars on the celestial sphere, the quantity called the *proper motion* of a star, μ, is defined as a quantity numerically equal to the angle at which the arc of the great circle is seen from the center of the heliocentric celestial sphere, representing the displacement of the star over a year, and having as its unit of measure (seconds of arc)/year. Thus:

$$\mu = \frac{\angle(\sigma O \sigma')}{\Delta t} = \frac{\Delta\theta}{\Delta t},$$

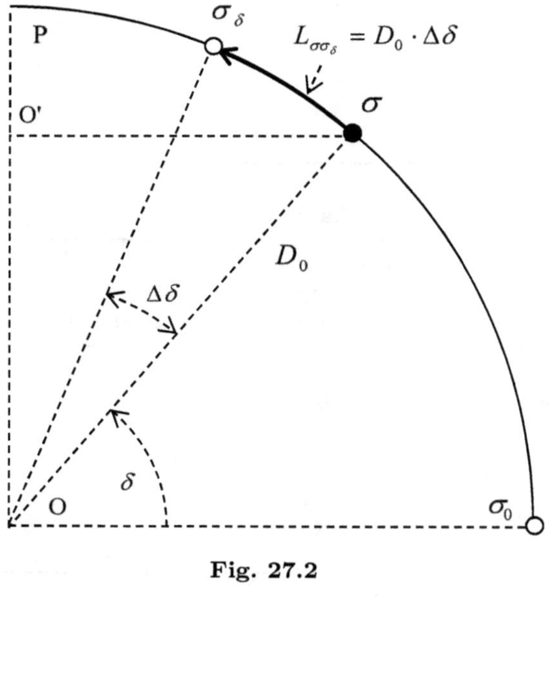

Fig. 27.2

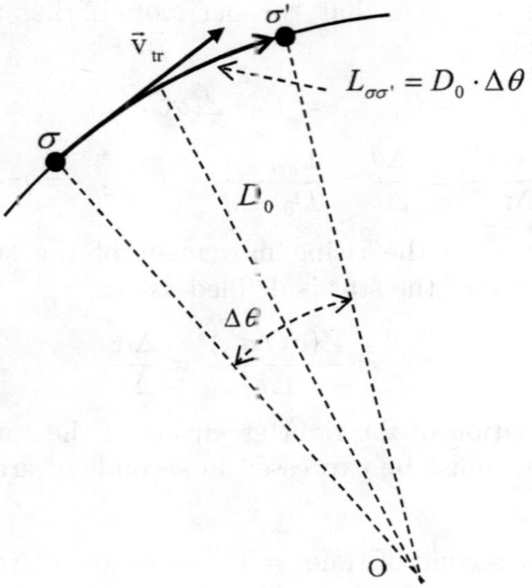

Fig. 27.3

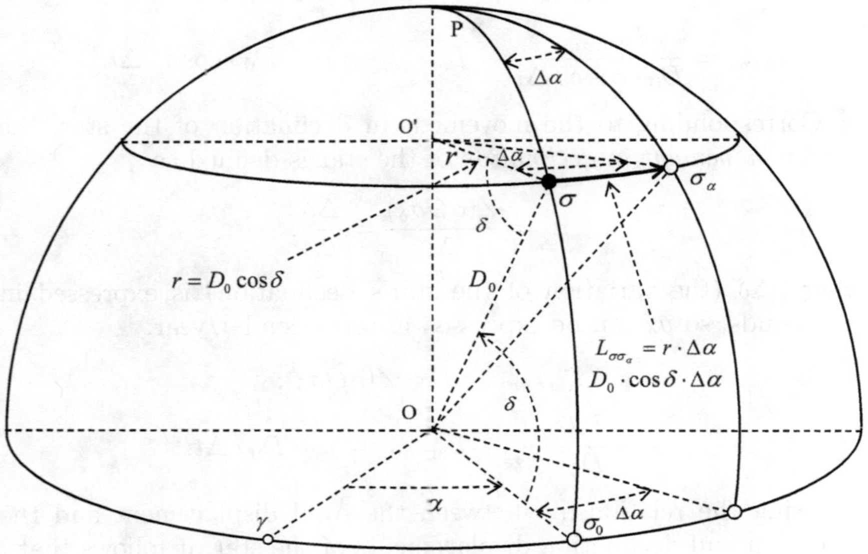

Fig. 27.4

from which we recognize that "proper motion" has the meaning of an angular velocity;

$$L_{\mathrm{arc}\,\sigma\sigma'} = D_0 \cdot \angle(\sigma O \sigma');$$

$$\mu = \frac{\angle(\sigma O \sigma')}{\Delta t} = \frac{\Delta\theta}{\Delta t} = \frac{L_{\mathrm{arc}\,\sigma\sigma'}}{D_0 \cdot \Delta t}; \quad L_{\mathrm{arc}\,\sigma\sigma'} = \mu \cdot D_0 \cdot \Delta t.$$

Corresponding to the rising movement of the star, the *proper upward movement* of the star is defined as

$$\mu_\alpha = \frac{\angle(\sigma O' \sigma_\alpha)}{\Delta t} = \frac{\Delta\alpha}{\Delta t},$$

where $\Delta\alpha$ (variation of the right ascension of the star, expressed in seconds of time) must be expressed in seconds of arc, based on the relation

$$1\,\mathrm{s}\,(\text{second of time}) = 15''\ (\text{seconds of arc}),$$

so that μ_α is expressed in (seconds of arc)/year:

$$L_{\mathrm{arc}\,\sigma\sigma_\alpha} = D_0 \cdot \cos\delta \cdot \angle(\sigma O' \sigma_\alpha);$$

$$\mu_\alpha = \frac{L_{\mathrm{arc}\,\sigma\sigma_\alpha}}{D_0 \cdot \cos\delta \cdot \Delta t}; \quad L_{\mathrm{arc}\,\sigma\sigma_\alpha} = \mu_\alpha \cdot D_0 \cdot \cos\delta \cdot \Delta t.$$

Corresponding to the movement in declination of the star, the *proper movement in declination* of the star is defined as

$$\mu_\delta = \frac{\angle(\sigma O \sigma_\delta)}{\Delta t} = \frac{\Delta\delta}{\Delta t},$$

where $\Delta\delta$ (the variation of the star's declination) is expressed in arcseconds, so μ_δ can be expressed in (arcseconds)/year:

$$L_{\mathrm{arc}\,\sigma\sigma_\delta} = D_0 \cdot \angle(\sigma O \sigma_\delta);$$

$$\mu_\delta = \frac{L_{\mathrm{arc}\,\sigma\sigma_\delta}}{D_0 \cdot \Delta t}; \quad L_{\mathrm{arc}\,\sigma\sigma_\delta} = \mu_\delta \cdot D_0 \cdot \Delta t.$$

Using the relationship between the total displacement and the ascension and declination displacements of the star, it follows that:

$$L_{\mathrm{arc}\,\sigma\sigma'} = D_0 \cdot \Delta\theta; \quad L_{\mathrm{arc}\,\sigma\sigma_\alpha} = D_0 \cdot \cos\delta \cdot \Delta\alpha;$$

$$L_{\mathrm{arc}\,\sigma\sigma_\delta} = D_0 \cdot \Delta\delta;$$

$$L_{\text{arc}\,\sigma\sigma'} = \sqrt{(L_{\text{arc}\,\sigma\sigma_\alpha})^2 + (L_{\text{arc}\,\sigma\sigma_\delta})^2};$$
$$\Delta\theta = \sqrt{(\cos\delta \cdot \Delta\alpha)^2 + (\Delta\delta)^2},$$

representing the relationship between the star's angular displacement in the sky, $\Delta\theta$, and the star's equatorial coordinates, α and δ;

$$L_{\text{arc}\,\sigma\sigma'} = \mu \cdot D_0 \cdot \Delta t; \quad L_{\text{arc}\,\sigma\sigma_\alpha} = \mu_\alpha \cdot D_0 \cdot \cos\delta \cdot \Delta t;$$
$$L_{\text{arc}\,\sigma\sigma_\delta} = \mu_\delta \cdot D_0 \cdot \Delta t;$$
$$L_{\text{arc}\,\sigma\sigma'} = \sqrt{(L_{\text{arc}\,\sigma\sigma_\alpha})^2 + (L_{\text{arc}\,\sigma\sigma_\delta})^2};$$
$$\mu = \sqrt{(\mu_\alpha \cos\delta)^2 + \mu_\delta^2}.$$

This represents the relationship between the true motion and the true ascension and declination motions of the star, where μ_α, expressed in (seconds of time)/year and (seconds of arc)/year, represents the proper motion of the rising star, and μ_δ, expressed in (seconds of arc)/year, is the proper motion of the star in declination:

$$\mu_\alpha = \frac{\Delta\alpha}{\Delta t}; \quad 0^0 < \alpha < 180^0; \quad 0^{\text{h}} < \alpha < 12^{\text{h}};$$
$$12^{\text{h}} \leftrightarrow 180^0; \quad 12 \cdot 3600^{\text{s}} \leftrightarrow 180 \cdot 60 \cdot 60'';$$
$$1^{\text{s}} \leftrightarrow 15''; \quad 1\ \text{s} \leftrightarrow 15\,\text{arcsec} = 15'';$$
$$\mu^*_{\alpha(\text{sec time})/\text{year}} = \mu^*_\alpha = \frac{(\Delta\alpha)_{(\text{seconds})}}{(\Delta t)_{(\text{year})}} = \frac{|(\Delta\alpha)_{(\text{sec time})}|}{|(\Delta t)_{(\text{year})}|}\frac{1\ \text{sec time}}{\text{year}}$$
$$= (\mu^*_\alpha)_{(\text{sec time})/\text{year}};$$
$$1\,\text{s} \leftrightarrow 15\,\text{arcsec} = 15'';$$
$$\mu_{\alpha(\text{arcsec})/\text{year}} = \frac{15''|(\Delta\alpha)_{(\text{sec time})}|}{(\Delta t)_{(\text{year})}} = \frac{|(\Delta\alpha)_{(\text{sec time})}| \cdot 15\,\text{arcsec}}{(\Delta t)_{(\text{year})}};$$
$$\mu_\alpha = \frac{|(\Delta\alpha)_{(\text{sec time})}| \cdot 15\,\text{arcsec}}{|(\Delta t)_{(\text{year})}| \cdot 1\,\text{year}} = \frac{15'' \cdot |(\Delta\alpha)_{(\text{sec time})}|}{|(\Delta t)_{(\text{year})}|}\frac{1}{\text{year}}$$
$$= (\mu_\alpha)_{(\text{arcsec})/\text{year}}.$$

Here, $|(\Delta\alpha)_{(\text{sec time})}|$ is the numerical value of $\Delta\alpha$, expressed in seconds of time, so that:

$$\mu_\alpha = (\mu_\alpha)_{(\text{arcsec/year})};$$

$$\mu_\alpha^* = \frac{(\Delta\alpha)_{(\text{sec time})}}{(\Delta t)_{\text{year}}} = \frac{|(\Delta\alpha)_{(\text{sec time})}|}{|(\Delta t)_{(\text{year})}|}\frac{\text{sec time}}{\text{year}} = (\mu_\alpha^*)_{(\text{sec time})/\text{year}};$$

$$|(\mu_\alpha^*)_{(\text{sec time})/\text{year}}| = \frac{|(\Delta\alpha)_{(\text{sec time})}|}{|(\Delta t)_{(\text{year})}|};$$

$$\mu_\alpha = 15\,\frac{|(\Delta\alpha)_{(\text{sec time})}|}{|(\Delta t)_{(\text{year})}|}\frac{\text{arcsec}}{\text{year}} = 15\cdot|(\mu^*_{\alpha(\text{sec time})/\text{year}})|\frac{\text{arcsec}}{\text{year}}$$

$$= |(\mu^*_{\alpha(\text{sec time})/\text{year}})|\cdot\frac{15''}{\text{year}};$$

$$\mu_\alpha = 15\cdot|(\mu^*_{\alpha(\text{sec time})/\text{year}})|\frac{\text{arcsec}}{\text{year}};\quad \mu_\alpha = 15''\cdot|(\mu_\alpha^*)|\frac{1}{\text{year}};$$

$$\mu_\alpha = 15''\cdot|(\mu^*_{\alpha(\text{sec time})/\text{year}})|\frac{1}{\text{year}};$$

$$\mu_\delta = \frac{\Delta\delta}{\Delta t};\quad 0^0 < \delta < 90^0;$$

$$\mu_\delta = \frac{\Delta\delta}{\Delta t} = \frac{(\Delta\delta)_{(\text{arcsec})}}{(\Delta t)_{(\text{year})}} = \frac{|(\Delta\delta)_{(\text{arcsec})}|}{|(\Delta t)_{(\text{year})}|}\frac{\text{arcsec}}{\text{year}}.$$

Here, $|(\Delta\delta)_{(\text{arcsec})}|$ is the numerical value of $\Delta\delta$, expressed in arcsecs, so that:

$$\mu_\delta = (\mu_\delta)_{(\text{arcsec/year})};$$

$$\mu = \sqrt{(\mu_\alpha\cos\delta)^2 + (\mu_\delta)^2},$$

representing the proper motion of the star,

$$\mu_\alpha^* = \frac{|(\Delta\alpha)_{\text{sec time}}|}{(\Delta t)_{\text{year}}},$$

expressed in 1/year;

$$\mu_\alpha = 15''\mu_\alpha^*,$$

expressed in (arcseconds)/year;

$$\mu = \sqrt{(15''\mu_\alpha^* \cos\delta)^2 + \mu_\delta^2},$$

where μ_α^* is expressed in 1/year, and μ_δ is expressed in (arcseconds)/year.

b) It is also possible to determine the angle between the direction of the tangent to the displacement of the star and the tangent to the celestial meridian of the star:

$$\text{tg}\,\eta = \frac{L_{\text{arc}\,\sigma\sigma_\sigma}}{L_{\text{arc}\,\sigma\sigma_\delta}} = \frac{\mu_\alpha \cdot \cos\delta}{\mu_\delta}; \quad \text{tg}\,\eta = \frac{15''\mu_\alpha^* \cos\delta}{\mu_\delta}.$$

c) The components of star σ's velocity are:

$$L_{\text{arc}\,\sigma\sigma'} = \Delta d = \text{v}_{\text{tr}} \cdot \Delta t;$$

$$\Delta d = D_0 \cdot \Delta\theta;$$

$$\Delta\theta = \frac{\text{v}_{\text{tr}} \cdot \Delta t}{D_0};$$

$$\mu = \frac{\Delta\theta}{\Delta t}; \quad \mu = \frac{\text{v}_{\text{tr}}}{D_0},$$

representing the relation between the proper motion and the transverse component of the star's velocity;

$$\text{v}_{\text{tr}} = \mu \cdot D_0.$$

According to the drawing in Figure 27.5, it follows that:

$$\tan p = \frac{r}{D_0} \approx p_{\text{rad}} = \frac{r_{(\text{pc})}}{D_{0(\text{pc})}};$$

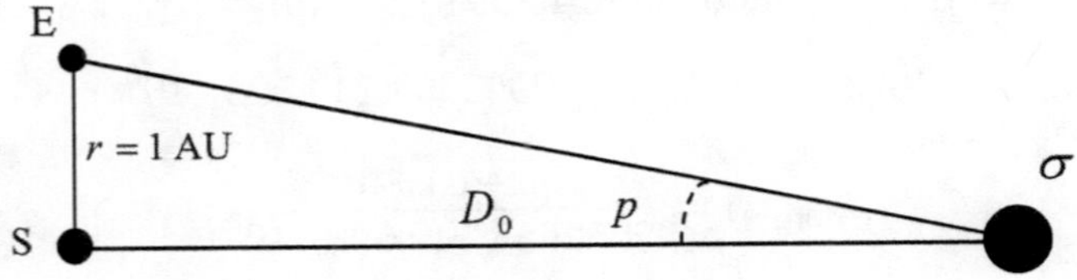

Fig. 27.5

$$1\,\text{rad} = 206265\,\text{arcsec} = 206265'';$$

$$1\,\text{pc} = 206265\,\text{AU};$$

$$D_{0(\text{pc})} = \frac{r_{(\text{pc})}}{p_{\text{rad}}} = \frac{\frac{r_{(\text{AU})}}{206265}}{p_{('')} \cdot \frac{1}{\frac{180}{3.14} \cdot 60 \cdot 60}} = \frac{\frac{r_{(\text{AU})}}{206265}}{p_{('')} \cdot \frac{1}{206265}} = \frac{r_{(\text{AU})}}{p_{('')}};$$

$$|D_{0(\text{pc})}| = \frac{|r_{(\text{AU})}|}{|p_{('')}|}; \quad r = 1\,\text{AU}; \quad |r_{(\text{AU})}| = 1;$$

$$|D_{0(\text{pc})}| = \frac{1}{|p_{('')}|}; \quad |p_{('')}| = \frac{1}{|D_{0(\text{pc})}|};$$

d)

$$\text{v}_{\text{tr (km/s)}} = \mu_{(\text{rad/s})} \cdot D_{0(\text{km})} = |\mu_{(\text{rad/s})}| \cdot \frac{1}{s} \cdot |D_{0(\text{km})}| \cdot \text{km};$$

$$\text{v}_{\text{tr (km/s)}} = |\mu_{(\text{rad/s})}| \cdot |D_{0(\text{km})}| \cdot \frac{\text{km}}{\text{s}};$$

$$\mu_{(\text{rad/s})} = |\mu_{(\text{rad/s})}| \cdot \frac{\text{rad}}{\text{s}} = |\mu_{(\text{rad/s})}| \cdot \frac{206265\,\text{arcsec}}{\frac{1\,\text{year}}{31.536 \cdot 10^6}};$$

$$\mu_{(\text{rad/s})} = |\mu_{(\text{rad/s})}| \cdot 206265 \cdot 31.05 \cdot 10^6\,\frac{\text{arcsec}}{\text{year}}$$

$$= |\mu_{(\text{arcsec/year})}| \cdot \frac{\text{arcsec}}{\text{year}};$$

$$|\mu_{(\text{arcsec/year})}| = |\mu_{(\text{rad/s})}| \cdot 206265 \cdot 31.536 \cdot 10^6;$$

$$|\mu_{(\text{rad/s})}| = \frac{|\mu_{(\text{arcsec/year})}|}{206265 \cdot 31.536 \cdot 10^6};$$

$$D_{0(\text{pc})} = |D_{0(\text{pc})}| \cdot \text{pc} = |D_{0(\text{pc})}| \cdot 206265\,\text{AU}$$

$$= |D_{0(\text{pc})}| \cdot 206265 \cdot 149.598 \cdot 10^6\,\text{km};$$

$$D_{0(\text{pc})} = |D_{0(\text{pc})}| \cdot 206265 \cdot 149.598 \cdot 10^6\,\text{km} = |D_{0(\text{km})}| \cdot \text{km};$$

$$|D_{0(\text{km})}| = |D_{0(\text{pc})}| \cdot 206265 \cdot 149.598 \cdot 10^6;$$

$$|D_{0(\text{pc})}| = \frac{|D_{0(\text{km})}|}{206265 \cdot 149.598 \cdot 10^6};$$

$$\text{v}_{\text{tr (km/s)}} = |\mu_{(\text{rad/s})}| \cdot |D_{0(\text{km})}| \cdot \frac{\text{km}}{\text{s}};$$

$$\mathrm{v}_{\mathrm{tr\,(km/s)}} = \frac{|\mu_{(\mathrm{arcsec/en})}|}{206265 \cdot 31.536 \cdot 10^6} \cdot |D_{0(\mathrm{pc})}|$$

$$\cdot 206265 \cdot 149.598 \cdot 10^6 \ \frac{\mathrm{km}}{\mathrm{s}};$$

$$\mathrm{v}_{\mathrm{tr\,(km/s)}} = \frac{|\mu_{(\mathrm{arcsec/year})}|}{31.536} \cdot |D_{0(\mathrm{pc})}| \cdot 149.598 \ \frac{\mathrm{km}}{\mathrm{s}};$$

$$\mathrm{v}_{\mathrm{tr\,(km/s)}} = 4.74 \cdot |\mu_{(\mathrm{arcsec/year})}| \cdot |D_{0(\mathrm{pc})}| \frac{\mathrm{km}}{\mathrm{s}},$$

representing the transverse component of star σ's velocity, expressed in km/s, where $|\mu_{(\mathrm{arcsec/year})}|$ is the numerical value of μ, expressed in arcsec/year, and $|D_{0(\mathrm{pc})}|$ is the numerical value of D_0, expressed in parsecs.

e) For the radial component of star σ's velocity, according to the Doppler effect, it follows that:

$$\frac{\Delta\lambda}{\lambda_0} = \frac{\mathrm{v}_{\mathrm{rad}}}{c}; \quad \mathrm{v}_{\mathrm{rad}} = c\frac{\Delta\lambda}{\lambda_0} = c\frac{\lambda - \lambda_0}{\lambda_0}.$$

So, the spatial velocity of the star σ is

$$\mathrm{v} = \sqrt{\mathrm{v}_{\mathrm{tr}}^2 + \mathrm{v}_{\mathrm{rad}}^2}.$$

f) According to Pogson's formula written for a star and for the Sun, it follows that:

$$\log \frac{E_{\mathrm{star}}}{E_{\mathrm{Sun}}} = -0.4(m_{\mathrm{star}} - m_{\mathrm{Sun}}),$$

where E_{star} and E_{Sun} represent the illumination produced by the star and the Sun, respectively, for the observer on Earth;

$$\log \frac{\frac{L_{\mathrm{star}}}{4\pi D_0^2}}{\frac{L_{\mathrm{Sun}}}{4\pi D_{\mathrm{ES}}^2}} = -0.4(m_{\mathrm{star}} - m_{\mathrm{Sun}}),$$

where L_{star} and L_{Sun} are the luminosity of the star and the luminosity of the Sun, and D_0 and D_{ES} are the distance from the Earth to the star and the distance from the Earth to the Sun, respectively;

$$\log \frac{L_{\mathrm{star}}}{L_{\mathrm{Sun}}} \left(\frac{D_{\mathrm{ES}}}{D_0}\right)^2 = -0.4(m_{\mathrm{star}} - m_{\mathrm{Sun}}); \quad m_{\mathrm{Sun}} = -26.8^m;$$

$$\frac{L_{\mathrm{star}}}{L_{\mathrm{Sun}}} \left(\frac{D_{\mathrm{ES}}}{D_0}\right)^2 = 10^{-0.4(m_{\mathrm{star}} - m_{\mathrm{Sun}})};$$

$$L_{\text{star}} = \left(\frac{D_0}{D_{\text{ES}}}\right)^2 \cdot 10^{-0.4(m_{\text{star}} - m_{\text{Sun}})} \cdot L_{\text{Sun}};$$

$$D_{\text{ES}} = 1\,\text{AU}; \quad 1\,\text{pc} = 206265\,\text{AU};$$

$$D_{0(\text{AU})} = |D_{0(\text{pc})}| \cdot 206265\,\text{AU};$$

$$\frac{D_{0(\text{AU})}}{D_{\text{ES(AU)}}} = |D_{0(\text{pc})}| \cdot 206265;$$

$$L_{\text{star}} = (|D_{0(\text{pc})}| \cdot 206265)^2 \cdot 10^{-0.4(m_{\text{star}} - m_{\text{Sun}})} \cdot L_{\text{Sun}},$$

representing the brightness of the star as a function of the brightness of the Sun.

Proper Motions of the Stars — Results

Table 27.5

No.	Star	Declination δ (° ′ ″)	Proper motion in ascension μ_β (10^{-3}arcsec/year)	Proper motion in declination μ_β (10^{-3}arcsec/year)
1	Barnard	+04°41′36.20″	−801.30	10327.12
2	Kapteyn	−45°01′06.28″	9203.56	−5730.84
3	Groombridge	+44°01′22.62″	5568.81	−5813.62
4	Lacaille	−35°51′11.04″	8350.64	1327.52
5	Gliese 1	−37°21′26.50″	7089.43	−2337.71
6	Lalande	+35°58′11.56″	−717.00	−4765.85
7	Epsilon Indi	−56°47′09.52″	7231.93	−2539.23

Table 27.6

No.	Star	Declination δ (°)	$\cos\delta$	μ_β (10^{-3}as/yr)	$\mu_\beta \cos\delta$ (10^{-3}as/yr)	μ_β (10^{-3}as/year)
1	Barnard	+4.693°	0.9966	−801.30	−798.57	10327.12
2	Kapteyn	−45.017°	0.7068	9203.56	6505.07	−5730.84
3	Groombridge	+44.022°	0.7190	5568.81	4003.97	−5813.62
4	Lacaille	−35.853°	0.8105	8350.64	6768.19	1327.52
5	Gliese 1	−37.357°	0.7948	7089.43	5634.67	−2337.71
6	Lalande	+35.969°	0.8093	−717.00	−580.26	−4765.85
7	Epsilon Indi	−56.785°	0.5477	7231.93	3960.92	−2539.23

Table 27.7

No.	Star	Proper motion μ (10^{-3} arcsec/year)	$\tan\eta = (\mu_\beta \cdot \cos\delta)/\mu_\beta$	Distance D_0 (pc)
1	Barnard	10358.94	−0.0773	1.7114
2	Kapteyn	8669.40	−1.1350	3.9114
3	Groombridge	7059.03	−0.6887	9.0917
4	Lacaille	6897.16	5.0983	3.2758
5	Gliese 1	6100.36	−2.4103	4.3399
6	Lalande	4801.04	0.1217	2.5468
7	Epsilon Indi	4704.96	−1.5598	3.6224

Table 27.8

No.	Star	Proper motion μ (10^{-3} arcsec/year)	Distance D_0 (pc)	Transversal velocity v_{tr} (km/s)
1	Barnard	10358.94	1.7114	84.03
2	Kapteyn	8669.40	3.9114	160.73
3	Groombridge	7059.03	9.0917	304.20
4	Lacaille	6897.16	3.2758	107.09
5	Gliese 1	6100.36	4.3399	125.49
6	Lalande	4801.04	2.5468	57.95
7	Epsilon Indi	4704.96	3.6224	80.78

Table 27.9

No.	Star	Radial velocity v_{rad} (km/s)	Transversal velocity v_{tr} (km/s)	Spatial velocity v (km/s)
1	Barnard	−110.51	84.03	138.82
2	Kapteyn	+245.19	160.73	293.17
3	Groombridge	−98.35	304.20	319.70
4	Lacaille	+8.81	107.09	107.45
5	Gliese 1	+25.38	125.49	127.03
6	Lalande	−84.69	57.95	102.61
7	Epsilon Indi	−40.00	80.78	90.14

Table 27.10

No.	Star	Distance D_0 (pc)	Distance D_0 (AU)	Apparent magnitude m (m)	$m - m_{Sun}$ (m)
1	Barnard	1.7114	353001.92	9.51	36.31^m
2	Kapteyn	3.9114	806784.92	8.85	35.65^m
3	Groombridge	9.0917	1875299.50	6.44	33.24^m
4	Lacaille	3.2758	675682.88	7.34	34.14^m
5	Gliese 1	4.3399	895169.47	8.57	35.37^m
6	Lalande	2.5468	525315.70	7.52	34.32^m
7	Epsilon Indi	3.6224	747174.33	4.83	31.63^m

Table 27.11

No.	Star	Distance D_0 (pc)	Distance D_0 (AU)	$10^{-0.4}$ $(m_{star} - m_{Sun})$	Luminosity L (10^{-4} L_{Sun})
1	Barnard	1.7114	353001.92	$10^{-14.52}$	3.6
2	Kapteyn	3.9114	806784.92	$10^{-14.26}$	35.3
3	Groombridge	9.0917	1875299.50	$10^{-13.29}$	1771.2
4	Lacaille	3.2758	675682.88	$10^{-13.65}$	99.6
5	Gliese 1	4.3399	895169.47	$10^{-14.14}$	57.4
6	Lalande	2.5468	525315.70	$10^{-13.72}$	50.6
7	Epsilon Indi	3.6224	747174.33	$10^{-12.65}$	1226.3

Problem 28

The Orbits of the Planets

It is assumed that the Earth's orbit around the Sun is a circle with radius $r_E = 1$ AU. In the Table 28.1 are the maximum eastern and western angular elongations of the planets Mercury and Venus at certain moments.

a) Assuming that the orbits of the three planets (Earth, Venus and Mercury) in relation to the Sun are concentric and coplanar circles, let us consider that Venus and Mercury are in the positions corresponding to the maximum eastern elongations. *Determine* the amount of time until Venus/Mercury will be:

1) for *the first time*, in the positions corresponding to the maximum western elongations;

2) *again* in positions corresponding to the maximum eastern elongations.

b) According to the data entered in Table 28.1, using a sheet of paper on which the circular orbit of the Earth is represented, with the Sun at its center, *locate*, approximately, the positions of the planets Mercury and Venus around the Sun and *determine* the average distance between Mercury and the Sun, as well as the average distance between Venus and the Sun.

c) *Determine* the exact values of the parameters of the orbits of Mercury and Venus $(a; b; e)$, expressed in AU, knowing that:

$$18^\circ \leq \alpha_{\text{max,east}}^{\text{Mercury}} \leq 28^\circ; \quad 18^\circ \leq \alpha_{\text{max,west}}^{\text{Mercury}} \leq 28^\circ;$$

$$45^\circ \leq \alpha_{\text{max,east}}^{\text{Venus}} \leq 48^\circ; \quad 45^\circ \leq \alpha_{\text{max,west}}^{\text{Venus}} \leq 48^\circ.$$

Table 28.1 Maximum elongations of the planets Mercury and Venus

Mercury: 1989–1990			Venus: 1983–1990		
Date	$\alpha_{\text{max,east}}$	$\alpha_{\text{max,west}}$	Date	$\alpha_{\text{max,east}}$	$\alpha_{\text{max,west}}$
January 8, 1989	19°		June 15, 1983	45°	
February 18, 1989		26°	November 4, 1983		47°
April 30, 1989	21°		January 21, 1985	47°	
June 18, 1989		23°	June 12, 1985		46°
August 28, 1989	20°		August 26, 1986	46°	
October 10, 1989		18°	January 15, 1987		47°
December 22, 1989	20°		April 2, 1988	46°	
February 1, 1990		25°	August 22, 1988	46°	
April 13, 1990	20°		November 8, 1988		47°
May 31, 1990		25°	March 30, 1990		46°
August 11, 1990	27°				
September 24, 1990		18°			
December 5, 1990	21°				

Solution

a) Assuming that the orbits of the three planets (Earth, Venus and Mercury) in relation to the Sun are concentric and coplanar circles, as indicated by the drawings in Figures 28.1 and 28.2, then the maximum angular elongations (distances) of each of the planets Venus and Mercury relative to the Sun, as viewed from Earth, will be constant over time and equal, $\alpha_{\text{max,east}} = \alpha_{\text{max,west}}$.

Under these conditions, the following values of the maximum elongations for the planets Mercury and Venus are accepted:

$$\alpha_{\text{max,east,Mercury}} = \alpha_{\text{max,west,Mercury}} = 27°;$$

$$\alpha_{\text{max,east,Venus}} = \alpha_{\text{max,west,Venus}} = 47°.$$

Knowing the previously specified values, let us consider that Venus/Mercury is in the position corresponding to the maximum eastern elongation.

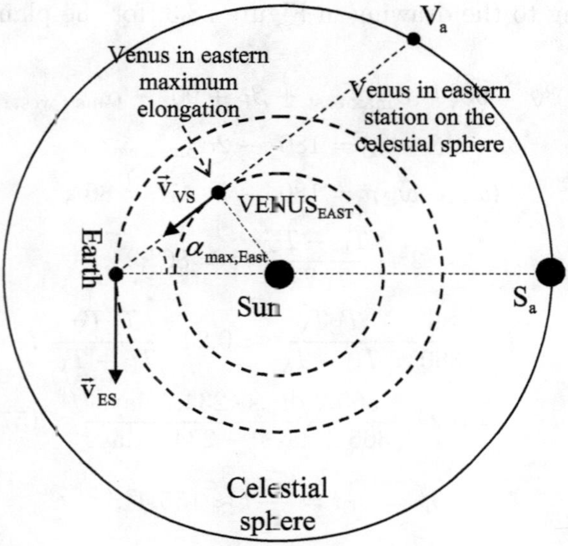

Fig. 28.1

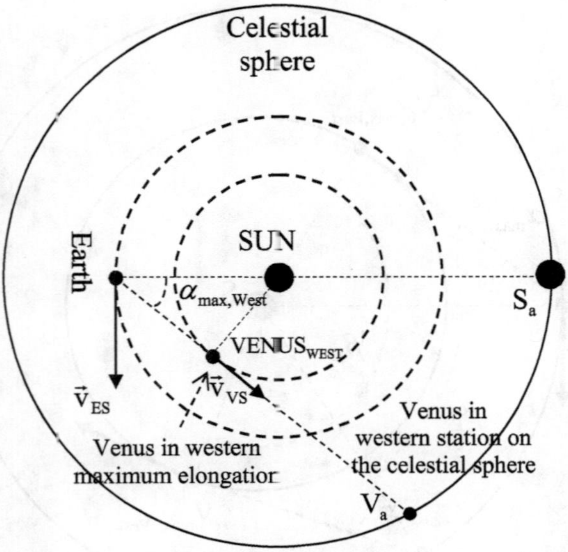

Fig. 28.2

1) According to the drawing in Figure 28.3, for the planet Venus, it follows that:

$$\beta_{\mathrm{V}} = 90^\circ - \alpha_{\mathrm{max,east}} + \beta_{\mathrm{P}} + 90^\circ - \alpha_{\mathrm{max,west}};$$

$$\beta_{\mathrm{V}} - \beta_{\mathrm{E}} = 180^\circ - 2\alpha_{\mathrm{max,east}};$$

$$(\omega_{\mathrm{V}} - \omega_{\mathrm{E}})t = 180^\circ - 2 \cdot 47^\circ = 86^\circ;$$

$$2\pi \cdot \frac{T_{\mathrm{E}} - T_{\mathrm{V}}}{T_{\mathrm{E}} T_{\mathrm{V}}} \cdot t = 86^\circ;$$

$$t = \frac{86^\circ}{360^\circ} \cdot \frac{T_{\mathrm{E}} T_{\mathrm{V}}}{T_{\mathrm{E}} - T_{\mathrm{V}}} \approx 0.24 \cdot \frac{T_{\mathrm{E}} T_{\mathrm{V}}}{T_{\mathrm{E}} - T_{\mathrm{V}}}$$

$$= 0.24 \cdot \frac{365.2 \text{ days} \cdot 234.7 \text{ days}}{365.2 \text{ days} - 234.7 \text{ days}} \approx 157.6 \text{ days};$$

$$\beta_{\mathrm{E}} = \omega_{\mathrm{E}} t = \frac{2\pi}{T_{\mathrm{E}}} t \approx 155.4^\circ;$$

$$\beta_{\mathrm{V}} = \omega_{\mathrm{V}} t = \frac{2\pi}{T_{\mathrm{V}}} t \approx 241.7^\circ.$$

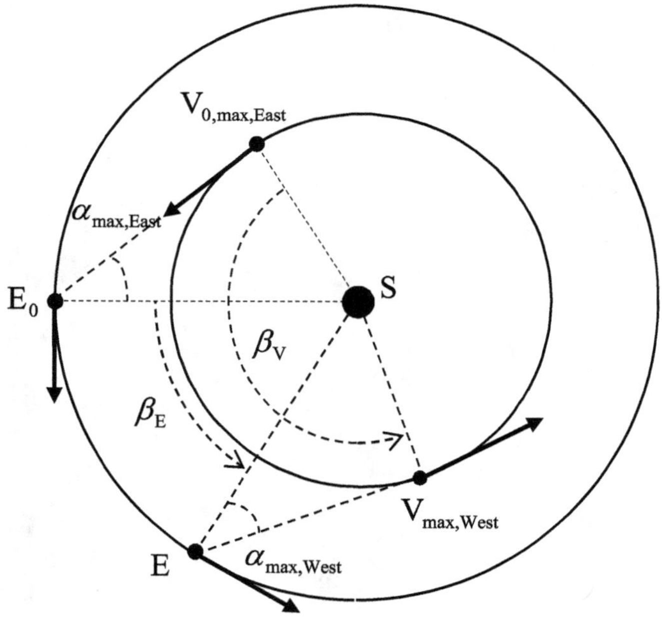

Fig. 28.3

Similarly, for the planet Mercury, it follows that:

$$\beta_{\mathrm{M}} = 90^\circ - \alpha_{\mathrm{max,east}} + \beta_{\mathrm{E}} + 90^\circ - \alpha_{\mathrm{max,west}};$$

$$\beta_{\mathrm{M}} - \beta_{\mathrm{E}} = 180^\circ - 2\alpha_{\mathrm{max,East}};$$

$$(\omega_{\mathrm{M}} - \omega_{\mathrm{E}})t = 180^\circ - 2 \cdot 27^\circ = 126^\circ;$$

$$2\pi \cdot \frac{T_{\mathrm{E}} - T_{\mathrm{V}}}{T_{\mathrm{E}}T_{\mathrm{V}}} \cdot t = 126^\circ;$$

$$t = \frac{126^\circ}{360^\circ} \cdot \frac{T_{\mathrm{E}}T_{\mathrm{M}}}{T_{\mathrm{E}} - T_{\mathrm{M}}} \approx 0.35 \cdot \frac{T_{\mathrm{E}}T_{\mathrm{M}}}{T_{\mathrm{E}} - T_{\mathrm{M}}}$$

$$= 0.35 \cdot \frac{365.2\ \text{days} \cdot 88\ \text{days}}{365.2\ \text{days} - 88\ \text{days}} \approx 40.6\ \text{days};$$

$$\beta_{\mathrm{E}} = \omega_{\mathrm{E}}t = \frac{2\pi}{T_{\mathrm{E}}}t \approx 40^\circ; \beta_{\mathrm{M}} = \omega_{\mathrm{M}}t = \frac{2\pi}{T_{\mathrm{M}}}t \approx 166^\circ.$$

2) According to the drawing in Figure 28.4, for the planet Venus, it follows that:

$$\beta_{\mathrm{V}} = 360^\circ + 90^\circ - \alpha_{\mathrm{max,east}} + \beta_{\mathrm{E}} - (90^\circ - \alpha_{\mathrm{max,east}});$$

$$\beta_{\mathrm{V}} = 360^\circ + \beta_{\mathrm{E}}; \quad (\omega_{\mathrm{V}} - \omega_{\mathrm{E}})t = 360^\circ;$$

$$2\pi \cdot \frac{T_{\mathrm{E}} - T_{\mathrm{V}}}{T_{\mathrm{E}}T_{\mathrm{V}}} \cdot t = 360^\circ;$$

$$t = \frac{T_{\mathrm{E}}T_{\mathrm{V}}}{T_{\mathrm{E}} - T_{\mathrm{V}}} = \frac{365.2\ \text{days} \cdot 234.7\ \text{days}}{365.2\ \text{days} - 234.7\ \text{days}} \approx 656.8\ \text{days};$$

$$\beta_{\mathrm{E}} = \omega_{\mathrm{E}}t = \frac{2\pi}{T_{\mathrm{E}}}t \approx 647.4^\circ \approx 360^\circ + 287^\circ;$$

$$\beta_{\mathrm{V}} = \omega_{\mathrm{V}}t = \frac{2\pi}{T_{\mathrm{V}}}t \approx 1007.4^\circ \approx 2 \cdot 360^\circ + 287^\circ = 360^\circ + \beta_{\mathrm{E}}.$$

Similarly, for the planet Mercury, it follows that:

$$t = \frac{T_{\mathrm{E}}T_{\mathrm{M}}}{T_{\mathrm{E}} - T_{\mathrm{M}}} = \frac{365.2\ \text{days} \cdot 88\ \text{days}}{365.2\ \text{days} - 88\ \text{days}} \approx 116\ \text{days};$$

$$\beta_{\mathrm{E}} = \omega_{\mathrm{E}}t = \frac{2\pi}{T_{\mathrm{E}}}t \approx 114.3^\circ;$$

$$\beta_{\mathrm{M}} = \omega_{\mathrm{M}}t = \frac{2\pi}{T_{\mathrm{M}}}t \approx 474.5^\circ = 360^\circ + 114.5^\circ \approx 360^\circ + \beta_{\mathrm{E}}.$$

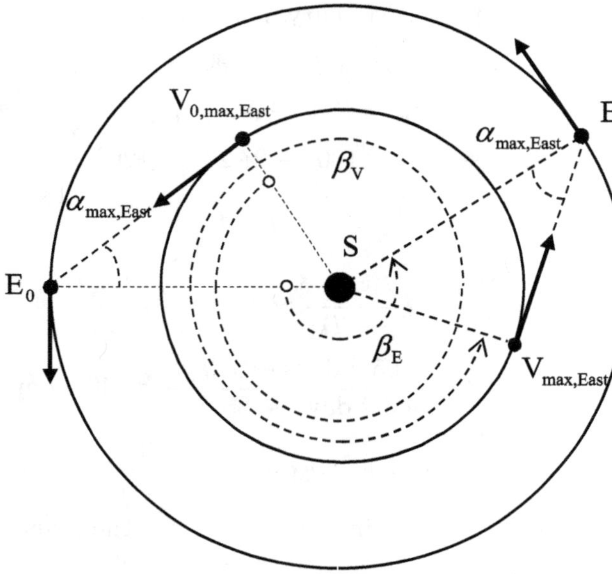

Fig. 28.4

b) Analyzing the data entered in Table 28.1, we find that the two maximum angular elongations for Mercury and Venus are also time-varying and different from each other, $\alpha_{\text{max,east}} \neq \alpha_{\text{max,west}}$. This means that the orbits of the two planets (Mercury and Venus) are ellipses with the Sun in one of the foci.

As you recall from the problem description, the Earth's orbit is given as circular, so we will consider the orbits of Mercury and Venus circular as well, and the positions of the two planets at their maximum eastern or western angular elongations are approximately indicated by the drawing in Figure 28.5.

For the circular orbit of the Earth, $r_{\text{E}} = 1$ AU, in Figures 28.6 and 28.7, two circles with radii of 5.5 cm have been drawn. Using the numerical information from Table 28.1, and having a protractor and a ruler available, the two drawings were created based on the method previously described, showing the approximate positions of the planets Mercury and Venus, respectively.

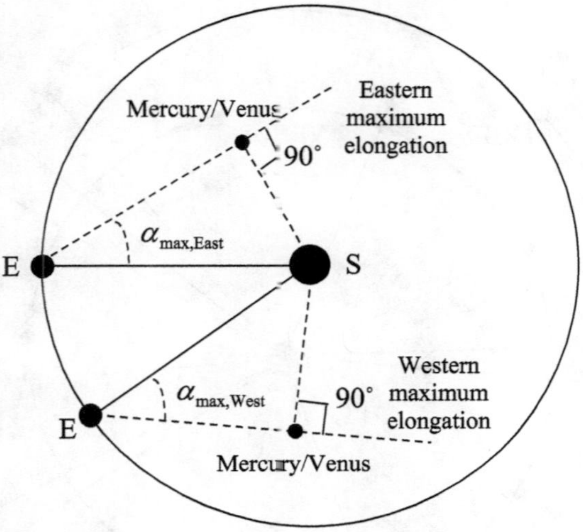

Fig. 28.5

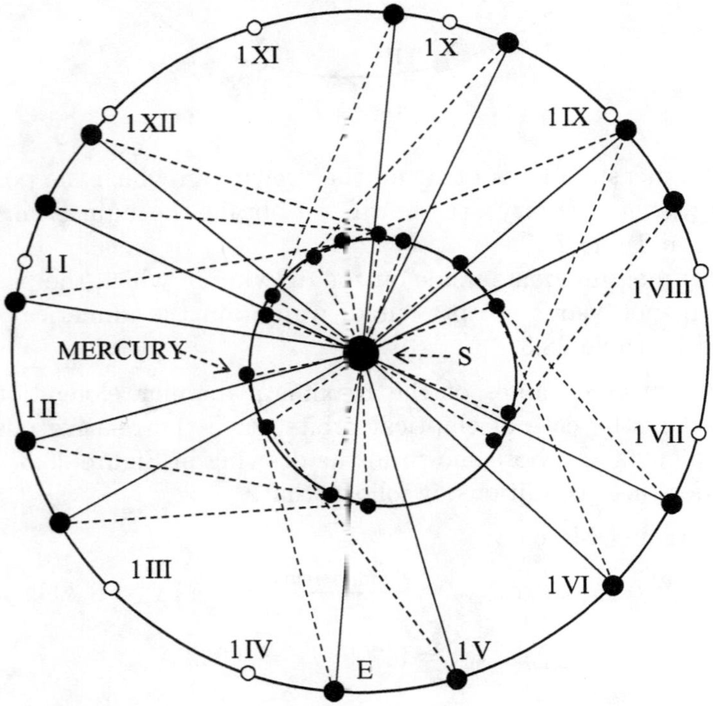

Fig. 28.6

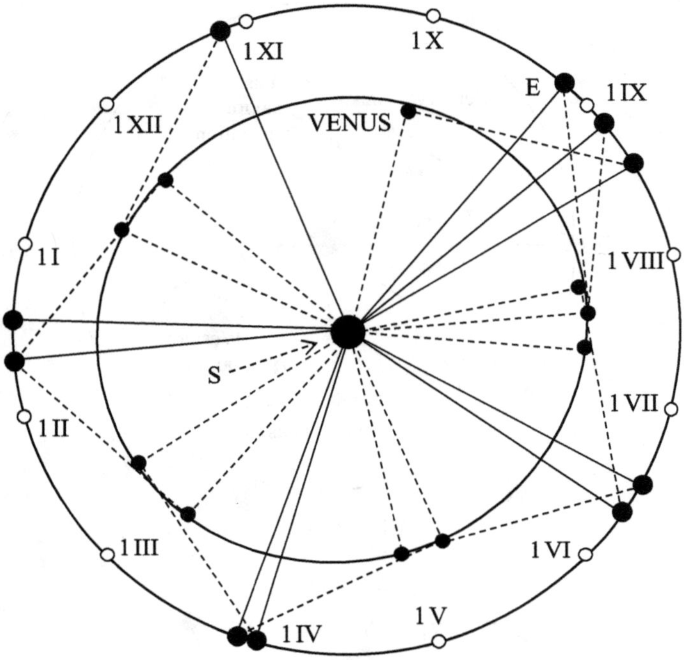

Fig. 28.7

From measurements made on the drawing in which the positions of the planet Mercury are shown, we obtain the numerical values entered in Table 28.2.

From measurements made on the drawing in which the positions of the planet Venus are presented, we obtain the numerical values entered in Table 28.3.

c) The extreme values of the maximum angular elongations are achieved in the case of elliptical orbits when the relative positions of the planets are those shown in the drawing in Figure 28.8.

Under these conditions, it follows that:

For the planet Mercury:

$$\sin \alpha_{\text{min,east,Mercury}} = \frac{r_{\text{min,Mercury}}}{r_{\text{E}}} = \sin 18° \approx 0.309;$$

$$r_{\text{min,Mercury}} = 0.309 \cdot r_{\text{E}} = 0.309 \text{ AU};$$

Table 28.2

Number of determination	M–S Segment d_{MS} (cm)	M–S distance r_{M} (AU)	Average M–S distance
1	1.7	0.30	
2	1.8	0.32	
3	1.9	0.34	
4	2.3	0.41	
5	2.4	0.43	0.360 AU
6	2.5	0.45	
7	2.4	0.43	
8	2.2	0.40	
9	2.0	0.36	
10	1.9	0.34	
11	1.8	0.32	
12	1.7	0.30	
13	1.6	0.29	

Table 28.3

Number of determination	V–S Segment d_{VS}(cm)	M–S distance r_{V}(AU)	Average V–S distance
1	3.9	0.70	
2	4.1	0.74	
3	4.2	0.76	
4	4.1	0.74	0.718 AU
5	3.9	0.70	
6	3.8	0.69	
7	4.0	0.72	
8	4.1	0.74	
9	3.9	0.70	
10	3.8	0.69	

$$\sin \alpha_{\text{max,west,Mercury}} = \frac{r_{\text{max,Mercury}}}{r_{\text{E}}} = \sin 28^\circ \approx 0.469;$$

$$r_{\text{max,Mercury}} = 0.469 \cdot r_{\text{E}} = 0.469 \text{ AU};$$

$$a_{\text{Mercury}} = \frac{r_{\text{min,Mercury}} + r_{\text{max,Mercury}}}{2} = 0.389 \text{ AU};$$

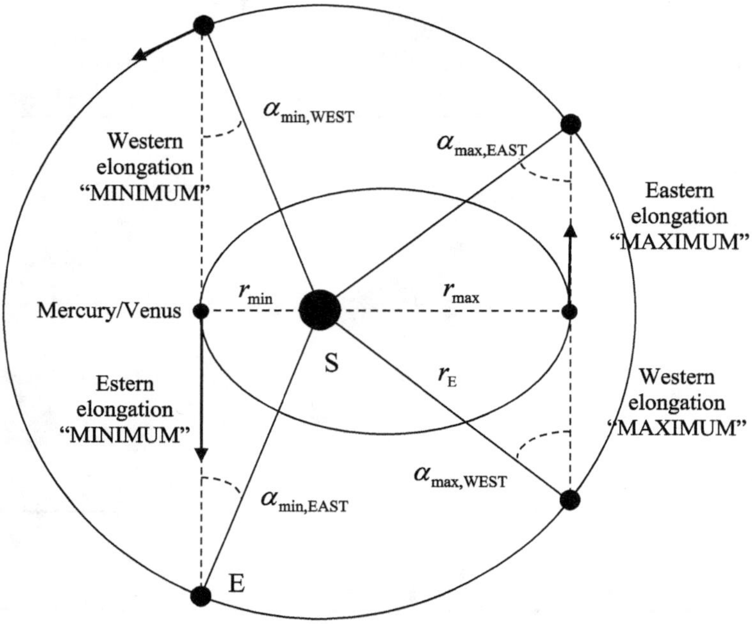

Fig. 28.8

$$e_{\text{Mercury}} = \frac{r_{\text{max,Mercury}} - r_{\text{min,Mercury}}}{r_{\text{min,Mercury}} + r_{\text{max,Mercury}}} \approx 0.020;$$

$$e_{\text{Mercury}} = \sqrt{1 - \frac{b^2_{\text{Mercury}}}{a^2_{\text{Mercury}}}};$$

$$b_{\text{Mercury}} = a_{\text{Mercury}} \cdot \sqrt{1 - e^2_{\text{Mercury}}} \approx 0.388 \text{ AU};$$

For the planet Venus:

$$\sin \alpha_{\text{min,east,Venus}} = \frac{r_{\text{min,Venus}}}{r_{\text{E}}} = \sin 45^\circ \approx 0.707;$$

$$r_{\text{min,Venus}} = 0.707 \cdot r_{\text{E}} = 0.707 \text{ AU};$$

$$\sin \alpha_{\text{max,east,Venus}} = \frac{r_{\text{max,Venus}}}{r_{\text{E}}} = \sin 48^\circ \approx 0.743;$$

$$r_{\text{max,Venus}} = 0.743 \cdot r_{\text{E}} = 0.743 \text{ AU};$$

$$a_{\text{Venus}} = \frac{r_{\text{min,Venus}} + r_{\text{max,Venus}}}{2} = 0.725 \text{ AU};$$

$$e_{\text{Venus}} = \frac{r_{\text{max,Venus}} - r_{\text{min,Venus}}}{r_{\text{min,Venus}} + r_{\text{max,Venus}}} \approx 0.024;$$

$$e_{\text{Venus}} = \sqrt{1 - \frac{b^2_{\text{Venus}}}{a^2_{\text{Venus}}}};$$

$$b_{\text{Venus}} = a_{\text{Venus}}\sqrt{1 - e^2_{\text{Venus}}} \approx 0.724 \text{ AU}.$$

Problem 29

The Apparent Magnitude of the Sun

Assuming that the radiation from the stars is black-body radiation, use the information in Table 29.1 to *determine* the apparent visual magnitude of the Sun.

Table 29.1

No.	Star	Angular diameter of the star (δ_{star})	Absolute temperature on the surface of the star (T_{star})	Apparent magnitude of the star (m_{star})	Apparent magnitude of the Sun (m_{Sun})
1	Betelgeuse	$0''.047$	3200 K	0.4^{m}	?
2	Aldebaran	$0''.020$	3800 K	0.9^{m}	?
3	Arcturus	$0''.020$	4300 K	-0.04^{m}	?
4	Herculis	$0''.030$	2650 K	3.15^{m}	?
5	Ceti Mira	$0''.056$	2400 K	3.04^{m}	?
6	Antares	$0''.040$	3100 K	0.88^{m}	?
7	Sun	$32'$	6000 K	?	?

Solution

According to the Stefan–Boltzmann law, the radiance (total energy) of a black body (star) corresponding to all wavelengths emitted in a unit of time by a unit area of the surface of the star is directly proportional to the fourth power of its absolute temperature, so that

$$Q_{\text{star}} = \frac{E_{\text{emitted, star}}}{tS_{\text{star}}} = \sigma T^4_{\text{star}},$$

where σ is a constant.

Under these conditions, the energy emitted by the entire surface of the star in a unit of time is:

$$P_{\text{emitted, star}} = 4\pi R^2_{\text{star}} \cdot Q_{\text{star}} = 4\pi\sigma R^2_{\text{star}} T^4_{\text{star}};$$

$$\frac{E_{\text{emitted, star}}}{t} = P_{\text{emitted, star}}; \quad \sigma T^4_{\text{star}} = \frac{P_{\text{emitted, star}}}{4\pi R^2_{\text{star}}};$$

$$P_{\text{emitted, star}} = \sigma T^4_{\text{star}} 4\pi R^2_{\text{star}}.$$

The energy flux density of the star, at the distance $r_{\text{Earth, star}}$, is the energy of all the radiation emitted by the star that crosses a unit area of the surface of Earth under normal incidence in a unit of time:

$$\phi_{\text{star},r_{\text{E,star}}} = \frac{P_{\text{emitted, star}}}{4\pi r^2_{\text{E,star}}};$$

$$\phi_{\text{star},r_{\text{E,star}}} = \frac{\sigma T^4_{\text{star}} 4\pi R^2_{\text{star}}}{4\pi r^2_{\text{E,star}}} = \frac{\sigma R^2_{\text{star}} T^4_{\text{star}}}{r^2_{\text{E,star}}}.$$

In particular, for the Sun, we have

$$\phi_{\text{Sun},r_{\text{E,Sun}}} = \frac{\sigma T^4_{\text{Sun}} 4\pi R^2_{\text{Sun}}}{4\pi r^2_{\text{E,Sun}}} = \frac{\sigma R^2_{\text{Sun}} T^4_{\text{Sun}}}{r^2_{\text{E,Sun}}}.$$

According to Pogson's formula, it follows that:

$$\log \frac{\phi_{\text{Sun},r_{\text{E,Sun}}}}{\phi_{\text{star},r_{\text{E,star}}}} = -0.4(m_{\text{Sun}} - m_{\text{star}});$$

$$\log \frac{\frac{\sigma R^2_{\text{Sun}} T^4_{\text{Sun}}}{r^2_{\text{E,Sun}}}}{\frac{\sigma R^2_{\text{star}} T^4_{\text{star}}}{r^2_{\text{E,star}}}} = -0.4(m_{\text{Sun}} - m_{\text{star}});$$

$$\log \frac{\left(\frac{R_{\text{Sun}}}{r_{\text{E,Sun}}}\right)^2 T^4_{\text{Sun}}}{\left(\frac{R_{\text{star}}}{r_{\text{E,star}}}\right)^2 T^4_{\text{star}}} = -0.4(m_{\text{Sun}} - m_{\text{star}});$$

$$\frac{R_{\text{Sun}}}{r_{\text{E,Sun}}} = \frac{1}{2}\delta_{\text{Sun}}; \qquad \frac{R_{\text{star}}}{r_{\text{E,star}}} = \frac{1}{2}\delta_{\text{star}};$$

$$\log \frac{\left(\frac{1}{2}\delta_{\text{Sun}}\right)^2 T_{\text{Sun}}^4}{\left(\frac{1}{2}\delta_{\text{star}}\right)^2 T_{\text{star}}^4} = -0.4(m_{\text{Sun}} - m_{\text{star}});$$

$$\log \frac{\delta_{\text{Sun}}^2 \cdot T_{\text{Sun}}^4}{\delta_{\text{star}}^2 \cdot T_{\text{star}}^4} = -0.4(m_{\text{Sun}} - m_{\text{star}});$$

$$\log \left(\frac{\delta_{\text{Sun}}}{\delta_{\text{star}}}\right)^2 \left(\frac{T_{\text{Sun}}}{T_{\text{star}}}\right)^4 = -0.4(m_{\text{Sun}} - m_{\text{star}});$$

$$2\log \frac{\delta_{\text{Sun}}}{\delta_{\text{star}}} + 4\log \frac{T_{\text{Sun}}}{T_{\text{star}}} = -0.4(m_{\text{Sun}} - m_{\text{star}});$$

$$\log \frac{\delta_{\text{Sun}}}{\delta_{\text{star}}} + 2\log \frac{T_{\text{Sun}}}{T_{\text{star}}} = -\frac{1}{5}(m_{\text{Sun}} - m_{\text{star}});$$

$$\log \frac{\delta_{\text{Sun}}}{\delta_{\text{star}}} + 2\log \frac{T_{\text{Sun}}}{T_{\text{star}}} = \frac{1}{5}(m_{\text{star}} - m_{\text{Sun}});$$

$$m_{\text{Sun}} = m_{\text{star}} - 5 \cdot \log \frac{\delta_{\text{Sun}}}{\delta_{\text{star}}} - 10 \cdot \log \frac{T_{\text{Sun}}}{T_{\text{star}}}.$$

The results of the determinations are presented in Tables 29.2 and 29.3:

$$\overline{m}_{\text{Sun}} = -25.195^{\text{m}}.$$

Table 29.2

No.	Star	Angular diameter of the star (δ_{star})	Absolute temperature on the surface of the star (T_{star})	Apparent magnitude of the star (m_{star})	Apparent magnitude of the Sun (m_{Sun})
1	Betelgeuse	$0''.047$	3200 K	0.4^{m}	?
2	Aldebaran	$0''.020$	3800 K	0.9^{m}	?
3	Arcturus	$0''.020$	4300 K	-0.04^{m}	?
4	Herculis	$0''.030$	2650 K	3.15^{m}	?
5	Ceti Mira	$0''.056$	2400 K	3.04^{m}	?
6	Antares	$0''.040$	3100 K	0.88^{m}	?
7	Sun	$32' = 1920''$	6000 K	?	?

Table 29.3

No.	Star	$\log \frac{\delta_{\text{Sun}}}{\delta_{\text{star}}}$	$\log \frac{T_{\text{Sun}}}{T_{\text{star}}}$	m_{star}	m_{Sun}
1	Betelgeuse	4.611	0.273	0.4^{m}	-25.385^{m}
2	Aldebaran	4.982	0.198	0.9^{m}	-25.99^{m}
3	Arcturus	4.982	0.144	-0.04^{m}	-26.39^{m}
4	Herculis	4.806	0.354	3.15^{m}	-24.42^{m}
5	Ceti Mira	4.535	0.397	3.04^{m}	-23.605^{m}
6	Antares	4.681	0.286	0.88^{m}	-25.385^{m}

Annex. The Simplified Form of Pogson's Formula

In a certain time interval, t, through its entire surface, with area S, a star emits the total energy E. As a result, the total energy that the star emits in a unit of time, through a unit of its surface area, called the *radiance* of the star, is

$$Q = \frac{E}{tS} = \frac{\frac{E}{t}}{4\pi R^2} = \frac{L}{4\pi R^2},$$

where $L = \frac{E}{t}$ represents the *brightness* of the star, the *energy flow* of the star, and the energy emitted by the star through its entire surface in a unit of time, and R is the radius of the star.

According to the Stefan–Boltzmann law, the *radiance* of the star is

$$Q = \sigma T^4,$$

which means that the energy emitted by a star, per unit time, per unit area of its surface, is directly proportional to the absolute temperature of the star to the 4th power, so that:

$$Q = \frac{L}{4\pi R^2} = \sigma T^4; \quad L = \sigma T^4 \cdot 4\pi R^2.$$

We now define the *energy flux density* of a star at the distance Δ, where an observer is located, as representing the fraction of the total energy emitted by the star that, for the observer, passes in a unit of time through a unit area of a surface placed perpendicular to the star–observer direction:

$$\varphi = \frac{\frac{E}{t}}{S} = \frac{E}{tS} = \frac{L}{S} = \frac{L}{4\pi\Delta^2}.$$

For two stars, according to Pogson's formula, it follows that:

$$\log\frac{\varphi_1}{\varphi_2} = -0.4\cdot(m_1 - m_2),$$

where m_1 and m_2 are the apparent magnitudes of the two stars;

$$\log\frac{\frac{L_1}{4\pi\Delta_1^2}}{\frac{L_2}{4\pi\Delta_2^2}} = -0.4\cdot(m_1 - m_2);$$

$$\log\frac{L_1\cdot\Delta_2^2}{L_2\cdot\Delta_1^2} = -0.4\cdot(m_1 - m_2);$$

$$\log\frac{L_1}{L_2}\cdot\left(\frac{\Delta_2}{\Delta_1}\right)^2 = -0.4\cdot(m_1 - m_2);$$

$$\log\frac{L_1}{L_2} + 2\cdot\log\frac{\Delta_2}{\Delta_1} = -0.4\cdot(m_1 - m_2);$$

$$m_1 = M_1 - 5 + 5\cdot\log|\Delta_{1(\mathrm{pc})}|;$$

$$m_2 = M_2 - 5 + 5\cdot\log|\Delta_{2(\mathrm{pc})}|,$$

where M_1 and M_2 are the absolute magnitudes of the two stars, and $|\Delta_{1(\mathrm{pc})}|$ and $|\Delta_{2(\mathrm{pc})}|$ represent the values of the distances from the observer to the two stars, expressed in parsecs;

$$\log\frac{L_1}{L_2} + 2\cdot\log\frac{\Delta_2}{\Delta_1}$$
$$= -0.4\cdot|(M_1 - 5 + 5\cdot\log|\Delta_{1(\mathrm{pc})}|) - (M_2 - 5 + 5\cdot\log|\Delta_{2(\mathrm{pc})}|)|;$$

$$\log\frac{L_1}{L_2} + 2\cdot\log\frac{\Delta_2}{\Delta_1}$$
$$= -0.4\cdot(M_1 - M_2 + 5\cdot(\log|\Delta_{1(\mathrm{pc})}| - \log|\Delta_{2(\mathrm{pc})}|));$$

$$\log\frac{L_1}{L_2} + 2\cdot\log\frac{\Delta_2}{\Delta_1}$$
$$= -0.4\cdot(M_1 - M_2 + 5\cdot(\log|\Delta_{1(\mathrm{pc})}| - \log|\Delta_{2(\mathrm{pc})}|));$$

$$\log\frac{L_1}{L_2} + 2\cdot\log\frac{\Delta_2}{\Delta_1}$$
$$= -0.4\cdot(M_1 - M_2 - 5\cdot(\log|\Delta_{2(\text{pc})}| - \log|\Delta_{1(\text{pc})}|));$$

$$\log\frac{L_1}{L_2} + 2\cdot\log\frac{\Delta_2}{\Delta_1} = -0.4\cdot\left(M_1 - M_2 - 5\cdot\log\frac{|\Delta_{2(\text{pc})}|}{|\Delta_{1(\text{pc})}|}\right);$$

$$\log\frac{L_1}{L_2} + 2\cdot\log\frac{\Delta_2}{\Delta_1} = -0.4\cdot(M_1 - M_2) + 0.4\cdot 5\cdot\log\frac{|\Delta_{2(\text{pc})}|}{|\Delta_{1(\text{pc})}|};$$

$$\log\frac{L_1}{L_2} + 2\cdot\log\frac{\Delta_2}{\Delta_1} = -0.4\cdot(M_1 - M_2) + 2\cdot\log\frac{|\Delta_{2(\text{pc})}|}{|\Delta_{1(\text{pc})}|};$$

$$\log\frac{L_1}{L_2} + 2\cdot\log\frac{\Delta_2}{\Delta_1} = -0.4\cdot(M_1 - M_2) + 2\cdot\log\frac{\Delta_2}{\Delta_1};$$

$$\log\frac{L_1}{L_2} = -0.4\cdot(M_1 - M_2),$$

representing the simplified form of Pogson's formula.

Problem 30

Altair and the Sun

For the star Altair (the star α in the constellation Aquila, represented in the drawing in Figure 30.1), the following are known: current annual parallax, $p_0 = 0.198''$; proper motion, $\mu = 0.658''/\text{year}$; radial velocity, $v_r = -26$ km/s; and current apparent visual magnitude, $m_0 = 0.89^m$.

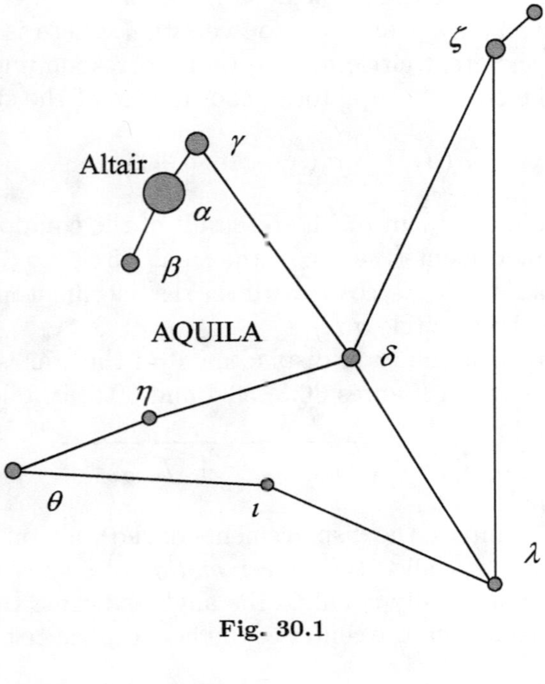

Fig. 30.1

Determine:

a) the time interval after which the distance between the star Altair and the Sun will be minimal, τ, considering that the movement of Altair in relation to the Sun is rectilinear and uniform;
b) the minimum distance between the star Altair and the Sun, D_{min};
c) the apparent magnitude of the star Altair, m, when the distance between it and the Sun is minimal.

Given: 1 rad = 206265 arcsec = 206265″; 1 pc = 206265 AU; the distance between the Earth and the Sun is d = 1 AU ≈ 150000000 km.

Solution

By comparing observations of the same stars at very long time intervals, the astronomer Edmond Halley discovered important differences between the coordinates of the same star, thus highlighting that the stars are not "fixed" on the celestial sphere.

As the drawing in Figure 30.2 indicates, in a time interval Δt, the displacement of a star σ on the celestial sphere is represented by the arc of the great circle $\sigma\sigma'$, so that, corresponding to the two positions of the star, the equatorial coordinates of the star are

$$\sigma(\alpha, \delta); \quad \sigma'(\alpha + \Delta\alpha, \delta + \Delta\delta).$$

The total displacement $\sigma\sigma'$ is the result of the composition of the ascending displacement (the arc of the small circle $\sigma\sigma_\alpha$, centered at O′ and with radius $r = D_0 \cos\delta$) with the displacement in declination (the arc of the great circle $\sigma\sigma_\delta$).

Considering that the total displacement of the star is very small, using the drawings in Figures 30.3, 30.4 and 30.5, it follows that

$$L_{\text{arc } \sigma\sigma'} = \sqrt{(L_{\text{arc } \sigma\sigma_\alpha})^2 + (L_{\text{arc } \sigma\sigma_\delta})^2}.$$

In order to compare the displacements of the stars on the celestial sphere, the quantity called the *proper motion* of a star, μ, is defined as a quantity numerically equal to the angle at which the arc of the great circle is seen from the center of the heliocentric celestial sphere,

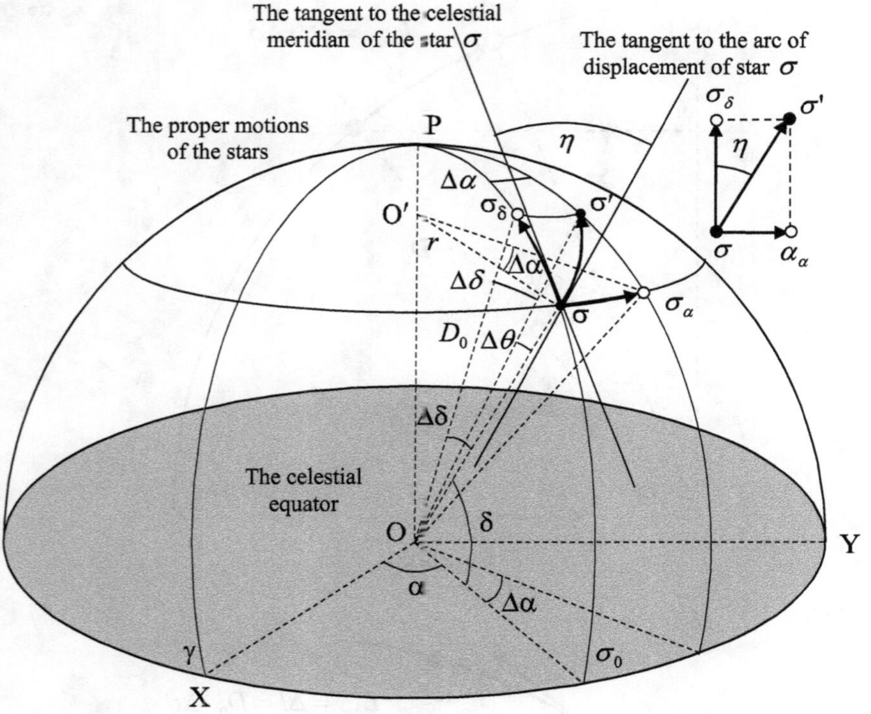

Fig. 30.2

representing the displacement of the star over a year, and having as its unit of measure (seconds of arc)/year. Thus:

$$\mu = \frac{\angle(\sigma \mathrm{O} \sigma')}{\Delta t} = \frac{\Delta\theta}{\Delta t},$$

from which we recognize that "proper motion" has the meaning of an angular velocity;

$$L_{\text{arc } \sigma\sigma'} = D_0 \cdot \angle(\sigma \mathrm{O} \sigma');$$

$$\mu = \frac{\angle(\sigma \mathrm{O} \sigma')}{\Delta t} = \frac{\Delta\theta}{\Delta t} = \frac{L_{\text{arc } \sigma\sigma'}}{D_0 \cdot \Delta t}; \quad L_{\text{arc } \sigma\sigma'} = \mu \cdot D_0 \cdot \Delta t.$$

Corresponding to the rising movement of the star, the *proper upward movement* of the star is defined as

$$\mu_\alpha = \frac{\angle(\sigma \mathrm{O}' \sigma_\alpha)}{\Delta t} = \frac{\Delta\alpha}{\Delta t},$$

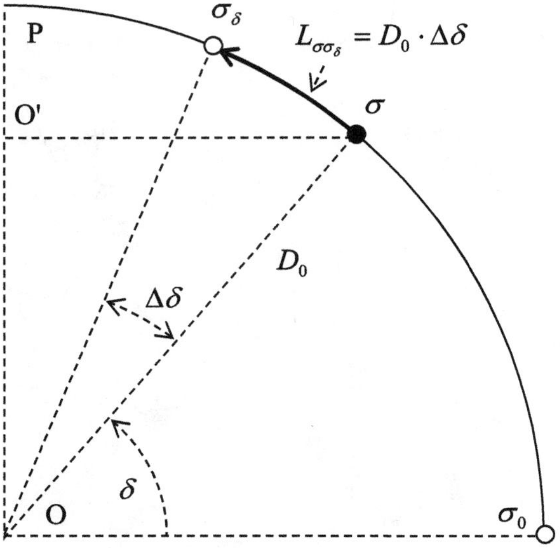

Fig. 30.3

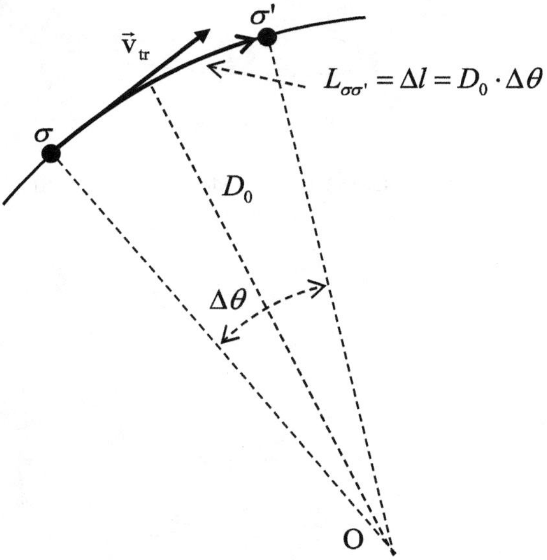

Fig. 30.4

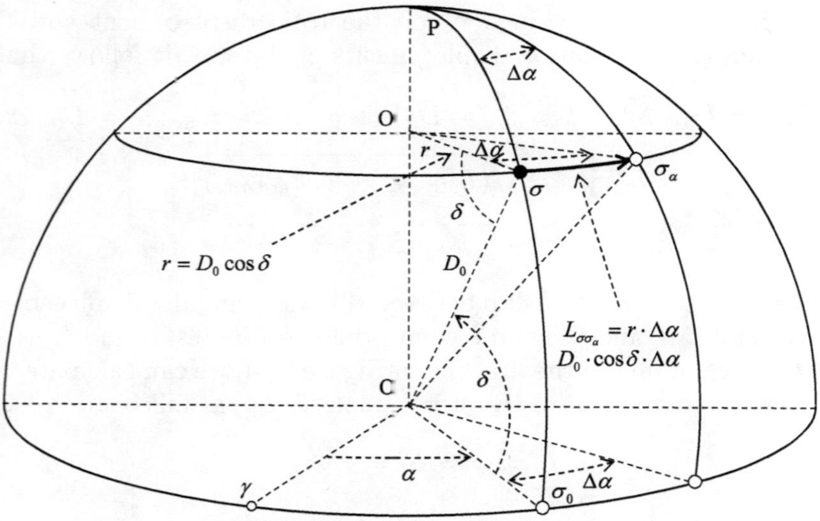

Fig. 30.5

where $\Delta\alpha$ (variation of the right ascension of the star, expressed in seconds of time) must be expressed in seconds of arc, based on the relation

$$1 \text{ s (seconds of time)} = 15'' \text{ (seconds of arc)},$$

so that μ_α is expressed in (seconds of arc)/year;

$$L_{\text{arc } \sigma\sigma_\alpha} = D_0 \cdot \cos\delta \cdot \angle(\sigma \text{O}' \sigma_\alpha);$$

$$\mu_\alpha = \frac{L_{\text{arc } \sigma\sigma_\alpha}}{D_0 \cdot \cos\delta \cdot \Delta t}; \quad L_{\text{arc } \sigma\sigma_\alpha} = \mu_\alpha \cdot D_0 \cdot \cos\delta \cdot \Delta t.$$

Corresponding to the movement in declination of the star, the *proper movement in declination* of the star is defined as

$$\mu_\delta = \frac{\angle(\sigma \text{O} \sigma_\delta)}{\Delta t} = \frac{\Delta\delta}{\Delta t},$$

where $\Delta\delta$ (the variation of the star's declination) is expressed in arcseconds, so that μ_δ can be expressed in (arcseconds)/year:

$$L_{\text{arc } \sigma\sigma_\delta} = D_0 \cdot \angle(\sigma \text{O} \sigma_\delta);$$

$$\mu_\delta = \frac{L_{\text{arc } \sigma\sigma_\delta}}{D_0 \cdot \Delta t}; \quad L_{\text{arc } \sigma\sigma_\delta} = \mu_\delta \cdot D_0 \cdot \Delta t.$$

Using the relationship between the total displacement and the ascension and declination displacements of the star, it follows that:

$$L_{\text{arc }\sigma\sigma'} = D_0 \cdot \Delta\theta; \quad L_{\text{arc }\sigma\sigma_\alpha} = D_0 \cdot \cos\delta \cdot \Delta\alpha; \quad L_{\text{arc }\sigma\sigma_\delta} = D_0 \cdot \Delta\delta;$$

$$L_{\text{arc }\sigma\sigma'} = \sqrt{(L_{\text{arc }\sigma\sigma_\alpha})^2 + (L_{\text{arc }\sigma\sigma_\delta})^2};$$

$$\Delta\theta = \sqrt{(\cos\delta \cdot \Delta\alpha)^2 + (\Delta\delta)^2},$$

representing the relationship between the star's angular displacement in the sky, $\Delta\theta$, and the star's equatorial coordinates, α and δ.

Corresponding to the drawing in Figure 30.4, we can calculate the tangential component of the star's velocity, $\mathrm{v_{tg}}$, as follows:

$$L_{\text{arc }\sigma\sigma'} = \Delta l = \mathrm{v_{tg}} \cdot \Delta t;$$

$$\Delta l = D_0 \cdot \Delta\theta;$$

$$\Delta\theta = \frac{\mathrm{v_{tg}} \cdot \Delta t}{D_0};$$

$$\mu = \frac{\Delta\theta}{\Delta t}; \quad \mu = \frac{\mathrm{v_{tg}}}{D_0},$$

representing the relationship between the proper motion of the star, μ, and the tangential component of the star's velocity;

$$\mathrm{v_{tg}} = \mu \cdot D_0.$$

Thus:

$$L_{\text{arc }\sigma\sigma'} = \mu \cdot D_0 \cdot \Delta t; \quad L_{\text{arc }\sigma\sigma_\alpha} = \mu_\alpha \cdot D_0 \cdot \cos\delta \cdot \Delta t;$$

$$L_{\text{arc }\sigma\sigma_\delta} = \mu_\delta \cdot D_0 \cdot \Delta t;$$

$$L_{\text{arc }\sigma\sigma'} = \sqrt{(L_{\text{arc }\sigma\sigma_\alpha})^2 + (L_{\text{arc }\sigma\sigma_\delta})^2};$$

$$\mu = \sqrt{(\mu_\alpha \cos\delta)^2 + \mu_\delta^2},$$

representing the relationship between the true motion and the true ascension and declination motions of the star, where μ_α, expressed in (seconds of time)/year, and to be expressed in (seconds of arc)/year, represents the proper motion of the rising star, and μ_δ, expressed in (seconds of arc)/year, represents the proper motion of the star in declination.

According to the drawing in Figure 30.6, it follows that:

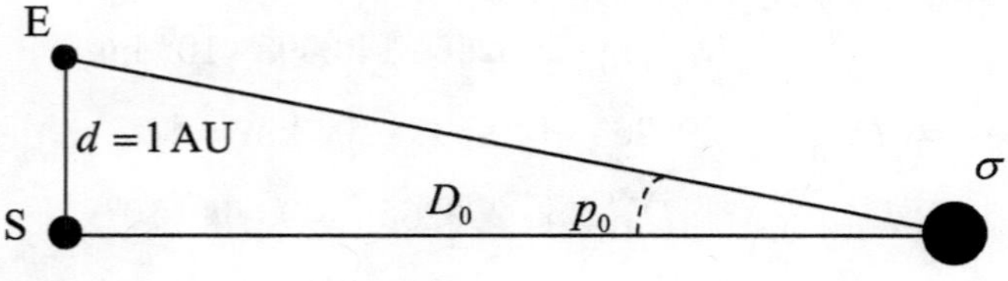

Fig. 30.6

$$\tan p_0 = \frac{d}{D_0} \approx p_{\rm rad} = \frac{d_{\rm (pc)}}{D_{0\,\rm (pc)}};$$

$$1 \text{ rad} = 206265 \text{ arcsec} = 206265'';$$

$$1 \text{ pc} = 206265 \text{ AU};$$

$$D_{0\,\rm (pc)} = \frac{d_{\rm (pc)}}{p_{0\,\rm (rad)}} = \frac{\frac{d_{\rm (AU)}}{206265}}{p_{0('')} \cdot \frac{1}{\frac{180}{3,14} \cdot 60 \cdot 60}} = \frac{\frac{d_{\rm (AU)}}{206265}}{p_{0('')} \cdot \frac{1}{206265}} = \frac{d_{\rm (AU)}}{p_{0('')}};$$

$$|D_{0\,\rm (pc)}| = \frac{|d_{\rm (AU)}|}{|p_{0\,('')}|}; \quad d = 1 \text{ AU}; \quad |d_{\rm (AU)}| = 1;$$

$$|D_{0\,\rm (pc)}| = \frac{1}{|p_{0('')}|}; \quad |p_{0('')}| = \frac{1}{|D_{0\,\rm (pc)}|};$$

$$v_{\rm tg\,(km/s)} = \mu_{\rm (rad/s)} \cdot D_{0\,\rm (km)} = |\mu_{\rm (rad/s)}| \cdot \frac{1}{s} \cdot |D_{0\,\rm (km)}| \cdot \text{km};$$

$$v_{\rm tg\,(km/s)} = |\mu_{\rm (rad/s)}| \cdot |D_{0\,\rm (km)}| \cdot \frac{\text{km}}{\text{s}};$$

$$\mu_{\rm (rad/s)} = |\mu_{\rm (rad/s)}| \cdot \frac{\text{rad}}{\text{s}} = |\mu_{\rm (rad/s)}| \cdot \frac{206265 \text{ arcsec}}{\frac{1 \text{ year}}{31.536 \cdot 10^6}};$$

$$\mu_{\rm (rad/s)} = |\mu_{\rm (rad/s)}| \cdot 206265 \cdot 31.05 \cdot 10^6 \frac{\text{arcsec}}{\text{year}}$$

$$= |\mu_{\rm (arcsec/year)}| \cdot \frac{\text{arcsec}}{\text{year}};$$

$$|\mu_{\rm (arcsec/year)}| = |\mu_{\rm (rad/s)}| \cdot 206265 \cdot 31.536 \cdot 10^6;$$

$$\left|\mu_{(\mathrm{rad/s})}\right| = \frac{\left|\mu_{(\mathrm{arcsec/year})}\right|}{206265 \cdot 31.536 \cdot 10^6};$$

$$D_{0\,(\mathrm{pc})} = \left|D_{0\,(\mathrm{pc})}\right| \cdot \mathrm{pc} = \left|D_{0\,(\mathrm{pc})}\right| \cdot 206265\ \mathrm{AU}$$

$$= \left|D_{0\,(\mathrm{pc})}\right| \cdot 206265 \cdot 149.598 \cdot 10^6\ \mathrm{km};$$

$$D_{0\,(\mathrm{pc})} = \left|D_{0\,(\mathrm{pc})}\right| \cdot 206265 \cdot 149.598 \cdot 10^6\ \mathrm{km} = \left|D_{0\,(\mathrm{km})}\right| \cdot \mathrm{km};$$

$$\left|D_{0\,(\mathrm{km})}\right| = \left|D_{0\,(\mathrm{pc})}\right| \cdot 206265 \cdot 149.598 \cdot 10^6;$$

$$\left|D_{0\,(\mathrm{pc})}\right| = \frac{\left|D_{0\,(\mathrm{km})}\right|}{206265 \cdot 149.598 \cdot 10^6};$$

$$\mathrm{v}_{\mathrm{tg}\,(\mathrm{km/s})} = \left|\mu_{(\mathrm{rad/s})}\right| \cdot \left|D_{0\,(\mathrm{km})}\right| \cdot \frac{\mathrm{km}}{\mathrm{s}};$$

$$\mathrm{v}_{\mathrm{tg}\,(\mathrm{km/s})} = \frac{\left|\mu_{(\mathrm{arcsec/year})}\right|}{206265 \cdot 31.536 \cdot 10^6} \cdot \left|D_{0\,(\mathrm{pc})}\right|$$

$$\cdot 206265 \cdot 149.598 \cdot 10^6\ \frac{\mathrm{km}}{\mathrm{s}};$$

$$\mathrm{v}_{\mathrm{tg}\,(\mathrm{km/s})} = \frac{\left|\mu_{(\mathrm{arcsec/year})}\right|}{31.536} \cdot \left|D_{0\,(\mathrm{pc})}\right| \cdot 149.598\ \frac{\mathrm{km}}{\mathrm{s}};$$

$$\mathrm{v}_{\mathrm{tg}\,(\mathrm{km/s})} = 4.74 \cdot \left|\mu_{(\mathrm{arcsec/an})}\right| \cdot \left|D_{0\,(\mathrm{pc})}\right|\ \frac{\mathrm{km}}{\mathrm{s}},$$

representing the tangential component of star σ's velocity expressed in km/s, where $\left|\mu_{(\mathrm{arcsec/year})}\right|$ is its numerical value μ, expressed in arcsec/year, and $\left|D_{0\,(\mathrm{pc})}\right|$ is the numerical value of D_0, expressed in parsecs.

For the radial component, $\mathrm{v}_{\mathrm{rad}}$, of star σ's velocity in accordance with the Doppler effect, it follows that:

$$\frac{\Delta\lambda}{\lambda_0} = \frac{\mathrm{v}_{\mathrm{rad}}}{c}; \quad \mathrm{v}_{\mathrm{rad}} = c\frac{\Delta\lambda}{\lambda_0} = c\frac{\lambda - \lambda_0}{\lambda_0}.$$

Thus, the spatial velocity, v, of the star σ is

$$\mathrm{v} = \sqrt{\mathrm{v}_{\mathrm{tg}}^2 + \mathrm{v}_{\mathrm{rad}}^2}.$$

According to the drawing represented in Figure 30.7, given the fact that the movement of the star Altair, in relation to the Sun, is

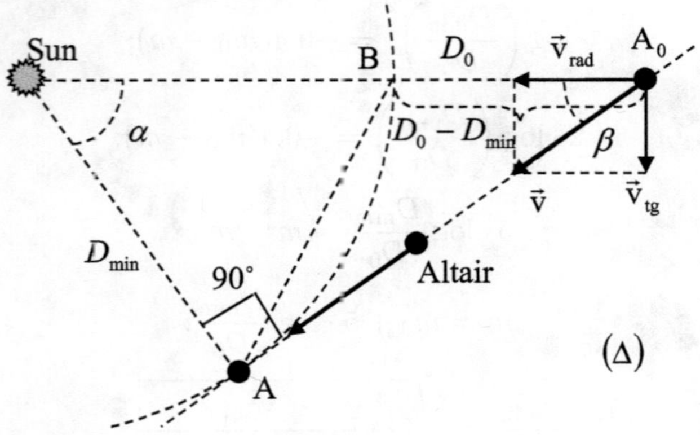

Fig. 30.7

rectilinear and uniform, it follows that:

$$D_0 - D_{\min} = v_{\rm rad}\tau;$$

$$v_{\rm rad} = v \cdot \cos\beta; \quad \cos\beta = \frac{v_{\rm rad}}{v};$$

$$\alpha + \beta = 90^\circ; \quad \alpha = 90^\circ - \beta;$$

$$\cos\alpha = \cos(90^\circ - \beta) = \sin\beta;$$

$$\cos\alpha = \frac{D_{\min}}{D_0} = \sin\beta = \sqrt{1 - \cos^2\beta} = \sqrt{1 - \frac{v_{\rm rad}^2}{v^2}};$$

$$v_{\rm tg} = \mu \cdot D_0;$$

$$v^2 = v_{\rm rad}^2 + v_{\rm tg}^2 = v_{\rm rad}^2 + (\mu \cdot D_0)^2;$$

$$\frac{D_{\min}}{D_0} = \sqrt{1 - \frac{v_{\rm rad}^2}{v^2}};$$

$$\frac{D_{\min}}{D_0} = \sqrt{1 - \frac{v_{\rm rad}^2}{v_{\rm rad}^2 + (\mu \cdot D_0)^2}}.$$

According to Pogson's formula, it follows that:

$$\log\frac{E_0}{E} = -0.4(m_0 - m);$$

$$E_0 = \frac{L}{4\pi D_0^2}; \quad E = \frac{L}{4\pi D_{\min}^2}; \quad \frac{E_0}{E} = \frac{D_{\min}^2}{D_0^2};$$

$$\log\left(\frac{D_{\text{min}}}{D_0}\right)^2 = -0.4(m_0 - m);$$

$$2 \cdot \log\left(\frac{D_{\text{min}}}{D_0}\right) = -0.4(m_0 - m);$$

$$5 \cdot \log\frac{D_{\text{min}}}{D_0} = m - m_0;$$

$$m = m_0 + 5 \cdot \log\frac{D_{\text{min}}}{D_0};$$

$$\frac{D_{\text{min}}}{D_0} = \sqrt{1 - \frac{\text{v}_{\text{rad}}^2}{\text{v}_{\text{rad}}^2 + (\mu \cdot D_0)^2}};$$

$$m = m_0 + 5 \cdot \log\left(\sqrt{1 - \frac{\text{v}_{\text{rad}}^2}{\text{v}_{\text{rad}}^2 + (\mu \cdot D_0)^2}}\right);$$

$$m = m_0 + 5 \cdot \log\left(\sqrt{\frac{\text{v}_{\text{rad}}^2 + (\mu D_0)^2 - \text{v}_{\text{rad}}^2}{\text{v}_{\text{rad}}^2 + (\mu \cdot D_0)^2}}\right);$$

$$m = m_0 + 5 \cdot \log\left(\sqrt{\frac{(\mu D_0)^2}{\text{v}_{\text{rad}}^2 + (\mu \cdot D_0)^2}}\right);$$

$$m = m_0 + 5 \cdot \log\frac{\mu \cdot D_0}{\sqrt{\text{v}_{\text{rad}}^2 + (\mu \cdot D_0)^2}};$$

$$\tan p_0 = \frac{d}{D_0} \approx p_0; \quad D_0 = \frac{d}{p_0};$$

$$m = m_0 + 5 \cdot \log\frac{\frac{\mu \cdot d}{p_0}}{\sqrt{\text{v}_{\text{rad}}^2 + \left(\frac{\mu \cdot d}{p_0}\right)^2}};$$

$$p_0 = 0.198'' = 0.198 \cdot \frac{3,14}{180 \cdot 60 \cdot 60}\ \text{rad} \approx 10^{-6}\ \text{rad};$$

$$\mu = 0.658''/\text{year} = 0,658 \cdot \frac{3.14}{180 \cdot 60 \cdot 60} \cdot \frac{\text{rad}}{365 \cdot 24 \cdot 3600\ \text{s}}$$

$$\approx 10^{-13}\frac{\text{rad}}{\text{s}};$$

$$\mathrm{v_{tg}} = \mu \cdot D_0; \quad D_0 = \frac{d}{p_0}; \quad \frac{\mu \cdot d}{p_0} = 15\ \frac{\mathrm{km}}{\mathrm{s}} = \mathrm{v_{tg}};$$

$$d = 1\ \mathrm{UA} \approx 150000000\ \mathrm{km};$$

$$\mathrm{v_{rad}} = -26\ \frac{\mathrm{km}}{\mathrm{s}};$$

$$\log \frac{\frac{\mu \cdot d}{p_0}}{\sqrt{\mathrm{v_{rad}^2} + \left(\frac{\mu \cdot d}{p_0}\right)^2}} = \log \frac{15 \frac{\mathrm{km}}{\mathrm{s}}}{\sqrt{\left(-26\ \frac{\mathrm{km}}{\mathrm{s}}\right)^2 + \left(15\ \frac{\mathrm{km}}{\mathrm{s}}\right)^2}}$$

$$= \log \frac{15}{\sqrt{676 + 225}} \approx -0.3;$$

$$m = m_0 + 5^{\mathrm{m}} \cdot (0.3) = 0.89^{\mathrm{m}} - 1.5^{\mathrm{m}} = -0.61^{\mathrm{m}};$$

$$\frac{D_{\min}}{D_0} = \sqrt{1 - \frac{\mathrm{v_{rad}^2}}{\mathrm{v_{rad}^2} + (\mu \cdot D_0)^2}};$$

$$D_0 = \frac{d}{p_0} = \frac{15 \cdot 10^7\ \mathrm{km}}{10^{-6}} = 15 \cdot 10^{13}\ \mathrm{km};$$

$$\frac{D_{\min}}{D_0} = \sqrt{1 - \frac{\mathrm{v_{rad}^2}}{\mathrm{v_{rad}^2} + (\mu \cdot D_0)^2}}; \quad \frac{D_{\min}}{D_0} = \sqrt{1 - \frac{\mathrm{v_{rad}^2}}{\mathrm{v_{rad}^2} + \mathrm{v_{tg}^2}}};$$

$$\frac{D_{\min}}{D_0} = \sqrt{\frac{\mathrm{v_{rad}^2} + \mathrm{v_{tg}^2} - \mathrm{v_{rad}^2}}{\mathrm{v_{rad}^2} + \mathrm{v_{tg}^2}}};$$

$$\frac{D_{\min}}{D_0} = \sqrt{\frac{\mathrm{v_{tg}^2}}{\mathrm{v_{rad}^2} + \mathrm{v_{tg}^2}}}; \quad D_0 = 15 \cdot 10^{13}\ \mathrm{km}; \quad \mathrm{v_{tg}} = 15\ \frac{\mathrm{km}}{\mathrm{s}};$$

$$\mathrm{v_{rad}} = -26 \frac{\mathrm{km}}{\mathrm{s}};$$

$$D_{\min} = D_0 \cdot \frac{\mathrm{v_{tg}}}{\sqrt{\mathrm{v_{rad}^2} + \mathrm{v_{tg}^2}}} = 15 \cdot 10^{13}\ \mathrm{km} \cdot \frac{1}{2} = 7.5 \cdot 10^{13}\ \mathrm{km};$$

$$D_0 - D_{\min} = \mathrm{v_{rad}} \tau;$$

$$\tau = \frac{D_0 - D_{\min}}{\mathrm{v_{rad}}} \approx 3 \cdot 10^{12}\ \mathrm{s} \approx 95130\ \mathrm{years}.$$

Problem 31

The Radii of Curvature of the Moon's Trajectory

Relative to the center of the Earth, the trajectory of the center of the Moon is a circle of radius $r_{\mathrm{M}} = 2.57 \cdot 10^{-3}$ AU. Relative to the center of the Sun, the trajectory of the center of the Earth is a circle of radius $r_{\mathrm{E}} = 1$ AU. As a result, the trajectory of the center of the Moon, relative to the center of the Sun, considered fixed, is much more complicated.

Determine the radii of curvature of the trajectory of the center of the Moon, in the positions indicated by the drawing in Figure 31.1, corresponding to the phases:

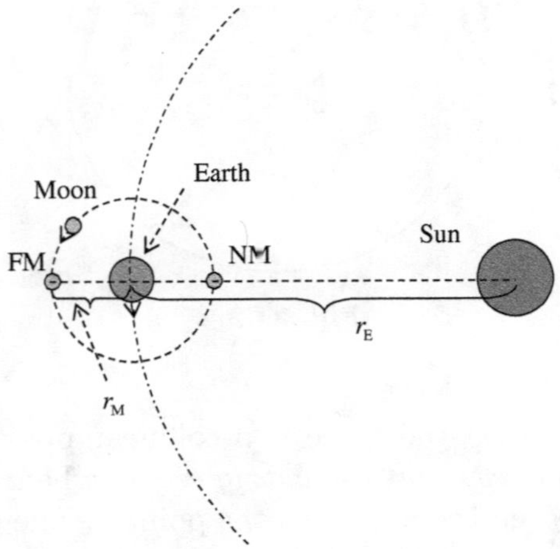

Fig. 31.1

a) Full Moon;
b) New Moon.

Locate the centers of curvature of the trajectory of the center of the Moon in the two cases, in relation to the center of the Sun. The mass ratio $M_E/M_S = 3 \cdot 10^{-6}$ is known.

It is known that every infinitesimal, but not circular, sector of a plane trajectory centered around a point of this sector belongs to a circle, called a *circle of curvature*, whose center is called the *center of curvature* and whose radius is called the *radius of curvature.*

Solution

It is known that through any three coplanar, non-collinear points, a circle can be constructed. As a result, three neighboring points, P_1, P and P_2, which are non-collinear on some plane curve, as indicated by the drawing in Figure 31.2, define a circle and a plane containing this circle.

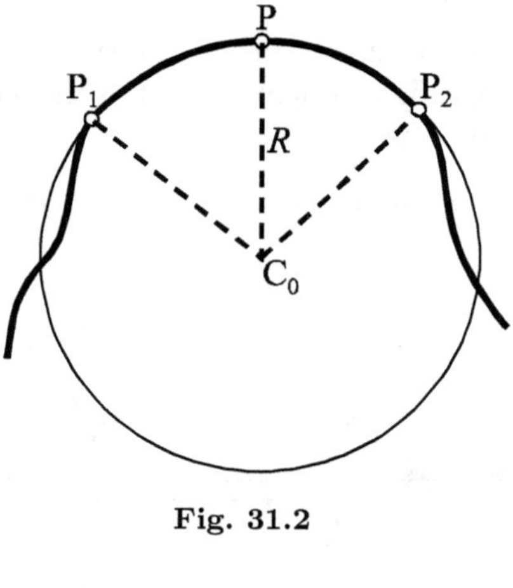

Fig. 31.2

The circle built on the three non-collinear points (P_1, P, P_2) is called a *circle of curvature (osculating circle)* when, at the limit, the points P_1 and P_2 tend to approach the point P. The plane containing the osculating circle is called the *osculating plane.*

The center of the oscillating circle (C_0) and the radius of the oscillating circle (R) represent the center of curvature of the trajectory and the radius of curvature of the trajectory, corresponding to point P.

The *curvature of the trajectory*, at the current point P, is the quantity

$$C = \frac{1}{R}.$$

To establish the geometric significance of the curvature of a trajectory, let's consider the points P and P′, neighbors on the flat curved trajectory represented in the drawing in Figure 31.3, where we also constructed the vertices $\vec{\tau}$ and $\vec{\tau}'$ and tangents to the trajectory at the two points, as well as the perpendiculars to the two tangents that intersect at point C_0.

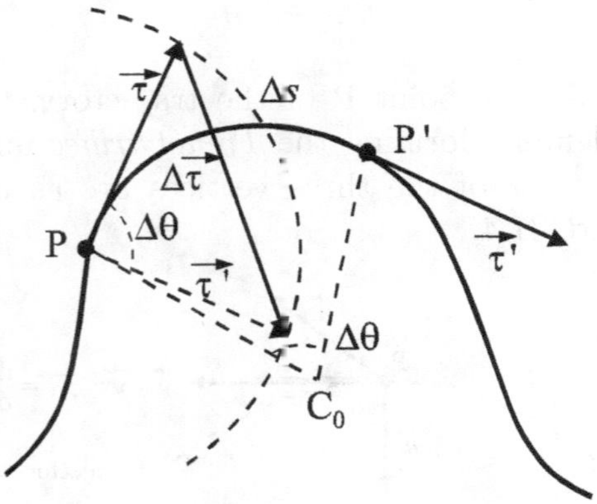

Fig. 31.3

At the limit, when $P' \to P$, the directions of the vertices $\vec{\tau}$ and $\vec{\tau}'$ define the osculating plane of the trajectory at point P, and the arc of the curve Δs approximates an arc of a circle (osculating circle), with radius $PC_0 = R$ and center at C_0.

The curvature of the trajectory at point P is the magnitude:

$$C = \lim_{\Delta s \to 0} \frac{\Delta \theta}{\Delta s} = \frac{\mathrm{d}\theta}{\mathrm{d}s}; \quad \langle C \rangle_{\mathrm{IS}} = \frac{\mathrm{rad}}{\mathrm{m}}.$$

The curvature of the trajectory at point P measures the degree of deviation of the trajectory from the tangent to the trajectory at point P.

The curvature of the trajectory is the ratio between the angle formed by two tangents to neighboring points and the length of the arc between the two points.

The curvature of the trajectory is the angle by which the tangent to the trajectory rotates when we move along the trajectory by one unit of length.

The normal direction to the tangent to the trajectory at point P, contained in the osculating plane, is called the *main normal* and has the direction $\vec{n} \perp \vec{\tau}$, oriented towards the center of curvature of the trajectory.

The normal direction to the trajectory plane at point P (perpendicular to the osculating plane) is called the *binormal* and has the direction $\vec{b}$, whose orientation is such that

$$\vec{b} = \vec{\tau} \times \vec{n}.$$

As a result, at any point P of the trajectory, three orthogonal directions are defined, forming the *Frenet trihedron*, in such a way that the orientations of the three vertices are as indicated by the drawing in Figure 31.4.

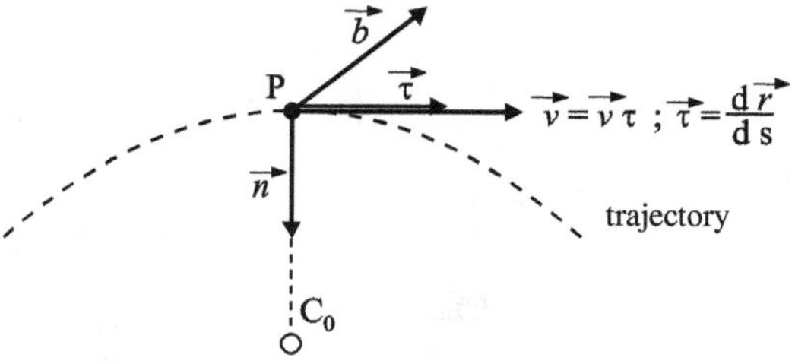

Fig. 31.4

Relative to the Frenet trihedral, the instantaneous velocity vector has a single component, along $\vec{\tau}$.

Every infinitesimal sector of a plane trajectory, other than a circle, centered around a point of this sector belongs to a circle, called a circle of curvature, whose center is called the *center of curvature* and whose radius is called the *radius of curvature*.

The forces acting on the Moon from the Earth and from the Sun in each of the proposed cases, as well as the velocities of the system elements in relation to the Sun, considered fixed, are those represented in the drawing in Figure 31.5.

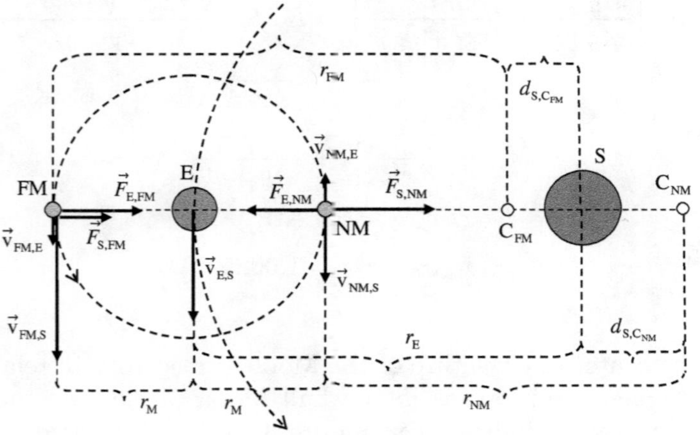

Fig. 31.5

a) For the Full Moon, we use the following notation: $\vec{v}_{FM,E}$ – the speed of the Full Moon in relation to the Earth; $\vec{v}_{FM,S}$ – the speed of the Full Moon in relation to the Sun; $\vec{v}_{E,S}$ – the speed of the Earth relative to the Sun.

The results are:

$$F_{E,FM} + F_{S,FM} = \frac{M_M v_{FM,S}^2}{r_{FM}};$$

$$K\frac{M_M M_E}{r_M^2} + K\frac{M_M M_S}{(r_M + r_E)^2} = \frac{M_M v_{FM,S}^2}{r_{FM}};$$

$$\vec{v}_{FM,S} = \vec{v}_{FM,E} + \vec{v}_{E,S}; \quad v_{FM,S} = v_{FM,E} + v_{E,S};$$

$$K\frac{M_E}{r_M^2} + K\frac{M_S}{(r_M + r_E)^2} = \frac{(v_{FM,E} + v_{E,S})^2}{r_{FM}};$$

$$v_{FM,E} = \sqrt{K\frac{M_E}{r_M}}; \quad v_{E,S} = \sqrt{K\frac{M_S}{r_E}};$$

$$K\frac{M_E}{r_M^2} + K\frac{M_S}{(r_M + r_E)^2} = \frac{\left(\sqrt{K\frac{M_E}{r_M}} + \sqrt{K\frac{M_S}{r_E}}\right)^2}{r_{FM}};$$

$$KM_S\left[\frac{M_E}{M_S}\frac{1}{r_M^2} + \frac{1}{(r_M + r_E)^2}\right] = KM_S\frac{\left(\sqrt{\frac{1}{r_E}} + \sqrt{\frac{M_E}{M_S}\frac{1}{r_M}}\right)^2}{r_{FM}};$$

$$r_{FM} = \frac{\left(\sqrt{\frac{1}{r_E}} + \sqrt{\frac{M_E}{M_S}\frac{1}{r_M}}\right)^2}{\frac{M_E}{M_S}\frac{1}{r_M^2} + \frac{1}{(r_M+r_E)^2}};$$

$$r_{ME} \approx 0.7\ \text{AU};$$

$$d_{S,FM} = r_E + r_M = 1.00257\ \text{AU};$$

$$r_{FM} < d_{S,FM}.$$

Thus, the center of curvature of the Moon's trajectory in relation to the Sun when the Moon is in the Full Moon phase, i.e., the point C_{FM}, is located as indicated in Figure 31.5. In relation to the Sun, it is at the distance

$$d_{S,C_{FM}} = (r_E + r_M) - r_{FM}$$
$$= 1\ \text{AU} + 0.00257\ \text{AU} - 0.7\ \text{AU} = 0.30257\ \text{AU}.$$

b) For the New Moon, we use the following notation: $\vec{v}_{NM,E}$ – the speed of the New Moon in relation to the Earth; $\vec{v}_{NM,S}$ – the speed of the New Moon in relation to the Sun.

The results are:

$$F_{S,FM} - F_{E,NM} = \frac{M_M v_{NM,S}^2}{r_{NM}};$$

$$K\frac{M_M M_S}{(r_E - r_M)^2} - K\frac{M_M M_E}{r_M^2} = \frac{M_M v_{NM,S}^2}{r_{NM}};$$

$$\vec{v}_{NM,S} = \vec{v}_{NM,E} + \vec{v}_{E,S}; \quad v_{NM,S} = v_{E,S} - v_{NM,E};$$

$$K\frac{M_S}{(r_E - r_M)^2} - K\frac{M_E}{r_M^2} = \frac{(v_{E,S} - v_{NM,E})^2}{r_{NM}};$$

$$v_{NM,E} = \sqrt{K\frac{M_E}{r_M}}; \quad v_{E,S} = \sqrt{K\frac{M_S}{r_E}};$$

$$K\frac{M_S}{(r_E - r_M)^2} - K\frac{M_E}{r_M^2} = \frac{\left(\sqrt{K\frac{M_S}{r_E}} - \sqrt{K\frac{M_E}{r_M}}\right)^2}{r_{NM}};$$

$$KM_S\left[\frac{1}{(r_E - r_M)^2} - \frac{M_E}{M_S}\frac{1}{r_M^2}\right] = KM_S\frac{\left(\sqrt{\frac{1}{r_E}} - \sqrt{\frac{M_E}{M_S}\frac{1}{r_M}}\right)^2}{r_{NM}};$$

$$r_{NM} = \frac{\left(\sqrt{\frac{1}{r_E}} - \sqrt{\frac{M_E}{M_S}\frac{1}{r_M}}\right)^2}{\frac{1}{(r_E - r_M)^2} - \frac{M_E}{M_S}\frac{1}{r_M^2}};$$

$$r_{NM} \approx 1.8\ \text{AU};$$

$$d_{S,NM} = r_E - r_M = 0.99743\ \text{AU};$$

$$r_{NM} > d_{S,NM}.$$

Thus, the center of curvature of the Moon's trajectory in relation to the Sun when the Moon is in the New Moon phase, i.e., the point C_{NM}, is located as indicated in Figure 31.5. In relation to the Sun, it is at the distance

$$d_{S,C_{NM}} = r_{NM} - (r_E - r_M) = 1.8\ \text{AU} - 0.99743\ \text{AU} = 0.80257\ \text{AU}.$$

Conclusion: The two centers of curvature are located on either side of the Sun, arranged asymmetrically.

Problem 32

Magnitudes of Stellar Systems

a) The absolute magnitudes of the components σ_1 and σ_2 belonging to a visual double star system are M_1 and M_2.
Determine the absolute magnitude, M_{ds}, of the visual binary star system.

b) The absolute magnitude of a triple star system is M_{ts}, and the absolute magnitudes of the components σ_1 and σ_2 of the visual triple star system are M_1 and M_2.
Determine the absolute magnitude, M_3, of the component σ_3 of the visual triple star system.

Solution

a) If L_S is the luminosity of the Sun, and the luminosity of the binary star system is

$$L_{\mathrm{ds}} = L_1 + L_2,$$

then, according to Pogson's formula, it follows that:

$$\log \frac{L_{\mathrm{ds}}}{L_{\mathrm{Sun}}} = -0.4(M_{\mathrm{ds}} - M_{\mathrm{Sun}}) = \log_{10} \frac{L_{\mathrm{ds}}}{L_{\mathrm{Sun}}};$$

$$\frac{L_{\mathrm{ds}}}{L_{\mathrm{Sun}}} = 10^{-0.4(M_{\mathrm{ds}} - M_{\mathrm{Sun}})};$$

$$\frac{L_1 + L_2}{L_{\mathrm{Sun}}} = 10^{-0.4(M_{\mathrm{ds}} - M_{\mathrm{Sun}})};$$

$$\frac{L_1}{L_{\text{Sun}}} + \frac{L_2}{L_{\text{Sun}}} = 10^{-0.4(M_{\text{ds}} - M_{\text{Sun}})};$$

$$\log \frac{L_1}{L_{\text{S}}} = -0.4(M_1 - M_{\text{S}}); \quad \frac{L_1}{L_{\text{S}}} = 10^{-0.4(M_1 - M_{\text{S}})};$$

$$\log \frac{L_2}{L_{\text{S}}} = -0.4(M_2 - M_{\text{S}}); \quad \frac{L_2}{L_{\text{S}}} = 10^{-0.4(M_2 - M_{\text{S}})};$$

$$10^{-0.4(M_1 - M_{\text{S}})} + 10^{-0.4(M_2 - M_{\text{S}})} = 10^{-0.4(M_{\text{ds}} - M_{\text{S}})};$$

$$\log 10^{-0.4(M_{\text{ds}} - M_{\text{S}})} = \log[10^{-0.4(M_1 - M_{\text{S}})} + 10^{-0.4(M_2 - M_{\text{S}})}];$$

$$-0.4(M_{\text{ds}} - M_{\text{S}}) = \log[10^{-0.4(M_1 - M_{\text{S}})} + 10^{-0.4(M_2 - M_{\text{S}})}];$$

$$M_{\text{ds}} - M_{\text{S}} = -2.5 \cdot \log[10^{-0.4(M_1 - M_{\text{S}})} + 10^{-0.4(M_2 - M_{\text{S}})}];$$

$$M_{\text{ds}} = M_{\text{S}} - 2.5 \cdot \log[10^{-0.4(M_1 - M_{\text{S}})} + 10^{-0.4(M_2 - M_{\text{S}})}];$$

$$M_{\text{ds}} = M_{\text{S}} - 2.5 \cdot \log[10^{-0.4 \cdot M_1} \cdot 10^{0.4 \cdot M_{\text{S}}} + 10^{-0.4 \cdot M_2} \cdot 10^{0.4 \cdot M_{\text{S}}}];$$

$$M_{\text{ds}} = M_{\text{S}} - 2.5 \cdot \log[10^{0.4 \cdot M_{\text{S}}}(10^{-0.4 \cdot M_1} + 10^{-0.4 \cdot M_2})];$$

$$M_{\text{ds}} = M_{\text{S}} - 2.5 \cdot \log 10^{0.4 \cdot M_{\text{S}}} - 2.5 \cdot \log[(10^{-0.4 \cdot M_1} + 10^{-0.4 \cdot M_2})];$$

$$M_{\text{ds}} = M_{\text{S}} - 2.5 \cdot 0.4 \cdot M_{\text{S}} - 2.5 \cdot \log[(10^{-0.4 \cdot M_1} + 10^{-0.4 \cdot M_2})];$$

$$M_{\text{ds}} = -2.5 \cdot \log(10^{-0.4 \cdot M_1} + 10^{-0.4 \cdot M_2}).$$

b) If L_{S} is the luminosity of the Sun, and the luminosity of the triple star system is

$$L_{\text{ts}} = L_1 + L_2 + L_3,$$

then, according to Pogson's formula, it follows that:

$$\log \frac{L_{\text{ts}}}{L_{\text{S}}} = -0.4(M_{\text{ts}} - M_{\text{S}}) = \log_{10} \frac{L_{\text{ts}}}{L_{\text{S}}};$$

$$\frac{L_{\text{ts}}}{L_{\text{S}}} = 10^{-0.4(M_{\text{ts}} - M_{\text{S}})};$$

$$\frac{L_1 + L_2 + L_3}{L_{\text{S}}} = 10^{-0.4(M_{\text{ts}} - M_{\text{S}})};$$

$$\frac{L_1}{L_{\text{S}}} + \frac{L_2}{L_{\text{S}}} + \frac{L_3}{L_{\text{S}}} = 10^{-0.4(M_{\text{ts}} - M_{\text{S}})};$$

$$\log \frac{L_1}{L_S} = -0.4(M_1 - M_S); \quad \frac{L_1}{L_S} = 10^{-0.4(M_1 - M_S)};$$

$$\log \frac{L_2}{L_S} = -0.4(M_2 - M_S); \quad \frac{L_2}{L_S} = 10^{-0.4(M_2 - M_S)};$$

$$\log \frac{L_3}{L_S} = -0.4(M_3 - M_S); \quad \frac{L_3}{L_S} = 10^{-0.4(M_3 - M_S)};$$

$$10^{-0.4(M_1 - M_S)} + 10^{-0.4(M_2 - M_S)} + 10^{-0.4(M_3 - M_S)} = 10^{-0.4(M_{st} - M_S)};$$

$$10^{-0.4(M_3 - M_S)} = 10^{-0.4(M_{st} - M_S)} - 10^{-0.4(M_1 - M_S)} - 10^{-0.4(M_2 - M_S)};$$

$$\log 10^{-0.4(M_3 - M_S)} = \log[10^{-0.4(M_{ts} - M_S)} - 10^{-0.4(M_1 - M_S)} - 10^{-0.4(M_2 - M_S)}];$$

$$-0.4(M_3 - M_S) = \log[10^{-0.4(M_{ts} - M_S)} - 10^{-0.4(M_1 - M_S)} - 10^{-0.4(M_2 - M_S)}];$$

$$M_3 - M_S = -2.5 \cdot \log[10^{-0.4(M_{ts} - M_S)} - 10^{-0.4(M_1 - M_S)} - 10^{-0.4(M_2 - M_S)}];$$

$$M_3 = M_S - 2.5 \cdot \log[10^{-0.4(M_{ts} - M_S)} - 10^{-0.4(M_1 - M_S)} - 10^{-0.4(M_2 - M_S)}];$$

$$M_3 = M_S - 2.5 \cdot \log[10^{-0.4 \cdot M_{ts}} \cdot 10^{0.4 \cdot M_S} - 10^{-0.4 \cdot M_1} \cdot 10^{0.4 \cdot M_S} - 10^{-0.4 \cdot M_2} \cdot 10^{0.4 \cdot M_S}];$$

$$M_3 = M_S - 2.5 \cdot \log[10^{0.4 \cdot M_S}(10^{-0.4 \cdot M_{ts}} - 10^{-0.4 \cdot M_1} - 10^{-0.4 \cdot M_2})];$$

$$M_3 = M_S - 2.5 \cdot \log 10^{0.4 \cdot M_S} - 2.5 \cdot \log[(10^{-0.4 \cdot M_{ts}} - 10^{-0.4 \cdot M_1} - 10^{-0.4 \cdot M_2})];$$

$$M_3 = M_S - 2.5 \cdot 0.4 \cdot M_S - 2.5 \cdot \log(10^{-0.4 \cdot M_{ts}} - 10^{-0.4 \cdot M_1} - 10^{-0.4 \cdot M_2});$$

$$M_3 = -2.5 \cdot \log(10^{-0.4 \cdot M_{ts}} - 10^{-0.4 \cdot M_1} - 10^{-0.4 \cdot M_2}).$$

Problem 33

Visible Star?

The parallax of the Sun is $p_{\text{Sun}} = 8.8''$, and the parallax of a star, σ, which has the same absolute brightness (luminosity) as the Sun, is $p_{\text{star}} = 0.022''$.

Specify whether the star in question can be observed with the naked eye in the night sky. The following are known: the distance between the Earth and the Sun, $r_{\text{ES}} = 149000000$ km, and the radius of the Earth, $R_{\text{E}} = 6380$ km.

Solution

According to Pogson's formula, it follows that:

$$\log \frac{E_{\text{Sun}}}{E_{\text{star}}} = -0.4(m_{\text{Sun}} - m_{\text{star}});$$

$$E_{\text{Sun}} = \frac{L_{\text{Sun}}}{4\pi \cdot r^2_{\text{Earth, Sun}}} = \frac{L_{\text{Sun}}}{4\pi \cdot r^2_{\text{ES}}}; \quad E_{\text{star}} = \frac{L_{\text{star}}}{4\pi \cdot r^2_{\text{Sun,star}}} = \frac{L_{\text{Sun}}}{4\pi \cdot r^2_{\text{S},\sigma}};$$

$$\frac{E_{\text{Sun}}}{E_{\text{star}}} = \frac{r^2_{\text{S},\sigma}}{r^2_{\text{ES}}} = \left(\frac{r_{\text{S},\sigma}}{r_{\text{ES}}}\right)^2.$$

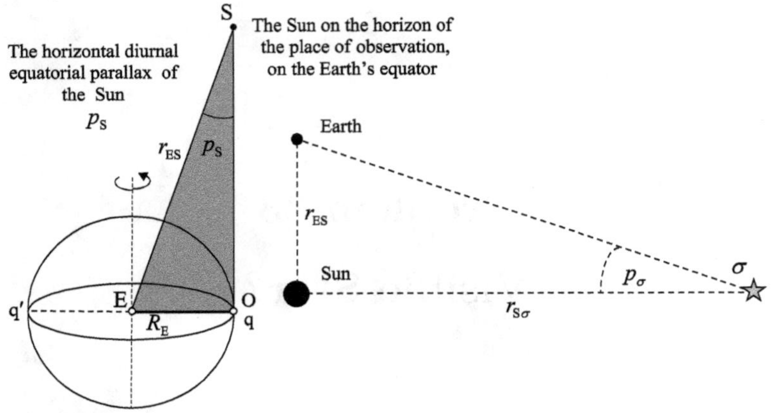

Fig. 33.1

According to the notation in Figure 33.1, knowing the definition of the parallax of a star, it follows that:

$$\sin p_S \approx p_S = \frac{R_E}{r_{ES}}; \quad r_{ES} = \frac{R_E}{p_S};$$

$$\sin p_\sigma \approx p_\sigma = \frac{r_{ES}}{r_{S\sigma}}; \quad r_{S\sigma} = \frac{r_{ES}}{p_\sigma};$$

$$\frac{E_{Sun}}{E_{star}} = \left(\frac{\frac{r_{ES}}{p_\sigma}}{\frac{R_E}{p_S}}\right)^2 = \left(\frac{r_{ES}}{R_E} \cdot \frac{p_S}{p_\sigma}\right)^2;$$

$$\log \frac{E_{Sun}}{E_{star}} = \log \left(\frac{r_{ES}}{R_E} \cdot \frac{p_S}{p_\sigma}\right)^2 = -0.4(m_{Sun} - m_{star});$$

$$2 \cdot \log \left(\frac{r_{ES}}{R_E} \cdot \frac{p_S}{p_\sigma}\right) = -0.4(m_{Sun} - m_{star});$$

$$m_{Sun} - m_{star} = -5 \cdot \log \left(\frac{r_{ES}}{R_E} \cdot \frac{p_S}{p_\sigma}\right);$$

$$m_{star} = m_{Sun} + 5 \cdot \log \left(\frac{r_{ES}}{R_E} \cdot \frac{p_S}{p_\sigma}\right);$$

$$m_{star} = -26.78^{m} + 5^{m} \cdot \log \left(\frac{149000000 \text{ km}}{6380 \text{ km}} \cdot \frac{8.8''}{0.022''}\right);$$

$$m_{\text{star}} = -26.78^{\text{m}} + 5^{\text{m}} \cdot 6.97;$$
$$m_{\text{star}} \approx 8^{\text{m}},$$

representing the apparent magnitude of the star.

Knowing that the human eye can see stars at the limit of magnitude $m_{\text{limit}} = 6^{\text{m}}$, it follows that the star analyzed in the proposed problem cannot be observed with the naked eye in the clear night sky.

Problem 34

The Meeting of the Stars

A star with mass m falls freely towards another star with mass M. At the initial moment, the two stars are at rest relative to each other, the distance between their centers being r_0.

Determine how long it takes for the two stars, considered material points, to meet.

The constant of universal attraction, K, is known. It is also known that

$$\int \sqrt{\frac{x}{1-x}}\mathrm{d}x = -\sqrt{x(1-x)} + \frac{1}{2}\arcsin(2x-1).$$

Solution

If at some moment, t, in the evolution of the system, when the distance between the stars is r, as indicated by the drawing in Figure 34.1, and the result of their gravitational interaction is $F = K\frac{mM}{r^2}$, then, after an elementary time $\mathrm{d}t$, during which the elementary displacements of the two stars in relation to the center of mass are $\mathrm{d}X$ and $\mathrm{d}x$, respectively, when it can be admitted that $F =$ constant, in accordance with the fundamental principles of dynamics and the law of gravitational attraction, we have:

$$M\vec{a}_1 = \vec{F}; \quad Ma_1 = F;$$

$$m\vec{a}_2 = -\vec{F}; \quad ma_2 = F;$$

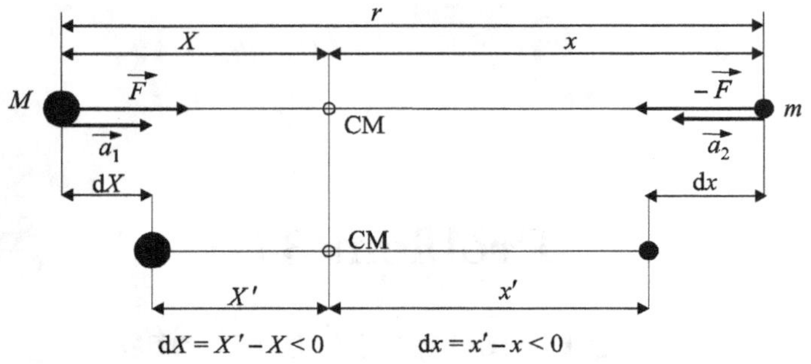

Fig. 34.1

$$\mathrm{d}X < 0; \quad a_1 = -\frac{\mathrm{d}^2X}{\mathrm{d}t^2} = -\frac{\mathrm{d}}{\mathrm{d}t}\left(\frac{\mathrm{d}X}{\mathrm{d}t}\right) > 0;$$

$$-M\frac{\mathrm{d}^2X}{\mathrm{d}t^2} = K\frac{mM}{r^2};$$

$$\mathrm{d}x < 0; \quad a_2 = -\frac{\mathrm{d}^2x}{\mathrm{d}t^2} = -\frac{\mathrm{d}}{\mathrm{d}t}\left(\frac{\mathrm{d}x}{\mathrm{d}t}\right) > 0;$$

$$-m\frac{\mathrm{d}^2x}{\mathrm{d}t^2} = K\frac{mM}{r^2};$$

$$mM\left(\frac{\mathrm{d}^2X}{\mathrm{d}t^2} + \frac{\mathrm{d}^2x}{\mathrm{d}t^2}\right) = -K\frac{mM}{r^2}(m+M);$$

$$X + x = r;$$

$$\frac{\mathrm{d}^2r}{\mathrm{d}t^2} = -K\frac{m+M}{r^2},$$

representing the differential equation associated with the movement of the two stars, falling towards each other;

$$r = \rho r_0,$$

where the dimensionless quantity ρ has values in the interval $0 \leq \rho \leq 1$;

$$\frac{\mathrm{d}^2r}{\mathrm{d}t^2} = r_0\frac{\mathrm{d}^2\rho}{\mathrm{d}t^2};$$

$$\frac{\mathrm{d}^2\rho}{\mathrm{d}t^2} = -K\frac{m+M}{r_0^3}\frac{1}{\rho^2}.$$

In this form, the differential equation of motion shows the advantage of being related to a dimensionless quantity. The significance of the constant $K\frac{m+M}{r_0^3}$ will be established next.

For this purpose, according to Figure 34.2, let's consider that the two stars, located at the distance r_0, evolve around their center of mass on concentric circles with radii X_0 and x_0, having speeds V_0 and v_0, respectively.

Under these conditions, we have:

$$\frac{M\mathrm{V}_0^2}{X_0} = K\frac{mM}{r_0^2};$$

$$\frac{m\mathrm{v}_0^2}{x_0} = K\frac{mM}{r_0^2};$$

$$\mathrm{V}_0 = \frac{2\pi X_0}{T_0}; \quad \mathrm{v}_0 = \frac{2\pi x_0}{T_0},$$

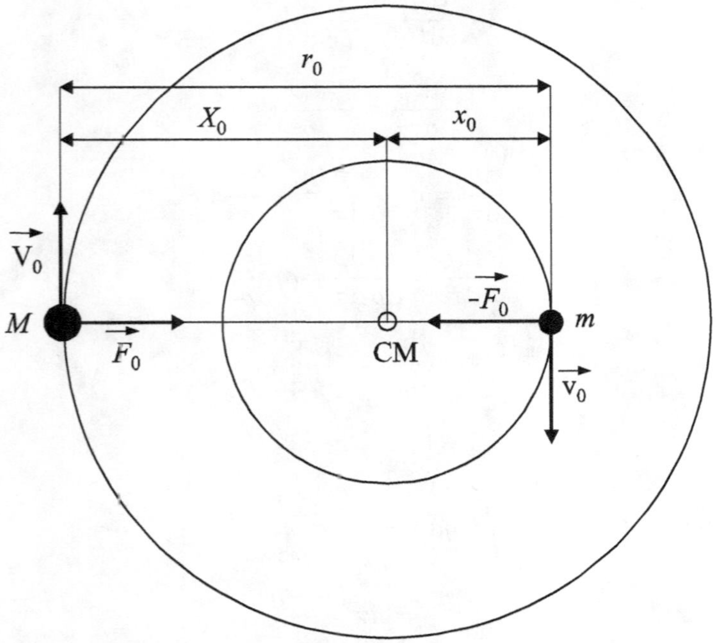

Fig. 34.2

where T_0 is the period of movement of the two stars around their center of mass;

$$\frac{4\pi^2}{T_0^2}X_0 = K\frac{m}{r_0^2};$$

$$\frac{4\pi^2}{T_0^2}x_0 = K\frac{M}{r_0^2};$$

$$K\frac{m+M}{r_0^3} = \frac{4\pi^2}{T_0^2};$$

$$\frac{\mathrm{d}^2\rho}{\mathrm{d}t^2} = -\frac{4\pi^2}{T_0^2}\frac{1}{\rho^2};$$

$$t = \tau T_0,$$

where the dimensionless quantity τ must be determined;

$$\frac{\mathrm{d}^2\rho}{\mathrm{d}t^2} = \frac{1}{T_0^2}\frac{\mathrm{d}^2\rho}{\mathrm{d}\tau^2};$$

$$\frac{\mathrm{d}^2\rho}{\mathrm{d}\tau^2} = -\frac{4\pi^2}{\rho^2};$$

$$\frac{\mathrm{d}\rho}{\mathrm{d}\tau} = \eta; \qquad \frac{\mathrm{d}\eta}{\mathrm{d}\tau} = -\frac{4\pi^2}{\rho^2};$$

$$\frac{\mathrm{d}\eta}{\mathrm{d}\tau} = \frac{\mathrm{d}\eta}{\mathrm{d}\rho}\frac{\mathrm{d}\rho}{\mathrm{d}\tau} = \eta\frac{\mathrm{d}\eta}{\mathrm{d}\rho};$$

$$\eta\frac{\mathrm{d}\eta}{\mathrm{d}\rho} = -\frac{4\pi^2}{\rho^2};$$

$$\eta\mathrm{d}\eta = -4\pi^2\frac{\mathrm{d}\rho}{\rho^2};$$

$$\int_0^\eta \eta\mathrm{d}\eta = -4\pi^2\int_1^\rho \frac{\mathrm{d}\rho}{\rho^2};$$

$$\frac{\eta^2}{2} = 4\pi^2\frac{1-\rho}{\rho};$$

$$\eta < 0;$$

$$\eta = -2\pi\sqrt{2}\sqrt{\frac{1-\rho}{\rho}} = \frac{\mathrm{d}\rho}{\mathrm{d}\tau};$$

$$\int_1^\rho \frac{\mathrm{d}\rho}{\sqrt{\frac{1-\rho}{\rho}}} = -2\pi\sqrt{2}\int_0^\tau \mathrm{d}\tau;$$

$$\frac{1}{\sqrt{\frac{1-\rho}{\rho}}} = \frac{\sqrt{\frac{1-\rho}{\rho}}}{\sqrt{\left(\frac{1-\rho}{\rho}\right)^2}} = \frac{\sqrt{\frac{1-\rho}{\rho}}}{\pm\frac{1-\rho}{\rho}};$$

$$\frac{1}{\sqrt{\frac{1-\rho}{\rho}}} = -\frac{\rho}{1-\rho}\sqrt{\frac{1-\rho}{\rho}} = -\sqrt{\frac{\rho}{1-\rho}};$$

$$\int_1^\rho \sqrt{\frac{\rho}{1-\rho}}\mathrm{d}\rho = 2\pi\sqrt{2}\tau;$$

$$\left[-\sqrt{\rho(1-\rho)} + \frac{1}{2}\arcsin(2\rho-1)\right]\Bigg|_1^\rho = 2\pi\sqrt{2}\tau;$$

$$-\sqrt{\rho(1-\rho)} + \frac{1}{2}\arcsin(2\rho-1) - \frac{\pi}{4} = 2\pi\sqrt{2}\tau;$$

$$\rho = 0; \quad r = 0; \quad \tau = \tau_{\text{down}};$$

$$\tau_{\text{down}} = \frac{1}{4\sqrt{2}};$$

$$t_{\text{down}} = \tau_{\text{down}} \cdot T_0;$$

$$t_{\text{down}} = \frac{T_0}{4\sqrt{2}};$$

$$t_{\text{down}} = \frac{1}{2}\pi r_0\sqrt{\frac{r_0}{2K(m+M)}}.$$

Problem 35

Law of Gravitational Attraction

Using the information from Figure 35.1, representing the graph of the dependence $\log|T_{(\text{years})}| = f(\log|r_{(\text{AU})}|)$, where $|r_{(\text{AU})}|$ is the numerical value of the radius of the circular orbit of a planet, P, around the Sun, S, expressed in AU, and $|T_{(\text{years})}|$ is the numerical value

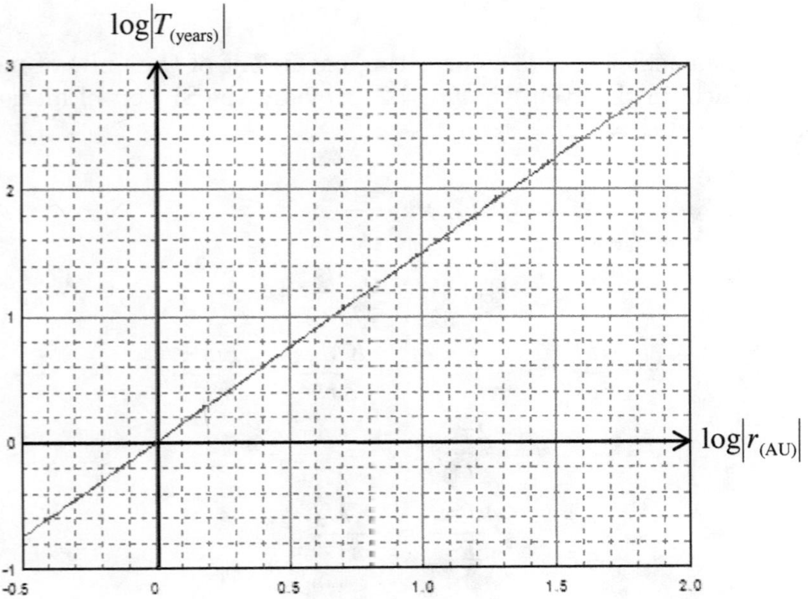

Fig. 35.1

of the period of the planet's rotation around the Sun, expressed in years, *determine* coefficients x and n, from the law of gravitational attraction, considering that it is of the form

$$F_{\text{grav}} = K\frac{M_{\text{P}}M_{\text{S}}}{x \cdot r^n},$$

where: $K = 6.67 \cdot 10^{-11}$ Nm^2 kg^{-2} is the constant of gravitational attraction; $M_{\text{S}} = 1.979 \cdot 10^{30}$ kg is the mass of the sun and M_{P} is the mass of the planet.

Solution

Accepting that under the action of the force of gravitational attraction that the Sun exerts on a planet, the trajectory of the planet is a circle, regardless of the form of the law of gravitational attraction, means accepting that the force of gravitational attraction, is a centripetal force. So, we can write that:

$$F_{\text{grav}} = K\frac{M_{\text{P}}M_{\text{S}}}{xr^n},$$

where the coefficient x is a correcting coefficient of the units of measure, which, in the event that $n \neq 2$, provides the SI unit of measure for force, $\langle F\rangle_{\text{IS}} = 1$ N;

$$F_{\text{cp}} = \frac{M_{\text{P}}\text{v}^2}{r};$$

$$F_{\text{grav}} = F_{\text{cp}}; \quad K\frac{M_{\text{P}}M_{\text{S}}}{xr^n} = \frac{M_{\text{P}}\text{v}^2}{r};$$

$$K\frac{M_{\text{S}}}{xr^n} = \frac{\text{v}^2}{r}; \quad \text{v}^2 = \frac{KM_{\text{S}}r}{xr^n} = \frac{KM_{\text{S}}}{xr^{n-1}};$$

$$\text{v} = \frac{2\pi r}{T}; \quad \text{v}^2 = \frac{4\pi^2 r^2}{T^2};$$

$$\frac{4\pi^2 r^2}{T^2} = \frac{KM_{\text{S}}}{xr^{n-1}};$$

$$T^2 = 4\pi^2 x\frac{r^{n+1}}{KM_{\text{S}}},$$

representing the expression of Kepler's third law when the force of gravitational attraction is

$$F_{\text{grav}} = K\frac{M_{\text{P}}M_{\text{S}}}{xr^n}.$$

Under these conditions, if the period of rotation of the planet around the Sun is expressed in years, and the radius of its circular orbit around the Sun is expressed in AU, it follows that:

$$T_{(\text{years})} = |T_{(\text{years})}| \cdot (1\,\text{year}); \quad T^2_{\text{years}} = |T_{(\text{years})}|^2 \cdot (1\text{ year})^2;$$

$$r_{(\text{AU})} = |r_{(\text{AU})}| \cdot (1\text{ AU}); \quad r^{n+1}_{(\text{AU})} = |r_{(\text{AU})}|^{n+1} \cdot (1\text{ AU})^{n+1};$$

$$|T_{(\text{years})}|^2 \cdot (1\text{ year})^2 = 4\pi^2 x\frac{|r_{(\text{AU})}|^{n+1} \cdot (1\text{ AU})^{n+1}}{KM_{\text{S}}};$$

$$|T_{(\text{years})}|^2 \cdot (1\text{ year})^2 = 4\pi^2 x\frac{|r_{(\text{AU})}|^{n+1} \cdot (1\text{ AU})^3 \cdot (1\text{ AU})^{n-2}}{KM_{\text{S}}};$$

$$|T_{(\text{years})}|^2 \cdot \frac{(1\,\text{year})^2 \cdot M_{\text{S}}}{(1\text{ AU})^3} = 4\pi^2 x\frac{|r_{(\text{AU})}|^{n+1} \cdot (1\text{ AU})^{n-2}}{K};$$

$$|T_{(\text{years})}|^2 \cdot \frac{(1\,\text{year})^2 \cdot M_{\text{S}}}{(1\text{ AU})^3} = \frac{4\pi^2}{K}x \cdot |r_{(\text{AU})}|^{n+1} \cdot (1\text{ AU})^{n-2};$$

$$\frac{(1\text{ years})^2 \cdot\ M_{\text{S}}}{(1\text{ AU})^3} = \frac{(365 \cdot 24 \cdot 3600)^2\text{ s}^2 \cdot 1.989 \cdot 10^{30}\text{ kg}}{(15 \cdot 10^{10})^3\text{ m}^3}$$

$$\approx 5.86 \cdot 10^{11}\ \frac{\text{s}^2\text{ kg}}{\text{m}^3};$$

$$\frac{4\pi^2}{K} = \frac{4 \cdot 3.14 \cdot 3.14}{6.67 \cdot 10^{-11}\text{ Nm}^2\text{ kg}^{-2}} \approx 5.91 \cdot 10^{11}\ \frac{\text{s}^2\text{ kg}}{\text{m}^3};$$

$$\frac{(1\,\text{year})^2\ \cdot M_{\text{S}}}{(1\text{ AU})^3} \approx \frac{4\pi^2}{K};$$

$$|T_{(\text{years})}|^2 = |r_{(\text{AU})}|^{n+1} \cdot x \cdot (1\text{ AU})^{n-2},$$

where the terms $|T_{(\text{years})}|^2$ and $|r_{(\text{AU})}|^3$ are numbers. So, to ensure the homogeneity of the previous expression, we must accept that

$$x = (1\text{ AU})^{2-n},$$

and we get:

$$|T_{\text{years}}|^2 = |r_{(\text{AU})}|^{n+1} \cdot (1\ \text{AU})^{2-n} \cdot (1\ \text{AU})^{n-2};$$

$$|T_{(\text{years})}|^2 = |r_{(\text{AU})}|^{n+1}.$$

From this, by logarithmization, it follows that:

$$2 \cdot \log |T_{(\text{years})}| = (n+1) \cdot \log |r_{(\text{AU})}|;$$

$$\log |T_{(\text{years})}| = \frac{n+1}{2} \cdot \log |r_{(\text{AU})}|,$$

which justifies, in the drawing in the problem statement, the linear dependence graph $\log |T_{(\text{years})}| = f(\log |r_{(\text{UA})}|)$.

The results are:

$$\tan \alpha = \frac{3}{2} = \frac{n+1}{2};$$

$$n = 2;$$

$$x = (1\ \text{AU})^{2-n} = 1;$$

$$F_{\text{grav}} = K\frac{M_{\text{P}} M_{\text{S}}}{x r^n}; \quad F_{\text{grav}} = K\frac{M_{\text{P}} M_{\text{S}}}{r^2}.$$

Problem 36

Radial Velocities of Stars

In the drawings of Figures 36.1 and 36.2, the relative elliptical orbit of the secondary star S is represented, with respect to the main star Σ, considered to be at rest with respect to the observer. In Figure 36.1, the secondary star S approaches the observer and, in Figure 36.2 the secondary star S moves away from the observer. In both variants, we consider that at the initial moment the secondary star S passes through the periastron of the relative orbit.

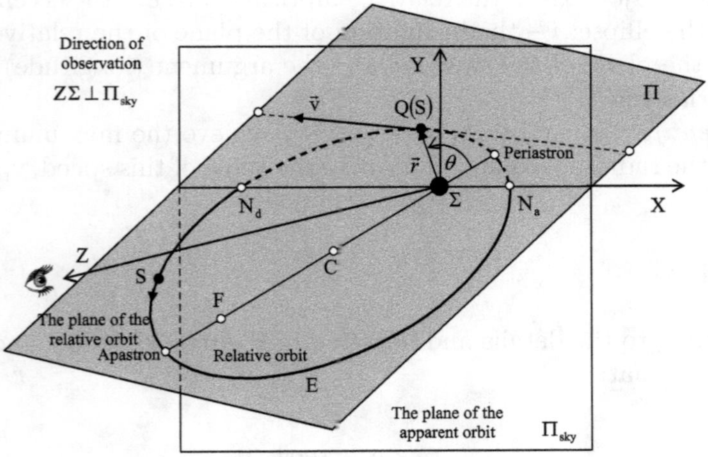

Fig. 36.1

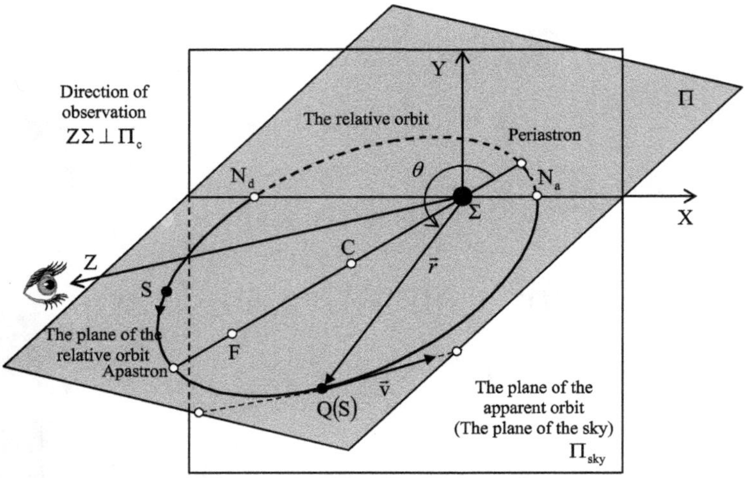

Fig. 36.2

a) *Establish* the dependence of the radial speed of the secondary star on the plane polar coordinates, $v_{rad} = f(r; \theta)$, in both variants, knowing: T – the rotation period of the secondary star; a – the semi-major axis of the relative elliptical orbit; e – the eccentricity of the ellipse; i – the inclination of the plane of the relative orbit to the plane of the sky; and ω – the argument (longitude) of the periastron.

b) *Identify* the conditions necessary to achieve the maximum value of the radial speed and *determine* the value of this speed, $v_{rad,max}$.

Solution

According to the details and notation in Figures 36.3, 36.4 and 36.5, it follows that:

$$0 < \theta < 180^0;$$

$$\sin i = \frac{z}{u}; \quad z = u \cdot \sin i;$$

$$\sin[\pi - (\theta + \omega)] = \frac{u}{r} = -\cos\pi \cdot \sin(\theta + \omega) = \sin(\theta + \omega);$$

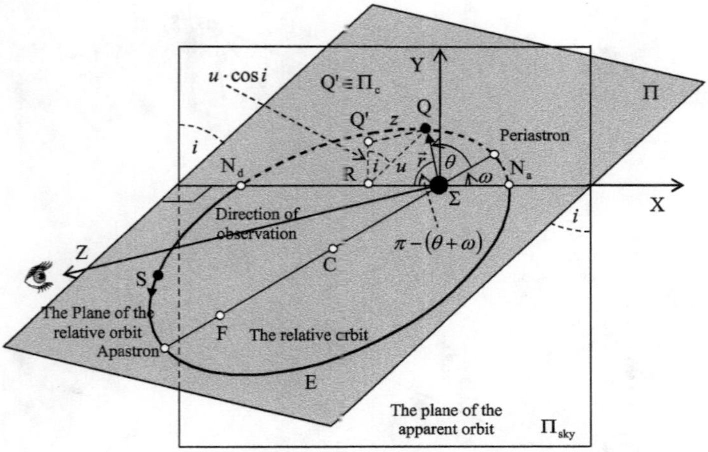

Fig. 36.3

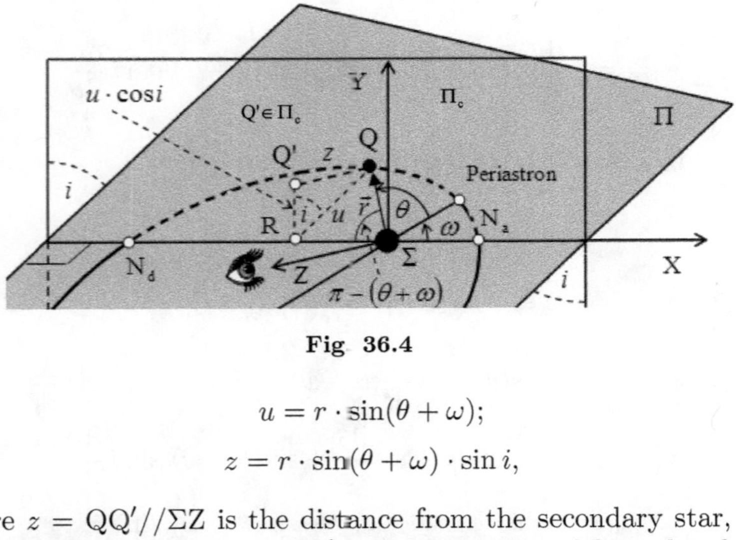

Fig 36.4

$$u = r \cdot \sin(\theta + \omega);$$

$$z = r \cdot \sin(\theta + \omega) \cdot \sin i,$$

where $z = \mathrm{QQ'}//\Sigma\mathrm{Z}$ is the distance from the secondary star, S, to the plane of the sky, Π_c, and Q′ is the projection of Q on the plane of the sky (the plane $\Pi_c \equiv \mathrm{X}\Sigma\mathrm{Y}$), which means that z is the coordinate of the star S corresponding to the axis $\Sigma\mathrm{Z} \perp \Pi_c$. Thus:

$$\mathrm{v_{rad}} = \frac{\mathrm{d}z}{\mathrm{d}t} = \frac{\mathrm{d}}{\mathrm{d}t}[r\ \sin(\theta + \omega)\ \sin i]; \quad \theta = \theta(t); \quad r = r(t);$$

$$i = \text{constant}; \quad \omega = \text{constant};$$

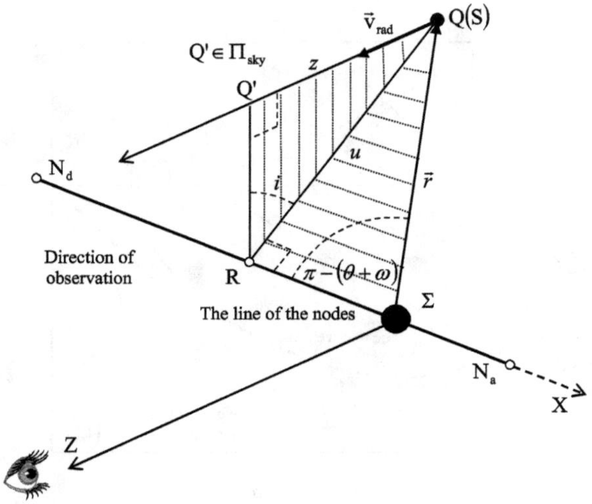

Fig. 36.5

$$v_{\text{rad}} = r\frac{\mathrm{d}}{\mathrm{d}t}[\sin(\theta+\omega)\ \sin i] + \sin(\theta+\omega)\ \sin i\,\frac{\mathrm{d}r}{\mathrm{d}t};$$

$$v_{\text{rad}} = r\ \sin(\theta+\omega)\,\frac{\mathrm{d}}{\mathrm{d}t}(\sin i) + r\sin i\,\frac{\mathrm{d}}{\mathrm{d}t}[\sin(\theta+\omega)]$$

$$+ \sin(\theta+\omega)\ \sin i\,\frac{\mathrm{d}r}{\mathrm{d}t};$$

$$i = \text{constant};\qquad \frac{\mathrm{d}}{\mathrm{d}t}(\sin i) = 0;$$

$$v_{\text{rad}} = r\ \sin i\ \cos(\theta+\omega)\,\frac{\mathrm{d}}{\mathrm{d}t}(\theta+\omega) + \sin(\theta+\omega)\ \sin i\,\frac{\mathrm{d}r}{\mathrm{d}t};$$

$$v_{\text{rad}} = r\ \sin i\ \cos(\theta+\omega)\,\frac{\mathrm{d}\theta}{\mathrm{d}t} + \sin(\theta+\omega)\ \sin i\,\frac{\mathrm{d}r}{\mathrm{d}t};$$

$$v_{\text{rad}} = r\ \sin i\ \cos(\theta+\omega)\,\dot{\theta} + \sin(\theta+\omega)\ \sin i\,\dot{r};$$

$$v_{\text{rad}} = [r\,\dot{\theta}\ \cos(\theta+\omega) + \dot{r}\ \sin(\theta+\omega)]\ \sin i;$$

$$r = \frac{p}{1+e\ \cos\theta} = \frac{a(1-e^2)}{1+e\ \cos\theta};$$

$$\dot{r} = \frac{\mathrm{d}r}{\mathrm{d}t} = \frac{\mathrm{d}}{\mathrm{d}t}\left[\frac{a(1-e^2)}{1+e\ \cos\theta}\right];$$

$$\dot{r} = \frac{\mathrm{d}r}{\mathrm{d}t} = \frac{(1 + e\cos\theta)\,\frac{\mathrm{d}}{\mathrm{d}t}[a(1-e^2)] - a(1-e^2)\,\frac{\mathrm{d}}{\mathrm{d}t}(1 + e\cos\theta)}{(1 + e\cos\theta)^2};$$

$$\dot{r} = \frac{\mathrm{d}r}{\mathrm{d}t} = \frac{a(1-e^2)\,e\sin\theta\,\frac{\mathrm{d}\theta}{\mathrm{d}t}}{(1 + e\cos\theta)^2};$$

$$\dot{r} = \frac{\mathrm{d}r}{\mathrm{d}t} = \frac{a(1-e^2)}{1 + e\cos\theta}\,\frac{e\,\frac{\mathrm{d}\theta}{\mathrm{d}t}\sin\theta}{1 + e\cos\theta};$$

$$r = \frac{p}{1 + e\cos\theta} = \frac{a(1-e^2)}{1 + e\cos\theta};$$

$$\dot{r} = \frac{r\,e\,\dot{\theta}\sin\theta}{1 - e\cos\theta};$$

$$\frac{\mathrm{d}A}{\mathrm{d}t} = \frac{1}{2}\,r^2\dot{\theta};$$

$$\frac{A}{T} = \frac{1}{2}\,r^2\dot{\theta};$$

$$A = \pi ab; \quad b = a\sqrt{1-e^2};$$

$$A = \pi a^2\sqrt{1-e^2};$$

$$\frac{\pi a^2\sqrt{1-e^2}}{T} = \frac{1}{2}\,r^2\dot{\theta};$$

$$r\,\dot{\theta} = \frac{2\pi a^2\sqrt{1-e^2}}{rT}; \quad r\,\dot{\theta} = \frac{1}{r}\,\frac{2\pi a^2\sqrt{1-e^2}}{T};$$

$$r\,\dot{\theta} = \frac{1 + e\cos\theta}{a(1-e^2)}\,\frac{2\pi a^2\sqrt{1-e^2}}{T};$$

$$r\dot{\theta} = \frac{2\pi a(1 + e\cos\theta)}{T\sqrt{1-e^2}};$$

$$\dot{r} = \frac{r\,e\,\dot{\theta}\sin\theta}{1 + e\cos\theta} = r\dot{\theta}\,\frac{e\sin\theta}{1 + e\cos\theta};$$

$$\dot{r} = \frac{2\pi a(1 + e\cos\theta)}{T\sqrt{1-e^2}}\,\frac{e\sin\theta}{1 + e\cos\theta};$$

$$\dot{r} = \frac{2\pi\,a\,e\sin\theta}{T\sqrt{1-e^2}};$$

$$\mathrm{v_{rad}} = [r\,\dot{\theta}\,\cos(\theta+\omega) + \dot{r}\,\sin(\theta+\omega)]\sin i;$$

$$\mathrm{v_{rad}} = \left[\frac{2\pi a(1+e\,\cos\theta)}{T\sqrt{1-e^2}}\,\cos(\theta+\omega) + \frac{2\pi ae\sin\theta}{T\sqrt{1-e^2}}\,\sin(\theta+\omega)\right]\,\sin i;$$

$$\mathrm{v_{rad}} = \frac{2\pi a\sin i}{T\sqrt{1-e^2}}[(1+e\cos\theta)\,\cos(\theta+\omega) + e\,\sin\theta\,\sin(\theta+\omega)];$$

$$\mathrm{v_{rad}} = \frac{2\pi a\sin i}{T\sqrt{1-e^2}}[\cos(\theta+\omega) + e\,\cos\theta\,\cos(\theta+\omega)$$
$$+\,e\,\sin\theta\,\sin(\theta+\omega)];$$

$$\cos(\theta+\omega) = \cos\theta\,\cos\omega - \sin\theta\,\sin\omega;$$

$$\sin(\theta+\omega) = \sin\theta\,\cos\omega + \cos\theta\,\sin\omega;$$

$$[\cos(\theta+\omega) + e\,\cos\theta\,\cos(\theta+\omega) + e\,\sin\theta\,\sin(\theta+\omega)]$$
$$= \cos\theta\,\cos\omega - \sin\theta\,\sin\omega + e\,\cos\omega = \cos(\theta+\omega) + e\,\cos\omega;$$

$$\mathrm{v_{rad}} = \frac{2\pi\,a\,\sin i}{T\sqrt{1-e^2}}[\cos(\theta+\omega) + e\,\cos\omega].$$

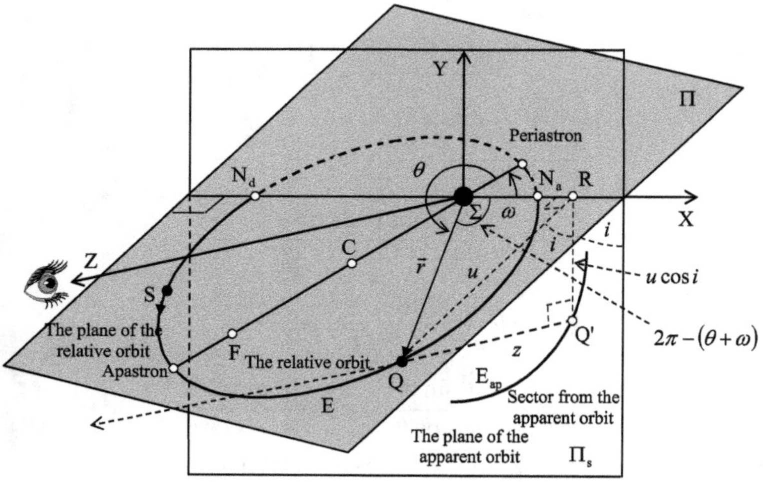

Fig. 36.6

For the variant represented in the drawing in Figure 36.6, considering that at the initial moment the secondary star S passes through

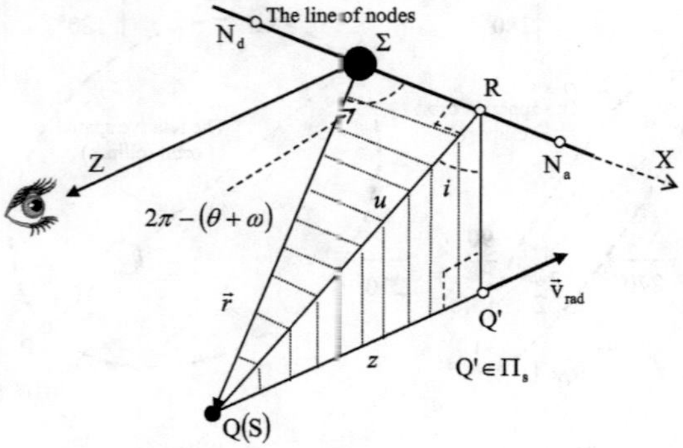

Fig. 36.7

periastron, in accordance with the details in Figure 36.7, it follows that:

$$180^0 < \theta < 360^0;$$

$$\sin i = \frac{z}{u}; \quad z = x \sin i; \quad z = u \cdot \sin i;$$

$$\sin[2\pi - (\theta + \omega)] = \frac{u}{r} = -\cos 2\pi \cdot \sin(\theta + \omega) = -\sin(\theta + \omega);$$

$$u = -r \cdot \sin(\theta + \omega);$$

$$z = -r \cdot \sin(\theta + \omega) \cdot \sin i;$$

$$\mathrm{v_{rad}} = -\frac{\mathrm{d}z}{\mathrm{d}t} = \frac{\mathrm{d}}{\mathrm{d}t}[r \sin(\theta + \omega) \sin i];$$

....

$$\mathrm{v_{rad}} = \frac{2\pi\, a \sin i}{T\sqrt{1 - e^2}}[\cos(\theta + \omega) + e \cos \omega].$$

The apparent orbit (ellipse) of the secondary star represented in the drawing in Figure 36.8 is the projection in the plane of the sky of the relative (true) orbit (ellipse). Numerous methods allow the determination of the elements of the relative ellipse using information resulting from measurements made on the apparent orbit (ellipse).

To the observer on Earth, the apparent motion of the secondary star around the primary star, as seen in the plane of the sky, follows an elliptical path (apparent orbit), specifically, a circle or line

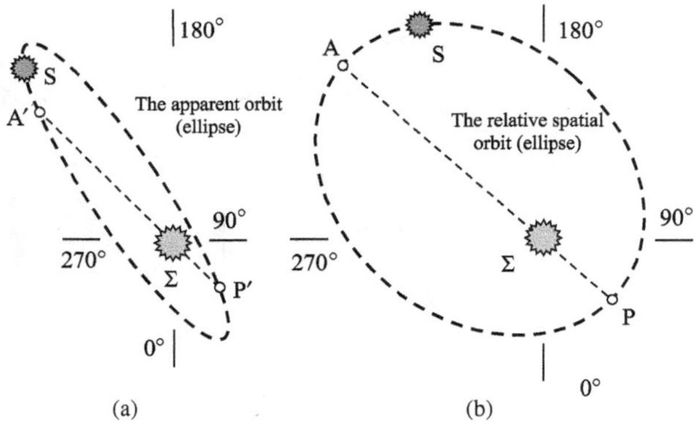

Fig. 36.8

segment. The primary star is always inside the apparent ellipse, but not always at its focus. On the ellipse of the apparent orbit, the vector radius of the secondary star, relative to the main star, describes surfaces whose areas are directly proportional to the duration of its displacement. As a result, Kepler's second law, the law of areas, is also true for the displacement of the secondary star in its apparent orbit.

The elements of the relative orbit (ellipse) can also be determined from the analysis of the curve that represents the time variation of the radial velocity of the secondary star. In general, the radial velocity of a star is the component of the star's velocity in the direction of the observer. The drawings in Figures 36.9–36.14 illustrate the radial

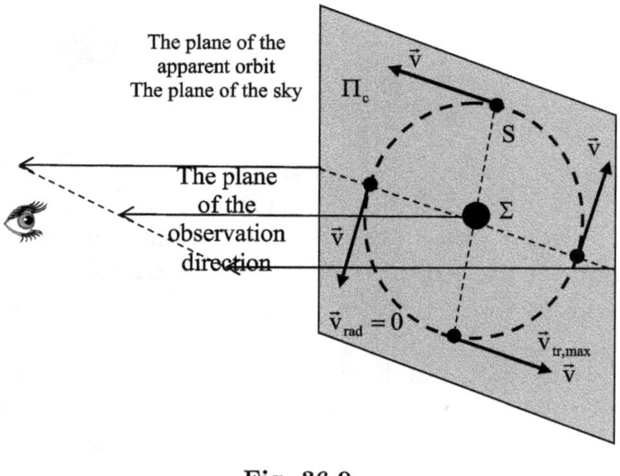

Fig. 36.9

velocities in different variants, for which:

$$v_{rad} = v \cdot \sin\alpha = v_{rad,max} \cdot \sin\omega t = v_{rad,max} \cdot \sin\frac{2\pi}{T}t;$$

$$v_{rad} = v \cdot \sin i \cdot \sin\alpha = v_{rad,max} \cdot \sin\omega t = v_{rad,max} \cdot \sin\frac{2\pi}{T}t;$$

$$v_{rad,max} = v \cdot \sin i.$$

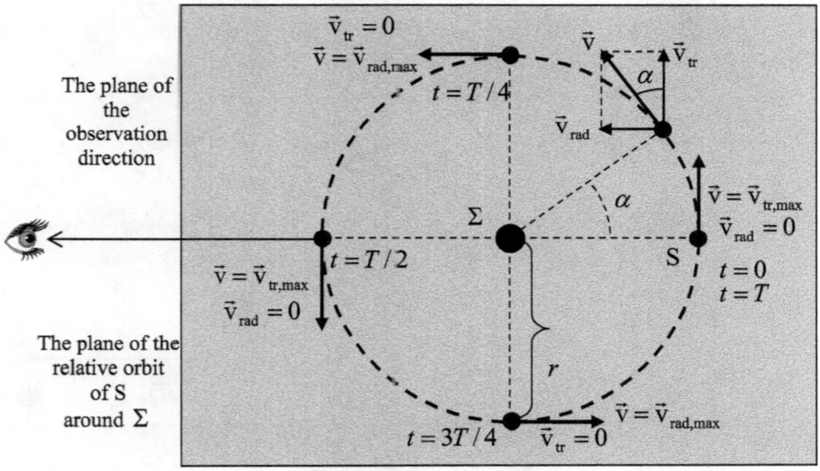

Fig. 36.10

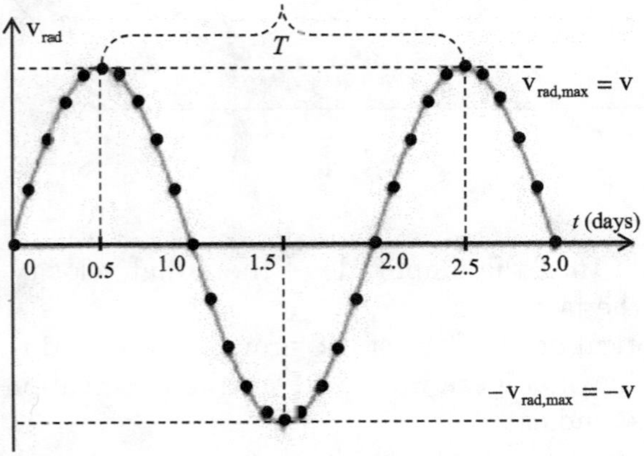

Fig. 36.11

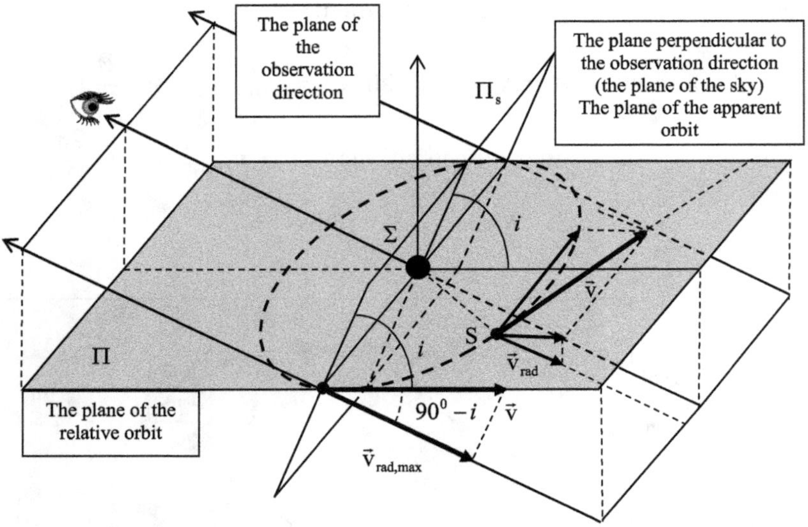

Fig. 36.12

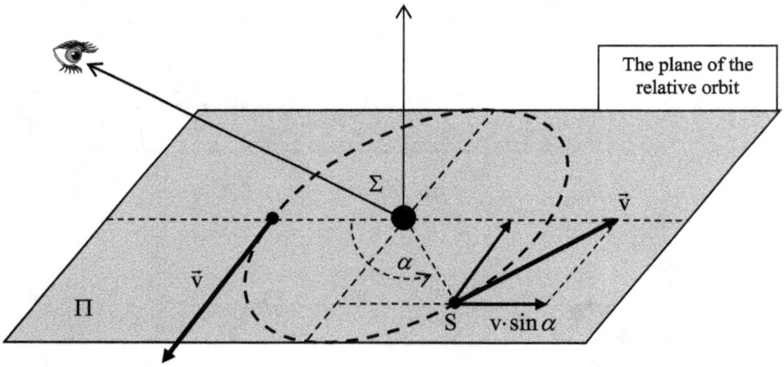

Fig. 36.13

If $i \neq 90^0$, then the amplitude of the radial velocity variation is reduced by the factor $\sin i$.

The elliptical orbit of the star S around the star Σ is represented in the drawing in Figure 36.15, where the observation line of the system is also indicated.

For the secondary star S, which at a certain moment has the speed $\vec{v}$ relative to an observer O, as shown in the drawing in Figure 36.16, we define: the radial speed, $\vec{v}_{rad}$, as the component of the speed

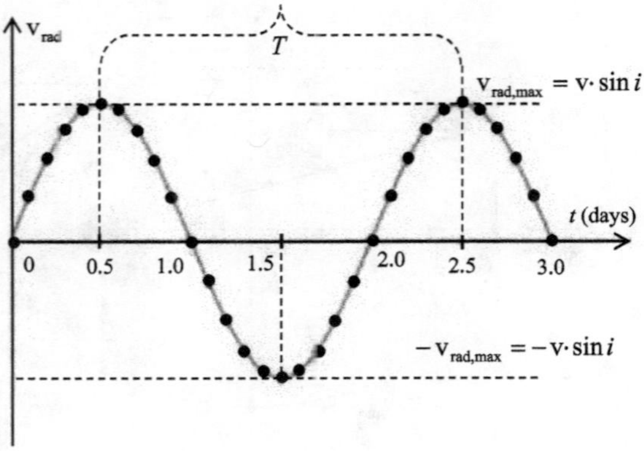

Fig. 36.14

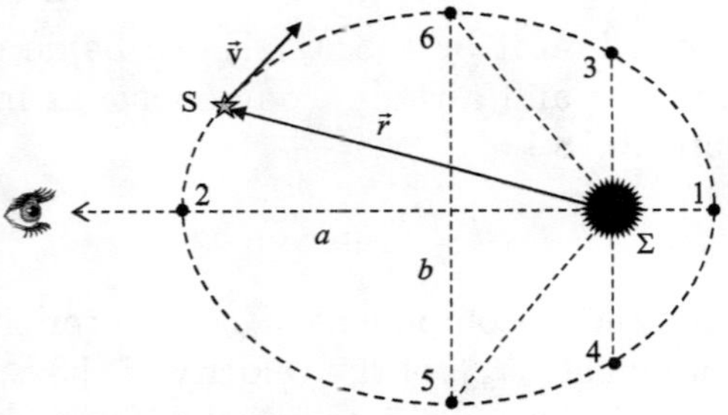

Fig. 36.15

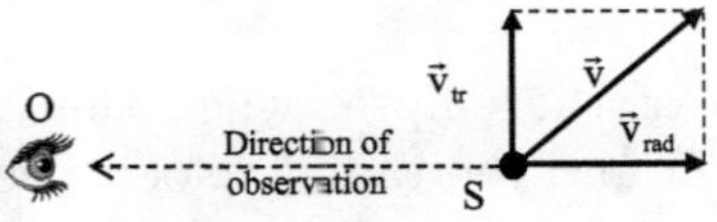

Fig. 36.16

oriented along the direction of observation of the star, and the transverse velocity, $\vec{v}_{tr}$, as the component of velocity perpendicular to the direction of observation.

Under these conditions, as shown in the drawing in Figure 36.17, it follows that:

$$v_1 = v_{max} = v_{tr.\,max}; \quad v_2 = v_{min} = v_{tr.\,min};$$

$$v_{rad,1} = v_{rad,2} = 0;$$

$$v_5 = v_6 = v = v_{rad}.$$

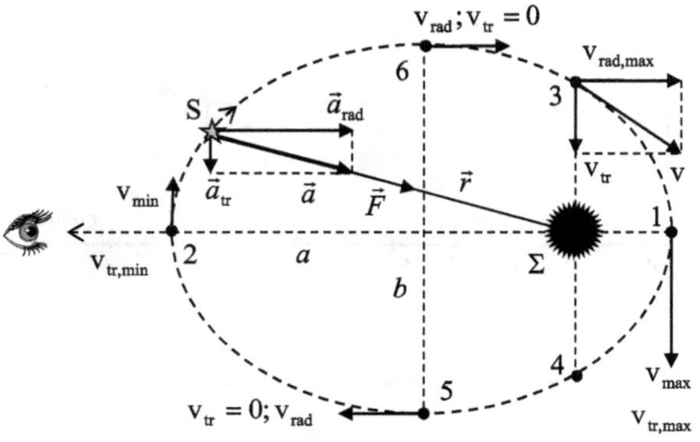

Fig. 36.17

The acceleration of the star S due to the central gravitational force, $\vec{a} = \frac{\vec{F}}{m}$, exerted on it by the star Σ can be decomposed into a transverse component and a radial component, as indicated by the drawing in Figure 36.18:

$$\vec{a} = \vec{a}_{\text{rad}} + \vec{a}_{\text{tr}}.$$

Of these, only the radial component, $\vec{a}_{\text{rad}}$, determines the variation of the radial component, $\vec{v}_{\text{rad}}$, of the velocity of the secondary star S.

The drawing in Figure 36.17 shows the evolution of the radial and transverse components of the velocity and acceleration vectors, relative to the observer, when the line of sight is in the plane of the orbit.

On sector 2–6–3 of the ellipse, when the angle α between the acceleration vector, $\vec{a}$, and the radial velocity vector, $\vec{v}_{\text{rad}}$, is

$$0 \leq \alpha \leq 90°,$$

the effect of acceleration (the effect of gravitational attraction) on the radial component of the velocity is an accelerating effect. As a result, in this sector, the radial component of the velocity is

$$0 \leq v_{\text{rad}} \leq v_{\text{rad,max}}.$$

On sector 3–1 of the ellipse, when the angle α between the acceleration vector, $\vec{a}$, and the radial velocity vector, $\vec{v}_{\text{rad}}$, is

$$90 \leq \alpha \leq 180°,$$

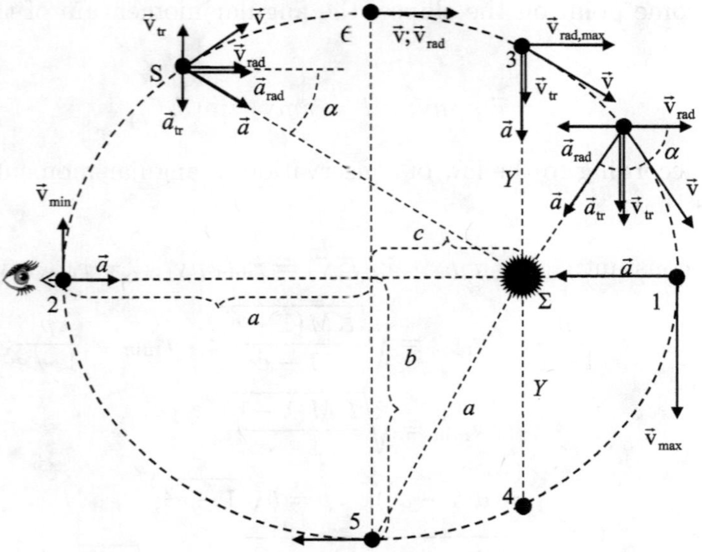

Fig. 36.18

the effect of acceleration (the effect of gravitational attraction) on the radial component of velocity is a retarding effect. As a result, in this sector, the radial component of the velocity is

$$0 \leq v_{rad} \leq v_{rad,max}.$$

Conclusions:

- For $\alpha = 90°$, when the star S is in position 3, the radial component of its velocity has its maximum value.
- On sector 2–3 of the ellipse, the radial effect of the gravitational attraction force is an accelerating effect, and on sector 3–1 of the ellipse, the radial effect of the gravitational attraction force is a decelerating effect.
- On sector 2–3 of the ellipse, the tangential effect of the gravitational attraction force is a slowing effect, and on sector 3–1 of the ellipse, the tangential effect of the gravitational attraction force is an accelerating effect.
- On sector 2–3 of the ellipse, the vectors $\vec{v}_{rad}$ and $\vec{a}_{rad}$ have identical orientations, and on sector 3–1, the vectors $\vec{v}_{rad}$ and $\vec{a}_{rad}$ have opposite orientations.
- At point 3, where the direction of the vector $\vec{a}_{rad}$ changes, the vector $\vec{v}_{rad}$ has the extreme (maximum) value.

At some point on the ellipse, the angular momentum of the star σ is:

$$\vec{L} = \vec{r} \times m\vec{\mathrm{v}}; \quad L = rm\mathrm{v} \cdot \sin(\vec{r}; \vec{\mathrm{v}}).$$

Thus, according to the law of conservation of angular momentum, it follows that:

$$\vec{L} = \text{constant}; \quad L = rm\mathrm{v} \cdot \sin(\vec{r}; \vec{\mathrm{v}}) = r_{\min} m\mathrm{v}_{\max} = r_{\max} m\mathrm{v}_{\min};$$

$$r_{\min} = \frac{p}{1+e}; \quad \mathrm{v}_{\max} = \sqrt{\frac{KM(1+e)}{1-e}}; \quad r_{\min} = \frac{p}{1-e};$$

$$\mathrm{v}_{\min} = \sqrt{\frac{KM(1-e)}{1+e}};$$

$$p = a(1-e^2); \quad p = b\sqrt{1-e^2};$$

$$L = m\sqrt{\frac{KMa^2(1-e)^2(1+e)}{a(1-e)}} = mb\sqrt{\frac{KM}{a}}.$$

Corresponding to position 3 of star S, when its angular momentum is

$$L = Ym\mathrm{v}_{\mathrm{rad,max}},$$

it results that:

$$Ym\mathrm{v}_{\mathrm{rad,max}} = mb\sqrt{\frac{KM}{a}}; \quad \mathrm{v}_{\mathrm{rad,max}} = \frac{b}{Y} \cdot \sqrt{\frac{KM}{a}};$$

$$\frac{x^2}{a^2} + \frac{y^2}{b^2} = 1;$$

$$x = c; \quad y = Y; \quad \frac{c^2}{a^2} + \frac{Y^2}{b^2} = 1; \quad c^2 = a^2 - b^2; \quad Y = \frac{b^2}{a};$$

$$\mathrm{v}_{\mathrm{rad,max}} = \frac{a}{b} \cdot \sqrt{\frac{KM}{a}}.$$

If τ_1 is the time interval in which the radial component of the velocity of the star S increases from zero to the maximum value and

τ_2 is the time interval in which the same component decreases from the maximum value to zero, it follows that:

$$\Delta v_{rad,23} = v_{rad,max} - 0 = v_{rad,max}; \quad \Delta t_{23} = \tau_1;$$

$$\Delta v_{rad,31} = 0 - v_{rad,max} = -v_{rad,max}; \quad \Delta t_{31} = \tau_2;$$

$$\frac{\Delta S_1}{\tau_1} = \frac{\Delta S_2}{\tau_2} = \frac{S_{\text{ellipse}}}{T} = \frac{\pi ab}{T}; \quad \Delta S_1 = \pi ab \cdot \frac{\tau_1}{T}; \quad \Delta S_2 = \pi ab \cdot \frac{\tau_2}{T};$$

$$\Delta S_1 + \Delta S_2 = \frac{1}{2} \cdot S_{\text{ellipse}}; \quad \pi ab \cdot \frac{\tau_1}{T} + \pi ab \cdot \frac{\tau_2}{T} = \frac{1}{2} \cdot \pi ab;$$

$$\tau_1 + \tau_2 = \frac{1}{2} T.$$

In Figure 36.19, these curves are shown, as well as their shape according to the shape of the relative orbit and its position in relation to the observer's line of sight.

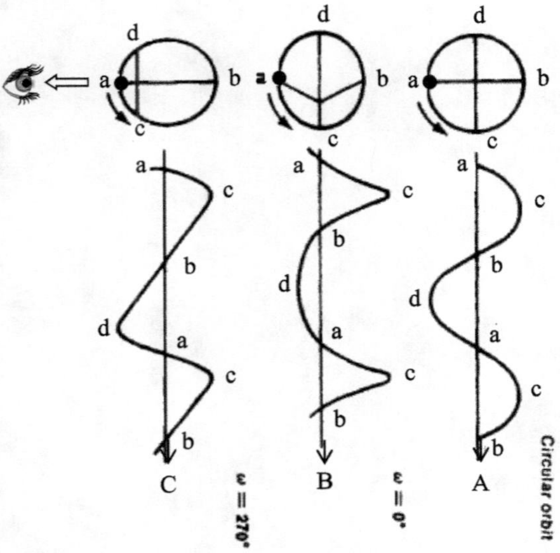

Fig. 36.19

Problem 37

Bombarding a Very Dangerous Asteroid!

A potentially dangerous gigantic asteroid is approaching the Earth, as illustrated in Figure 37.1. The collision of the asteroid with the Earth is inevitable. While monitoring the asteroid's approach, the decision to launch a nuclear projectile (nuclear bomb) from an artificial satellite orbiting around the Earth is made. The projectile will either meet and pulverize the asteroid very far from the Earth, so that the small fragments it is transformed into will not cause any damage even if they reach the Earth, or it will change the asteroid's trajectory to prevent collision with the Earth.

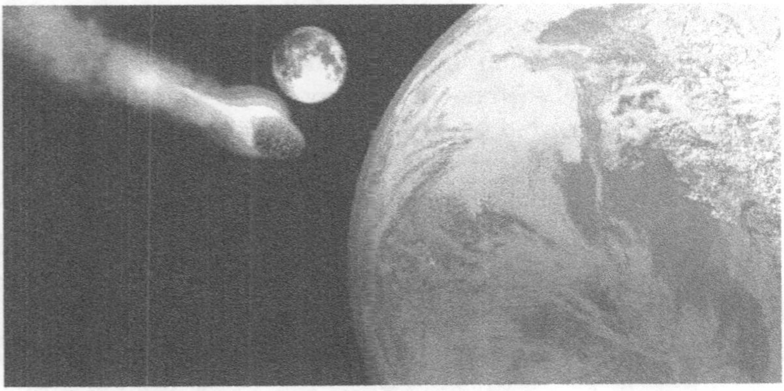

Fig. 37.1 (Credit: Catmando on Shutterstock)

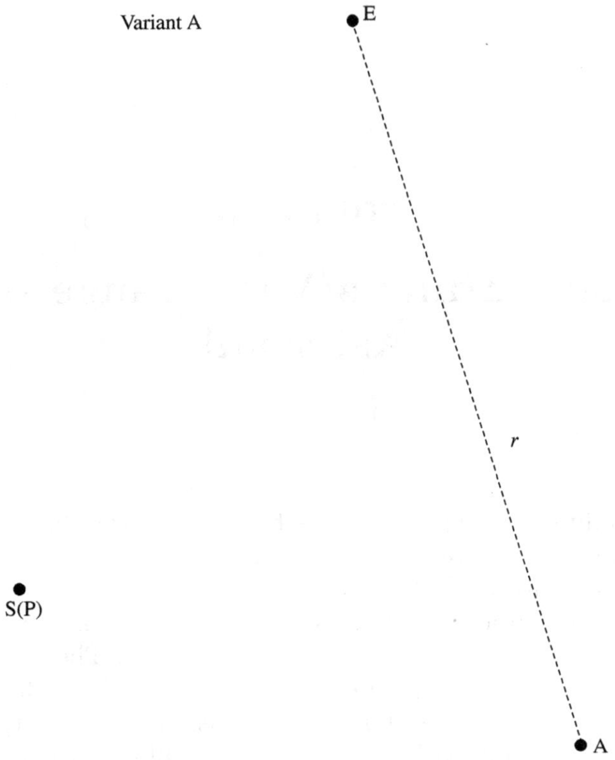

Fig. 37.2

In Figure 37.2, we use the following notation: E – the center of the Earth; S – the position of the satellite at the moment when the projectile P is launched; and A – the point at which the projectile should meet the asteroid at a distance of $r = 30000\,\text{km}$ from the Earth's surface. The positions of the three points in the diagram illustrate at a certain scale the real placement of the bodies in space.

A. A Single Solution

Considering that the problem has a single solution (for a given value v_0 of the projectile's initial velocity relative to the Earth, there is a single trajectory on which the projectile can travel from point S to point A), *determine:*

a) the elements of the projectile's orbit that would ensure its collision with the asteroid;

b) the direction of the projectile's initial velocity $\vec{v}_0$ at the launching point for a given value v_0 that will allow the projectile to meet the asteroid;
c) the projectile's velocity at the launching moment, knowing that the Earth's mass is $M = 6 \cdot 10^{24}$ kg and the universal attraction constant is $K = 6.67 \cdot 10^{-11}\,\mathrm{N\,m^2\,kg^{-2}}$;
d) the duration of the projectile's movement from the moment it is launched until it meets the asteroid;
e) the distance the projectile travels from the moment it is launched until it meets the asteroid.

Available materials: A self-adhesive plasticine plate, a ruler, string, a knife, scissors, adhesive sheets, adhesive tape, a board for support, and straight pins.

B. Two Solutions

The trajectory of the same asteroid is monitored by another satellite while it approaches the Earth. From this satellite orbiting around the Earth at a different altitude, a second projectile is simultaneously launched, aiming to intercept the asteroid at the same point as the first projectile described in the previous case. In Figure 37.3, the following notation is used: E – the center of the Earth; S – the position of the new satellite at the moment when the projectile P is launched; and A – the point at which the second projectile must reach the asteroid when the asteroid is at a distance of $r = 30000$ km from the Earth. The location of the three points in Figure 37.3 represents the real positions of the celestial bodies in space at a different scale to the first case.

Considering that the problem in this new variant has two solutions (for the new value of the initial velocity of the projectile, v_0, relative to the Earth, there are two trajectories on which the projectile can move from point S to point A), *determine*:

a) the elements of the two projectile's orbits that allow them to meet the asteroid, if on the diagram the position of a fixed point X is also marked;
b) the directions of the projectile's initial velocities, $\vec{v}_0$, at the launching point, for an absolute velocity value v_0, that allow the projectile to meet the asteroid;

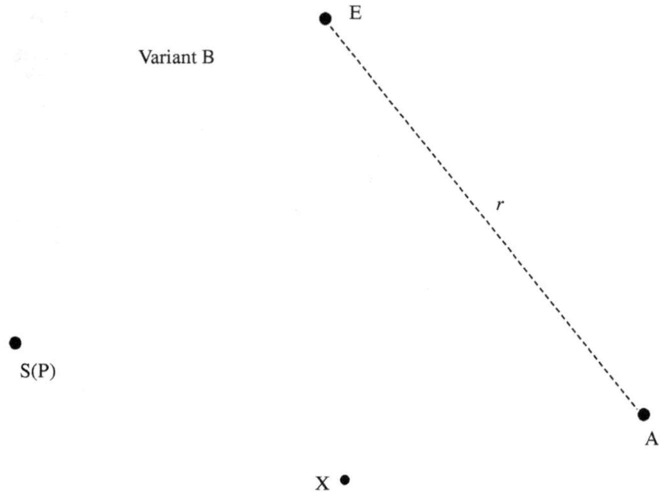

Fig. 37.3

c) the projectile's velocity, v_0, at the launching moment, knowing that the Earth's mass is $M = 6 \cdot 10^{24}$ kg and the universal attraction constant is $K = 6.67 \cdot 10^{-11}\,\mathrm{Nm^2\,kg^{-2}}$;

d) the duration of the projectile's movement from the moment it is launched until it reaches the asteroid, calculated for each of the two trajectories;

e) the distances each projectile travels until impact with the asteroid.

Available materials: A self-adhesive plasticine plate, a ruler, string, a knife, scissors, adhesive sheets, adhesive tape, a board for support, and straight pins.

C. The Security Ellipse

If projectile P launched from point S reaches point A at the same time as the asteroid, traveling on the only variant of the transfer orbit, it means that point A moves on a *security ellipse*, different from the transfer ellipse.

a) *Define* the security ellipse of the projectile, *draw* its ellipse, and *determine* its elements (a_0, b_0, c_0, e_0).

b) *Indicate* where the asteroid should be, relative to the projectile's security ellipse, so that:

- the projectile's transfer to the asteroid is possible on a single orbit;
- the projectile's transfer to the asteroid is possible on two orbits;
- the projectile's transfer to the asteroid is impossible.

c) One of the fragments resulting from the impact of the projectile with the asteroid continues its movement on the security ellipse. *Determine* the time interval until this fragment reaches the maximum distance from the Earth.

Available materials: A self-adhesive plasticine plate, a ruler, string, a knife, scissors, adhesive sheets, adhesive tape, a board for support, and straight pins.

Solution

A.

a) If the projectile P launched from point S meets the asteroid at point A, it means that points A and S must be on the same ellipse. F_1, the focus of the ellipse, is in the center of the Earth, E, as presented in Figures 37.4 and 37.5.

Since the problem has a single solution, the ellipse's second focus, F_2, belongs to the SA segment and is the tangent point for the two

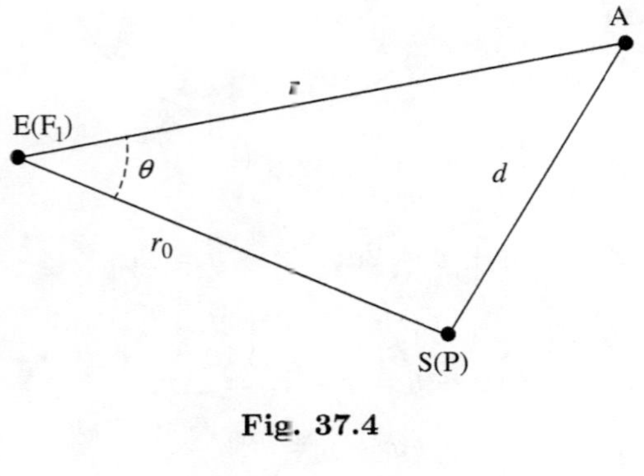

Fig. 37.4

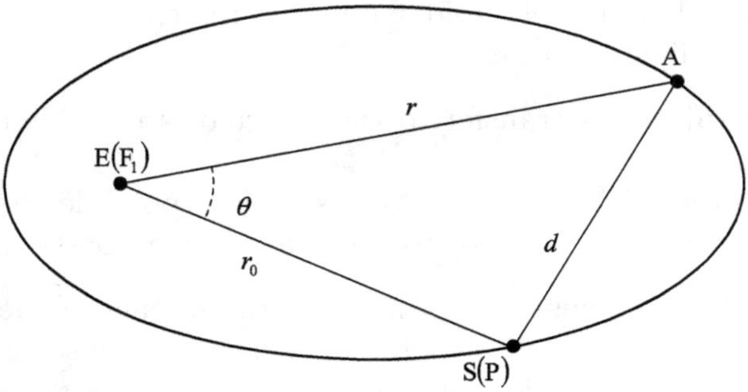

Fig. 37.5

circles of radius x and y, with centers at points S and A, respectively, as presented in Figures 37.6 and 37.7. We can locate the F_2 focus on the SA segment using a known relation for the ellipse:

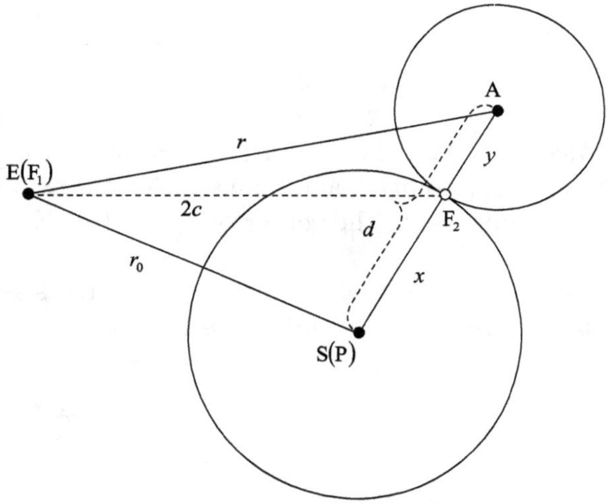

Fig. 37.6

$$r_0 + x = 2a; \quad r + y = 2a;$$

$$r_0 + x = r + y;$$

$$x - y = r - r_0 = \Delta r;$$

$$x + y = d;$$

$$x = \frac{1}{2}(d + \Delta r); \quad y = \frac{1}{2}(d - \Delta r);$$

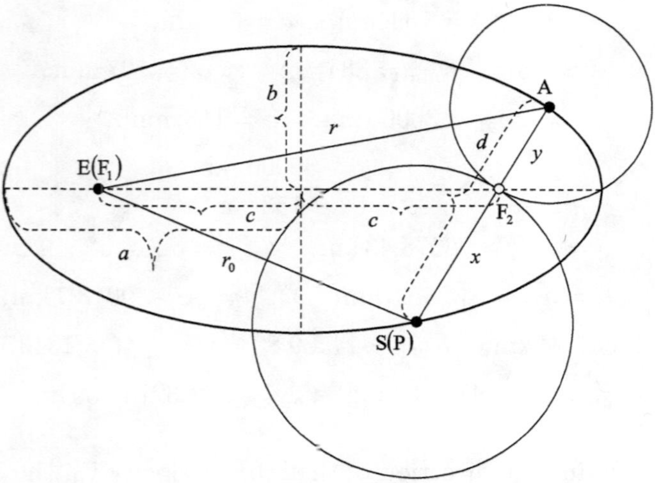

Fig. 37.7

$$a = \frac{1}{2}(r_0 + x) = \frac{1}{2}\left[r_0 + \frac{1}{2}(d + \Delta r)\right] = \frac{1}{2}\left[r_0 + \frac{1}{2}(d + r - r_0)\right];$$

$$a = \frac{1}{2}\left[r_0 + \frac{1}{2}(d + r) - \frac{r_0}{2}\right] = \frac{1}{4}(r_0 + r + d);$$

$$2a = \frac{1}{2}(r_0 + r - d); \quad F_1F_2 = 2c;$$

$$c = \sqrt{a^2 - b^2}; \quad b = \sqrt{a^2 - c^2};$$

$$e = \sqrt{1 - \frac{b^2}{a^2}}; \quad e = \frac{r_{\max} - r_{\min}}{r_{\max} + r_{\min}};$$

$$r_{\min} = a(1 - e); \quad r_{\max} = a(1 + e); \quad r_{\min} + r_{\max} = 2a.$$

Using the lengths measured on the drawing, by calculus, it results that:

$$r_0 = 133\,\text{mm}; \quad r = 153\,\text{mm}; \quad d = 115\,\text{mm};$$

$$\Delta r = r - r_0 = 20\,\text{mm};$$

$$x = 67.5\,\text{mm}; \quad y = 47.5\,\text{mm};$$

$$2a = 200\,\text{mm}; \quad a = 100\,\text{mm};$$

$$2b = 148\,\text{mm}; \quad b = 74\,\text{mm};$$

$$2c = 134\,\text{mm}; \quad c = 67\,\text{mm};$$

$$e \approx 0.67; \quad r_{\text{min}} = 33\,\text{mm}; \quad r_{\text{max}} = 167\,\text{mm};$$

$$r_{\text{real}} = 30000\,\text{km}; \quad r = 153\,\text{mm};$$

$$S = \frac{r_{\text{real}}}{r} = \frac{30000}{153}\,\frac{\text{km}}{\text{mm}};$$

$$r_{0,\text{real}} = r_0 S \approx 26078.43\,\text{km}; \quad d_{\text{real}} = dS \approx 22549\,\text{km};$$

$$x_{\text{real}} = xS \approx 13235.3\,\text{km}; \quad y_{\text{real}} = yS \approx 9313.7\,\text{km};$$

$$a_{\text{real}} \approx 19607.84\,\text{km}; \quad b_{\text{real}} \approx 14509.80\,\text{km}; \quad c_{\text{real}} \approx 13137.25\,\text{km};$$

$$r_{\text{min,real}} \approx 6470.58\,\text{km}; \quad r_{\text{max,real}} \approx 32745.09\,\text{km}.$$

b) To determine the direction of the initial velocity $\vec{v}_0$, the direction of the tangent to the ellipse at point S must be established. This can be done using the optical properties of the ellipse. According to these properties, a light beam emitted from the focus of a concave ellipsoidal mirror will pass through the other focus of the mirror after reflexion.

As a consequence, the direction of the tangent to the ellipse forms equal angles with the vector radii of point S having their origins in the two foci, as presented in the Figures 37.8, 37.9 and 37.10. The

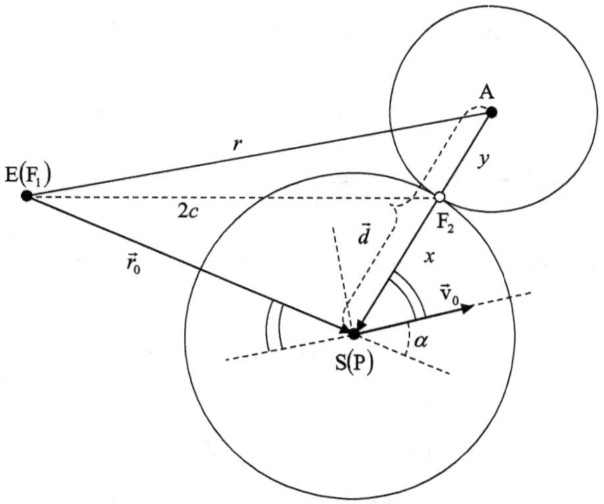

Fig. 37.8

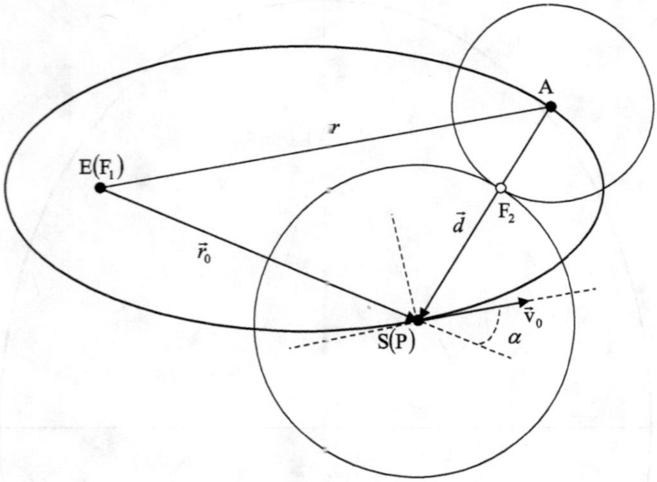

Fig. 37.9

tangent to the ellipse at point S is perpendicular to the ASP angle's bisector.

Under these conditions, the $\vec{v}_0$ direction makes an angle α with the direction of $\vec{r}_0$. The angle α can be measured: $\alpha \approx 54^0$.

c) If the projectile P launched from point S passes through point A, then points S and A are on the same ellipse that has the Earth, E, in its focus, as presented in Figure 37.11.

The projectile moves on this ellipse following the energy and the angular momentum conservation laws. For the moments when the projectile passes through points B_1 or B_2 (at the ellipse's apogee and perigee, respectively) the $E = E_0$ and $L = L_0$ equations lead to:

$$\frac{v_{1,2}^2}{2} - K\frac{M}{r_{1,2}} = \frac{v_0^2}{2} - K\frac{M}{r_0};$$

$$v_{1,2}r_{1,2} = v_0 r_0 \sin\alpha;$$

$$\left(\frac{v_0^2}{2} - K\frac{M}{r_0}\right) r_{1,2}^2 + KMr_{1,2} - \frac{1}{2}v_0^2 r_0^2 \sin^2\alpha = 0.$$

The two square roots r_1 and r_2 of this equation represent the $r_{1,2}$ values at the apogee and at the perigee; thus,

$$a = \frac{1}{2}(r_1 + r_2).$$

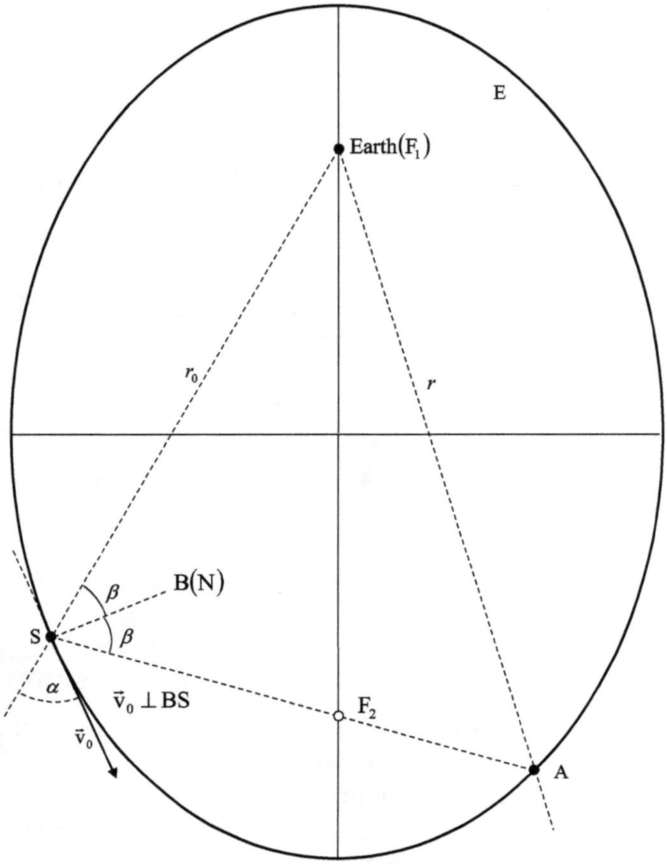

Fig. 37.10

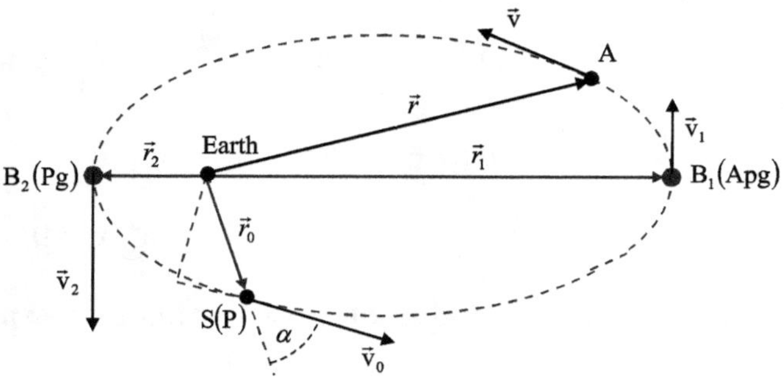

Fig. 37.11

From Viète's formulas, it results that:

$$a = \frac{KMr_0}{2KM - r_0 \mathrm{v}_0^2},$$

a relation which is independent of α (the orientation of the initial injection velocity $\vec{\mathrm{v}}_0$);

$$\mathrm{v}_0 = \sqrt{KM \frac{2a_{\mathrm{real}} - r_{0,\mathrm{real}}}{a_{\mathrm{real}} r_{0,\mathrm{real}}}} = \sqrt{\frac{KM}{r_{0,\mathrm{real}}} \cdot \frac{2a_{\mathrm{real}} - r_{0,\mathrm{real}}}{a_{\mathrm{real}}}},$$

representing the velocity of the projectile at its launching moment;

$$S = \frac{30000\,\mathrm{km}}{153\,\mathrm{mm}};$$

$$r_{0,\mathrm{real}} = 133\,\mathrm{mm} \cdot \frac{30000\,\mathrm{km}}{153\,\mathrm{mm}} \approx 26078\,\mathrm{km};$$

$$M = 6 \cdot 10^{24}\,\mathrm{kg}; \quad K = 6.67 \cdot 10^{-11}\,\mathrm{Nm^2\,kg^{-2}};$$

$$2a_{\mathrm{real}} = 200\,\mathrm{mm} \cdot S;$$

$$\mathrm{v}_0 = \sqrt{\frac{6.67 \cdot 10^{-11}\,\mathrm{Nm^2\,kg^{-2}} \cdot 6 \cdot 10^{24}\,\mathrm{kg}}{26078 \cdot 10^3\,\mathrm{m}} \cdot \frac{200 - 133}{100}};$$

$$\mathrm{v}_0 = \sqrt{\frac{6.67 \cdot 10^{-11} \cdot 6 \cdot 10^{24}}{26078 \cdot 10^3} \cdot \frac{200 - 133}{100}}\,\frac{\mathrm{m}}{\mathrm{s}} \approx 3200\,\frac{\mathrm{m}}{\mathrm{s}} = 3.2\,\frac{\mathrm{km}}{\mathrm{s}}.$$

d)

$$T^2 = \frac{4\pi^2}{K(M+m)} \cdot a_{\mathrm{real}}^3; \quad m \ll M; \quad T^2 = \frac{4\pi^2}{KM} \cdot a_{\mathrm{real}}^3;$$

$$M = 6 \cdot 10^{24}\,\mathrm{kg}; \quad K = 6.67 \cdot 10^{-11}\,\mathrm{Nm^2\,kg^{-2}};$$

$$S = \frac{30000\,\mathrm{km}}{153\,\mathrm{mm};}$$

$$a_{\mathrm{real}} = 100\,\mathrm{mm} \cdot S \approx 19608\,\mathrm{km};$$

$$T = 2\pi\sqrt{\frac{a_{\mathrm{real}}^3}{KM}} = 2 \cdot 3.14\sqrt{\frac{19608^3 \cdot 10^9}{6.67 \cdot 10^{-11} \cdot 6 \cdot 10^{24}}}\,\mathrm{s} \approx 27240\,\mathrm{s};$$

$$T \approx 454\,\mathrm{min} \approx 7.56\,\mathrm{h}.$$

The equilibrium of the system represented in Figure 37.12 is achieved:

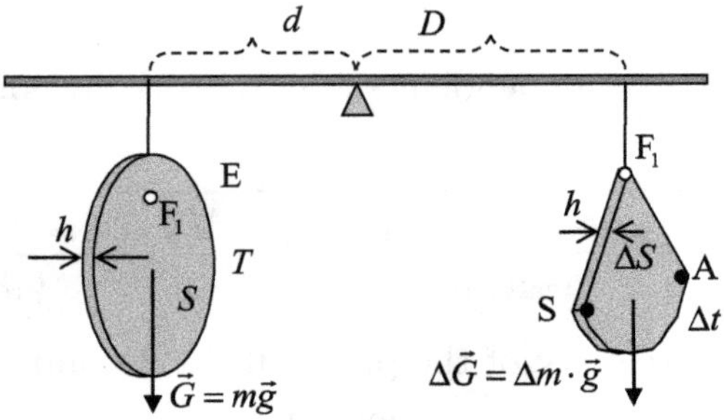

Fig. 37.12

$$G \cdot d = \Delta G \cdot D; \quad mg \cdot d = \Delta m \cdot g \cdot D;$$

$$m \cdot d = \Delta m \cdot D; \quad \rho \cdot V \cdot d = \rho \cdot \Delta V \cdot D;$$

$$V \cdot d = \Delta V \cdot D; \quad S \cdot h \cdot d = \Delta S \cdot h \cdot D;$$

$$S \cdot d = \Delta S \cdot D; \quad \frac{\Delta S}{S} = \frac{d}{D}.$$

According to Kepler's second law (the law of equal areas), it results that:

$$T \ldots\ldots\ldots\ldots\ldots\ldots S;$$

$$\Delta t \ldots\ldots\ldots\ldots\ldots \Delta S;$$

$$\Delta t = \frac{\Delta S}{S} \cdot T = \frac{d}{D} \cdot T,$$

representing the duration for which the projectile moves until it reaches the asteroid.

The results from the collected data are presented in the table below. From this table, the duration of the projectile's movement until it reaches the asteroid can be determined.

D	d	T	Δt
26 cm	11 cm	7.56 h	3.19 h

e) A thread is aligned along the ellipse's sector between S and A. Measuring the length of this thread, as presented Figures 37.13 and 37.14, it results that:

$$l_{\mathrm{SA}} = 135\,\mathrm{mm};$$

$$l_{\mathrm{SA,real}} = l_{\mathrm{SA}} \cdot S = 135\,\mathrm{mm} \cdot \frac{30000\,\mathrm{km}}{153\,\mathrm{mm}} \approx 26470.58\,\mathrm{km}.$$

B.

a) The two ellipses have a common focus, F_1, which is the center of the Earth. The projectile's injection on to any of the two ellipses occurs at the same point $\vec{r}_0$, with the same initial velocity v_0.

Thus, the semi-major axes of the two ellipses are identical:

$$a = \frac{KMr_0}{2KM - r_0\mathrm{v}_0^2}.$$

The differences between the two ellipses are: the distances between foci $2c_1 \neq 2c_2$; the minor axes $2b_1 \neq 2b_2$; and the eccentricities $e_1 \neq e_2$.

The unknown foci of the two ellipses, F_2' and F_2'', will be the intersection points of the circles with their centers at point S and point A, respectively, as presented in Figure 37.15. They are symmetrical relative to the SA line. The S and A points pertain to both ellipses

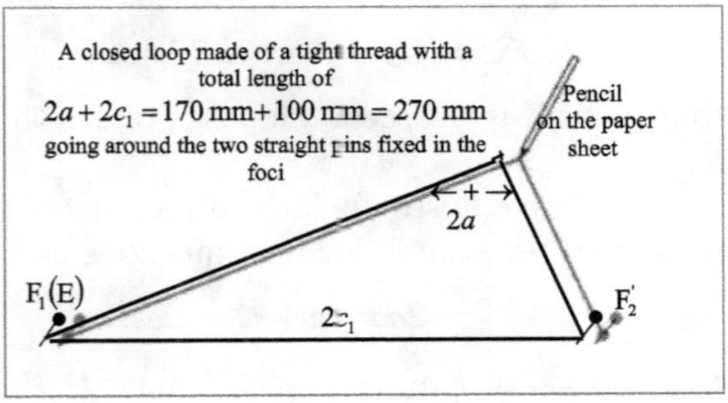

Fig. 37.13

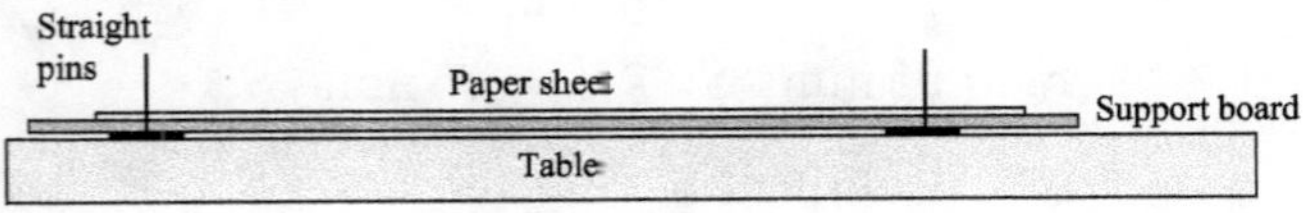

Fig. 37.14

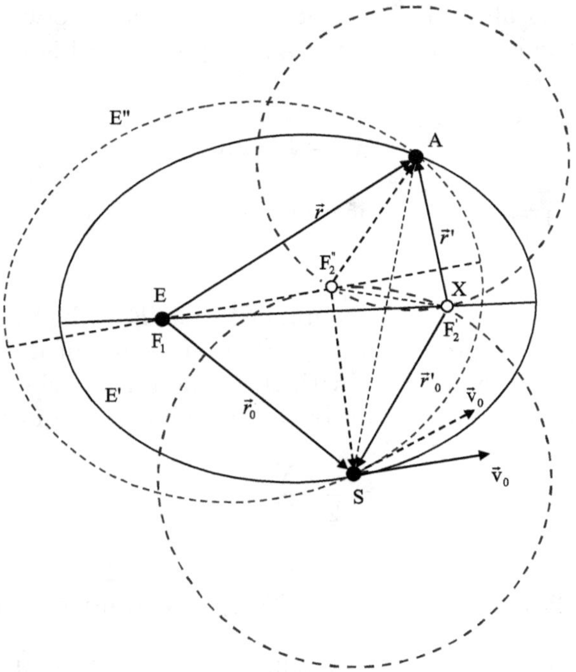

Fig. 37.15

(they are the intersection points for the two ellipses). The F_2'' focus is symmetrical to F_2' relative to the SA direction.

By measuring the distances on the given diagram, it results that:

$$\mathrm{ES} + \mathrm{SX} = \mathrm{EA} + \mathrm{AX} = 170\,\mathrm{mm}.$$

This implies that point X is the second focus of one of the two ellipses, $\mathrm{X} \equiv F_2'$.

After locating the two ellipses' foci, the directions of their axes can be drawn. For each ellipse, the following equations can be written:

$$r_0 + r_0' = 2a; \quad r + r' = 2a.$$

Measuring r_0 and r_0', or r and r', we calculate that:

$$S = \frac{30000\,\mathrm{km}}{107\,\mathrm{mm}};$$

$$r_0 = 95\,\mathrm{mm} \cdot S; \quad r_0' = 75\,\mathrm{mm} \cdot S;$$

$$r = 107\,\mathrm{mm} \cdot S; \quad r' = 63\;\mathrm{mm} \cdot S;$$

$$2a = 170\,\text{mm} \cdot S \approx 47664\,\text{km};$$

$$a = \frac{1}{2}(r_0 + r_0') = \frac{1}{2}(r + r') = 85\,\text{mm} \cdot S = 85\,\text{mm} \cdot \frac{30000\,\text{km}}{107\,\text{mm}}$$
$$\approx 23832\,\text{km}.$$

Measuring the distances between the foci of the two ellipses, it results that:

$$F_1F_2' = 2c_1; \quad b_1 = \sqrt{a^2 - c_1^2};$$
$$2c_1 = 100\,\text{mm} \cdot S; \quad c_1 = 50\,\text{mm} \cdot S;$$
$$b_1 \approx 69\,\text{mm} \cdot S \approx 19346\,\text{km};$$
$$F_1F_2'' = 2c_2; \quad b_2 = \sqrt{a^2 - c_2^2};$$
$$2c_2 = 60\,\text{mm} \cdot S; \quad c_2 = 30\,\text{mm} \cdot S;$$
$$b_2 \approx 80\,\text{mm} \cdot S \approx 22430\,\text{km}.$$

Using the two ellipses, we draw the diagrams while applying the previously determined distances and the method presented in Figures 37.16–37.20.

b) According to the optical properties of an ellipse, the α' and the α'' angles can be measured as follows:

$$\alpha' \approx 50^0; \quad \alpha'' \approx 70^0.$$

c)

$$\text{v}_0 = \sqrt{KM\frac{2a_{\text{real}} - r_{0\,\text{real}}}{a_{\text{real}}r_{0,\text{real}}}} = \sqrt{\frac{KM}{r_{0,\text{real}}} \cdot \frac{2a - r_0}{a}};$$
$$r_0 = 95\,\text{mm} \cdot S \qquad S = \frac{30000\,\text{km}}{107\,\text{mm}};$$
$$r_{0,\text{real}} \approx 26636\,\text{km}; \quad 2a_{\text{real}} = 170\,\text{mm} \cdot S;$$
$$a = 85\,\text{mm} \cdot S; \quad a_{\text{real}} = 23831.77\,\text{km};$$

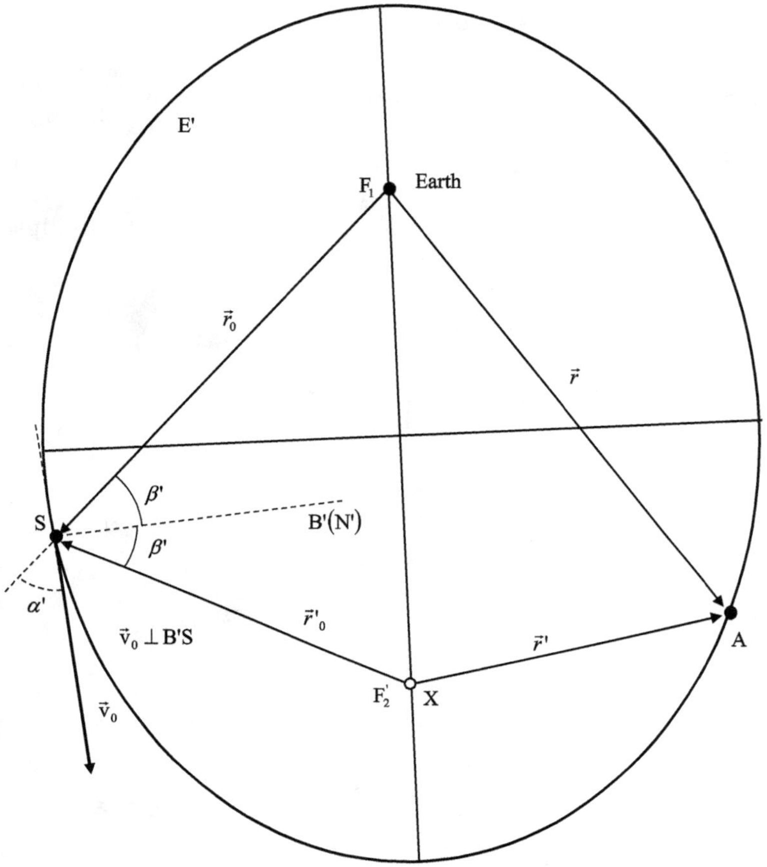

Fig. 37.16

$$2a = 170\,\text{mm}; \quad 2a_{\text{real}} = 47663.55\,\text{km};$$

$$\text{v}_0 = \sqrt{\frac{6.67 \cdot 10^{-11}\,\text{Nm}^2\,\text{kg}^{-2} \cdot 6 \cdot 10^{24}\,\text{kg}}{26636 \cdot 10^3\,\text{m}} \cdot \frac{170 - 95}{85}};$$

$$\text{v}_0 = \sqrt{\frac{6.67 \cdot 10^{-11} \cdot 6 \cdot 10^{24}}{26636 \cdot 10^3} \cdot \frac{170 - 95}{85}}\,\frac{\text{m}}{\text{s}} \approx 3640\,\frac{\text{m}}{\text{s}} \approx 3.6\,\frac{\text{km}}{\text{s}}.$$

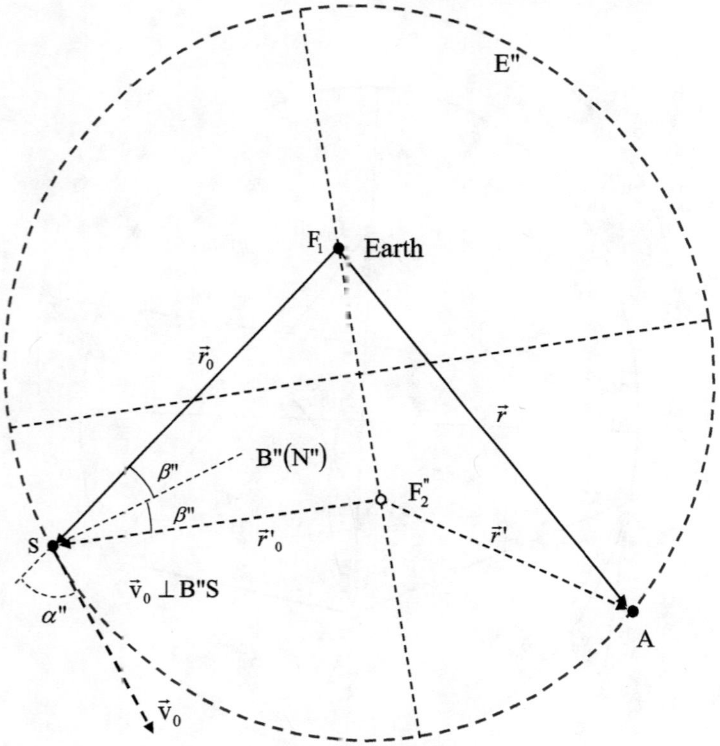

Fig. 37.17

d)

$$T^2 = \frac{4\pi^2}{K(M+m)} \cdot a_{\text{real}}^3; \quad m \ll M; \quad T^2 = \frac{4\pi^2}{KM} \cdot a_{\text{real}}^3;$$

$$M = 6 \cdot 10^{24}\,\text{kg}; \quad K = 6.67 \cdot 10^{-11}\,\text{Nm}^2\,\text{kg}^{-2};$$

$$a_{\text{real}} = 23832\,\text{km};$$

$$T = 2\pi\sqrt{\frac{a_{\text{real}}^3}{KM}} = 2 \cdot 3.14\sqrt{\frac{23832^3 \cdot 10^9}{6.67 \cdot 10^{-11} \cdot 6 \cdot 10^{24}}}\,\text{s} \approx 36523\,\text{s};$$

$$T \approx 608\,\text{min} \approx 10\,\text{h}.$$

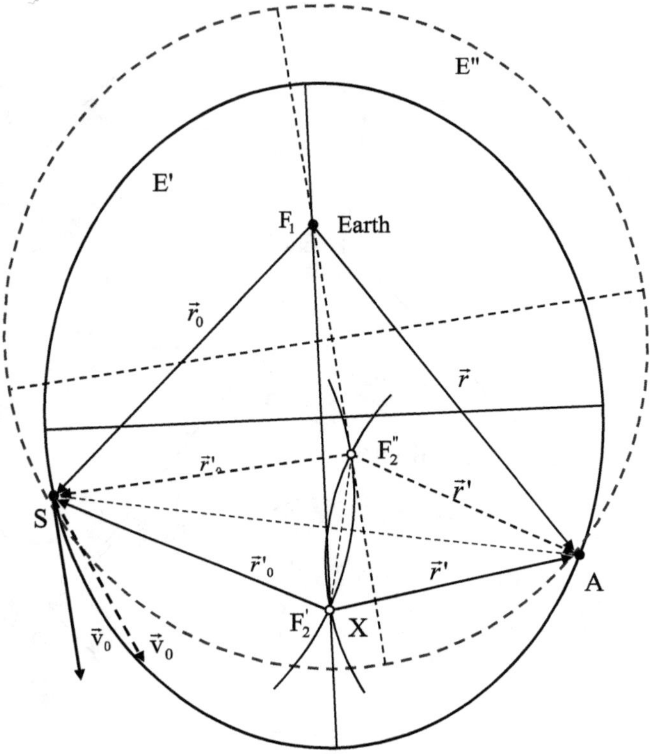

Fig. 37.18

For each of the two ellipses, the system's equilibrium is achieved, as presented in Figure 37.19:

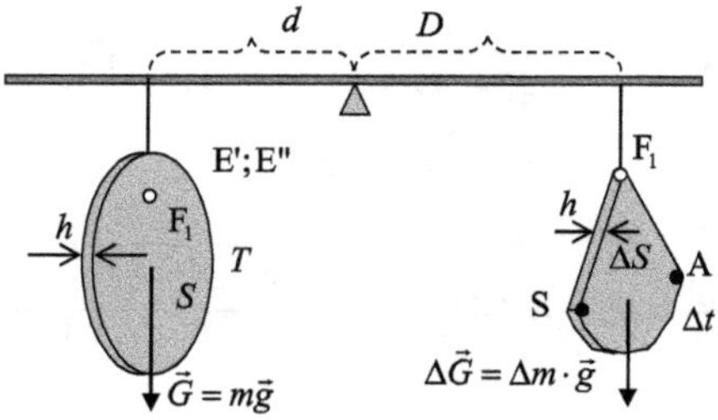

Fig. 37.19

$$G \cdot d = \Delta G \cdot D; \quad mg \cdot d = \Delta m \cdot g \cdot D;$$

$$m \cdot d = \Delta m \cdot D; \quad \rho \cdot V \cdot d = \rho \cdot \Delta V \cdot D;$$

$$V \cdot d = \Delta V \cdot D; \quad S \cdot h \cdot d = \Delta S \cdot h \cdot D;$$

$$S \cdot d = \Delta S \cdot D; \quad \frac{\Delta S}{S} = \frac{d}{D}.$$

According to Kepler's second law (the law of equal areas), it results that:

$$T \ldots\ldots\ldots\ldots\ldots\ldots\ldots\ldots S;$$

$$\Delta t \ldots\ldots\ldots\ldots\ldots\ldots\ldots \Delta S;$$

$$\Delta t = \frac{\Delta S}{S} \cdot T = \frac{d}{D} \cdot T.$$

From measurements for the projectile's movement on the E' ellipse, it results that:

$$d = 12.8\,\text{cm}; \quad D = 23\,\text{cm}; \quad T = 10\,\text{h};$$

$$\Delta t = \frac{d}{D} \cdot T = \frac{12.8\,\text{cm}}{23\,\text{cm}} \cdot 10\,\text{h} \approx 5.56\,\text{h};$$

$$d = 10.7\,\text{cm}; \quad D = 25\,\text{cm};$$

$$\Delta \tau = \frac{10.7\,\text{cm}}{25\,\text{cm}} \cdot 10\,\text{h} \approx 4.28\,\text{h};$$

$$\Delta t = T - \Delta \tau = 5.72\,\text{h};$$

$$\Delta t = \frac{5.56\,\text{h} + 5.72\,\text{h}}{2} = 5.64\,\text{h}.$$

From measurements for the projectile's movement on the E'' ellipse, it results that:

$$d = 8.5\,\text{cm}; \quad D = 22.3\,\text{cm}; \quad T = 10\,\text{h};$$

$$\Delta t = \frac{d}{D} \cdot T = \frac{8.5\,\text{cm}}{22.3\,\text{cm}} \cdot 10\,\text{h} \approx 3.81\,\text{h};$$

$$d = 13.5\,\text{cm}; \quad D = 23\,\text{cm};$$

$$\Delta \tau = \frac{13.5\,\text{cm}}{23\,\text{cm}} \cdot 10\,\text{h} \approx 5.86\,\text{h};$$

$$\Delta t = T - \Delta\tau = 4.14\,\text{h};$$

$$\Delta t = \frac{3.81\,\text{h} + 4.14\,\text{h}}{2} = 3.975\,\text{h}.$$

e) Using a thread to model each SA sector of the two ellipses, it results that:

$$l'_{\text{SA}} = 183\,\text{mm}; \quad l'_{\text{SA,real}} = l'_{\text{SA}}S = 183\,\text{mm} \cdot \frac{30000\,\text{km}}{107\,\text{mm}} \approx 51308.41\,\text{km};$$

$$l''_{\text{SA}} = 156\,\text{mm}; \quad l''_{\text{SA,real}} = l''_{\text{SA}}S = 156\,\text{mm} \cdot \frac{30000\,\text{km}}{107\,\text{mm}} \approx 43738.31\,\text{km}.$$

C.

a) Figure 37.20 presents the projectile's transfer ellipse, E, to the asteroid, from point S to point A, for the case in which there is only one solution for this transfer. Points S and A pertain to this ellipse. The elements of this ellipse have previously been determined.

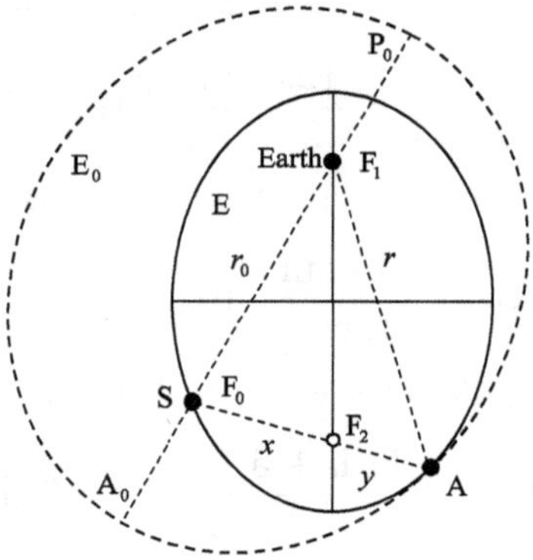

Fig. 37.20

We can consider that point A pertains to another ellipse, with F_1 (Earth) and F_0 (S) as its foci, whose major axis is $2a_0$. Thus, it results that:

$$\text{PA} + \text{AS} = 2a_0;$$

$$r + x + y = 2a_0;$$

$$r_0 + x = 2a; \quad r + y = 2a;$$

$$2a + 2a - r_0 = 2a_0;$$

$$2a_0 = 4a - r_0,$$

representing the major axis of the *security ellipse*;

$$2a_0 = 222\,\text{mm} - 74\,\text{mm} = 148\,\text{mm};$$

$$S = \frac{30000\,\text{km}}{85\,\text{mm}};$$

$$2a_{0,\text{real}} = 2a_0 S = 148\,\text{mm} \cdot \frac{30000\,\text{km}}{85\,\text{mm}} \approx 52235.29\,\text{km}.$$

Or, referring to point A on the diagram:

$$2a_0 = 400\,\text{mm} - 133\,\text{mm} = 267\,\text{mm};$$

$$S = \frac{30000\,\text{km}}{153\,\text{mm}};$$

$$2a_{0,\text{real}} = 2a_0 S = 267\,\text{mm} \cdot \frac{30000\,\text{km}}{153\,\text{mm}} \approx 52352.94\,\text{km};$$

$$a_{0,\text{real}} = 26176.47\,\text{km}.$$

The *security ellipse* is a section of the *security ellipsoid*, in the transfer orbit plane, obtained by rotating the transfer ellipse around the PS axis corresponding to the first variant.

In addition, for the security ellipse E_0, we have:

$$2c_{0,\text{real}} = r_{0,\text{real}} = 26078\,\text{km}; \quad c_{0,\text{real}} = 13039\,\text{km};$$

$$b_{0,\text{real}} = \sqrt{a_{0,\text{real}}^2 - c_{0,\text{real}}^2} \approx 22697.84\,\text{km};$$

$$e_0 = \sqrt{1 - \frac{b_{0,\text{real}}^2}{a_{0,\text{real}}^2}} \approx 0.5.$$

The outline of the security ellipse can be drawn as presented in Figures 37.21 and 37.22.

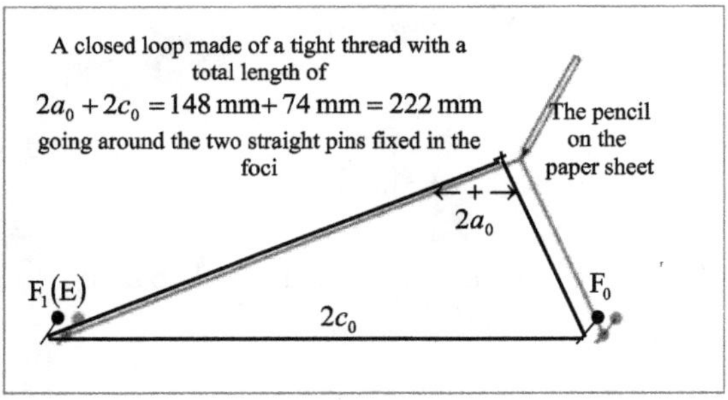

Fig. 37.21

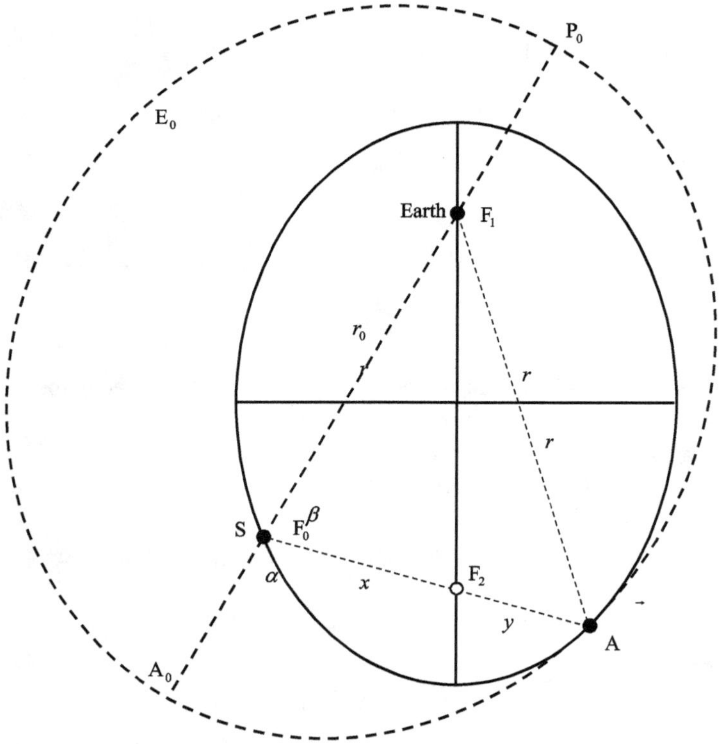

Fig. 37.22

b) If point A is on the security ellipsoid of the projectile, then the projectile's transfer to the asteroid can take place on a single orbit.

If point A is inside the projectile's security ellipsoid, then the transfer of the projectile to the asteroid can take place on two orbits.

The projectile's transfer to the asteroid is not possible if the point A is outside the projectile's security ellipsoid.

c) For the security ellipse E_0 and its sector $\mathrm{EAA_0}$, marked on plasticine plates and modeled using the known method, the equilibrium for the system presented in Figure 37.23 is achieved:

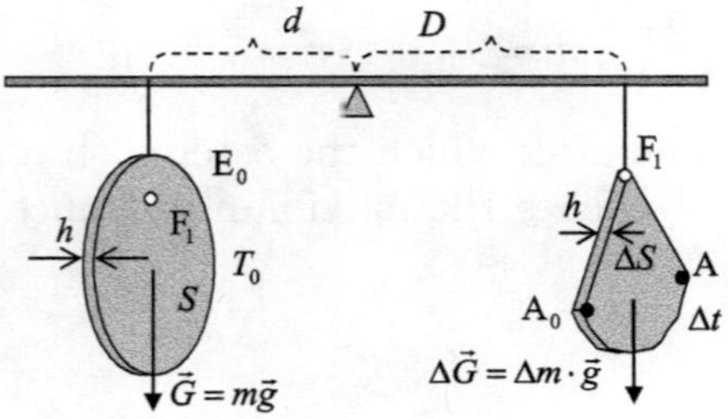

Fig. 37.23

$$G \cdot d = \Delta G \cdot D; \quad mg \cdot d = \Delta m \cdot g \cdot D;$$

$$m \cdot d = \Delta m \cdot D; \quad \rho \cdot V \cdot d = \rho \cdot \Delta V \cdot D;$$

$$V \cdot d = \Delta V \cdot D; \quad S \cdot h \cdot d = \Delta S \cdot h \cdot D;$$

$$S \cdot d = \Delta S \cdot D; \quad \frac{\Delta S}{S} = \frac{d}{D}.$$

According to Kepler's second law (the law of equal areas), it results that:

$$T_0 \ldots\ldots\ldots\ldots\ldots\ldots\ldots S;$$

$$\Delta t \ldots\ldots\ldots\ldots\ldots\ldots \Delta S;$$

$$\Delta t = \frac{\Delta S}{S} \cdot T_0 = \frac{d}{D} \cdot T_0;$$

$$T_0^2 = \frac{4\pi^2}{KM} a_{0,\mathrm{real}}^3; \quad a_{0,\mathrm{real}} = 26176.47\,\mathrm{km};$$

$$M = 6 \cdot 10^{24}\,\mathrm{kg}; \quad K = 6.67 \cdot 10^{-11}\,\mathrm{Nm^2\,kg^{-2}};$$

$$T_0 = 2\pi \cdot a_{0,\mathrm{real}} \cdot \sqrt{\frac{a_{0,\mathrm{real}}}{KM}} \approx 42042.42\,\mathrm{s};$$

$$T_0 \approx 700.7\ \mathrm{min} \approx 11.67\,\mathrm{h}.$$

For the asteroid fragment moving on the security ellipse, E_0, from our measurements, it results that:

$$d = 8.5\,\text{cm}; \quad D = 22.3\,\text{cm}; \quad T = 11.67\,\text{h};$$

$$\Delta\tau = \frac{d}{D} \cdot T = \frac{8.5\,\text{cm}}{23\,\text{cm}} \cdot 11.67\,\text{h} \approx 4.31\,\text{h};$$

$$\Delta t = T_0 - \Delta\tau = 7.36\,\text{h},$$

representing the time after which the asteroid fragment traveling on the security ellipse reaches the maximum distance from the Earth's center.

Problem 38

Virial Theorem

Prove the following statement: The relationship between the time-averaged kinetic and potential energies and the degree of homogeneity of the system's potential energy function is expressed by the following relation:

$$2 \cdot \langle E_{\mathrm{c}} \rangle_{\mathrm{t}} = q \cdot \langle E_{\mathrm{p}} \rangle_{\mathrm{t}}.$$

Solution

In its historical form, Kepler's third law referring to planets moving around the Sun is

$$\frac{R_1^3}{T_1^2} = \frac{R_2^3}{T_2^2},$$

where T_1 and T_2 are the periods of two planets' movements, and R_1 and R_2 are the mean distances between the two planets and the Sun, without specifying which kind of mean it is.

In a subsequent form derived from Newton's laws, Kepler's third law has the form

$$\frac{a_1^3}{T_1^2} = \frac{a_2^3}{T_2^2},$$

where a_1 and a_2 are the semi-major axes of the two elliptic orbits on which the planets are moving around the Sun.

Knowing that the *temporal mean* of a periodical function dependent on time, $x(t)$, is given by the expression

$$\langle x \rangle_{\mathrm{t}} = \frac{1}{\mathrm{T}} \int_0^{\mathrm{T}} x(t)\mathrm{d}t,$$

by direct integration, we find that the temporal mean of the distance between the ellipse's focus and the points on the parabola is:

$$\langle r \rangle_{\mathrm{t}} = \frac{3a^2 - b^2}{2a};$$

$$a > b; \quad \langle r \rangle_{\mathrm{t}} > a,$$

which proves that the mean distance $R = a$, presented in the two forms of Kepler's third law, differs from the mean temporal distance.

By defining the *spatial mean* of the same variable quantity x, for the points on a curve C, as

$$\langle x \rangle_{\mathrm{c}} = \frac{1}{C} \int_0^{\mathrm{C}} x(s)\mathrm{d}s,$$

when the C curve is an ellipse, we find through integration that the spatial mean of the distance between the ellipse's focus and the points on the ellipse is

$$\langle r \rangle_{\mathrm{c}} = a = R,$$

which proves that the mean distance presented in the two forms of Kepler's third law is the spatial mean distance.

Further, we will demonstrate that the previous result can be more intuitively obtained by using elements of the geometry of the ellipse and symmetry arguments.

It is known that the sum of distances from any point P on an ellipse to the two foci F and F′ of the ellipse is equal to the ellipse's major axis:

$$\mathrm{PF} + \mathrm{PF}' = 2a.$$

Let's consider that points P and P′ on the ellipse are symmetrical relative to the minor axis, as presented in Figure 38.1.

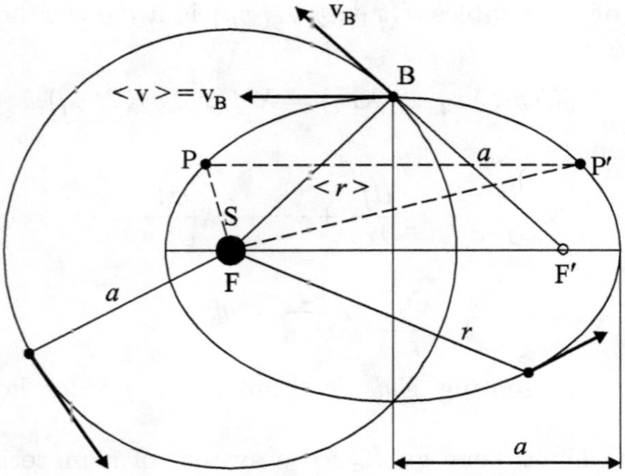

Fig. 38.1

The mean distances from the focus F to all points on the ellipse can be calculated by adding up the distances from the focus F to all pairs of symmetrical points, i.e.,

$$\sum_{1}^{n} (\mathrm{FP} + \mathrm{FP}'),$$

where, taking into account the symmetry of P and P′ relative to the minor axis of the ellipse, FP′ = PF′, the spatial mean of the distance from focus F to any point P on the ellipse is

$$\langle \mathrm{FP} \rangle = \frac{\sum_1^n (\mathrm{FP} + \mathrm{FP}')}{2n} = \frac{\sum_1^n (\mathrm{PF} + \mathrm{PF}')}{2n} = \frac{2an}{2n} = a = \langle r \rangle.$$

With this result, the distance R in Kepler's third law can be estimated as the mean of the orbit's geometry and not as the mean of the orbit's dynamics.

Another way to understand the nature of these means is offered by the *Virial theorem*, which relates the average of the total kinetic and potential energy of a physical system over time with the power q of the distance the potential energy of the system depends on.

To deduce the relation between the previously mentioned elements (in the Virial theorem), we recall that in mathematical analysis, if a function of n variables $f(x_1, x_2, \dots x_n)$ is a q-order homogeneous function, i.e.,

$$f(\lambda x_1, \lambda x_2, \dots \lambda x_n) = \lambda^q f(x_1, x_2 \dots x_n),$$

then the identity:

$$x_1 \frac{\partial f}{\partial x_1} + x_2 \frac{\partial f}{\partial x_2} + \dots + x_n \frac{\partial f}{\partial x_n} = qf,$$

$$\sum_{k=1}^{n} x_k \frac{\partial f}{\partial x_k} = qf,$$

is satisfied, representing *Euler's theorem* for q-order homogeneous functions.

Since the kinetic energy E_{c} for a system of n material points is a homogeneous function of second degree (of order $q = 2$), for components $\vec{\mathrm{v}}_1, \vec{\mathrm{v}}_2, \dots \vec{\mathrm{v}}_n$, according to the previously presented *Euler's theorem* we have:

$$\vec{\mathrm{v}}_1 \frac{\partial E_{\mathrm{c}}}{\partial \vec{\mathrm{v}}_1} + \vec{\mathrm{v}}_2 \frac{\partial E_{\mathrm{c}}}{\partial \vec{\mathrm{v}}_2} + \dots + \vec{\mathrm{v}}_n \frac{\partial E_{\mathrm{c}}}{\partial \vec{\mathrm{v}}_{\mathrm{n}}} = 2E_{\mathrm{c}};$$

$$\sum_{k=1}^{n} \vec{\mathrm{v}}_k \frac{\partial E_{\mathrm{c}}}{\partial \vec{\mathrm{v}}_k} = 2E_{\mathrm{c}};$$

$$\frac{\partial E_{\mathrm{c}}}{\partial \vec{\mathrm{v}}_k} = m_k \vec{\mathrm{v}}_k = \vec{p}_k;$$

$$\sum_{k=1}^{n} \vec{p}_k \vec{\mathrm{v}}_k = 2E_{\mathrm{c}};$$

$$\sum_{k=1}^{n} \vec{p}_k \frac{\mathrm{d}\vec{r}_k}{\mathrm{d}t} = 2E_{\mathrm{c}};$$

$$\frac{\mathrm{d}}{\mathrm{d}t} \sum_{k=1}^{n} \vec{p}_k \vec{r}_k - \sum_{k=1}^{n} \vec{r}_k \frac{\mathrm{d}\vec{p}_k}{\mathrm{d}t} = 2E_{\mathrm{c}};$$

$$\frac{\mathrm{d}\vec{p}_k}{\mathrm{d}t} = \vec{F}_k = -\nabla_k E_{\mathrm{p}} = -\frac{\partial E_{\mathrm{p}}}{\partial \vec{r}_k} = \left(\frac{\partial E_{\mathrm{p}}}{\partial x_k} \vec{i} + \frac{\partial E_{\mathrm{p}}}{\partial y_k} \vec{j} + \frac{\partial E_{\mathrm{p}}}{\partial z_k} \vec{k} \right);$$

$$\sum_{k=1}^{n} \vec{r}_k \frac{\mathrm{d}\vec{p}_k}{\mathrm{d}t} = -\sum_{k=1}^{n} \vec{r}_k \frac{\partial E_{\mathrm{p}}}{\partial \vec{r}_k} = -qE_{\mathrm{p}},$$

according to Euler's theorem, if we admit that the potential energy of the system is a q-order homogeneous function;

$$\frac{\mathrm{d}}{\mathrm{d}t}\sum_{k=1}^{n}\vec{p}_k\vec{r}_k + qE_{\mathrm{p}} = 2E_{\mathrm{c}}.$$

To calculate the mean of this value relative to time, we note that:

- The mean value of any function of time is the quantity $f(t)$:

$$\bar{f} = \lim_{\tau\to\infty}\frac{1}{\tau}\int_0^{\tau} f(t)\mathrm{d}t,$$

- If function $f(t)$ is the derivative of function $F(t)$ with respect to the time variable, i.e., $f(t) = \frac{\mathrm{d}F(t)}{\mathrm{d}t}$, which is bounded (does not have infinite values), then its mean value is zero:

$$\bar{f} = \lim_{\tau\to\infty}\frac{1}{\tau}\int_0^{\tau}\frac{\mathrm{d}F}{\mathrm{d}t}\mathrm{d}t = \lim_{\tau\to\infty}\frac{F(\tau)-F(0)}{\tau} = 0;$$

  this is true if function $F(t)$ refers to a limited domain of space.

Under these conditions, we have:

$$\overline{\frac{\mathrm{d}}{\mathrm{d}t}\sum_{k=1}^{n}\vec{p}_k\vec{r}_k} + q\langle E_{\mathrm{p}}\rangle_{\mathrm{t}} = 2\langle E_{\mathrm{c}}\rangle_{\mathrm{t}};$$

$$\overline{\frac{\mathrm{d}}{\mathrm{d}t}\sum_{k=1}^{n}\vec{p}_k\vec{r}_k} = \lim_{\tau\to\infty}\frac{1}{\tau}\int_0^{\tau}\frac{\mathrm{d}}{\mathrm{d}t}\left(\sum_{k=1}^{n}\vec{p}_k\vec{r}_k\right)\mathrm{d}t = 0,$$

since each product $\vec{p}_k\vec{r}_k$ remains finite;

$$2\langle E_{\mathrm{c}}\rangle_{\mathrm{t}} = q\langle E_{\mathrm{p}}\rangle_{\mathrm{t}}.$$

This relation represents the *virial theorem* and shows the *link between the temporal means of kinetic energy and potential energy and the homogeneity order of the homogeneous function by which the system's potential energy is expressed.*

For the planet–Sun mechanical system, the kinetic energy is $E_{\mathrm{c}} = \frac{1}{2}m\mathrm{v}^2$ the potential energy is $E_{\mathrm{p}} = -G\frac{mM}{r}$, and the homogeneity order of the E_p function is $q = -1$ (the same as the power of r in the homogeneous function E_p).

According to the virial theorem for this system, we have:

$$2\langle E_c\rangle_t = -\langle E_p\rangle_t; \quad 2\left\langle \frac{m\mathrm{v}^2}{2}\right\rangle = -\left\langle -G\frac{mM}{r}\right\rangle_t;$$

$$\langle \mathrm{v}^2\rangle_t = GM\left\langle \frac{1}{r}\right\rangle_t.$$

This represents the relation between the temporal means of the velocity's second power and the second power of the inverse of distance.

Let's define the *Kepler mean velocity* of the planet as

$$\langle \mathrm{v}\rangle = \frac{2\pi a}{T}.$$

According to Kepler's third law, this relation is the same for all elliptical orbits with identical major axes, 2a, and for the circle of radius a with its center in one of the foci.

The total energy of the planet–Sun system is

$$E = -G\frac{mM}{2a},$$

and according to the conservation rule, it is identical to the total energy when the planet passes through the minor point B, i.e.:

$$-G\frac{mM}{2a} = \frac{1}{2}m\mathrm{v}_B^2 - G\frac{mM}{a};$$

$$\mathrm{v}_B^2 = \frac{GM}{a},$$

which shows that at point B the planet's velocity v_B depends (besides M) on the distance $r_B = a$ between focus F and point B.

So, the velocity v_B of the planet at minor vertex B of the ellipse must be the same as the velocity on a circular orbit of radius equal to the ellipse's semi-major axis:

$$\mathrm{v}_B = \frac{2\pi a}{T} = \langle \mathrm{v}\rangle.$$

From the previous relations, it results that

$$\frac{\langle \mathrm{v}^2\rangle_\mathrm{t}}{\mathrm{v}_\mathrm{B}^2} = \frac{\left\langle \frac{1}{r}\right\rangle_\mathrm{t}}{\frac{1}{R}} = \frac{\langle \mathrm{v}^2\rangle_\mathrm{t}}{\langle \mathrm{v}\rangle^2} = c,$$

a ratio of constant value for any elliptic orbit. In the special case of a circular orbit for which the mean values are identical to the circle's radius and the velocity on the orbit, $c = 1$.

This result shows that the Kepler mean of the planet–Sun distance is the inverse of the temporal mean of the inverse of the planet–Sun distance, i.e.,

$$R = \frac{1}{\left\langle \frac{1}{r}\right\rangle_\mathrm{t}},$$

and the Kepler mean velocity of the planet is the square root of the temporal mean of the orbital velocity's second power, i.e.,

$$\langle \mathrm{v}\rangle = \sqrt{\langle \mathrm{v}^2\rangle_\mathrm{t}}.$$

Through direct integration, we demonstrate that

$$\langle \mathrm{v}\rangle = \sqrt{\langle \mathrm{v}\rangle_\mathrm{t}\langle \mathrm{v}\rangle_\mathrm{c}}.$$

The Kepler mean of the planet–Sun distance, $R = a$, is a mean over the orbit's geometry, better presented graphically by the oblique focus–vertex distance, i.e., the distance from the Sun in focus F to the minor vertex B.

The Kepler mean of the orbital velocity, $\langle \mathrm{v}\rangle = \frac{2\pi a}{T} = \mathrm{v}_\mathrm{B}$, is the square root of the temporal mean of the orbital velocity's second power, and it coincides with the instantaneous velocity on the elliptic orbit at the minor vertex B.

Problem 39

The Gravitational Potential Energy of a Spherical Cluster

In diagram (a) of Figure 39.1 are presented N bodies of masses $m_1, m_2, \ldots\ldots, m_N$ placed very far apart, so that there are no gravitational interactions between them. The gravitational potential energy of such a system is zero.

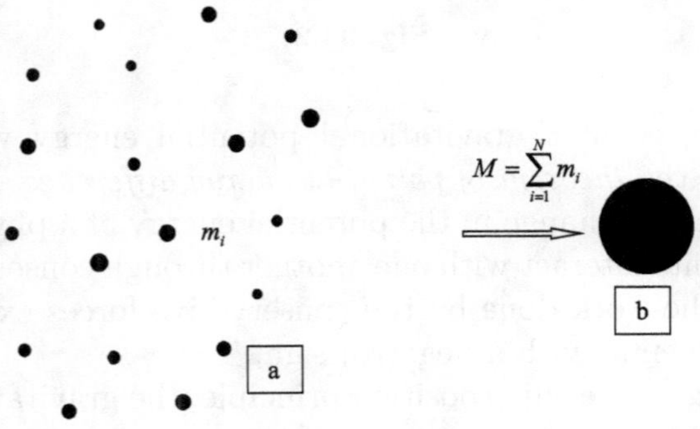

Fig. 39.1

Determine the gravitational potential energy of the same mass distributed continuously to form a single spherical body, as shown in diagram (b), with radius R, total mass $M = \sum_{i=1}^{N} m_i$, and uniform density ρ.

Solution

In diagram (c) of Figure 39.2, the N bodies, placed at finite distances from one another, interacting gravitationally, form an insulated system of discontinuous structure. The potential energy of a specific pair is

$$E_{\mathrm{p},ij} = -G\frac{m_i m_j}{r_{ij}}.$$

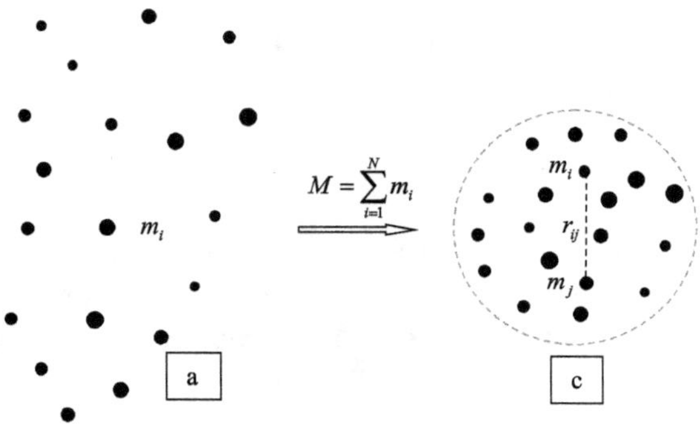

Fig. 39.2

This expression of gravitational potential energy was obtained according to the *theorem of potential energy difference.* According to this theorem, the change in the potential energy of a physical system whose elements interact with one another through conservative forces is equal to the work done by the conservative forces exerted on the system's elements, with a negative sign.

According to the superposition principle, the gravitational potential energy of the system represents the sum of the potential energies of all possible pairs of bodies in the given system, i.e.,

$$E_{\mathrm{p}} = \sum_{i,j=i;i\neq j}^{N} E_{p,ij} = \sum_{i,j=1;i\neq j}^{N} \left(-G\frac{m_i m_j}{r_{ij}}\right).$$

As presented in Figure 39.3, let's admit that the N bodies located far apart, without gravitational interactions, form a single spherical

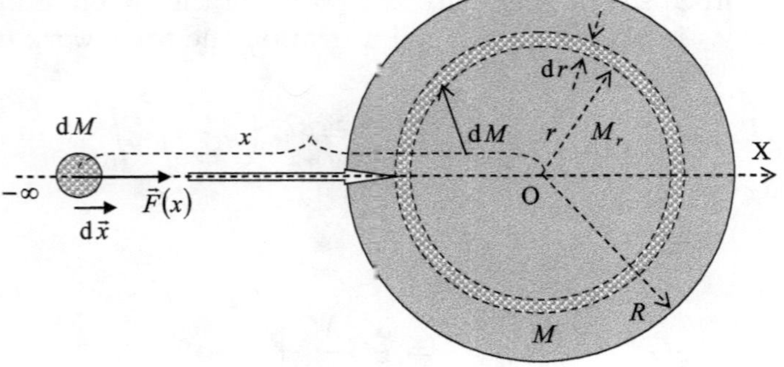

Fig. 39.3

body of radius R, mass $M = \sum_{i=1}^{N} m_i$ and density ρ with a fcontinuous structure. Now, we determine the gravitational potential energy of this system of continuous structure

Let's imagine that we are building a sphere by adding homogeneous, thin, spherical layers of mass dM and elementary thickness dr to a sphere of radius r and mass M_r, as presented in Figure 39.3. The process continues until we reach a sphere of radius R and mass M.

The elementary work done to bring the body of elementary mass dM from infinity to the surface of the sphere of radius r and mass M_r is:

$$\begin{aligned}
dL_r &= \int_{-\infty}^{-r} \vec{F}(x) \cdot d\vec{x} = \int_{-\infty}^{-r} G\frac{M_r dM_r}{x^2} dx \\
&= GM_r dM_r \int_{-\infty}^{-r} \frac{dx}{x^2} = -GM_r \cdot dM_r \cdot \frac{1}{x}\bigg|_{-\infty}^{-r} \\
&= GM_r \cdot dM_r \cdot \frac{1}{r} = K\rho\frac{4\pi r^3}{3} \cdot d\left(\rho\frac{4\pi r^3}{3}\right) \cdot \frac{1}{r} \\
&= G\rho\frac{4\pi r^3}{3}\rho\frac{4\pi}{3}3r^2 dr\frac{1}{r} \\
&= G\rho\frac{4\pi r^3}{3}\rho\frac{4\pi}{3}3r^2 dr\frac{1}{r} = 3G\left(\rho\frac{4\pi}{3}\right)^2 r^4 dr.
\end{aligned}$$

If the process continues until the radius of the sphere becomes R and its mass is M, we obtain by integration the total work done:

$$L = \int_0^R \left[3G\left(\rho\frac{4\pi}{3}\right)^2 r^4 \mathrm{d}r\right] = 3G\left(\rho\frac{4\pi}{3}\right)^2 \int_0^R r^4 \mathrm{d}r$$

$$= 3G\left(\rho\frac{4\pi}{3}\right)^2 \frac{R^5}{5}$$

$$= \frac{3}{5}G\left(\rho\frac{4\pi R^3}{3}\right)^2 \frac{1}{R} = \frac{3}{5}G\frac{M^2}{R}.$$

According to the gravitational potential energy theorem, it results that the gravitational potential energy of the sphere of mass M and radius R is

$$E_{\mathrm{p}} = -L = -\frac{3}{5}G\frac{M^2}{R},$$

representing the gravitational potential energy of the spherical cluster.

Application

For an insulated spherical cluster formed by N galaxies, each of mass m, according to the virial theorem, it results that:

$$2\langle E_{\mathrm{c}}\rangle_{\mathrm{t}} = -\langle E_{\mathrm{p}}\rangle_{\mathrm{t}};$$

$$-2\left\langle \sum_{i=1}^{N} \frac{1}{2} m_i \mathrm{v}_i^2 \right\rangle_{\mathrm{t}} = \langle E_{\mathrm{p}}\rangle_{\mathrm{t}}; \quad -\left\langle \sum_{i=1}^{N} m_i \mathrm{v}_i^2 \right\rangle_{\mathrm{t}} = \langle E_{\mathrm{p}}\rangle_{\mathrm{t}};$$

$$-m\left\langle \sum_{i=1}^{N} \mathrm{v}_i^2 \right\rangle_{\mathrm{t}} = \langle E_{\mathrm{p}}\rangle_{\mathrm{t}};$$

$$-\frac{m}{N}\left\langle \sum_{i=1}^{N} \mathrm{v}_i^2 \right\rangle_{\mathrm{t}} = \frac{1}{N}\langle E_{\mathrm{p}}\rangle_{\mathrm{t}};$$

$$E_{\mathrm{p}} = -\frac{3}{5}G\frac{M^2}{R};$$

$$-\frac{m}{N}\left\langle\sum_{i=1}^{N}\mathrm{v}_i^2\right\rangle = -\frac{1}{N}\frac{3}{5}G\frac{M^2}{R};$$

$$\frac{M}{N} = m;$$

$$\frac{m}{N}\left\langle\sum_{i=1}^{N}\mathrm{v}_i^2\right\rangle_{\mathrm{t}} = m\frac{3}{5}G\frac{M}{R};$$

$$\frac{1}{N}\left\langle\sum_{i=1}^{N}\mathrm{v}_i^2\right\rangle_{\mathrm{t}} = \frac{3}{5}\frac{GM}{R};$$

$$\frac{1}{N}\left\langle\sum_{i=1}^{N}\mathrm{v}_i^2\right\rangle_{\mathrm{t}} = \left\langle\frac{\sum_{i=1}^{N}\mathrm{v}_i^2}{N}\right\rangle = \left\langle\frac{\mathrm{v}_1^2+\mathrm{v}_2^2+\cdots\cdots\cdots+\mathrm{v}_N^2}{N}\right\rangle;$$

$$\mathrm{v}_1 \approx \mathrm{v}_2 \approx \cdot\ \cdots\cdots\cdot \approx \mathrm{v}_N;$$

$$\frac{1}{N}\left\langle\sum_{i=1}^{N}\mathrm{v}_i^2\right\rangle_{\mathrm{t}} = \left\langle\frac{N\mathrm{v}^2}{N}\right\rangle = \langle\mathrm{v}^2\rangle.$$

The position vector of a mobile body moving on a spatial curve $\vec{r} = \vec{r}(t)$ is presented in Figure 39.4, and the parametric equations for the path are:

$$r = r(t); \quad \theta = \theta(t); \quad \varphi = \varphi(t),$$

where r, θ and φ are spherical coordinates.

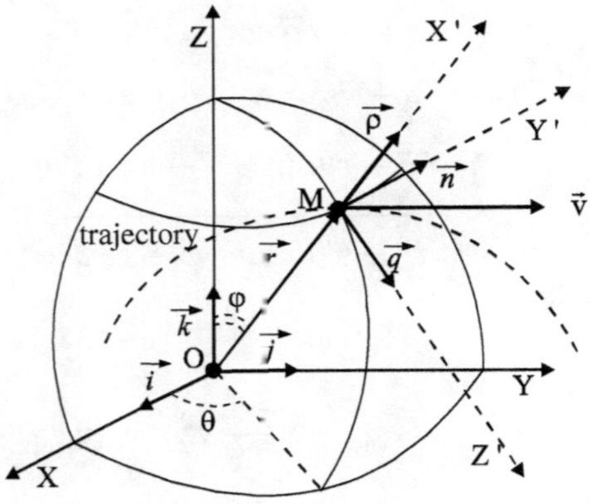

Fig. 39.4

To the fixed system XYZ, we associate a mobile system X′Y′Z′, whose axes have the following directions: OX′ axis along $\vec{r}$; Y′ axis along the tangent to the "parallel" at point M; and Z′ axis along the tangent to the "meridian" at point M. See Figure 39.4.

The versors of the new system's axes are given by the expressions:

$$\vec{\rho} = \cos\theta \sin\varphi \vec{i} + \sin\theta \sin\varphi \vec{j} + \cos\varphi \vec{k};$$

$$\vec{n} = -\sin\theta \vec{i} + \cos\theta\, \vec{j};$$

$$\vec{q} = \cos\theta \cos\varphi \vec{i} + \sin\theta \cos\varphi \vec{j} - \sin\varphi \vec{k}.$$

We demonstrate that:

$$\frac{\mathrm{d}\vec{\rho}}{\mathrm{d}t} = \dot{\vec{\rho}} = \dot{\theta}\, \sin\varphi \vec{n} + \dot{\varphi}\, \vec{q};$$

$$\frac{\mathrm{d}\vec{n}}{\mathrm{d}t} = \dot{\vec{n}} = -\dot{\theta}(\cos\theta\, \vec{i} + \sin\theta\, \vec{j});$$

$$\sin\varphi \vec{\rho} + \cos\varphi \vec{q} = \cos\theta\, \vec{i} + \sin\theta\, \vec{j};$$

$$\dot{\vec{n}} = -\dot{\theta}\, (\sin\, \varphi\, \vec{\rho} + \cos\, \varphi\, \vec{q});$$

$$\frac{\mathrm{d}\vec{q}}{\mathrm{d}t} = \dot{\vec{q}} = +\dot{\theta} \cos\, \varphi\, \vec{n} - \dot{\varphi}\, \vec{\rho}.$$

From the definition of the instantaneous velocity vector, it results that:

$$\vec{\mathrm{v}} = \frac{\mathrm{d}\vec{r}}{\mathrm{d}t} = \dot{\vec{r}}(t); \quad \vec{r}(t) = r(t)\vec{\rho}(t);$$

$$\vec{\mathrm{v}} = \dot{r}\vec{\rho} + r\dot{\vec{\rho}};$$

$$\vec{\mathrm{v}} = \vec{\mathrm{v}}_{\mathrm{rad}} + \vec{\mathrm{v}}_{\theta} + \vec{\mathrm{v}}_{\varphi} = \mathrm{v}_{\mathrm{rad}}\vec{\rho} + \mathrm{v}_{\theta}\vec{n} + \mathrm{v}_{\varphi}\vec{q};$$

$$\vec{\mathrm{v}} = \dot{r}\vec{\rho} + r\dot{\theta} \sin\varphi\, \vec{n} + r\, \dot{\varphi}\, \vec{q};$$

$$\mathrm{v} = \sqrt{\dot{r}^2 + r^2\dot{\theta}^2 \sin^2\varphi + r^2\dot{\varphi}^2};$$

$$\mathrm{v}^2 = \mathrm{v}_{\mathrm{rad}}^2 + \mathrm{v}_{\theta}^2 + \mathrm{v}_{q}^2;$$

$$\frac{1}{N}\left\langle \sum_{i=1}^{N} \mathrm{v}_i^2 \right\rangle_{\mathrm{t}} = \langle \mathrm{v}^2 \rangle = \langle \mathrm{v}_{\mathrm{rad}}^2 + \mathrm{v}_{\theta}^2 + \mathrm{v}_{\varphi}^2 \rangle = \langle \mathrm{v}_{\mathrm{rad}}^2 \rangle + \langle \mathrm{v}_{\theta}^2 \rangle + \langle \mathrm{v}_{\varphi}^2 \rangle;$$

$$\langle \mathrm{v}_{\mathrm{rad}}^2 \rangle \approx \langle \mathrm{v}_{\theta}^2 \rangle \approx \langle \mathrm{v}_{\varphi}^2 \rangle;$$

$$\frac{1}{N}\left\langle\sum_{i=1}^{N} \mathrm{v}_i^2\right\rangle_{\mathrm{t}} = 3\langle \mathrm{v}_{\mathrm{rad}}^2\rangle;$$

$$\frac{1}{N}\left\langle\sum_{i=1}^{N} \mathrm{v}_i^2\right\rangle_{\mathrm{t}} = \frac{3}{5}\frac{GM}{R};$$

$$\frac{3}{5}\frac{GM}{R} = 3\langle \mathrm{v}_{\mathrm{rad}}^2\rangle;$$

$$\langle \mathrm{v}_{\mathrm{rad}}^2\rangle_{\mathrm{t}} = \frac{1}{5}\frac{GM}{R};$$

$$M = \frac{5R\langle \mathrm{v}_{\mathrm{rad}}^2\rangle_{\mathrm{t}}}{G}.$$

Using Figure 39.5, we find that:

$$\sin\frac{\phi}{2} = \frac{R}{\mathrm{d}} \approx \frac{\phi}{2}; \quad R = \frac{\phi d}{2} \approx 3.14\,\mathrm{Mpc};$$

$$\sigma_{\mathrm{v}_{\mathrm{rad}}} = \sqrt{\langle \mathrm{v}_{\mathrm{rad}}^2\rangle} = 1000\,\frac{\mathrm{km}}{\mathrm{s}};$$

$$M_{\mathrm{virial}} = \frac{5R\langle \mathrm{v}_{\mathrm{rad}}^2\rangle_{\mathrm{t}}}{G} = \frac{5R\sigma_{\mathrm{v}_{\mathrm{rad}}}^2}{G} \approx 3.6\cdot 10^{15}\,M_{\mathrm{S}}.$$

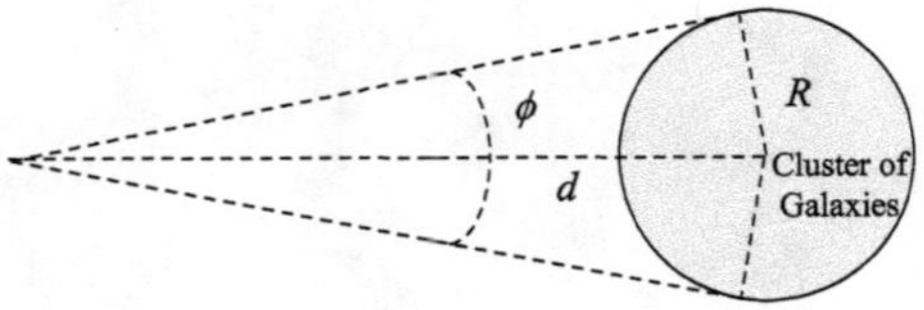

Fig. 39.5

$$\frac{M_{\mathrm{cluster}}}{L_{\mathrm{cluster}}} = \frac{M_{\mathrm{S}}}{L_{\mathrm{S}}}; \quad M_{\mathrm{cluster}} = \frac{L_{\mathrm{cluster}}}{L_{\mathrm{S}}} M_{\mathrm{S}} = 5\cdot 10^{12} M_{\mathrm{S}};$$

$$\frac{M_{\mathrm{virial}}}{L_{\mathrm{cluster}}} = \frac{3.6\cdot 10^{15}\,M_{\mathrm{S}}}{5\cdot 10^{12}\,L_{\mathrm{S}}} = 0.72\cdot 10^3\,\frac{M_{\mathrm{S}}}{L_{\mathrm{S}}} = 7.2\cdot 10^2\,\frac{M_{\mathrm{S}}}{L_{\mathrm{S}}};$$

$$M_{\mathrm{virial}} = 3.6\cdot 10^{15}\,M_{\mathrm{S}};$$

$$M_{\mathrm{cluster}} < M_{\mathrm{virial}}.$$

Problem 40

Jeans Mass

The Jeans mass of a stellar cloud is the critical mass of the cloud above which gravity dominates. For perturbations below the Jeans mass, pressure forces dominate, so the perturbation will re-expand when being compressed.

However, for perturbations more massive than the Jeans mass, gravity dominates, and so the perturbation will collapse even futher when compressed, leading to runaway collapse.

The conditions for a cloud of interstellar gas to collapse and form stars were first formulated by James Jean in 1902 while at Trinity College, Cambridge.

The conditions for the equilibrium of a stable, gravitationally bound system is given by the virial theorem:

$$2K + U = 0,$$

where K is the internal kinetic energy, and U is the potential energy of the system.

Consider now what happens if such a system is perturbed from equilibrium. If $2K > |U|$, the force due to gas pressure will dominate the gravitational force, and the cloud will expand. On the other hand, if $2K < |U|$, the reverse will be true, and the cloud will collapse under the force of gravity.

For this case, *determine* the mass of the cloud, M_{Jeans}.

Solution

The gravitational potential energy can be written as

$$U = -\frac{3}{5} \cdot \frac{GM_{\text{cloud}}^2}{R_{\text{cloud}}},$$

and we know that the average kinetic energy per particle is

$$K_1 = \frac{3}{2}kT,$$

where k is the Boltzmann constant.

Under these conditions, the total internal kinetic energy of the cloud is:

$$K = N_{\text{H}_1} \cdot K_1 = \frac{3}{2} N_{\text{H}_1} \cdot k \cdot T,$$

where N_{H_1} is the total number of particles (hydrogen atoms) in the cloud;

$$N_{\text{H}_2} = \frac{M_{\text{cloud}}}{\mu_{\text{H}_2}} = 2 \cdot N_{\text{H}_1}; \quad N_{\text{H}_1} = \frac{M_{\text{cloud}}}{2 \cdot \mu_{\text{H}_2}};$$

$$K = \frac{3}{2} \cdot \frac{M_{\text{cloud}}}{2 \cdot \mu_{\text{H}_2}} \cdot k \cdot T; \quad K = \frac{3}{4} \cdot \frac{M_{\text{cloud}}}{\mu_{\text{H}_2}} \cdot k \cdot T.$$

We rewrite the conditions for gravitational collapse, $2K < |U|$, as follows:

$$2 \cdot \frac{3}{4} \cdot \frac{M_{\text{cloud}}}{\mu_{\text{H}_2}} \cdot k \cdot T < \frac{3}{5} \cdot \frac{GM_{\text{cloud}}^2}{R_{\text{cloud}}};$$

$$\frac{1}{2} \cdot \frac{k \cdot T}{\mu_{\text{H}_2}} < \frac{1}{5} \cdot \frac{GM_{\text{cloud}}}{R_{\text{cloud}}};$$

$$M_{\text{cloud}} = \rho_0 \cdot \frac{4\pi R_{\text{cloud}}^3}{3}; \quad R_{\text{cloud}} = \left(\frac{3 \cdot M_{\text{cloud}}}{4\pi \cdot \rho_0}\right)^{1/3};$$

$$2K < |U|;$$

$$2 \cdot \frac{3}{4} \cdot \frac{M_{\text{cloud}}}{\mu_{\text{H}_2}} \cdot k \cdot T < \frac{3}{5} \cdot \frac{GM_{\text{cloud}}^2}{R_{\text{cloud}}};$$

$$\frac{1}{2} \cdot \frac{M_{\text{cloud}}}{\mu_{\text{H}_2}} \cdot k \cdot T < \frac{1}{5} \cdot \frac{GM_{\text{cloud}}^2}{R_{\text{cloud}}};$$

$$\frac{k \cdot T}{2 \cdot \mu_{\text{H}_2}} < \frac{1}{5} \cdot \frac{G \cdot M_{\text{cloud}}}{R_{\text{cloud}}};$$

$$M_{\text{cloud}} = \rho_0 \cdot \frac{4\pi R_{\text{cloud}}^3}{3}; \quad R_{\text{cloud}} = \left(\frac{3 \cdot M_{\text{cloud}}}{4\pi \cdot \rho_0}\right)^{1/3},$$

where ρ_0 is the initial density of the cloud prior to collapse, under the assumption that the cloud is a sphere of constant density;

$$\frac{k \cdot T}{2 \cdot \mu_{\text{H}_2}} < \frac{1}{5} \cdot \frac{G \cdot M_{\text{cloud}}}{\left(\frac{3 \cdot M_{\text{cloud}}}{4\pi \cdot \rho_0}\right)^{1/3}};$$

$$\frac{5 \cdot k \cdot T}{2 \cdot G \cdot \mu_{\text{H}_2}} < \frac{M_{\text{cloud}}}{\left(\frac{3}{4\pi \cdot \rho_0}\right)^{1/3} \cdot M_{\text{cloud}}^{1/3}};$$

$$\frac{5 \cdot k \cdot T}{2 \cdot G \cdot \mu_{\text{H}_2}} < \frac{M_{\text{cloud}}^{2/3}}{\left(\frac{3}{4\pi \cdot \rho_0}\right)^{1/3}};$$

$$\frac{5 \cdot k \cdot T}{2 \cdot G \cdot \mu_{\text{H}_2}} \cdot \left(\frac{3}{4\pi \cdot \rho_0}\right)^{1/3} < \frac{M_{\text{cloud}}^{2/3}}{\left(\frac{3}{4\pi \cdot \rho_0}\right)^{1/3}} \cdot \left(\frac{3}{4\pi \cdot \rho_0}\right)^{1/3};$$

$$M_{\text{cloud}}^{2/3} > \frac{5 \cdot k \cdot T}{2 \cdot G \cdot \mu_{\text{H}_2}} \cdot \left(\frac{3}{4\pi \cdot \rho_0}\right)^{1/3};$$

$$\left(M_{\text{cloud}}^{2/3}\right)^{3/2} > \left(\frac{5 \cdot k \cdot T}{2 \cdot G \cdot \mu_{\text{H}_2}}\right)^{3/2} \cdot \left[\left(\frac{3}{4\pi \cdot \rho_0}\right)^{1/3}\right]^{3/2};$$

$$M_{\text{cloud}} > \left(\frac{5 \cdot k \cdot T}{2 \cdot G \cdot \mu_{\text{H}_2}}\right)^{3/2} \cdot \left(\frac{3}{4\pi \cdot \rho_0}\right)^{1/2} = M_{\text{Jeans}};$$

$$M_{\text{Jeans}} = \left(\frac{5 \cdot k \cdot T}{2 \cdot G \cdot \mu_{\text{H}_2}}\right)^{3/2} \cdot \left(\frac{3}{4\pi \cdot \rho_0}\right)^{1/2}.$$

If the mass of a cloud exceeds the Jeans mass, the cloud will be unstable and prone to gravitational collapse.

Note that for a given chemical composition (i.e., for a given μ), the Jeans mass depends only on temperature and density: the lower the temperature and the higher the density, the smaller the mass of the cloud that is at risk of gravitational collapse. Note also that this is an oversimplification of the real situation, not only because we have ignored rotation, internal macroscopic velocity gradients and magnetic fields, but also because we have neglected any external pressure on the cloud (such as the external pressure of an encompassing giant molecular cloud on an embedded dense core).

The same criteria for gravitational collapse can also be expressed in terms of the Jeans length,

$$R_J \approx \left(\frac{15 \cdot k \cdot T}{4\pi \cdot G \cdot \mu_{\mathrm{H}_2} \cdot m_{\mathrm{H}_1} \cdot \rho_0}\right)^{1/2},$$

where the condition for gravitational collapse is $R_{\mathrm{cloud}} > R_J$, or the Jeans density,

$$\rho_J \approx \frac{3}{4\pi \cdot M_{\mathrm{cloud}}^2} \cdot \left(\frac{5kT}{G \cdot \mu \cdot m_H}\right),$$

where the condition for gravitational collapse is $\rho_{\mathrm{cloud}} > \rho_J$.

Problem 41

Free Fall Timescale

From the initial moment, when the radius of a star is r_0 and its density is ρ_0, *determine* the duration of the free fall of the star in gravitational collapse.

Solution

For a moment, t, after the gravitational collapse begins (the initial moment, $t_0 = 0$), when the radius of the star is r, and the mass of the spherical star in collapse is M_r, the equation of gravitational acceleration is:

$$\frac{\mathrm{d}^2 r}{\mathrm{d}t^2} = -G \cdot \frac{M_r}{r^2},$$

where the mass of the star, M_r, remains constant for the entire collapse duration;

$$M_r = M_{r_0} = \rho_0 \cdot \frac{4 \cdot \pi \cdot r_0^3}{3};$$

$$\frac{\mathrm{d}^2 r}{\mathrm{d}t^2} = -\frac{4 \cdot \pi}{3} \cdot G \cdot \rho_0 \cdot r_0^3 \cdot \frac{1}{r^2};$$

$$\frac{\mathrm{d}^2 r}{\mathrm{d}t^2} \cdot \frac{\mathrm{d}r}{\mathrm{d}t} = -\frac{4 \cdot \pi}{3} \cdot G \cdot \rho_0 \cdot r_0^3 \cdot \frac{1}{r^2} \cdot \frac{\mathrm{d}r}{\mathrm{d}t};$$

$$\frac{\mathrm{d}^2 r}{\mathrm{d}t^2} \cdot \frac{\mathrm{d}r}{\mathrm{d}t} = -\left(\frac{4 \cdot \pi}{3} \cdot G \cdot \rho_0 \cdot r_0^3\right) \cdot \frac{1}{r^2} \cdot \frac{\mathrm{d}r}{\mathrm{d}t};$$

$$\frac{\mathrm{d}r}{\mathrm{d}t}\cdot\frac{\mathrm{d}^2r}{\mathrm{d}t^2}=-\left(\frac{4\cdot\pi}{3}\cdot G\cdot\rho_0\cdot r_0^3\right)\cdot\frac{1}{r^2}\cdot\frac{\mathrm{d}r}{\mathrm{d}t};$$

$$\frac{\mathrm{d}r}{\mathrm{d}t}\cdot\frac{\mathrm{d}}{\mathrm{d}t}\left(\frac{\mathrm{d}r}{\mathrm{d}t}\right)=-\left(\frac{4\cdot\pi}{3}\cdot G\cdot\rho_0\cdot r_0^3\right)\cdot\frac{1}{r^2}\cdot\frac{\mathrm{d}r}{\mathrm{d}t};$$

$$\frac{\mathrm{d}r}{\mathrm{d}t}\cdot\frac{\mathrm{d}}{\mathrm{d}t}\left(\frac{\mathrm{d}r}{\mathrm{d}t}\right)=\left(\frac{4\cdot\pi}{3}\cdot G\cdot\rho_0\cdot r_0^3\right)\cdot\frac{\mathrm{d}}{\mathrm{d}t}\left(\frac{1}{r}\right);$$

$$\frac{\mathrm{d}r}{\mathrm{d}t}=x;$$

$$x\cdot\frac{\mathrm{d}x}{\mathrm{d}t}=\left(\frac{4\cdot\pi}{3}\cdot G\cdot\rho_0\cdot r_0^3\right)\cdot\frac{\mathrm{d}}{\mathrm{d}t}\left(\frac{1}{r}\right);$$

$$x\cdot\frac{\mathrm{d}x}{\mathrm{d}t}\cdot\mathrm{d}t=\left(\frac{4\cdot\pi}{3}\cdot G\cdot\rho_0\cdot r_0^3\right)\cdot\frac{\mathrm{d}}{\mathrm{d}t}\left(\frac{1}{r}\right)\cdot\mathrm{d}t;$$

$$x\cdot\mathrm{d}x=\left(\frac{4\cdot\pi}{3}\cdot G\cdot\rho_0\cdot r_0^3\right)\cdot\mathrm{d}\left(\frac{1}{r}\right);$$

$$\int x\cdot\mathrm{d}x=\left(\frac{4\cdot\pi}{3}\cdot G\cdot\rho_0\cdot r_0^3\right)\cdot\int\mathrm{d}\left(\frac{1}{r}\right);$$

$$\frac{1}{2}\cdot x^2=\left(\frac{4\cdot\pi}{3}\cdot G\cdot\rho_0\cdot r_0^3\right)\cdot\frac{1}{r}+C_1,$$

where the integration constant C_1 is determined under the boundary condition that the in-fall velocity is zero at the onset of collapse, that is, $\frac{\mathrm{d}r}{\mathrm{d}t}=0$, when $r=r_0$;

$$\frac{1}{2}\cdot x_0^2=\left(\frac{4\cdot\pi}{3}\cdot G\cdot\rho_0\cdot r_0^3\right)\cdot\frac{1}{r_0}+C_1;$$

$$x_0=0;\quad C_1=-\frac{4\cdot\pi}{3}\cdot G\cdot\rho_0\cdot r_0^2;$$

$$\frac{1}{2}\cdot x^2=\left(\frac{4\cdot\pi}{3}\cdot G\cdot\rho_0\cdot r_0^3\right)\cdot\frac{1}{r}+C_1;\quad\frac{\mathrm{d}r}{\mathrm{d}t}=x;$$

$$\frac{1}{2}\cdot\left(\frac{\mathrm{d}r}{\mathrm{d}t}\right)^2=\left(\frac{4\cdot\pi}{3}\cdot G\cdot\rho_0\cdot r_0^3\right)\cdot\frac{1}{r}-\frac{4\cdot\pi}{3}\cdot G\cdot\rho_0\cdot r_0^2;$$

$$\left(\frac{\mathrm{d}r}{\mathrm{d}t}\right)^2=\left(\frac{8\cdot\pi}{3}\cdot G\cdot\rho_0\cdot r_0^3\right)\cdot\frac{1}{r}-\frac{8\cdot\pi}{3}\cdot G\cdot\rho_0\cdot r_0^2;$$

$$\left(\frac{\mathrm{d}r}{\mathrm{d}t}\right)^2 = \frac{8\cdot\pi}{3}\cdot G\cdot\rho_0\cdot r_0^2\cdot\left(\frac{r_0}{r}-1\right);$$

$$\frac{\mathrm{d}r}{\mathrm{d}t} = \pm\sqrt{\frac{8\cdot\pi}{3}\cdot G\cdot\rho_0\cdot r_0^2\cdot\left(\frac{r_0}{r}-1\right)};$$

$$\frac{\mathrm{d}r}{\mathrm{d}t} = -r_0\cdot\sqrt{\frac{8\cdot\pi}{3}\cdot G\cdot\rho_0\cdot\left(\frac{r_0}{r}-1\right)},$$

where we have chosen the negative root because the cloud is collapsing.

For the integration of this expression, we will substitute the following:

$$\lambda = \frac{r}{r_0};\quad \Gamma = \sqrt{\frac{8\cdot\pi}{3}\cdot G\cdot\rho_0};$$

$$\frac{\mathrm{d}r}{\mathrm{d}t} = -\Gamma\cdot r_0\cdot\sqrt{\frac{1}{\lambda}-1};\quad r = \lambda\cdot r_0;$$

$$r_0\cdot\frac{\mathrm{d}\lambda}{\mathrm{d}t} = -\Gamma\cdot r_0\cdot\sqrt{\frac{1}{\lambda}-1};\quad \frac{\mathrm{d}\lambda}{\mathrm{d}t} = -\Gamma\cdot\sqrt{\frac{1}{\lambda}-1};$$

$$\frac{\mathrm{d}\lambda}{\mathrm{d}t} = -\Gamma\ \left(\frac{1}{\lambda}-1\right)^{1/2};$$

$$\lambda = \cos^2\varphi;$$

$$\frac{\mathrm{d}(\cos^2\varphi)}{\mathrm{d}t} = -\Gamma\cdot\left(\frac{1}{\cos^2\varphi}-1\right)^{1/2};$$

$$\frac{\mathrm{d}(\cos^2\varphi)}{\mathrm{d}t} = -\Gamma\cdot\left(\frac{1-\cos^2\varphi}{\cos^2\varphi}\right)^{1/2};$$

$$\frac{\mathrm{d}(\cos^2\varphi)}{\mathrm{d}t} = -\Gamma\cdot\left(\frac{\sin^2\varphi}{\cos^2\varphi}\right)^{1/2};\quad \frac{\mathrm{d}(\cos^2\varphi)}{\mathrm{d}t} = -\Gamma\cdot\frac{\sin\varphi}{\cos\varphi};$$

$$\mathrm{d}(\cos^2\varphi) = -\Gamma\cdot\frac{\sin\varphi}{\cos\varphi}\cdot\mathrm{d}t;$$

$$2\cdot\cos\varphi\cdot(-\sin\varphi)\cdot\mathrm{d}\varphi = -\Gamma\cdot\frac{\sin\varphi}{\cos\varphi}\cdot\mathrm{d}t;$$

$$2\cdot\cos\varphi\cdot\mathrm{d}\varphi = \Gamma\cdot\frac{1}{\cos\varphi}\cdot\mathrm{d}t;$$

$$2 \cdot \cos^2 \varphi \cdot \mathrm{d}\varphi = \Gamma \cdot \mathrm{d}t; \quad \cos^2 \varphi \cdot \mathrm{d}\varphi = \frac{\Gamma}{2} \cdot \mathrm{d}t;$$

$$\int \cos^2 \varphi \cdot \mathrm{d}\varphi = \frac{\Gamma}{2} \cdot t + C_2;$$

$$\frac{\varphi}{2} + \frac{\sin 2\varphi}{4} = \frac{\Gamma}{2} \cdot t + C_2; \quad r = \lambda \cdot r_0; \quad \lambda = \cos^2 \varphi;$$

$$t = 0; \quad r = r_0; \quad \lambda = 1; \quad \varphi = 0;$$

$$C_2 = 0;$$

$$\frac{\varphi}{2} + \frac{\sin 2\varphi}{4} = \frac{\Gamma}{2} \cdot t;$$

$$\varphi + \frac{1}{2} \cdot \sin 2\varphi = \Gamma \cdot t.$$

We define the free fall timescale as the time taken by a cloud in free fall to collapse from $r = r_0$ to $r = 0$. But, in reality, this condition is never reached, so we consider that $r_{\text{final}} \ll r_0$.

For $r = 0$, when $t = t_{\text{free fall}}$, we will obtain:

$$\lambda = 0; \quad \varphi = \frac{\pi}{2};$$

$$t_{\text{ff}} = \frac{\pi}{2 \cdot \Gamma}; \quad \Gamma = \sqrt{\frac{8 \cdot \pi}{3} \cdot G \cdot \rho_0};$$

$$t_{\text{ff}} = \frac{\pi}{2 \cdot \sqrt{\frac{8 \cdot \pi}{3} \cdot G \cdot \rho_0}}; \quad t_{\text{ff}} = \frac{\pi}{2} \cdot \sqrt{\frac{3}{8 \cdot \pi \cdot G \cdot \rho_0}};$$

$$t_{\text{ff}} = \sqrt{\frac{3 \cdot \pi^2}{4 \cdot 8 \cdot \pi \cdot G \cdot \rho_0}}; \quad t_{\text{ff}} = \sqrt{\frac{3 \cdot \pi}{32 \cdot G \cdot \rho_0}}.$$

Observation: The free fall timescale is independent of the initial radius of the sphere, r_0, and depends only on the initial density, ρ_0.

Problem 42

85 Pegasi A and B

Represented in Figures 42.1 and 42.2 are the possible locations in the plane of the sky, Π_S, for the apparent positions of the star Pegasi B in relation to the star Pegasi A, using the angular coordinates θ, angular position (AP), and ρ, angular separation (AS).

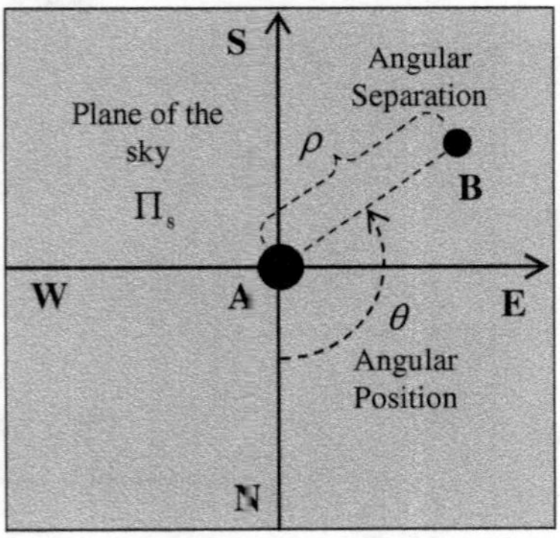

Fig. 42.1

a) Using the data in Table 42.1, plot the ellipse representing the apparent orbit of the companion star, Pegasi B, around the main star, Pegasi A, belonging to the multiple star system 85 Pegasi in the Pegasus constellation. In the drawing in Figure 42.3, the direction X′Y′ is the direction of the projection of the line of the apsides (large axis, PA) of the relative orbit (ellipse).

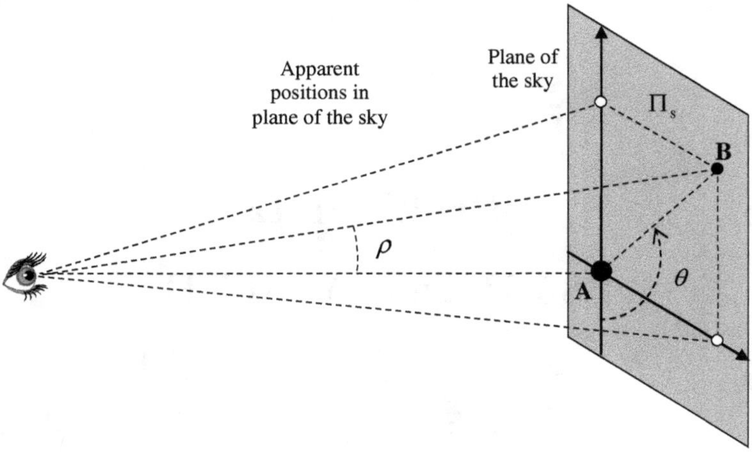

Fig. 42.2

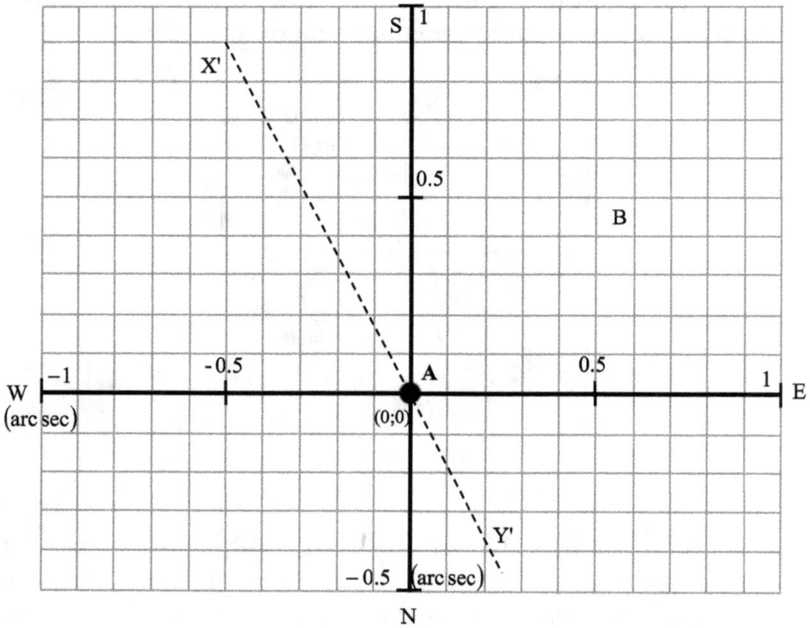

Fig. 42.3

Table 42.1

Year	2005	2006	2007	2008	2009	2010	2011	2012
Angular position θ (degrees)	232	241	249	257	265	273	282	292
Angular separation ρ (arcsecs)	0.80	0.82	0.84	0.85	0.85	0.84	0.80	0.73

Year	2013	2014	2015	2016	2017	2018	2019	2020
Angular position θ (degrees)	304	323	356	44	79	99	112	123
Angular separation ρ (arcsecs)	0.62	0.49	0.36	0.36	0.48	0.80	0.70	0.75

Year	2021	2022	2023	2024	2025	2026	2027	2028
Angular position θ (degrees)	133	142	151	161	170	180	191	201
Angular separation ρ (arcsecs)	0.78	0.79	0.78	0.77	0.76	0.75	0.75	0.75

Year	2029	2030
Angular position θ (degrees)	211	221
Angular separation ρ (arcsecs)	0.76	0.78

b) *Determine* the eccentricity, e, of the relative elliptical orbit of Pegasi A around Pegasi B.

c) *Determine* the distance $d = \mathrm{A'P'}$, in the plane of the sky, representing the length of the projection of the line of apsides, AP, in the plane of the relative orbit in the plane of the sky. The distance from Earth to the star system Pegasi A and B, $\Delta = 40\,\text{ly}$, is known.

d) *Determine* the eccentricity, e', of the apparent elliptical orbit.

The center of the apparent orbit, C_{ap}, is the center of the circle that circumscribes, by inner tangency, the apparent elliptical orbit.

Solution

a) The apparent orbit of the Pegasi B star in relation to the Pegasi A star is represented in the drawing in Figure 42.4.

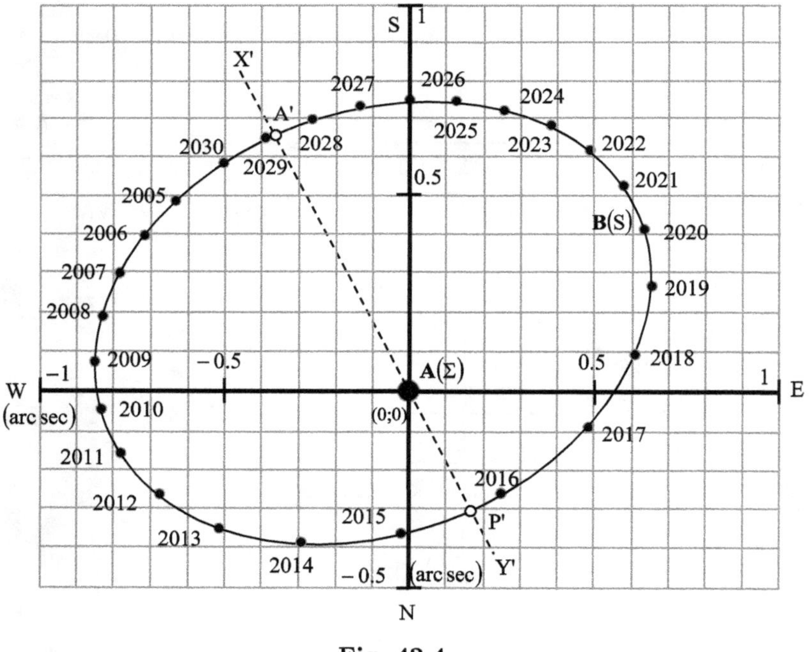

Fig. 42.4

b) In the drawing in Figure 42.5, we use the following notation: Σ – the main star (Pegasi A); S – the secondary star (Pegasi B); A – apastron (of the star S on the ellipse E in relation to the star Σ in the focus of the ellipse); P – peristron (of the star S on the ellipse E with respect to the star Σ); AP – the line of the apsides (the large

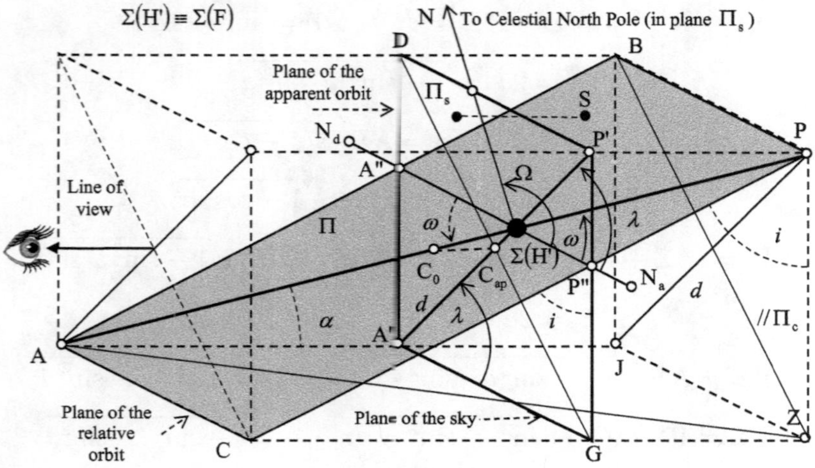

Fig. 42.5

axis of the ellipse, representing the relative orbit); A′P′ – projection of the line of the apsides in the plane of the sky; $\mathrm{N_aN_d}$ – the line of the nodes; i – the angle between the plane of the relative orbit and the plane of the sky; ω – the angle between the line of the apsides and the line of the nodes; Π(ABPC) – the plane of the relative orbit; Π_c(DP′GA′) – the plane of the sky (the plane of the apparent orbit); $2a$ – the distance between the apastron and periastron (the large axis of the relative ellipse); and A″P″ – the projection of the large axis of the orbit (ellipse) relative to the nodes line.

The orbit of the star S relative to the star Σ is an ellipse (E) located in the plane Π(ABPC).

The apparent orbit of the star S is an ellipse, $\mathrm{E_{ap}}$, located in the plane of the sky, Π_s(DP′GA′). The ellipse $\mathrm{E_{ap}}$ is the projection of the ellipse E.

From Figure 42.5, it follows that:

$$\mathrm{A\Sigma} = r_{\max} = a(1+e); \qquad \mathrm{AA'} = r_{\max}\cos\alpha;$$

$$\mathrm{P\Sigma} = r_{\min} = a\,(1-e)\,; \qquad \mathrm{JA'} = r_{\min}\cos\alpha;$$

$$\mathrm{AA'} + \mathrm{JA'} = \mathrm{AJ} = (r_{\max} + r_{\min})\cos\alpha = 2a\cdot\cos\alpha;$$

$$\frac{\mathrm{A\Sigma}}{\mathrm{P\Sigma}} = \frac{r_{\max}}{r_{\min}} = \frac{A'\Sigma}{P'\Sigma} = k = \frac{1+e}{1-e};$$

$$\mathrm{A'P'} = \mathrm{A'\Sigma} + \mathrm{P'\Sigma} = d; \quad \cos\alpha = \sin\omega \cdot \sin i;$$

$$d = 2a \cdot \sqrt{1 - \sin^2\omega \cdot \sin^2 i};$$

$$\mathrm{A'\Sigma} = \mathrm{A\Sigma} \cdot \sin\alpha = \mathrm{A\Sigma} \cdot \sqrt{1 - \cos^2\alpha};$$

$$\mathrm{P'\Sigma} = \mathrm{P\Sigma} \cdot \sin\alpha = \mathrm{P\Sigma} \cdot \sqrt{1 - \cos^2\alpha};$$

$$\mathrm{A'P'} = (\mathrm{A\Sigma} + \mathrm{P\Sigma}) \sin\alpha = \mathrm{AP} \cdot \sin\alpha = \mathrm{AP} \cdot \sqrt{1 - \sin^2\omega \sin^2 i};$$

$$\mathrm{A'P'} = 2a \cdot \sqrt{1 - \sin^2\omega \cdot \sin^2 i} = d;$$

$$\mathrm{A'\Sigma} = \mathrm{A\Sigma} \cdot \sqrt{1 - \sin^2\omega \cdot \sin^2 i} = r_{\max} \cdot \sqrt{1 - \sin^2\omega \cdot \sin^2 i};$$

$$\mathrm{P'\Sigma} = \mathrm{P\Sigma} \cdot \sqrt{1 - \sin^2\omega \cdot \sin^2 i} = r_{\min} \cdot \sqrt{1 - \sin^2\omega \cdot \sin^2 i};$$

$$\frac{\mathrm{A'\Sigma}}{\mathrm{P'\Sigma}} = \frac{\mathrm{A\Sigma}}{\mathrm{P\Sigma}} = \frac{r_{\max} \cdot \sqrt{1 - \sin^2\omega \cdot \sin^2 i}}{r_{\min} \cdot \sqrt{1 - \sin^2\omega \cdot \sin^2 i}}$$

$$= \frac{r_{\max}}{r_{\min}} = \frac{a(1+e)}{a\,(1-e)} = \frac{1+e}{1-e} = k;$$

$$k = \frac{1+e}{1-e}; \quad e = \frac{k-1}{k+1},$$

representing the numerical eccentricity of the relative orbit (ellipse);

$$k = \frac{\mathrm{A'\Sigma}}{\mathrm{P'\Sigma}},$$

whose value is determined from measurements made in the plane of the apparent orbit (Π_s, the plane of the sky);

$$(\mathrm{A'\Sigma})_{\text{measured}} = 5.7\,\text{cm}; \quad (\mathrm{P'\Sigma})_{\text{measured}} = 2.6\,\text{cm};$$

$$\text{Scale} = 3.5\,\text{cm} \ldots\ldots\ldots\ldots\ldots 0.5\,\text{arcsec};$$

$$\mathrm{A'\Sigma} = (\mathrm{A'\Sigma})_{\text{measured}} \cdot \text{scale}; \quad \mathrm{P'\Sigma} = (\mathrm{P'\Sigma})_{\text{measured}} \cdot \text{scale};$$

$$k = \frac{5.7\,\text{cm} \cdot \text{scale}}{2.6\,\text{cm} \cdot \text{scale}} = \frac{5.7}{2.6} = 2.192;$$

$$e = \frac{k-1}{k+1} = \frac{1.192}{3.192} = 0.373.$$

c) From measurements made on the drawing in Figure 42.4, it follows that:

$$d_{\text{measured}} = (\mathrm{A'P'})_{\text{measured}} = 8.3\,\text{cm};$$

$$\text{Scale} = 3.5\,\text{cm} \ldots\ldots\ldots\ldots\ldots 0.5\,\text{arcsec};$$

$$3.5\,\text{cm}\ldots\ldots\ldots\ldots 0.5\,\text{arcsec};$$

$$8.3\,\text{cm}\ldots\ldots\ldots\ldots \gamma;$$

$$\gamma = 1.185\,\text{arcsec}; \quad 1\,\text{arcsec} = \frac{3.14}{180 \cdot 3600}\,\text{rad};$$

$$\gamma = 1.185 \cdot \frac{3.14}{180 \cdot 3600} \approx 0.000005742\,\text{rad}; \quad \Delta = 40.0\,\text{ly}.$$

So, using the drawing in Figure 42.6, where $d = \mathrm{A'P'}$, measurements are made of the apparent orbit (ellipse) described in the problem statement. Corresponding to the scale at which the apparent orbit is represented, it results that:

$$d = \Delta \cdot \gamma = 40.0 \cdot 0.000005742\,\text{ly} = 0.000229685\,\text{ly};$$

$$1\,\text{ly} = 63241\ \text{AU}; \quad d = 14.5255\ \text{AU} = \mathrm{A'P'}.$$

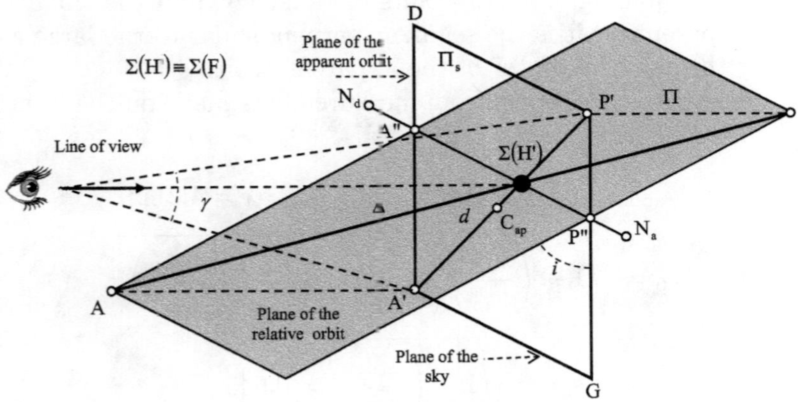

Fig. 42.6

d) In the drawing in Figure 42.7, the center of the apparent orbit, C_{ap}, is the center of the circle that circumscribes, by inner tangency, the apparent elliptical orbit. The large axis of the apparent orbit is

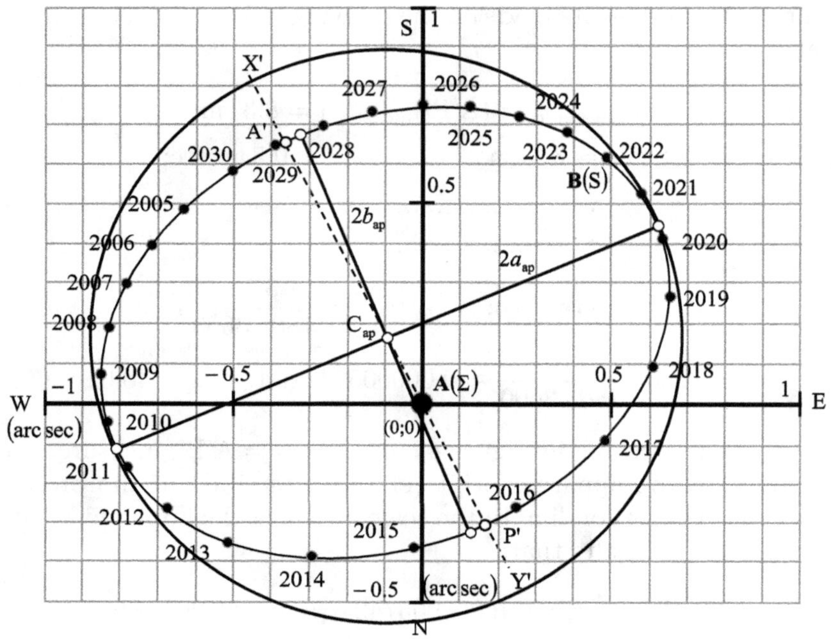

Fig. 42.7

the segment joining the two points of tangency, and the small axis of the apparent orbit is the segment perpendicular to the large axis, passing through the center of the apparent orbit.

Under these conditions, from measurements made on the drawing in Figure 42.7, we obtain:

$$a_{\text{ap,measured}} = 5.5\,\text{cm}; \quad b_{\text{ap,measured}} = 4.2\,\text{cm};$$

$$e_{\text{ap}} = \sqrt{1 - \left(\frac{b_{\text{ap}}}{a_{\text{ap}}}\right)^2} = \sqrt{1 - \left(\frac{b_{\text{ap,measured}}}{a_{\text{ap,measured}}}\right)^2};$$

$$e_{\text{ap}} = \sqrt{1 - \left(\frac{4.2}{5.5}\right)^2} = 0.645.$$

Problem 43

Convergent Proper Motions

The component stars of a cluster may have convergent movements towards a well defined point on the celestial sphere, called the point of convergence, C. To this infinite point converge all the common parallel movement directions of the cluster's stars. For one of the stars in the cluster, σ, with equatorial coordinates α and δ, as seen in Figure 43.1, we also indicate the point of convergence C and the star's speed vector $\vec{v}//OC$ (parallel to OC), together with its three perpendicular components, two of them in the plane of the sky and one in the radial direction.

The angle η between the arc of the great circle σC and the celestial meridian of star σ is also shown.

For eight stars from the same cluster, Table 43.1 gives the values for:

- $(\alpha; \delta)$ – the equatorial coordinates of the star;
- the product $\mu_\alpha \cos\delta$, where μ_α is the proper motion in ascension, and δ is its declination;
- μ_δ – each star's proper motion in declination.

All the data were extracted from the Hipparcos catalog.

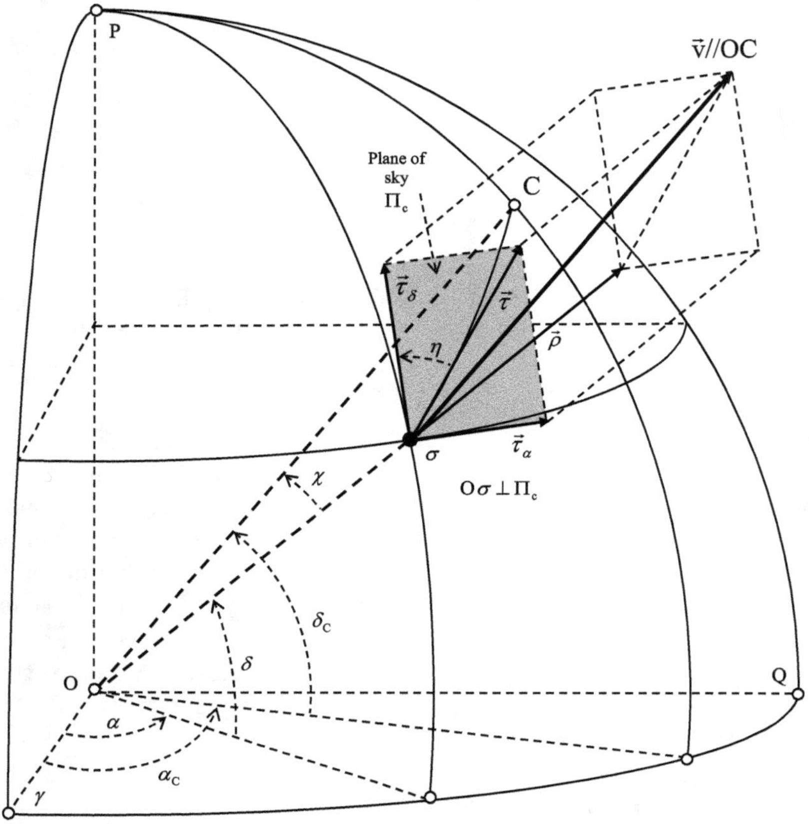

Fig. 43.1

Table 43.1

Star	α (h m s)	δ (° ′ ″)	$\mu_\alpha \cos\delta$ 10^{-3} $\frac{\text{arcsec}}{\text{years}}$	μ_δ 10^{-3} $\frac{\text{arcsec}}{\text{years}}$	p 10^{-3} arcsec
18170	03 53 09.96	+17 19 37.8	143.97	−29.93	24.14
19554	04 11 20.20	+05 31 22.9	146.86	+5.00	25.89
20261	04 20 36.24	+15 05 43.8	108.79	−20.67	21.20
20901	04 28 50.10	+13 02 51.5	105.17	−15.08	20.33
21589	04 38 09.40	+12 30 39.1	101.73	−14.90	21.79
22157	04 46 01.70	+11 42 20.2	67.48	−7.09	12.24
23479	05 03 05.70	+21 35 24.2	68.94	−40.85	20.01
24019	05 09 45.06	+28 01 50.2	55.86	−60.57	18.28

a) *Calculate* the equatorial position coordinates of the convergence point C for the stars in the cluster ($\alpha_C; \delta_C$), knowing that:

$$\vec{v} = \vec{\tau} + \vec{\rho} = \vec{\tau}_\alpha + \vec{\tau}_\delta + \vec{\rho};$$

$$v = \sqrt{\tau_\alpha^2 + \tau_\delta^2 + \rho^2};$$

$$\operatorname{tg}\eta = \frac{\tau_\alpha}{\tau_\delta}; \quad \tau_\alpha = 71.10\frac{\mu_\alpha}{p}\cos\delta;$$

$$\tau_\delta = 4.74\frac{\mu_\delta}{p}; \quad \operatorname{tg}\eta = \frac{71.10}{4.74}\cdot\frac{\mu_\alpha\cos\delta}{\mu_\delta};$$

$$\operatorname{tg}\eta = 15\cdot\frac{\mu_\alpha\cos\delta}{\mu_\delta}; \quad \operatorname{ctg}\eta = \frac{1}{15}\cdot\frac{\mu_\delta}{\mu_\alpha\cos\delta}.$$

b) *Determine* the angle between the visual radius of each star and the visual radius of the convergence point, χ.

c) *Determine* the distance between the Earth observer and each of the eight stars.

Solution

a) For one of the stars of the considered group, σ, with equatorial position coordinates α and δ, as indicated by the drawings in Figures 43.2 and 43.3, where the convergence point C is indicated, with equatorial position coordinates α_C and δ_C, as well as the speed $\vec{v}$ of the star and its three perpendicular components, it is shown that:

$$\vec{v} = \vec{\tau} + \vec{\rho} = \vec{\tau}_\alpha + \vec{\tau}_\delta + \vec{\rho};$$

$$v = \sqrt{\tau_\alpha^2 + \tau_\delta^2 + \rho^2};$$

$$\operatorname{tg}\eta = \frac{\tau_\alpha}{\tau_\delta}; \quad \tau_\alpha = 71.10\frac{\mu_\alpha}{p}\cos\delta;$$

$$\tau_\delta = 4.74\frac{\mu_\delta}{p}; \quad \operatorname{tg}\eta = \frac{71.10}{4.74}\cdot\frac{\mu_\alpha\cos\delta}{\mu_\delta};$$

$$\operatorname{tg}\eta = 15\cdot\frac{\mu_\alpha\cos\delta}{\mu_\delta}; \quad \operatorname{ctg}\eta = \frac{1}{15}\cdot\frac{\mu_\delta}{\mu_\alpha\cos\delta}.$$

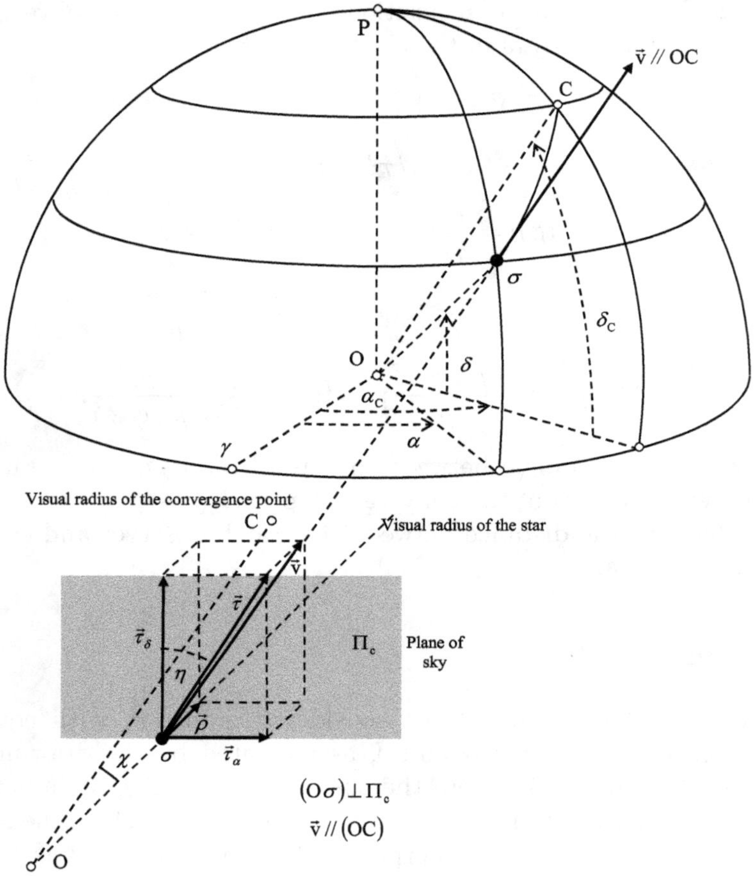

Fig. 43.2

If the spherical triangle PCσ, represented in Figure 43.4, is considered a standard spherical triangle ABC, the following relations hold:

$$\sin b \cdot \operatorname{ctg} c = \cos b \cdot \cos A + \sin A \cdot \operatorname{ctg} C;$$

$$\sin(90^\circ - \delta) \cdot \operatorname{ctg}(90^\circ - \delta_C) = \cos(90^\circ - \delta) \cdot \cos(\alpha_C - \alpha) + \sin(\alpha_C - \alpha) \cdot \operatorname{ctg} \eta;$$

$$\cos \delta \cdot \operatorname{tg} \delta_C = \sin \delta \cdot \cos(\alpha_C - \alpha) + \sin(\alpha_C - \alpha) \cdot \operatorname{ctg} \eta;$$

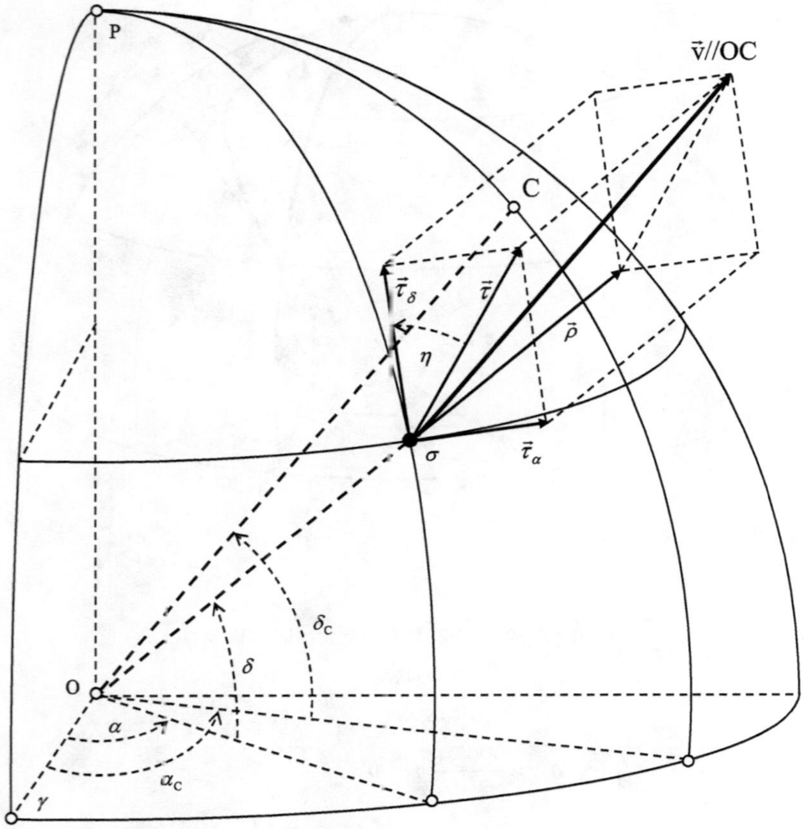

Fig 43.3

$$\cos\delta \cdot \operatorname{tg}\delta_C = \sin\delta \cdot (\cos\alpha_C \cdot \cos\alpha + \sin\alpha_C \cdot \sin\alpha) + (\sin\alpha_C \cdot \cos\alpha - \cos\alpha_C \cdot \sin\alpha) \cdot \operatorname{ctg}\eta;$$

$$\cos\delta \cdot \operatorname{tg}\delta_C = (\sin\delta \cdot \cos\alpha - \operatorname{ctg}\eta \cdot \sin\alpha) \cdot \cos\alpha_C + (\sin\delta \cdot \sin\alpha + \operatorname{ctg}\eta \cdot \cos\alpha) \cdot \sin\alpha_C.$$

The following notation is used:

$$x = \sin\delta \cdot \cos\alpha - \operatorname{ctg}\eta \cdot \sin\alpha;$$
$$y = \sin\delta \cdot \sin\alpha + \operatorname{ctg}\eta \cdot \cos\alpha.$$

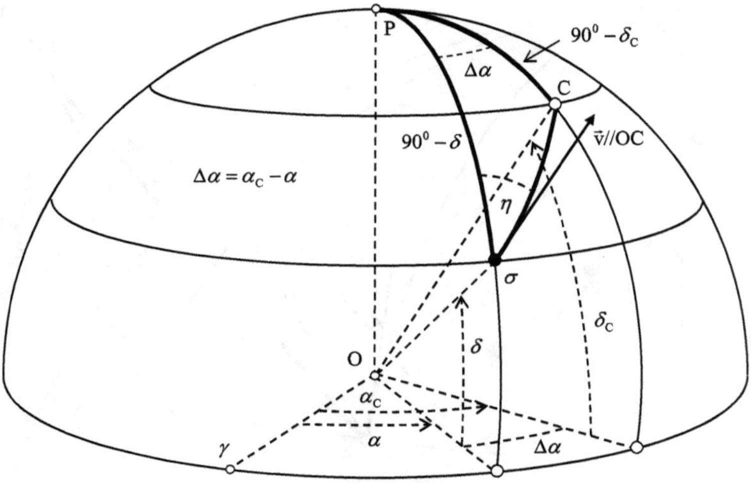

Fig. 43.4

Thus:

$$\cos\delta\cdot\operatorname{tg}\delta_C = x\cdot\cos\alpha_C + y\cdot\sin\alpha_C;$$

$$\cos\delta = x\cdot\frac{\cos\alpha_C}{\operatorname{tg}\delta_C} + y\cdot\frac{\sin\alpha_C}{\operatorname{tg}\delta_C};$$

$$a = \frac{\cos\alpha_C}{\operatorname{tg}\delta_C};\quad b = \frac{\sin\alpha_C}{\operatorname{tg}\delta_C};$$

$$\operatorname{tg}\alpha_C = \frac{b}{a};\quad \operatorname{tg}\delta_C = \frac{1}{\sqrt{a^2+b^2}};$$

$$\cos\alpha_C = a\cdot\operatorname{tg}\delta_C;\quad \sin\alpha_C = b\cdot\operatorname{tg}\delta_C;$$

$$\cos\delta\cdot\operatorname{tg}\delta_C = x\cdot a\cdot\operatorname{tg}\delta_C + y\cdot b\cdot\operatorname{tg}\delta_C;$$

$$\cos\delta = x\cdot a + y\cdot b;$$

$$x\cdot a + y\cdot b = \cos\delta.$$

So, for the considered eight stars, the following relationships can be written:

$$\begin{cases} x_1\cdot a + y_1\cdot b = \cos\delta_1 = f_1(a;b); \\ x_2\cdot a + y_2\cdot b = \cos\delta_2 = f_2(a;b); \\ \dots\dots\dots\dots\dots\dots\dots\dots\dots\dots \\ x_8\cdot a + y_8\cdot b = \cos\delta_8 = f_8(a;b). \end{cases}$$

The solutions of the system of eight equations will be used for eight experimental measurements of the coordinates $(\alpha_C; \delta_C)$ – the equatorial coordinates of the convergence point C.

We suggest that the smallest square method be applied to find out the most probable values of the unknown variables.

We use the derived system of equations – the system of errors equations:

$$\begin{cases} f_1(a;b) - \cos\delta_1 = \varepsilon_1; \\ f_2(a;b) - \cos\delta_2 = \varepsilon_2; \\ \dots\dots\dots\dots\dots\dots \\ f_8(a;b) - \cos\delta_8 = \varepsilon_8; \end{cases}$$

or

$$\begin{cases} x_1 \cdot a + y_1 \cdot b - \cos\delta_1 = \varepsilon_1; \\ x_2 \cdot a + y_2 \cdot b - \cos\delta_2 = \varepsilon_2; \\ \dots\dots\dots\dots\dots\dots\dots\dots \\ x_8 \cdot a + y_8 \cdot b - \cos\delta_8 = \varepsilon_8; \end{cases}$$

with the conditions:

$$S = \varepsilon_1^2 + \varepsilon_2^2 + \cdots\cdots + \varepsilon_8^2;$$

$$\frac{\partial S}{\partial a} = 0; \quad \frac{\partial S}{\partial b} = 0.$$

Thus:

$$\begin{cases} \dfrac{\partial S}{\partial a} = 2\varepsilon_1\dfrac{\partial \varepsilon_1}{\partial a} + 2\varepsilon_2\dfrac{\partial \varepsilon_2}{\partial a} + \cdots\cdots + 2\varepsilon_8\dfrac{\partial \varepsilon_8}{\partial a} = 0; \\ \dfrac{\partial S}{\partial b} = 2\varepsilon_1\dfrac{\partial \varepsilon_1}{\partial b} + 2\varepsilon_2\dfrac{\partial \varepsilon_2}{\partial b} + \cdots\cdots + 2\varepsilon_8\dfrac{\partial \varepsilon_8}{\partial b} = 0; \end{cases}$$

$$\begin{cases} \varepsilon_1\dfrac{\partial \varepsilon_1}{\partial a} + \varepsilon_2\dfrac{\partial \varepsilon_2}{\partial a} - \cdots\cdots + \varepsilon_8\dfrac{\partial \varepsilon_8}{\partial a} = 0; \\ \varepsilon_1\dfrac{\partial \varepsilon_1}{\partial b} + \varepsilon_2\dfrac{\partial \varepsilon_2}{\partial b} + \cdots\cdots + \varepsilon_8\dfrac{\partial \varepsilon_8}{\partial b} = 0; \end{cases}$$

$$\begin{cases} x_1 \cdot a + y_1 \; b - \cos\delta_1 = \varepsilon_1; \\ x_2 \cdot a + y_2 \; b - \cos\delta_2 = \varepsilon_2; \\ \dots\dots\dots\dots\dots\dots\dots\dots \\ x_8 \cdot a + y_8 \cdot b - \cos\delta_8 = \varepsilon_8; \end{cases}$$

$$\frac{\partial \varepsilon_1}{\partial a} = x_1; \quad \frac{\partial \varepsilon_2}{\partial a} = x_2; \ldots\ldots\ldots \frac{\partial \varepsilon_8}{\partial a} = x_8;$$

$$\frac{\partial \varepsilon_1}{\partial b} = y_1; \quad \frac{\partial \varepsilon_2}{\partial b} = y_2; \ldots\ldots\ldots \frac{\partial \varepsilon_8}{\partial b} = y_8;$$

$$\begin{cases} (x_1 a + y_1 b - \cos\delta_1)x_1 + (x_2 a + y_2 b - \cos\delta_2)x_2 \\ \qquad + \cdots + (x_8 a + y_8 b - \cos\delta_8)x_8 = 0; \\ (x_1 a + y_1 b - \cos\delta_1)y_1 + (x_2 a + y_2 b - \cos\delta_2)y_2 \\ \qquad + \cdots + (x_8 a + y_8 b - \cos\delta_8)y_8 = 0; \end{cases}$$

$$\begin{cases} a\sum_{i=1}^{8} x_i^2 + b\sum_{i=1}^{8} x_i y_i = \sum_{i=1}^{8} x_i \cos\delta_i; \\ a\sum_{i=1}^{8} x_i y_i + b\sum_{i=1}^{8} y_i^2 = \sum_{i=1}^{8} y_i \cos\delta_i; \end{cases}$$

$$\begin{cases} a\sum_{i=1}^{8} x_i^2 + b\sum_{i=1}^{8} x_i y_i = \sum_{i=1}^{8} x_i \cos\delta_i & \Big| \cdot \sum_{i=1}^{8} y_i^2; \\ a\sum_{i=1}^{8} x_i y_i + b\sum_{i=1}^{8} y_i^2 = \sum_{i=1}^{8} y_i \cos\delta_i & \Big| \cdot \left(-\sum_{i=1}^{8} x_i y_i\right); \end{cases}$$

$$\begin{cases} a \cdot \left(\sum_{i=1}^{8} x_i^2\right) \cdot \left(\sum_{i=1}^{8} y_i^2\right) + b \cdot \left(\sum_{i=1}^{8} x_i y_i\right) \cdot \left(\sum_{i=1}^{8} y_i^2\right) \\ \qquad = \left(\sum_{i=1}^{8} x_i \cos\delta_i\right) \cdot \left(\sum_{i=1}^{8} y_i^2\right); \\ -a \cdot \left(\sum_{i=1}^{8} x_i y_i\right)^2 - b \cdot \left(\sum_{i=1}^{8} x_i y_i\right) \cdot \left(\sum_{i=1}^{8} y_i^2\right) \\ \qquad = -\left(\sum_{i=1}^{8} y_i \cos\delta_i\right) \cdot \left(\sum_{i=1}^{8} x_i y_i\right); \end{cases}$$

$$a = \frac{\left(\sum_{i=1}^{8} x_i \cos\delta_i\right) \cdot \left(\sum_{i=1}^{8} y_i^2\right) - \left(\sum_{i=1}^{8} y_i \cos\delta_i\right) \cdot \left(\sum_{i=1}^{8} x_i y_i\right)}{\left(\sum_{i=1}^{8} x_i^2\right) \cdot \left(\sum_{i=1}^{8} y_i^2\right) - \left(\sum_{i=1}^{8} x_i y_i\right)^2};$$

$$\begin{cases} a\sum_{i=1}^{8} x_i^2 + b\sum_{i=1}^{8} x_i y_i = \sum_{i=1}^{8} x_i \cos\delta_i; & \Big| \cdot \left(-\sum_{i=1}^{8} x_i y_i\right); \\ a\sum_{i=1}^{8} x_i y_i + b\sum_{i=1}^{8} y_i^2 = \sum_{i=1}^{8} y_i \cos\delta_i; & \Big| \cdot \sum_{i=1}^{8} x_i^2; \end{cases}$$

$$\begin{cases} -a\cdot\left(\sum_{i=1}^{8} x_i^2\right)\cdot\left(\sum_{i=1}^{8} x_i y_i\right) - b\cdot\left(\sum_{i=1}^{8} x_i y_i\right)^2 \\ \qquad = -\left(\sum_{i=1}^{8} x_i \cos\delta_i\right)\cdot\left(\sum_{i=1}^{8} x_i y_i\right); \\ a\cdot\left(\sum_{i=1}^{8} x_i^2\right)\cdot\left(\sum_{i=1}^{8} x_i y_i\right) + b\cdot\left(\sum_{i=1}^{8} x_i^2\right)\cdot\left(\sum_{i=1}^{8} y_i^2\right) \\ \qquad = \left(\sum_{i=1}^{8} y_i \cos\delta_i\right)\cdot\left(\sum_{i=1}^{8} x_i^2\right); \end{cases}$$

$$b = \frac{\left(\sum_{i=1}^{8} y_i \cos\delta_i\right)\cdot\left(\sum_{i=1}^{8} x_i^2\right) - \left(\sum_{i=1}^{8} x_i \cos\delta_i\right)\cdot\left(\sum_{i=1}^{8} x_i y_i\right)}{\left(\sum_{i=1}^{8} x_i^2\right)\cdot\left(\sum_{i=1}^{8} y_i^2\right) - \left(\sum_{i=1}^{8} x_i y_i\right)^2}.$$

Using the data in Tables 43.2–43.11:

$$\operatorname{ctg}\eta = \frac{1}{15}\cdot\frac{\mu_\delta}{\mu_\alpha\cos\delta}.$$

Table 43.2

Star	α (h m s)	δ (° ′ ″)
18170	03 53 09.96	+17 19 37.8
19554	04 11 20.20	+05 31 22.9
20261	04 20 36.24	+15 05 43.8
20901	04 28 50.10	+13 02 51.5
21589	04 38 09.40	+12 30 39.1
22157	04 46 01.70	+11 42 20.2
23479	05 03 05.70	+21 35 24.2
24019	05 09 45.06	+28 01 50.2

Table 43.3

Star	α (h m s)	α (°)	α (rad)
18170	03 53 09.96	58.289	1.016
19554	04 11 20.20	62.830	1.096
20261	04 20 36.24	65.144	1.136
20901	04 28 50.10	67.200	1.172
21589	04 38 09.40	69.537	1.213
22157	04 46 01.70	71.506	1.247
23479	05 03 05.70	75.772	1.321
24019	05 09 45.06	77.430	1.350

Table 43.4

Star	$\cos\alpha$	$\sin\alpha$
18170	0.526	0.850
19554	0.457	0.889
20261	0.421	0.906
20901	0.388	0.921
21589	0.350	0.936
22157	0.318	0.948
23479	0.247	0.968
24019	0.219	0.975

Table 43.5

Star	δ (° ′ ″)	δ (°)	δ (rad)
18170	+17 19 37.8	+17.327	+0.302
19554	+05 31 22.9	+5.523	+0.096
20261	+15 05 43.8	+15.095	+0.263
20901	+13 02 51.5	+13.047	+0.227
21589	+12 30 39.1	+12.510	+0.218
22157	+11 42 20.2	+11.705	+0.204
23479	+21 35 24.2	+21.590	+0.376
24019	+28 01 50.2	+28.030	+0.488

Table 43.6

Star	$\cos\delta$	$\sin\delta$
18170	0.954	0.297
19554	0.995	0.095
20261	0.965	0.062
20901	0.974	0.225
21589	0.976	0.216
22157	0.979	0.202
23479	0.930	0.367
24019	0.883	0.468

Table 43.7

Star	$\mu_\alpha \cos\delta$ $10^{-3}\,\dfrac{\text{arcsec}}{\text{years}}$	μ_δ $10^{-3}\,\dfrac{\text{arcsec}}{\text{years}}$	$\text{ctg}\,\eta$
18170	143.97	−29.93	−0.01385
19554	146.86	+5.00	+0.00226
20261	108.79	−20.67	−0.01266
20901	105.17	−15.08	−0.00955
21589	101.73	−14.90	−0.00976
22157	67.48	−7.09	−0.00700
23479	68.94	−40.85	−0.03950
24019	55.86	−60.57	−0.07228

Table 43.8

Star	$\sin\delta \cdot \cos\alpha$	$\text{ctg}\,\eta \cdot \sin\alpha$	x
18170	0.01562	−0.01177	0.02739
19554	0.04341	0.00200	0.04141
20261	0.02610	−0.01146	0.03756
20901	0.08730	−0.00879	0.09609
21589	0.07560	−0.00913	0.08473
22157	0.06423	−0.00663	0.07708
23479	0.09064	−0.03823	0.12887
24019	0.10249	−0.07047	0.17296

Table 43.9

Star	$\sin\delta \cdot \sin\alpha$	$\text{ctg}\,\eta \cdot \cos\alpha$	y
18170	0.25245	−0.00728	0.24517
19554	0.08445	+0.00103	0.08548
20261	0.05617	−0.00532	0.05085
20901	0.20722	−0.00370	0.20352
21589	0.20217	−0.00341	0.19876
22157	0.19149	−0.00222	0.18927
23479	0.35525	−0.00975	0.34550
24019	0.45630	−0.01582	0.44048

Table 43.10

Star	x_i	x_i^2	$x_i \cos\delta_i$
18170	0.02739	0.00075	0.02613
19554	0.04141	0.00171	0.41202
20261	0.03756	0.00141	0.03624
20901	0.09609	0.00923	0.09359
21589	0.08473	0.00717	0.08269
22157	0.07708	0.00594	0.07546
23479	0.12887	0.01660	0.11984
24019	0.17296	0.02991	0.15272

Table 43.11

Star	y_i	y_i^2	$y_i \cos\delta_i$	$x_i y_i$
18170	0.24517	0.06010	0.23389	0.00671
19554	0.08548	0.00730	0.08505	0.00353
20261	0.05085	0.00258	0.04907	0.00190
20901	0.20352	0.04142	0.19822	0.01955
21589	0.19876	0.03950	0.19398	0.01684
22157	0.18927	0.03582	0.18529	0.01458
23479	0.34550	0.11937	0.32131	0.04452
24019	0.44048	0.19402	0.38894	0.07618

The final results are:

$$\sum_{i=1}^{8} x_i^2 = 0.07272; \quad \sum_{i=1}^{8} x_i \cos\delta_i = 0.99869;$$

$$\sum_{i=1}^{8} y_i^2 = 0.50011; \quad \sum_{i=1}^{8} y_i \cos\delta_i = 1.65575; \quad \sum_{i=1}^{8} x_i y_i = 0.18381;$$

$$\left(\sum_{i=1}^{8} x_i y_i\right)^2 = 0.03378;$$

$$a = \frac{\left(\sum_{i=1}^{8} x_i \cos\delta_i\right)\cdot\left(\sum_{i=1}^{8} y_i^2\right) - \left(\sum_{i=1}^{8} y_i \cos\delta_i\right)\cdot\left(\sum_{i=1}^{8} x_i y_i\right)}{\left(\sum_{i=1}^{8} x_i^2\right)\cdot\left(\sum_{i=1}^{8} y_i^2\right) - \left(\sum_{i=1}^{8} x_i y_i\right)^2};$$

$$a = \frac{0.99869 \cdot 0.50011 - 1.65575 \cdot 0.18381}{0.7272 \cdot 0.50011 - 0.03378} = \frac{0.19511}{0.00258} = 75.62403;$$

$$b = \frac{\left(\sum_{i=1}^{8} y_i \cos\delta_i\right)\cdot\left(\sum_{i=1}^{8} x_i^2\right) - \left(\sum_{i=1}^{8} x_i \cos\delta_i\right)\cdot\left(\sum_{i=1}^{8} x_i y_i\right)}{\left(\sum_{i=1}^{8} x_i^2\right)\cdot\left(\sum_{i=1}^{8} y_i^2\right) - \left(\sum_{i=1}^{8} x_i y_i\right)^2}.$$

$$b = \frac{1.65575 \cdot 0.07272 - 0.99869 \cdot 0.18381}{0.7272 \cdot 0.50011 - 0.03378}$$

$$= \frac{-0.06316}{0.00258} = -24.48062;$$

$$\operatorname{tg}\alpha_C = \frac{b}{a}; \quad \operatorname{tg}\delta_C = \frac{1}{\sqrt{a^2+b^2}};$$

$$\operatorname{tg}\alpha_C = \frac{-24.48062}{75.62403}; \quad \operatorname{tg}\alpha_C = -0.32371;$$

$$\operatorname{tg}\delta_C = \frac{1}{\sqrt{(75.62403)^2 + (-24.48062)^2}} = \frac{1}{\sqrt{6318.29466}} = \frac{1}{79.48770};$$

$$\operatorname{tg}\delta_C = 0.01258; \quad \operatorname{tg}\delta_C \approx \delta_C = 0.01258;$$

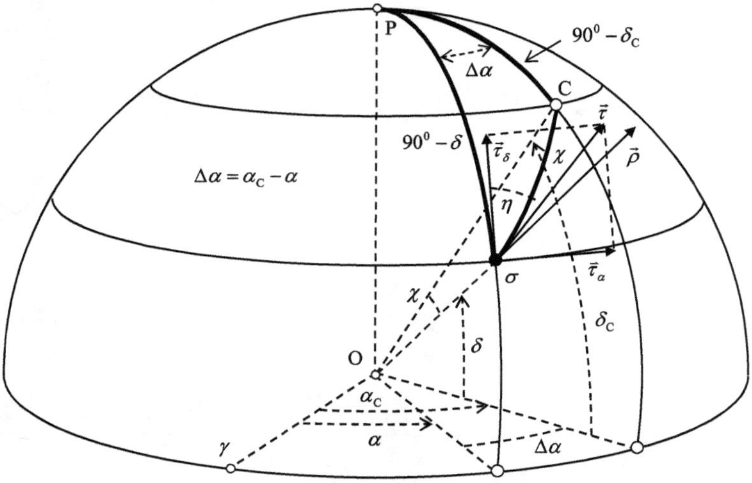

Fig. 43.5

$$\operatorname{tg}\alpha_C = -0.32371; \quad \operatorname{tg}\delta_C = 0.01258;$$

$$\alpha_C = 2.826\,\text{rad} = 162°;$$

$$\delta_C \approx 0.01258\,\text{rad} = 0.72° = 43'\,12''.$$

b) From the same spherical triangle, PCσ, represented in the drawing in Figure 43.5, where $\chi = \angle\sigma\text{OC}$ is the angle between the visual radius of the star and the visual radius of the convergence point, we obtain:

$$\cos\chi = \cos(90° - \delta) \cdot \cos(90° - \delta_C)$$
$$+ \sin(90° - \delta) \cdot \sin(90° - \delta_C) \cdot \cos(\alpha_C - \alpha);$$
$$\cos\chi = \sin\delta \cdot \sin\delta_C + \cos\delta \cdot \cos\delta_C \cdot \cos(\alpha_C - \alpha).$$

where $(\alpha_C; \delta_C)$ are determined by the method of the smallest squares and $(\alpha; \delta)$ are known;

$$\operatorname{tg}\delta_C = 0.01258;$$

$$\sin\delta_C = \frac{\operatorname{tg}\delta_C}{\sqrt{1 + \operatorname{tg}^2\delta_C}} = 0.01257;$$

$$\cos\delta_C = \sqrt{1-\sin^2\delta_C} = 0.99992;$$

$$\operatorname{tg}\alpha_C = -0.32371;$$

$$\sin\alpha_C = \frac{\operatorname{tg}\alpha_C}{\sqrt{1+\operatorname{tg}^2\alpha_C}} = 0.30797;$$

$$\cos\alpha_C = -\sqrt{1-\sin^2\alpha_C} = -0.95139;$$

$$\cos(\alpha_C - \alpha) = \cos\alpha_C\cos\alpha + \sin\alpha_C\sin\alpha;$$

$$\cos\chi = \sin\delta\cdot\sin\delta_C + \cos\delta\cdot\cos\delta_C\cdot\cos(\alpha_C-\alpha);$$

$$\cos\chi = \sin\delta\cdot\sin\delta_C + \cos\delta\cdot\cos\delta_C\cdot\cos(\alpha_C-\alpha).$$

c) The annual parallax of a star σ, located outside our Solar System, is the angle p_{an} below which the average radius of the Earth's orbit around the Sun, as viewed from the center of the star at the moment of the year when the Earth–star direction (Eσ) is perpendicular to the Sun–Earth (SE) direction, as indicated by the drawing in Figure 43.6. This results in:

$$\sin p_{\text{an}} = \frac{r_{\text{ES}}}{\Delta_{\text{E}\sigma}} \approx p_{\text{an}}; \quad \frac{r_{\text{ES}}}{\Delta_{\text{E}\sigma}} \approx p_{\text{an}};$$

$$\frac{r_{\text{ES(AU)}}}{\Delta_{\text{E}\sigma\text{(AU)}}} \approx p_{\text{an(rad)}}; \quad \frac{r_{\text{ES(pc)}}}{\Delta_{\text{E}\sigma\text{(pc)}}} \approx p_{\text{an(rad)}};$$

$$r_{\text{ES(pc)}} = |r_{\text{ES(pc)}}|\cdot 1\,\text{pc} = |r_{\text{ES(pc)}}|\cdot 206265\,\text{AU} = |r_{\text{ES(AU)}}|\cdot 1\,\text{AU};$$

$$|r_{\text{ES(pc)}}|\cdot 206265 = |r_{\text{ES(AU)}}|;$$

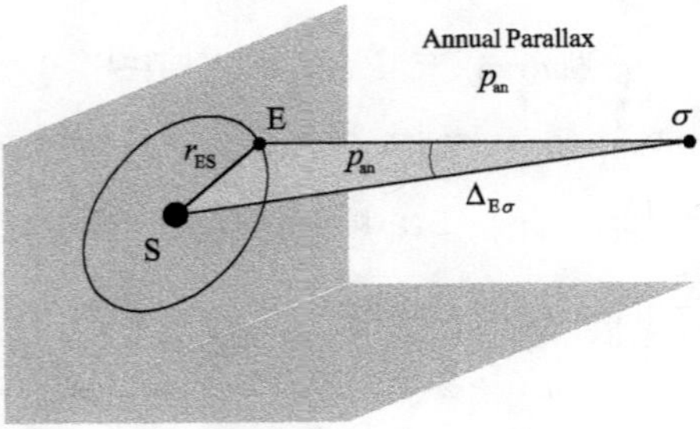

Fig. 43.6

$$|r_{\text{ES(pc)}}| = \frac{|r_{\text{ES(AU)}}|}{206265};$$

$$\Delta_{\text{E}\sigma\text{(pc)}} = |\Delta_{\text{E}\sigma\text{(pc)}}| \cdot 1\,\text{pc} = |\Delta_{\text{E}\sigma\text{(pc)}}| \cdot 206265\,\text{AU}$$
$$= |\Delta_{\text{E}\sigma\text{(AU)}}| \cdot 1\,\text{AU};$$

$$|\Delta_{\text{E}\sigma\text{(pc)}}| \cdot 206265 = |\Delta_{\text{E}\sigma\text{(AU)}}|;$$

$$|\Delta_{\text{E}\sigma\text{(pc)}}| = \frac{|\Delta_{\text{E}\sigma\text{(AU)}}|}{206265};$$

$$\frac{r_{\text{ES(pc)}}}{\Delta_{\text{E}\sigma\text{(pc)}}} = \frac{|r_{\text{ES(pc)}}|\,\text{pc}}{|\Delta_{\text{E}\sigma\text{(pc)}}|\,\text{pc}} = \frac{|r_{\text{ES(pc)}}|}{|\Delta_{\text{E}\sigma\text{(pc)}}|};$$

$$\frac{r_{\text{ES(pc)}}}{\Delta_{\text{E}\sigma\text{(pc)}}} = \frac{|r_{\text{ES(pc)}}|}{|\Delta_{\text{E}\sigma\text{(pc)}}|};$$

$$|r_{\text{ES(pc)}}| = \frac{|r_{\text{ES(AU)}}|}{206265};$$

$$\frac{r_{\text{ES(pc)}}}{\Delta_{\text{E}\sigma\text{(pc)}}} = \frac{\frac{|r_{\text{ES(AU)}}|}{206265}}{|\Delta_{\text{E}\sigma\text{(pc)}}|};$$

$$\frac{r_{\text{ES(pc)}}}{\Delta_{\text{E}\sigma\text{(pc)}}} = \frac{|r_{\text{ES(AU)}}|}{206265 \cdot |\Delta_{\text{E}\sigma\text{(pc)}}|};$$

$$|r_{\text{ES(AU)}}| = 1;$$

$$\frac{r_{\text{ES(pc)}}}{\Delta_{\text{E}\sigma\text{(pc)}}} = \frac{1}{206265 \cdot |\Delta_{\text{E}\sigma\text{(pc)}}|};$$

$$\frac{r_{\text{ES(pc)}}}{\Delta_{\text{E}\sigma\text{(pc)}}} = p_{\text{an(rad)}};$$

$$p_{\text{an(rad)}} = |p_{\text{an(rad)}}| \cdot 1\,\text{rad};$$

$$p_{\text{an(arcsec)}} = |p_{\text{an(arcsec)}}| \cdot 1\,\text{arcsec};$$

$$p_{\text{an(rad)}} = |p_{\text{an(rad)}}| \cdot 1\,\text{rad} = |p_{\text{an(rad)}}| \cdot 206265\,\text{arcsec}$$
$$= |p_{\text{an(arcsec)}}| \cdot 1\,\text{arcsec};$$

$$|p_{\text{an(rad)}}| \cdot 206265 = |p_{\text{an(arcsec)}}|;$$

$$|p_{\text{an(rad)}}| = \frac{|p_{\text{an(arcsec)}}|}{206265};$$

$$\frac{r_{\mathrm{ES(pc)}}}{\Delta_{\mathrm{E}\sigma(\mathrm{pc})}} = p_{\mathrm{an(rad)}};$$

$$\frac{r_{\mathrm{ES(pc)}}}{\Delta_{\mathrm{E}\sigma(\mathrm{pc})}} = |p_{\mathrm{an(rad)}}| \cdot 1\,\mathrm{rad} = |p_{\mathrm{an(rad)}}|,$$

$$\frac{r_{\mathrm{ES(pc)}}}{\Delta_{\mathrm{E}\sigma(\mathrm{pc})}} = |p_{\mathrm{an(rad)}}|;$$

$$|p_{\mathrm{an(rad)}}| = \frac{|p_{\mathrm{an(arcsec)}}|}{206265};$$

$$\frac{r_{\mathrm{ES(pc)}}}{\Delta_{\mathrm{E}\sigma(\mathrm{pc})}} = \frac{|p_{\mathrm{an(arcsec)}}|}{206265};$$

$$\frac{r_{\mathrm{ES(pc)}}}{\Delta_{\mathrm{E}\sigma(\mathrm{pc})}} = \frac{1}{206265 \cdot |\Delta_{P\sigma(\mathrm{pc})}|};$$

$$\frac{1}{206265 \cdot |\Delta_{\mathrm{E}\sigma(\mathrm{pc})}|} = \frac{|p_{\mathrm{an(arcsec)}}|}{206265};$$

$$|\Delta_{\mathrm{E}\sigma(\mathrm{pc})}| = \frac{1}{|p_{\mathrm{an(arcsec)}}|}.$$

The numerical results are shown in Table 43.12.

Table 43.12

Star	p 10^{-3} arcsec	Δ pc	Ranking
18170	24.14	41.425	2
19554	25.89	38.624	1
20261	21.20	47.169	4
20901	20.33	49.188	5
21589	21.79	45.892	3
22157	12.24	81.699	8
23479	20.01	49.975	6
24019	18.28	54.704	7

Problem 44

From Romania ... to the Antipode! A Ballistic Projectile Messenger

The organizers of IOAA 2014 devised a symbolic way to announce the start of the event in Suceava, Romania, by making an announcement at its antipode! A ballistic intercontinental projectile launched from Romania will carry the Olympic flag to the antipode (Figures 44.1 and 44.2). The rotational movement of the Earth is neglected.

a) *Locate* the antipode, knowing the geographical coordinates of the launching point: $\varphi_{\text{Romania}} = 44°$ north; $\lambda_{\text{Romania}} = 30°$ east.
b) *Determine* the elements of the vector $\vec{v}_0$, representing the minimum velocity with which the projectile must be launched relative to the center of the Earth in order to reach the antipode.
c) *Determine* the velocity of the projectile at the antipode.
d) *Determine* the minimum velocity of the projectile on its trajectory.
e) *Determine* the duration of the messenger projectile's flight from the launching point to the antipode. The following are considered known: gravitational acceleration at the ground, $g_0 = 9.81\ \text{ms}^{-2}$; the Earth's radius, $R = 6370$ km.
f) *Evaluate* the possibility of observing the projectile with the naked eye from the Earth's surface at the moment when it is at its maximum distance from the Earth. *The following are known:* the Moon's albedo, $\alpha_{\text{M}} = 0.12$; the Moon's radius, $R_{\text{M}} = 1738$ km;

Fig. 44.1

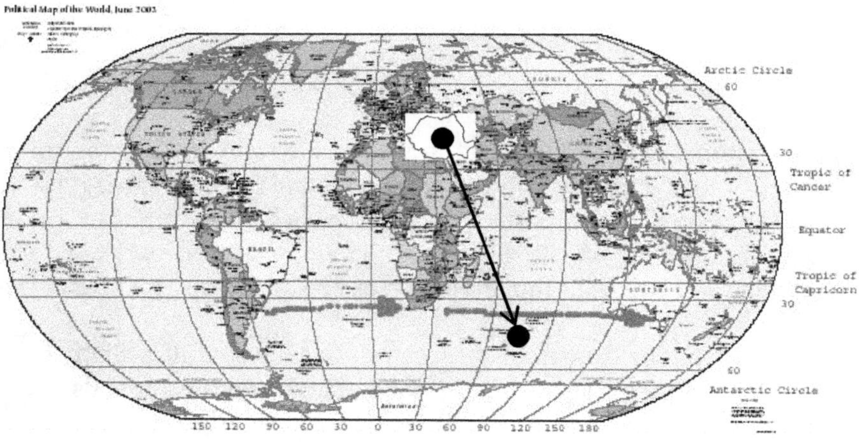

Fig. 44.2

the Earth–Moon distance, $r_{\text{EM}} = 384400$ km; and the apparent magnitude of the Full Moon, $m_{\text{M}} = -12.7^{\text{m}}$. *It is known that* the projectile is a metallic sphere with a perfectly reflecting surface and a radius $r_{\text{projectile}} = 400$ mm.

Solution

a) In Figure 44.3, two diametrically opposed places, X and Y, on the Earth's surface are presented. Under these conditions, the relations between their geographical coordinates are:

$$\varphi_Y = \varphi_{Y,\text{south}} = \varphi_{X,\text{north}} = \varphi_X;$$

$$\lambda_{Y,\text{west}} + \lambda_{X,\text{east}} = 180°; \quad \lambda_Y + \lambda_X = 180°.$$

Taking into account that

$$\varphi_{\text{Romania}} = 43° \text{ north}, \lambda_{\text{Romania}} = 30° \text{ east},$$

it results that

$$\varphi_{\text{antipode}} = 43° \text{ south}, \lambda_{\text{antipode}} = 150° \text{ west},$$

i.e., somewhere in the southeast of Tasmania (south of mainland Australia).

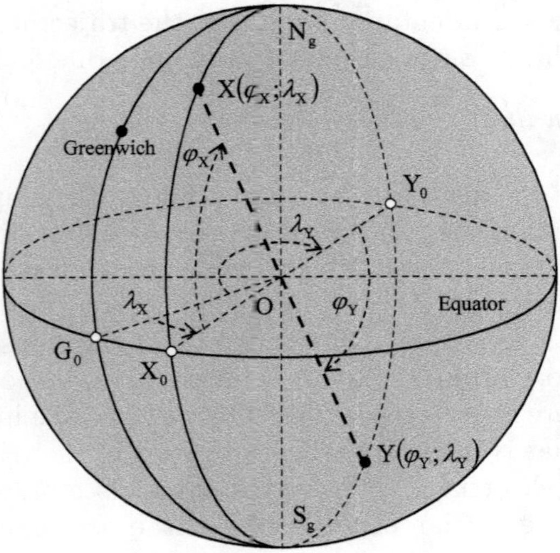

Fig. 44.3

b) As a consequence, the Romania–antipode "messenger projectile" can be analyzed according to the notation in Figure 44.4, where the trajectory plane is presented from the launching point to the landing point.

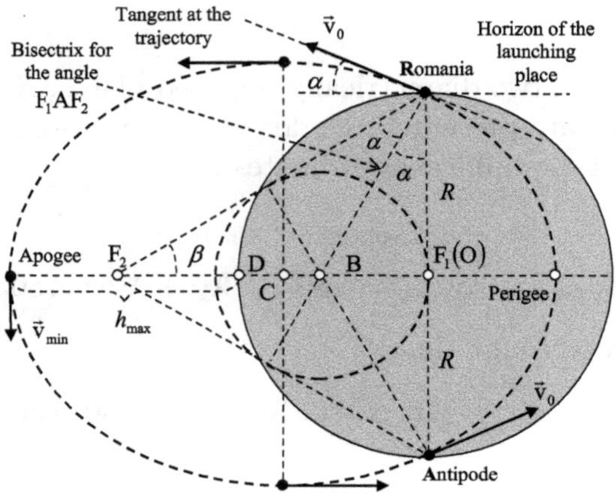

Fig. 44.4

In order to reach the antipode, the ballistic projectile, at the moment of launch from Romania, must have velocity $\vec{v}_0$, with an absolute value and orientation such that the trajectory is a sector of an ellipse with the Earth's center (O) in one of its foci (F_1).

It is known that:

1) the sum of the distances from any point on the ellipse to the two foci is constant, i.e., $2a$, which is the major axis of the ellipse;
2) the tangent at a point on the ellipse is perpendicular to the bisector of the angle between the lines joining the respective point and the ellipse's foci (optical characteristic of the ellipse);
3) the bisectors of an angle are concurrent – the point where the bisectors are concurrent is the center of the circle inscribed in the triangle that is interiorly tangent to each of the triangle's edges;
4) in an isosceles triangle, the vertex angle bisector, the altitude of the base, the median of the base and the perpendicular bisector coincide.

Under these conditions, B is the point at which the angle bisector of the isosceles triangle RF_2A splits the F_1F_2 segment in to two parts. Thus:

$$F_2B = 2 \cdot F_1B; \quad F_1F_2 = 3 \cdot F_1B.$$

It results that:

$$\tan 2\alpha = \frac{\mathrm{F_1F_2}}{R}; \quad \mathrm{F_1F_2} = R \cdot \tan 2\alpha;$$

$$\tan \alpha = \frac{\mathrm{F_1B}}{R}; \quad \mathrm{F_1}B = R \cdot \tan \alpha;$$

$$R \cdot \tan 2\alpha = \mathrm{F_1B} = R \cdot \tan \alpha;$$

$$\tan 2\alpha = 3 \cdot \tan \alpha;$$

$$\frac{\sin 2\alpha}{\cos 2\alpha} = 3\frac{\sin \alpha}{\cos \alpha};$$

$$\frac{2 \sin \alpha \cdot \cos \alpha}{\cos 2\alpha} = 3\frac{\sin \alpha}{\cos \alpha};$$

$$2\cos^2 \alpha = 3\cos 2\alpha; \quad 2\cos^2 \alpha = 3(\cos^2 \alpha - \sin^2 \alpha);$$

$$3\sin^2 \alpha = \cos^2 \alpha; \quad \tan^2 \alpha = \frac{1}{3};$$

$$\tan \alpha = \frac{\sqrt{3}}{3}; \quad \alpha = 30^\circ; \quad 2\alpha = 60^\circ; \quad \beta = 90^\circ - 2\alpha = 30^\circ; \quad 2\beta = 60^\circ;$$

$$\Delta(\mathrm{RF_2A}) \to \text{equilateral triangle};$$

$$\mathrm{RF_2} = \mathrm{AF_2} = \mathrm{RA} = 2R;$$

$$\mathrm{RF_2} + \mathrm{RF_1} = 2a = 3R;$$

$$a = \frac{3}{2}R;$$

$$\mathrm{v_0} = \sqrt{KM\left(\frac{2}{r} - \frac{1}{a}\right)}; \quad r = R; g_0 = K\frac{M}{R^2};$$

$$\mathrm{v_0} = \sqrt{\frac{KM}{R^2} \cdot R^2\left(\frac{2}{R} - \frac{2}{3R}\right)} = 2\sqrt{\frac{g_0 R}{3}}.$$

c)

$$\mathrm{v_{antipode}} = \mathrm{v_0}.$$

d)

$$\mathrm{F_1F_2} = R \cdot \tan 2\alpha = 2c; c = \frac{R}{2} \cdot \tan 2\alpha = \frac{R}{2} \cdot \tan 60^\circ = \frac{\sqrt{3}}{2}R;$$

$$b = \sqrt{a^2 - c^2} = \sqrt{\frac{3}{2}}R;$$

$$2a = 2r_{\text{min}} + 2c; \quad r_{\text{min}} = a - c = \frac{1}{2}(3 - \sqrt{3})R;$$

$$r_{\text{max}} = 2a - r_{\text{min}} = \frac{1}{2}\left(3 + \sqrt{3}\right) R;$$

$$\text{v}_{\text{min}} = \sqrt{KM\left(\frac{2}{r_{\text{max}}} - \frac{1}{a}\right)}; \quad r_{\text{max}} = \frac{1}{2}(3 + \sqrt{3})R;$$

$$\text{v}_{\text{min}} = \sqrt{\frac{KM}{R^2} \cdot R^2 \left(\frac{4}{(3 + \sqrt{3})\, R} - \frac{2}{3R}\right)} = \sqrt{\frac{2g_0 R}{3} \cdot \frac{3 - \sqrt{3}}{3 + \sqrt{3}}}.$$

e) According to Kepler's law, using Figure 44.5, it results that:

$$\Omega = \frac{\mathrm{d}S}{\mathrm{d}t} = \text{constant};$$

$$\frac{S_0}{T} = \frac{2\frac{S_0}{4} + 2S_1}{\Delta t}; \quad \frac{S_0}{T} = \frac{\frac{S_0}{2} + 2S_1}{\Delta t}; \quad \frac{S_0}{T} = \frac{S_0 + 4S_1}{2 \cdot \Delta t};$$

$$S_0 = \pi ab; \quad S_1 = \frac{ab}{2}\left[\sqrt{1 - \frac{b^2}{a^2}} \cdot \frac{b}{a} + \arcsin\sqrt{1 - \frac{b^2}{a^2}}\right];$$

$$\Delta t = \frac{S_0 + 4S_1}{2S_0} \cdot T = \left(\frac{1}{2} + 2\frac{S_1}{S_0}\right) \cdot T;$$

$$T = 2\pi\sqrt{\frac{a^3}{KM}}; \quad T = \frac{2\pi}{R}\sqrt{\frac{a^3}{g_0}};$$

$$\frac{2S_1}{S_0} = \frac{1}{\pi}\left(\frac{b}{a} \cdot \sqrt{1 - \frac{b^2}{a^2}} + \arcsin\sqrt{1 - \frac{b^2}{a^2}}\right);$$

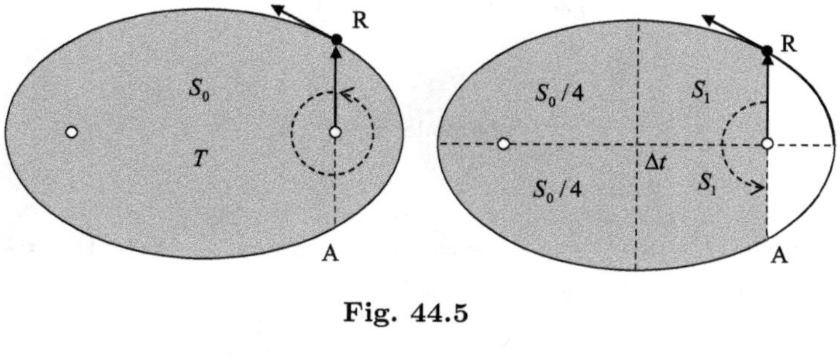

Fig. 44.5

$$\sqrt{1-\frac{b^2}{a^2}}=e;\qquad \frac{2S_1}{S_0}=\frac{1}{\pi}\left(\frac{b}{a}\cdot e+\arcsin e\right);$$

$$\Delta t=\left(\frac{1}{2}+\frac{eb}{\pi a}+\frac{\arcsin e}{\pi}\right)\cdot T.$$

f) The Sun's *integrated luminosity*, L_S, is the total energy emitted by the Sun in one time unit, through its entire surface, on all wavelengths, and in all directions:

$$L_S=\frac{E_{\text{emitted, Sun}}}{t}=3.86\cdot 10^{26}\ \text{W}.$$

Thus, from the dimensional point of view, luminosity is power.

Let us consider Σ to be the surface of the circumsolar sphere and its radius to be the distance between the center of the Sun and the center of the Earth (or the Moon), r_{ES}, as presented in Figure 44.6. Under these circumstances, the energy of solar radiation crossing the surface Σ in one time unit is equal to L_S.

The density of the Sun's energetic flux at a distance r_{ES} from the Sun (close to the Earth, the Moon and the ballistic projectile) is the energy of all radiation emitted by the Sun that crosses, at normal incidence, a unit area of a surface at the respective distance

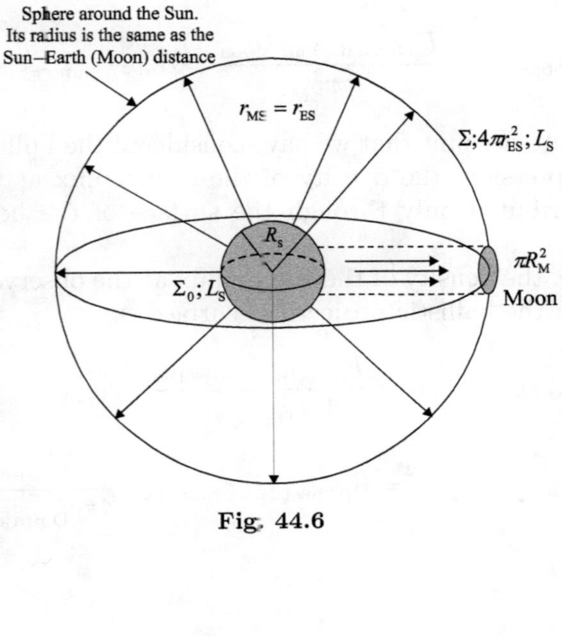

Fig. 44.6

per unit time, i.e.,

$$\phi_{\text{Sun},r_{\text{ES}}} = \frac{E_{\text{emitted, Sun}}}{St} = \frac{\frac{E_{\text{emitted, Sun}}}{t}}{S} = \frac{L_{\text{S}}}{S} = \frac{L_{\text{S}}}{4\pi r_{\text{ES}}^2} = \text{constant}.$$

The hemisphere of the Moon exposed to solar radiation is equivalent to a circular plane disc of radius R_{M} and surface πR_{M}^2, placed perpendicular to the Moon–Sun direction. Thus, the *flux* of incident solar radiation at the Moon's surface is

$$F_{\text{incident, Full Moon}} = \phi_{\text{Sun},r_{\text{ES}}} \cdot \pi R_{\text{M}}^2.$$

If α_{M} is the Moon's albedo, it results that:

$$\alpha_{\text{M}} = \frac{F_{\text{reflected, Full Moon}}}{F_{\text{incident, Full Moon}}},$$

where $F_{\text{reflected, Full Moon}}$ is the energetic flux of the radiation reflected by the Full Moon towards the observer on the Earth;

$$F_{\text{reflected, Full Moon}} = \alpha_{\text{M}} \cdot F_{\text{incident, Full Moon}} = \alpha_{\text{M}} \cdot \phi_{\text{Sun},r_{\text{ES}}} \cdot \pi R_{\text{M}}^2.$$

Consequently, the density of the energetic flux reaching the observer after being reflected by the Moon's surface is

$$\phi_{\text{Moon, observer}} = \frac{F_{\text{reflected, Full Moon}}}{2\pi r_{\text{EM}}^2} = \alpha_{\text{M}} \cdot \phi_{\text{Sun},r_{\text{ES}}} \cdot \frac{\pi R_{\text{M}}^2}{2\pi r_{\text{EM}}^2}.$$

Taking into account that we have considered the Full Moon in the previous expression, the density of the energy flux at the observer level is distributed only through the surface of the hemisphere of radius r_{EM}.

Similarly, the density of the energy flux at the observer level after reflection on the ballistic projectile's surface is:

$$\phi_{\text{projectile, observer}} = \frac{F_{\text{reflected, projectile}}}{4\pi r_{\text{D,projectile}}^2}$$

$$= \alpha_{\text{projectile}} \cdot \phi_{\text{Sun},r_{\text{ES}}} \cdot \frac{\pi R_{\text{projectile}}^2}{4\pi r_{\text{D,projectile}}^2}.$$

In the previous expression, we took into account that the density of the energy flux from the projectile to the observer results from its distribution on the surface of the sphere of radius $r_{\mathrm{E,projectile}}$.

Using Pogson's formula, we will compare the apparent visual magnitude of the Full Moon with the apparent visual magnitude of the ballistic projectile:

$$\log \frac{\phi_{\text{Moon, observer}}}{\phi_{\text{projectile, observer}}} = -0.4\left(m_{\text{Full Moon}} - m_{\text{projectile}}\right);$$

$$\log \frac{\phi_{\text{Moon, observer}}}{\phi_{\text{projectile,observer}}} = \log \frac{\alpha_{\mathrm{M}} \cdot \phi_{\mathrm{Sun}, r_{\mathrm{ES}}} \cdot \frac{\pi R_{\mathrm{M}}^2}{2\pi r_{\mathrm{EM}}^2}}{\alpha_{\text{projectile}} \cdot \phi_{\mathrm{Sun}, r_{\mathrm{ES}}} \cdot \frac{\pi R_{\text{projectile}}^2}{4\pi r_{\text{D,projectile}}^2}}$$

$$= \log \frac{\alpha_{\mathrm{M}} \cdot \frac{R_{\mathrm{M}}^2}{r_{\mathrm{EM}}^2}}{\alpha_{\text{projectile}} \cdot \frac{R_{\text{projectile}}^2}{2 r_{\text{D,projectile}}^2}};$$

$$\log \frac{\alpha_{\mathrm{M}} \cdot \frac{R_{\mathrm{M}}^2}{r_{\mathrm{EM}}^2}}{\alpha_{\text{projectile}} \cdot \frac{R_{\text{projectile}}^2}{2 r_{\text{D,projectile}}^2}} = -0.4\left(m_{\mathrm{M}} - m_{\text{projectile}}\right);$$

$$\log \frac{\alpha_{\mathrm{M}}}{\alpha_{\text{projectile}}} \cdot \left(\frac{R_{\mathrm{M}}}{R_{\text{projectile}}}\right)^2 \cdot 2 \cdot \left(\frac{r_{\text{D,projectile}}}{r_{\mathrm{EM}}}\right)^2$$
$$= -0.4\left(m_{\mathrm{M}} - m_{\text{projectile}}\right);$$

$$\alpha_{\mathrm{M}} = 0.12; \alpha_{\text{projectile}} = 1;$$

$$R_{\mathrm{M}} = 1738\,\mathrm{km}; R_{\text{projectile}} = 400\,\mathrm{mm};$$

$$r_{\text{D,projectile}} = r_{\text{max,observer}-\text{projectile}} = h_{\max} = r_{\max} - R;$$

$$r_{\max} = \frac{1}{2}\left(3 + \sqrt{3}\right) R;$$

$$h_{\max} = \frac{1}{2}\left(3 + \sqrt{3}\right) R - R = \frac{1}{2}\left(1 + \sqrt{3}\right) R \approx 8700\ \mathrm{km};$$

$$r_{\mathrm{EM}} = r_{\text{observer,Moon}} = 384400\,\mathrm{km}; \quad m_{\mathrm{M}} = -12.7^{\mathrm{m}};$$

$$\log \frac{\alpha_{\mathrm{M}}}{\alpha_{\text{projectile}}} + 2\log \frac{R_{\mathrm{M}}}{R_{\text{projectile}}} + \log 2 + 2\log \frac{r_{\text{D}-\text{projectile}}}{r_{\mathrm{EM}}}$$
$$= -0.4\left(m_{\mathrm{M}} - m_{\text{projectile}}\right);$$

$$\log(0.12) + 2\log\frac{1738000\ \text{m}}{0.400\ \text{m}} + \log 2 + 2\log\frac{8700\ \text{km}}{384400\ \text{km}}$$
$$= -0.4\left(m_{\text{M}} - m_{\text{projectile}}\right);$$
$$\log(0.12) + 2\log\frac{1738000}{0.400} + \log 2 + 2\log\frac{8700}{384400}$$
$$= -0.4\left(m_{\text{M}} - m_{\text{projectile}}\right);$$
$$-0.920818754 + 13.27597956 + 0.301029995 - 3.290528253$$
$$= -0.4\left(m_{\text{M}} - m_{\text{projectile}}\right);$$
$$23.4^{\text{m}} = 12.7^{\text{m}} + m_{\text{projectile}};$$
$$m_{\text{projectile}} = 10.7^{\text{m}};$$
$$m_{\max} \approx 6^{\text{m}};\quad m_{\text{projectile}} > m_{\max}.$$

Thus, the messenger projectile is not visible to the naked eye when it is at its apogee.

Annex 1. The Optical Characteristics of an Ellipse

The tangent at a point of an ellipse is perpendicular to the bisector of the angle between the directions joining the respective point and the ellipse's foci.

Figure 44.7 presents a concave mirror in the form of a rotational ellipsoid. In one of its foci (F_1) is a point light source. The incident beam is reflected on the mirror at point M. We have also represented the tangent to the ellipse and the normal MN at the respective incidence point. The reflected beam obeys the laws of reflection ($\theta_1 = \theta_2$), and the resultant beam is MP.

The equation for the incident beam of the SM line is:

$$y = m_1 x + n_1;$$
$$m_1 = \tan\alpha_1 = \frac{y_0}{x_0 + c};\quad n_1 = \frac{cy_0}{x_0 + c};$$
$$y = \frac{y_0}{x_0 + c}x + \frac{cy_0}{x_0 + c}.$$

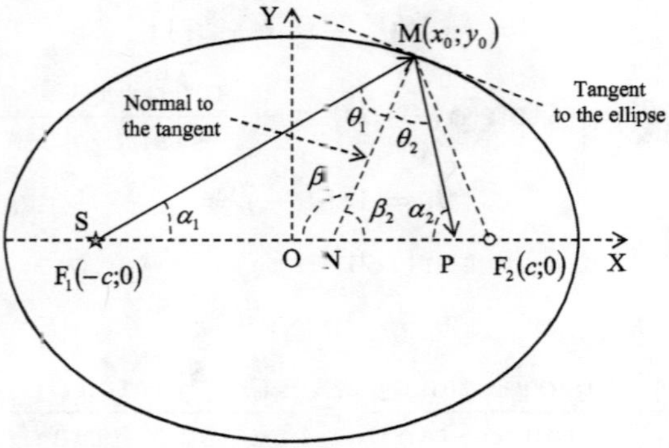

Fig. 44.7

The equation of the normal to the tangent of the ellipse at point M $(x_0; y_0)$, i.e., the equation of the MN line, is

$$y - y_0 = \frac{a^2 y_0}{b^2 x_0}(x - x_0),$$

with the conditions:

$$\frac{x_0^2}{a^2} + \frac{y_0^2}{b^2} = 1;$$

$$y = \frac{a^2 y_0}{b^2 x_0} x + y_0 \left(1 - \frac{a^2}{b^2}\right);$$

$$y = mx + n;$$

$$m = \frac{a^2 y_0}{b^2 x_0} = \tan \beta_2; \quad n = y_0 \left(1 - \frac{a^2}{b^2}\right).$$

The equation of the MP line representing the reflected beam is:

$$y - y_0 = m_2 (x - x_0);$$

$$m_2 = \tan (180^\circ - \alpha_2) = -\tan \alpha_2;$$

$$\alpha_2 = 180^\circ - (\beta_2 + \theta_2);$$

$$m_2 = \tan (\beta_2 + \theta_2);$$

$$m_2 = \frac{\tan \beta_2 + \tan \theta_2}{1 - \tan \beta_2 \cdot \tan \theta_2};$$

$$\theta_1 = 180^\circ - (\alpha_1 + \beta_1);$$

$$\tan\theta_1 = -\tan(\alpha_1 + \beta_1) = -\frac{\tan\alpha_1 + \tan\beta_1}{1 - \tan\alpha_1 \cdot \tan\beta_1};$$

$$\beta_1 = 180^\circ - \beta_2;$$

$$\tan\beta_1 = \tan(180^\circ - \beta_2) = -\tan\beta_2;$$

$$\theta_2 = \theta_1;$$

$$\tan\theta_1 = -\frac{\tan\alpha_1 - \tan\beta_2}{1 - \tan\alpha_1 \cdot \tan\beta_1} = \frac{\tan\beta_2 - \tan\alpha_1}{1 + \tan\alpha_1 \cdot \tan\beta_2} = \tan\theta_2;$$

$$m_2 = \frac{\tan\beta_2 + \tan\theta_2}{1 - \tan\beta_2 \cdot \tan\theta_2};$$

$$m_2 = \frac{\tan\beta_2 + \frac{\tan\beta_2 - \tan\alpha_1}{1 + \tan\alpha_1 \cdot \tan\beta_2}}{1 - \tan\beta_2 \cdot \frac{\tan\beta_2 - \tan\alpha_1}{1 + \tan\alpha_1 \cdot \tan\beta_2}}; \quad \tan\alpha_1 = \frac{y_0}{x_0 + c}; \quad \tan\beta_2 = \frac{a^2 y_0}{b^2 x_0};$$

$$m_2 = \frac{2a^2b^2x_0y_0(x_0 + c) + y_0\left(a^4y_0^2 - b^4x_0^2\right)}{2a^2b^2x_0y_0^2 - (x_0 + c)\left(a^4y_0^2 - b^4x_0^2\right)}.$$

The equation of MF_2, which is the line joining point M and focus F_2, is:

$$y = m_3x + n_3;$$

$$m_3 = \frac{y_0}{x_0 - c}; \quad n_3 = -\frac{y_0c}{x_0 - c}.$$

Let's compare the coefficients m_2 and m_3, representing the slopes of the lines MP and MF_2, where $m_2 = m_3$.

We find that:

$$\frac{2a^2b^2x_0y_0(x_0 + c) + y_0\left(a^4y_0^2 - b^4x_0^2\right)}{2a^2b^2x_0y_0^2 - (x_0 + c)\left(a^4y_0^2 - b^4x_0^2\right)} = \frac{y_0}{x_0 - c};$$

$$\frac{2a^2b^2x_0(x_0 + c) + \left(a^4y_0^2 - b^4x_0^2\right)}{2a^2b^2x_0y_0^2 - (x_0 + c)\left(a^4y_0^2 - b^4x_0^2\right)} = \frac{1}{x_0 - c};$$

$$2a^2b^2x_0\left(x_0^2 - c^2\right) + (x_0 - c)\left(a^4y_0^2 - b^4x_0^2\right)$$
$$= 2a^2b^2x_0y_0^2 - (x_0 + c)\left(a^4y_0^2 - b^4x_0^2\right);$$

$$2a^2b^2x_0\left(x_0^2 - c^2\right) + x_0\left(a^4y_0^2 - b^4x_0^2\right) - c\left(a^4y_0^2 - b^4x_0^2\right)$$
$$= 2a^2b^2x_0y_0^2 - x_0\left(a^4y_0^2 - b^4x_0^2\right) - c\left(a^4y_0^2 - b^4x_0^2\right);$$

$$2a^2b^2x_0\left(x_0^2 - c^2\right) + 2x_0\left(a^4y_0^2 - b^4x_0^2\right) = 2a^2b^2x_0y_0^2;$$
$$a^2b^2\left(x_0^2 - c^2\right) + \left(a^4y_0^2 - b^4x_0^2\right) = a^2b^2y_0^2;$$
$$c^2 = a^2 - b^2;$$
$$a^2b^2\left(x_0^2 - a^2 + b^2\right) + \left(a^4y_0^2 - b^4x_0^2\right) = a^2b^2y_0^2;$$
$$a^2b^2x_0^2 - a^4b^2 + a^2b^4 - a^4y_0^2 - b^4x_0^2 = a^2b^2y_0^2;$$
$$a^2b^2x_0^2 - b^4x_0^2 + a^2b^4 = a^2b^2y_0^2 - a^4y_0^2 + a^4b^2;$$
$$b^2\left(a^2x_0^2 - b^2x_0^2 + a^2b^2\right) = a^2\left(b^2y_0^2 - a^2y_0^2 + a^2b^2\right);$$
$$\frac{x_0^2}{a^2} + \frac{y_0^2}{b^2} = 1; \quad b^2x_0^2 + a^2y_0^2 = a^2b^2;$$
$$b^2\left(a^2x_0^2 - b^2x_0^2 + b^2x_0^2 + a^2y_0^2\right) = a^2\left(b^2y_0^2 - a^2y_0^2 + b^2x_0^2 + a^2y_0^2\right);$$
$$b^2\left(a^2x_0^2 + a^2y_0^2\right) = a^2\left(b^2y_0^2 + b^2x_0^2\right);$$
$$a^2b^2\left(x_0^2 + y_0^2\right) = a^2b^2\left(y_0^2 + x_0^2\right).$$

This proves that the hypothesis was true, i.e., $m_2 = m_3$, which means that the slopes for the lines MP and MF_2 are identical.

Conclusions:

- After the reflection at point M, the beam originating in focus F_1 will pass through focus F_2; all light beams emitted by the point source placed in focus F_1 will reflect on the concave ellipsoid mirror and then will pass through focus F_2, as presented in Figure 44.8.

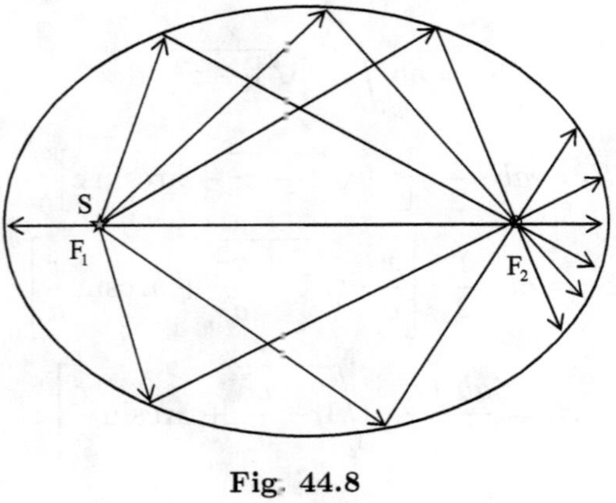

Fig. 44.8

- The tangent at a point on the ellipse is perpendicular to the bisector of the angle between the directions joining the respective point with the ellipse's foci.

Annex 2. The Surface of an Ellipse Sector

For the ellipse presented in Figure 44.9, it results that:

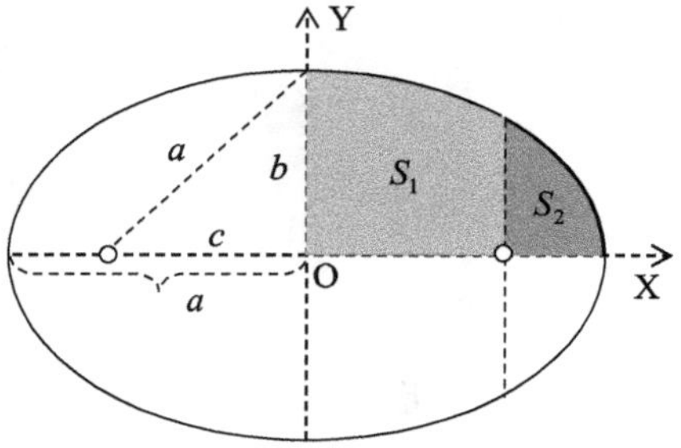

Fig. 44.9

$$\frac{x^2}{a^2}+\frac{y^2}{b^2}=1; \quad y=b\cdot\sqrt{1-\frac{x^2}{a^2}};$$

$$S_1=\int_0^c f(x)\cdot \mathrm{d}x=\int_0^c y\cdot \mathrm{d}x=b\int_0^c\sqrt{1-\frac{x^2}{a^2}}\cdot \mathrm{d}x;$$

$$\frac{x}{a}=z; \quad x=az; \quad \mathrm{d}x=a\cdot \mathrm{d}z;$$

$$S_1=ab\int_0^{c/a}\sqrt{1-z^2}\cdot \mathrm{d}z;$$

$$S_1=ab\cdot\frac{1}{2}\cdot\left[z\cdot\sqrt{1-z^2}+\arcsin z\right]_0^{c/a};$$

$$S_1=ab\cdot\frac{1}{2}\cdot\left[\frac{x}{a}\cdot\sqrt{1-\frac{x^2}{a^2}}+\arcsin\frac{x}{a}\right]_0^c;$$

$$S_1=\frac{ab}{2}\left[\frac{c}{a}\cdot\sqrt{1-\frac{c^2}{a^2}}+\arcsin\frac{c}{a}\right];$$

$$c^2 = a^2 - b^2; \quad c = \sqrt{a^2 - b^2} = a \cdot \sqrt{1 - \frac{b^2}{a^2}};$$

$$S_1 = \frac{ab}{2}\left[\sqrt{1 - \frac{b^2}{a^2}} \cdot \frac{b}{a} + \arcsin\sqrt{1 - \frac{b^2}{a^2}}\right];$$

$$S_2 = \int_c^a y \cdot \mathrm{d}x = b\int_c^a \sqrt{1 - \frac{x^2}{a^2}} \cdot \mathrm{d}x;$$

$$S_2 = ab\int_{c/a}^1 \sqrt{1 - z^2} \cdot \mathrm{d}z;$$

$$S_2 = ab \cdot \frac{1}{2} \cdot \left[z \cdot \sqrt{1 - z^2} + \arcsin z\right]_{c/a}^1;$$

$$S_2 = ab \cdot \frac{1}{2} \cdot \left[\frac{x}{a} \cdot \sqrt{1 - \frac{x^2}{a^2}} + \arcsin\frac{x}{a}\right]_c^a;$$

$$S_2 = ab \cdot \frac{1}{2} \cdot \left[\frac{a}{a} \cdot \sqrt{1 - \frac{a^2}{a^2}} + \arcsin\frac{a}{a} - \frac{c}{a}\sqrt{1 - \frac{c^2}{a^2}} - \arcsin\frac{c}{a}\right];$$

$$S_2 = ab \cdot \frac{1}{2} \cdot \left[\arcsin 1 - \sqrt{1 - \frac{b^2}{a^2}} \cdot \frac{b}{a} - \arcsin\sqrt{1 - \frac{b^2}{a^2}}\right];$$

$$S_2 = ab \cdot \frac{1}{2} \cdot \left[\frac{\pi}{2} - \sqrt{1 - \frac{b^2}{a^2}} \cdot \frac{b}{a} - \arcsin\sqrt{1 - \frac{b^2}{a^2}}\right];$$

$$\begin{aligned} S_1 + S_2 = {} & \frac{ab}{2}\left[\sqrt{1 - \frac{b^2}{a^2}} \cdot \frac{b}{a} + \arcsin\sqrt{1 - \frac{b^2}{a^2}}\right] \\ & + \frac{ab}{2}\left[\frac{\pi}{2} - \sqrt{1 - \frac{b^2}{a^2}} \cdot \frac{b}{a} - \arcsin\sqrt{1 - \frac{b^2}{a^2}}\right]; \end{aligned}$$

$$S_1 + S_2 = \frac{\pi ab}{4};$$

$$4\,(S_1 + S_2) = S_{\text{ellipse}} = \pi ab.$$

Problem 45

Ice Particle

A comet revolves around the Sun in a very elongated elliptical orbit. A particle of ice detaches from the comet when the comet is at the aphelion of its orbit, where the speed of the comet relative to the Sun is very low (negligible).

a) *Estimate* the radius of the ice particle that detaches from the comet such that the detached particle remains at rest in relation to the Sun. It is known that the ice particle is a perfectly reflective sphere.

b) *Determine* the pressure of the solar radiation corresponding to the distance at which the ice particle is located.

c) *Estimate* the temperature of the ice particle after the comet has detached, T_{particle}.

d) *Determine* the density of the energy of the solar radiation, w, at the distance corresponding to the ice particle, and *establish* its relation to the pressure of the solar radiation, p_{rad}.

Given: the density of ice in the structure of the comet, $\rho = 300\ \text{kg/m}^3$; the brightness of the Sun, $L_{\text{Sun}} = 3.86 \cdot 10^{26}$ W; the constant of gravitational attraction, $G = 6.67 \cdot 10^{-11}\ \text{Nm}^2\text{kg}^{-2}$; the speed of light in vacuum, $c = 300000$ km/s; the mass of the Sun, $M_{\text{Sun}} = 1.99 \cdot 10^{30}$ kg; the distance between the Sun and the comet at the aphelion, $R_{\max} = 35143615.62$ AU; 1 AU $\approx 15 \cdot 10^{10}$ m; and the Stefan–Boltzmann constant, $\sigma = 5.67 \cdot 10^{-8}\ \frac{\text{W}}{\text{m}^2\text{K}^4}$.

Solution

a) Consider that, at some point, when the comet is at a distance R_{max} from the Sun, at the aphelion of its orbit, as indicated in Figure 45.1, a spherical particle of ice with radius r and mass m detaches from the comet, its speed in relation to the Sun being very low (negligible).

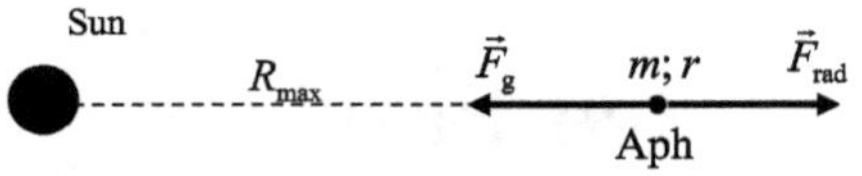

Fig. 45.1

The forces acting on the ice particle are: $\vec{F}_g$ – the force of gravitational attraction from the Sun; and $\vec{F}_{rad}$ – the repulsive force due to solar radiation pressure.

The force of gravitational attraction

$$F_{gravitational} = G\frac{m_{particle}M_{Sun}}{R_{max}^2};$$

$$m_{particle} = \rho \cdot \frac{4\pi r^3}{3};$$

$$F_{gravitational} = G\frac{\rho \cdot \frac{4\pi r^3}{3} M_{Sun}}{R_{max}^2};$$

$$F_{gravitational} = G\frac{4\pi \rho r^3 M_{Sun}}{3R_{max}^2}.$$

Radiation pressure force

The variation in the impulse of a photon, incident on the reflecting face of the spherical ice particle (Figure 45.2), is:

$$\Delta\vec{p} = \vec{p}_r - \vec{p}_i;$$

$$\Delta p = 2p_i \cos\theta = 2\frac{h}{\lambda}\cos\theta = 2\frac{hv}{c}\cos\theta.$$

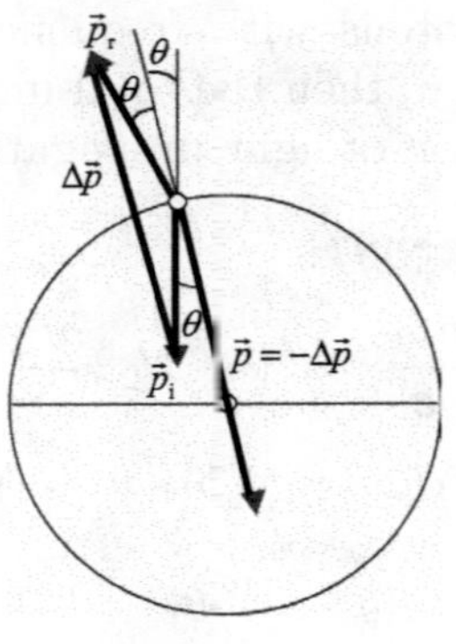

Fig. 45.2

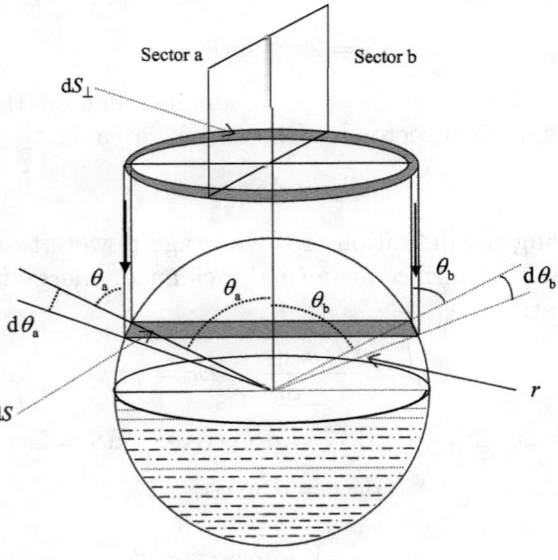

Fig. 45.3

In this case, the impulse transmitted to the sphere is:

$$\vec{p} = -\Delta\vec{p}; \quad p = \Delta p; \quad p = 2\frac{h}{\lambda}\cos\theta = 2\frac{hv}{c}\cos\theta.$$

If on each of the two elementary spherical sectors, a and b, on the reflecting surface of the spherical ice particle (Figure 45.3), under the same angle of incidence, $\theta_a = \theta_b = \theta$, $N_1/2$ photons with the frequency ν_1, $N_2/2$ photons with frequency ν_2, and so on, arrive with uniform distribution, then the total impulse transmitted to the sphere along the direction of light propagation is:

$$\begin{aligned} p_{//} &= p_{//,\mathrm{a}} + p_{//,\mathrm{b}} \\ &= N_1 2\frac{h\nu_1}{c}\cos^2\theta + N_2 2\frac{h\nu_2}{c}\cos^2\theta + \cdots \\ &= \frac{2}{c}\left(N_1 h\nu_1 + N_2 h\nu_2 + \cdots\right)\cdot\cos^2\theta \\ &= \frac{2}{c}W_{\theta;\theta+\mathrm{d}\theta}\cdot\cos^2\theta, \end{aligned}$$

where $W_{\theta;\theta+\mathrm{d}\theta}$ is the energy of all incident photons on both sectors, a and b, i.e., on the whole elementary spherical sector, whose area is

$$\mathrm{d}S = 2\pi r^2 \sin\theta\cdot\mathrm{d}\theta.$$

The cross-section of the light beam incident on the considered elementary spherical sector has the surface area

$$\mathrm{d}S_\perp = \mathrm{d}S\cdot\cos\theta.$$

Considering the definition of the average power of solar radiation per unit area of a surface at normal incidence (energy flow density), it results that:

$$\varphi = \frac{W_{\theta;\theta+\mathrm{d}\theta}}{\mathrm{d}S_\perp \mathrm{d}t}; \quad E_0 = \varphi;$$

$$W_{\theta;\theta+\mathrm{d}\theta} = \varphi\cdot\mathrm{d}S_\perp\cdot\mathrm{d}t;\ \mathrm{d}S_\perp = \mathrm{d}S\cdot\cos\theta; \quad \mathrm{d}S = 2\pi r^2\sin\theta\cdot\mathrm{d}\theta;$$

$$\mathrm{d}S_\perp = \mathrm{d}S\cdot\cos\theta;$$

$$p_{//} = \frac{2}{c}W_{\theta;\theta+\mathrm{d}\theta}\cdot\cos^2\theta;$$

$$p_{//} = \frac{2}{c}\varphi\cdot\mathrm{d}S_\perp\cdot\mathrm{d}t\cdot\cos^2\theta; \quad \mathrm{d}S_\perp = \mathrm{d}S\cdot\cos\theta;$$

$$p_{//} = \frac{2}{c}\varphi\cdot\mathrm{d}S\cdot\cos\theta\cdot\mathrm{d}t\cdot\cos^2\theta; \quad p_{//} = \frac{1}{c}\varphi\cdot\mathrm{d}S\cdot\mathrm{d}t\cdot\cos^3\theta;$$

$$\mathrm{d}S = 2\pi r^2\sin\theta\cdot\mathrm{d}\theta;$$

$$p_{//} = \frac{4\pi r^2\varphi}{c}\cos^3\theta\sin\theta\cdot\mathrm{d}\theta\cdot\mathrm{d}t.$$

Under these conditions, the elementary force acting on the sphere as a result of the photons incident on the considered elementary sector is:

$$\mathrm{d}F = \frac{p_{//}}{\mathrm{d}t} = \frac{4\pi r^2 \varphi}{c} \cdot \cos^3\theta \cdot \sin\theta \cdot \mathrm{d}\theta;$$

$$\mathrm{d}F = -\frac{4\pi r^2 \varphi}{c} \cdot \cos^3\theta \cdot \mathrm{d}(\cos\theta).$$

The force acting on the whole sphere as a result of photons incident on the reflecting hemisphere of the ice particle will be:

$$\begin{aligned} F &= -\frac{4\pi r^2 \varphi}{c}\left(\int_0^{\pi/2} \cos^3\theta \cdot d(\cos\theta)\right) \\ &= -\frac{4\pi r^2 \varphi}{c} \cdot \frac{1}{4}\left(\cos^4\frac{\pi}{2} - \cos^4 0\right) \\ &= -\frac{4\pi r^2 \varphi}{c} \cdot \frac{1}{4}(0-1) \\ &= \frac{\pi r^2 \varphi}{c}; \end{aligned}$$

$$\varphi = \frac{L_S}{4\pi R_{\max}^2};$$

$$F_{\mathrm{rad}} = \frac{L_S r^2}{4cR_{\max}^2},$$

where L_{Sun} is the brightness of the Sun, and c is the speed of light in vacuum.

Consider that at some point, when the comet is at a distance R from the Sun, as shown in the drawing in Figure 45.4, a spherical ice particle with radius r and mass m detaches from the comet, its velocity relative to the Sun being equal to the speed of the comet, $\vec{v}$.

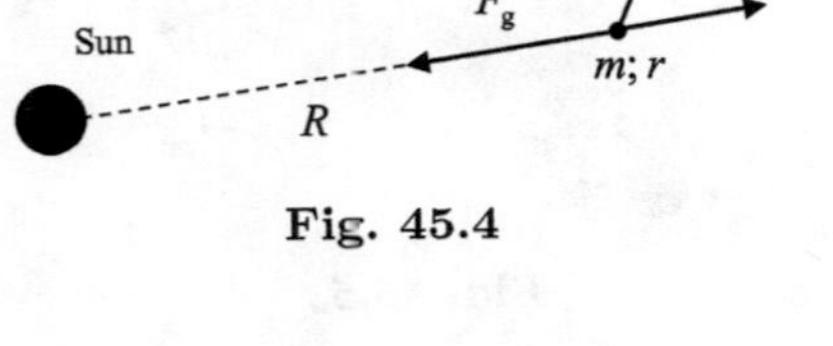

Fig. 45.4

The forces acting on the ice particle are: $\vec{F}_{\mathrm{g}}$ – the force of gravitational attraction from the Sun; and $\vec{F}_{\mathrm{rad}}$ – repulsive force due to solar radiation pressure.

$$F_{\mathrm{g}} = K\frac{mM_{\mathrm{S}}}{R^2};$$

$$F_{\mathrm{p}} = \frac{L_{\mathrm{S}}r^2}{4cR^2},$$

so that the resultant of the two collinear and opposite forces acting on the ice particle is:

$$F = F_{\mathrm{g}} - F_{\mathrm{p}} = K\frac{mM_{\mathrm{S}}}{R^2} - \frac{L_{\mathrm{S}}r^2}{2cR^2};$$

$$F = K\frac{m}{R^2}\left(M_{\mathrm{S}} - \frac{L_{\mathrm{S}}r^2}{2cKm}\right),$$

which is a central force resulting from the gravitational interaction of the ice particle and an equivalent Sun, having an effective mass

$$M_{\mathrm{S,effective}} = M_{\mathrm{S}} - \frac{L_{\mathrm{S}}r^2}{2cKm}.$$

The two interactions (gravitational and electromagnetic) between the ice particle and the Sun with mass M_{S} can be replaced by a single (gravitational) interaction between the ice particle and an effective equivalent Sun, having mass $M_{\mathrm{S,effective}}$, as shown in the drawing in Figure 45.5.

As $F < F_{\mathrm{g}}$, the trajectory of the ice particle will no longer be the same as the trajectory of the comet. From that moment, the ice particle is in the gravitational field of an effective Sun with a smaller mass, so that the trajectory of the particle can be another ellipse, a parabola, or a hyperbola, depending on the total energy of the particle–actual Sun system.

The total mechanical energy of the equivalent system, immediately after its formation (after the detachment of the ice particle

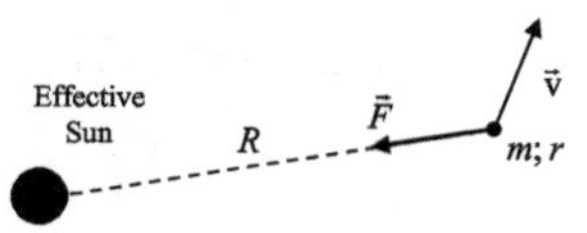

Fig. 45.5

from the comet), is

$$E = \frac{m\mathrm{v}^2}{2} - K\frac{mM_{\mathrm{ef}}}{R}.$$

The algebraic sign of E determines whether the ice particle leaves the Solar System or not. In order for the ice particle not to leave the Solar System, the following condition must be met:

$$E < 0.$$

Therefore,

$$\frac{m\mathrm{v}^2}{2} - K\frac{m}{R}\left(M_{\mathrm{S}} - \frac{L_{\mathrm{S}}r^2}{4cKm}\right) < 0.$$

Suppose that the detachment of the ice particle from the comet occurs when the comet is at the aphelion, $R = R_{\mathrm{max}}$, where its speed is very low. Hence:

$$\mathrm{v} \approx 0; \quad M_{\mathrm{S}} - \frac{L_{\mathrm{S}}r^2}{4cKm} > 0; \quad M_{\mathrm{S}} > \frac{Lr^2}{4cKm}; \quad m = \rho \cdot \frac{4\pi r^3}{3};$$

$$r > \frac{3L_{\mathrm{S}}}{16\pi c\rho K M_{\mathrm{S}}};$$

$$r > \frac{3 \cdot 3.86 \cdot 10^{26}\ \mathrm{W}}{16 \cdot 3.14 \cdot 3 \cdot 10^{8}\ \frac{\mathrm{m}}{\mathrm{s}} \cdot 300\ \frac{\mathrm{kg}}{\mathrm{m}^3} \cdot 6.67 \cdot 10^{-11}\ \frac{\mathrm{Nm}^2}{\mathrm{kg}^2} \cdot 1.99 \cdot 10^{30}\ \mathrm{kg}};$$

$$r > \frac{3 \cdot 3.86 \cdot 10^{26}}{16 \cdot 3.14 \cdot 3 \cdot 10^{8} \cdot 300 \cdot 6.67 \cdot 10^{-11} \cdot 1.99 \cdot 10^{30}}\ \mathrm{m};$$

$$r > \frac{3.86}{16 \cdot 3.14 \cdot 3 \cdot 6.67 \cdot 1,99}\ 10^{26} \cdot 10^{-8} \cdot 10^{-2} \cdot 10^{11} \cdot 10^{-30}\ \mathrm{m};$$

$$r > \frac{3.86}{16 \cdot 3.14 \cdot 3 \cdot 6.67 \cdot 1.99} \cdot 10^{-3}\ \mathrm{m};$$

$$r > 0.001929\ \mathrm{mm}; \quad r > 1.9 \cdot 10^{-6}\ \mathrm{m}.$$

b) We previously determined the pressure force exerted by the solar radiation on the spherical ice particle when the particle reflects the incident radiation:

$$F_{\text{rad}} = \frac{L_{\text{Sun}} r^2}{4cR_{\text{max}}^2}.$$

In this case, it results that:

$$p_{\text{rad}} = \frac{F_{\text{rad}}}{\pi r^2} = \frac{\frac{L_{\text{Sun}} r^2}{4cR_{\text{max}}^2}}{\pi r^2};$$

$$p_{\text{rad}} = \frac{L_{\text{Sun}}}{4\pi c R_{\text{max}}^2};$$

$$L_{\text{Sun}} = 4\pi\sigma T_{\text{Sun}}^4 R_{\text{Sun}}^2;$$

$$p_{\text{rad}} = \frac{4\pi\sigma T_{\text{Sun}}^4 R_{\text{Sun}}^2}{4\pi c R_{\text{max}}^2};$$

$$p_{\text{rad}} = \frac{\sigma T_{\text{Sun}}^4 R_{\text{Sun}}^2}{c R_{\text{max}}^2};$$

$$p_{\text{rad}} = \frac{3.86 \cdot 10^{26}\ \text{W}}{4 \cdot 3.14 \cdot 3 \cdot 10^8\ \frac{\text{m}}{\text{s}} \cdot (35143615.62 \cdot 15 \cdot 10^{10})^2\ \text{m}^2};$$

$$p_{\text{rad}} = \frac{3.86 \cdot 10^{26}}{4 \cdot 3.14 \cdot 3 \cdot 10^8 \cdot (35143615.62 \cdot 15 \cdot 10^{10})^2}\ \frac{\text{N}}{\text{m}^2};$$

$$p_{\text{rad}} = \frac{3.86}{4 \cdot 3.14 \cdot 3 \cdot 10^8 \cdot (35143615.62 \cdot 15)^2} \cdot 10^{26} \cdot 10^{-8} \cdot 10^{-20}\ \frac{\text{N}}{\text{m}^2};$$

$$p_{\text{rad}} = \frac{3.86}{4 \cdot 3.14 \cdot 3 \cdot (35143615.62 \cdot 15)^2} \cdot 10^{-2}\ \frac{\text{N}}{\text{m}^2};$$

$$p_{\text{rad}} \approx 3.68 \cdot 10^{-21}\ \frac{\text{N}}{\text{m}^2}.$$

c) According to the Stefan–Boltzmann law, the radiance of the Sun (considered an absolute black body), i.e., the total energy, corresponding to all wavelengths, emitted in a unit of time by one unit area of the Sun's surface, is directly proportional to the fourth power of the actual surface temperature. So:

$$Q_{\text{Sun}} = \frac{E_{\text{emitted,Sun}}}{tS_{\text{Sun}}} = \sigma T_{\text{Sun}}^4,$$

where σ is a constant;

$$\frac{E_{\text{emitted,Sun}}}{t} = P_{\text{emitted,Sun}} = L_{\text{Sun}};$$

$$\sigma T_{\text{Sun}}^4 = \frac{P_{\text{emitted,Sun}}}{4\pi R_{\text{Sun}}^2} = \frac{L_{\text{Sun}}}{4\pi R_{\text{Sun}}^2},$$

where L_{Sun} is the brightness of the Sun;

$$P_{\text{emitted,Sun}} = L_{\text{Sun}} = \sigma T_{\text{Sun}}^4 4\pi R_{\text{Sun}}^2.$$

The density of the Sun's energy flow at a distance D is the energy of all the radiation emitted by the Sun that crosses unit area of a surface, under normal incidence, in a unit of time. Thus:

$$\begin{aligned}\phi_{\text{Sun},\,D} &= \frac{E_{\text{emitted,Sun}}}{St} = \frac{\frac{E_{\text{emitted,Sun}}}{t}}{S} = \frac{P_{\text{emitted,Sun}}}{S}\\ &= \frac{P_{\text{emitted,Sun}}}{4\pi R_{\text{max}}^2} = \frac{L_{\text{Sun}}}{4\pi R_{\text{max}}^2},\end{aligned}$$

where D is the distance between the particle and the Sun;

$$\phi_{\text{Sun, D}} = \frac{\sigma T_{\text{Sun}}^4 4\pi R_{\text{Sun}}^2}{4\pi R_{\text{max}}^2}.$$

The hemisphere of the particle exposed to solar radiation is equivalent to a circular plane disk with radius r and surface area πr^2, placed perpendicular to the Sun–particle direction, so that the flow of incident stellar radiation, F_{incident}, at the particle's level (the solar energy incident on the particle) per unit time is:

$$F_{\text{incident}} = \phi_{\text{Sun},D} \cdot \pi r^2 = P_{\text{incident}} = P_{\text{emitted,Sun}};$$

$$F_{\text{incident}} = \frac{\sigma T_{\text{Sun}}^4 4\pi R_{\text{Sun}}^2}{4\pi R_{\text{max}}^2} \cdot \pi r^2 = P_{\text{incident}}.$$

Considering that the particle does not reflect any of the received radiation (it absorbs everything),

$$P_{\text{reflected,particle}} = 0.$$

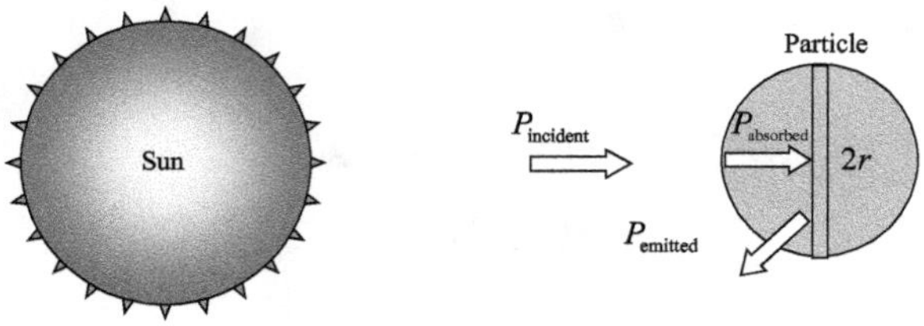

Fig. 45.6

Therefore, according to Figure 45.6, the energy balance equation of the analyzed process is:

$$P_{\text{incident,particle}} = P_{\text{absorbed,particle}};$$

$$\frac{\sigma T_{\text{Sun}}^4 4\pi R_{\text{Sun}}^2}{4\pi D^2} \cdot \pi r^2 = P_{\text{absorbed,particle}}.$$

In turn, the energy emitted by the particle, considered a black body, in a unit of time, through half of its surface (the particle does not rotate around its own axis) is

$$P_{\text{emitted,particle}} = \sigma T_{\text{particle}}^4 \cdot 2\pi r^2.$$

When the process becomes stationary,

$$P_{\text{emitted,particle}} = P_{\text{absorbed,particle}},$$

it results that:

$$\frac{\sigma T_{\text{Sun}}^4 4\pi R_{\text{Sun}}^2}{4\pi D^2} \cdot \pi r^2 = \sigma T_{\text{particle}}^4 \cdot 2\pi r^2;$$

$$T_{\text{particle}}^4 = \frac{T_{\text{Sun}}^4 R_{\text{Sun}}^2}{2D^2};$$

$$T_{\text{particle}} = T_{\text{Sun}} \cdot \sqrt[4]{\frac{R_{\text{Sun}}^2}{2D^2}};$$

$$T_{\text{particle}} = T_{\text{Sun}} \cdot \sqrt{R_{\text{Sun}}} \cdot \frac{1}{\sqrt[4]{2D^2}},$$

representing the temperature on the hemisphere of the particle exposed to solar radiation, if the particle does not rotate around its own axis;

$$L_{\text{Sun}} = \sigma T_{\text{Sun}}^4 4\pi R_{\text{Sun}}^2;$$

$$L_{\text{Sun}} = 4\pi\sigma T_{\text{Sun}}^4 R_{\text{Sun}}^2;$$

$$T_{\text{Sun}}^4 R_{\text{Sun}}^2 = \frac{L_{\text{Sun}}}{4\pi\sigma};$$

$$\sqrt[4]{T_{\text{Sun}}^4 R_{\text{Sun}}^2} = \sqrt[4]{\frac{L_{\text{Sun}}}{4\pi\sigma}};$$

$$T_{\text{Sun}} \cdot \sqrt{R_{\text{Sun}}} = \sqrt[4]{\frac{L_{\text{Sun}}}{4\pi\sigma}};$$

$$T_{\text{particle}} = T_{\text{Sun}} \cdot \sqrt{R_{\text{Sun}}} \cdot \frac{1}{\sqrt[4]{2} \cdot \sqrt{D}};$$

$$T_{\text{particle}} = \sqrt[4]{\frac{L_{\text{Sun}}}{4\pi\sigma}} \cdot \frac{1}{\sqrt[4]{2} \cdot \sqrt{D}};$$

$$T_{\text{particle}} = \sqrt[4]{\frac{L_{\text{Sun}}}{8\pi\sigma}} \cdot \frac{1}{\sqrt{D}};$$

$$T_{\text{particle}} = \sqrt[4]{\frac{3.86 \cdot 10^{26}\ \text{W}}{8 \cdot 3.14 \cdot 5.67 \cdot 10^{-8}\ \frac{\text{W}}{\text{m}^2\text{K}^4}}}$$

$$\cdot \frac{1}{\sqrt{35143615.62 \cdot 149.6 \cdot 10^9\ \text{m}}};$$

$$T_{\text{partilcle}} = \sqrt[4]{\frac{3.86 \cdot 10^{26}}{8 \cdot 3.14 \cdot 5.67 \cdot 10^{-8}}} \cdot \frac{1}{\sqrt{35143615.62 \cdot 149.6 \cdot 10^9}}\ \text{K};$$

$$T_{\text{particle}} = \sqrt[4]{\frac{3.86 \cdot 10^{24} \cdot 10^2 \cdot 10^8}{8 \cdot 3.14 \cdot 5.67}} \cdot \frac{1}{\sqrt{35143615.62 \cdot 149.6 \cdot 10^9}}\ \text{K};$$

$$T_{\text{particle}} = \sqrt[4]{\frac{386}{8 \cdot 3.14 \cdot 5.67}} \cdot \frac{1}{10^4 \cdot \sqrt{35143615.62 \cdot 1496}}\ \text{K};$$

$$T_{\text{particle}} = \sqrt[4]{\frac{386}{8 \cdot 3.14 \cdot 5.67}} \cdot \frac{1}{\sqrt{35143615.62 \cdot 1496}} \cdot 10^6 \cdot 10^2 \cdot 10^{-4}\,\text{K};$$

$$T_{\text{particle}} = \sqrt[4]{\frac{386}{8 \cdot 3.14 \cdot 5.67}} \cdot \frac{1}{\sqrt{35143615.62 \cdot 1496}} \cdot 10^4\ \text{K};$$

$$T_{\text{particle}} = \sqrt[4]{2.71} \cdot \frac{1}{229292.0604} \cdot 10^4\ \text{K};$$

$$T_{\text{particle}} = \sqrt[4]{2.71} \cdot \frac{1}{229292.0604} \cdot 10^4\ \text{K};$$

$$\sqrt[4]{2.71} \approx 1.28;$$

$$T_{\text{particle}} = \frac{12800}{229292.0604}\ \text{K};$$

$$T_{\text{particle}} \approx 0.0558\ K.$$

d) According to the Stefan–Boltzmann law, the radiance of the Sun (considered an absolute black body), i.e., the total energy, corresponding to all wavelengths, emitted in a unit of time by a unit area of the Sun's surface, is directly proportional to the fourth power of the actual surface temperature. So:

$$Q_{\text{Sun}} = \frac{E_{\text{emitted,Sun}}}{t \cdot S_{\text{Sun}}} = \sigma T_{\text{Sun}}^4,$$

where σ is a constant;

$$\frac{E_{\text{emitted,Sun}}}{t} = P_{\text{emitted,Sun}} = L_{\text{Sun}};$$

$$\sigma T_{\text{Sun}}^4 = \frac{P_{\text{emitted,Sun}}}{4\pi R_{\text{Sun}}^2} = \frac{L_{\text{Sun}}}{4\pi R_{\text{Sun}}^2},$$

where L_{Sun} is the brightness of the star;

$$P_{\text{emitted,Sun}} = L_{\text{Sun}} = \sigma T_{\text{Sun}}^4 4\pi R_{\text{Sun}}^2.$$

The density of the Sun's energy flow at a distance D is the energy of all the radiation emitted by the Sun that crosses a unit area of a surface, under normal incidence, in a unit of time. Hence:

$$\phi_{\text{Sun, }D} = \frac{E_{\text{emitted,Sun}}}{S \cdot t} = \frac{\frac{E_{\text{emitted, Sun}}}{t}}{S} = \frac{P_{\text{emitted,Sun}}}{S}$$

$$= \frac{P_{\text{emitted,Sun}}}{4\pi D^2} = \frac{L_{\text{Sun}}}{4\pi D^2};$$

$$\phi_{\text{Sun, }D} = \frac{\sigma T_{\text{Sun}}^4 4\pi R_{\text{Sun}}^2}{4\pi D^2} = \frac{\sigma T_{\text{Sun}}^4 R_{\text{Sun}}^2}{D^2};$$

$$\frac{\phi_{\text{Sun, }D}}{c} = \frac{\sigma T_{\text{Sun}}^4 R_{\text{Sun}}^2}{cD^2};$$

$$\phi_{\text{Sun, }D} = \frac{E_{\text{emitted,Sun}}}{S \cdot \Delta t} = \frac{E_{\text{emitted,Sun}}}{4\pi D^2 \cdot \Delta t};$$

$$V = \frac{4\pi D^3}{3};$$

$$\Delta V = \frac{4\pi}{3}(D + \Delta D)^3 - \frac{4\pi}{3} D^3$$

$$= \frac{4\pi}{3}\left[D^3 + 3D^2(\Delta D) + 3L(\Delta D)^2 + (\Delta D)^3 - D^3\right],$$

as shown in the drawing in Figure 45.7;

$$\Delta V = 4\pi D^2 \cdot \Delta D; \Delta D = c\Delta t;$$

$$\Delta V = 4\pi D^2 \cdot c \cdot \Delta t;$$

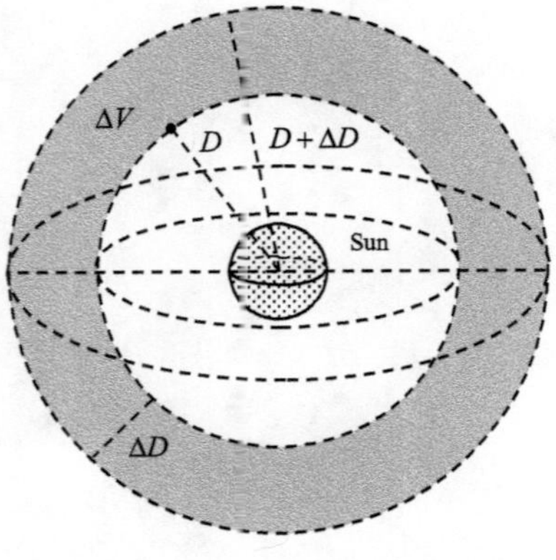

Fig. 45.7

$$\frac{\phi_{\text{Sun, } D}}{c} = \frac{E_{\text{emitted,Sun}}}{4\pi D^2 \cdot c \cdot \Delta t} = \frac{E_{\text{emitted,Sun}}}{\Delta V} = w;$$

$$\frac{\phi_{\text{Sun, } D}}{c} = \frac{\sigma T^4_{\text{Sun}} R^2_{\text{Sun}}}{cD^2} = \frac{E_{\text{emitted,star}}}{\Delta V} = w;$$

$$w = \frac{\sigma T^4_{\text{Sun}} R^2_{\text{Sun}}}{cD^2}; p_{\text{rad}} = \frac{\sigma T^4_{\text{Sun}} R^2_{\text{Sun}}}{cD^2};$$

$$w = p_{\text{rad}}.$$

That is, the energy density of the solar radiation is equal to the pressure of the solar radiation.

Other Books by Mihail Sandu

1. **PROBLEME DE FIZICĂ PENTRU GIMNAZIU**, *Editura Didactică şi Pedagogică*, Bucharest, 1977, 327 p.

2. **FIZICĂ, MANUAL PENTRU CLASA a VI-a**, coauthor Emanuel Nichita, *Editura Didactică şi Pedagogică*, Bucharest, 1978, 160 p.

3. **PROBLEME DE FIZICĂ PENTRU GIMNAZIU**, coauthors Emanuel Nichita and Tudorel Ştefan, *Editura Didactică şi Pedagogicş*, Bucharest, 1982, 223 p.

4. **CAIET METODIC CU PROBLEME DE FIZICĂ PENTRU GIMNAZIU**, *Casa Personalului Didactic*, Rm. Vâlcea, 1983, 181 p.

5. **GHIDUL PROFESORULUI ŞI AL ELEVULUI PENTRU CERCURILE DE FIZICĂ, VOL. I**, *Casa de Cultură a Ştiinţei şi Tehnicii pentru tineret*, Rm. Vâlcea, 1984, 498 p.

6. **GHIDUL PROFESORULUI ŞI AL ELEVULUI PENTRU CERCURILE DE FIZICĂ, VOL. II**, *Casa de Cultură a Ştiinţei şi Tehnicii pentru tineret*, Rm. Vâlcea, 1984, 405 p.

7. **CULEGERE DE PROBLEME DE FIZICĂ, VOL. I**, *Societatea de Ştiinţe Fizice şi Chimice din România*, Bucharest, 1986, 338 p.

8. **CULEGERE DE PROBLEME DE FIZICĂ, VOL. II**, *Societatea de Ştiinţe Fizice şi Chimice din România*, Bucharest, 1986, 118 p.
9. **PROBLEME DE FIZICĂ**, *Editura "Scrisul Românesc"*, Craiova, 1988, 277 p.
10. **GHID PENTRU CERCURILE DE FIZICĂ**, *Editura Academiei Române*, Bucharest, 1991, 325 p.
11. **PROBLEME DE FIZICĂ PENTRU GIMNAZIU**, *Editura Didactică şi Pedagogică*, Bucharest, 1991, 208 p.
12. **500 PROBLEME DE FIZICĂ**, *Editura Tehnică*, Bucharest, 1991, 283 p.
13. **PROBLEME DE PERFORMANŢĂ ÎN FIZICĂ**, *Editura Tehnică*, Bucharest, 1992, 340 p.
14. **PROBLEME DE FIZICĂ PENTRU GIMNAZIU**, *Editura "Lumina"*, Chişinău, Republic of Moldova, 1993, 272 p.
15. **CAIET METODIC CU PROBLEME DE FIZICĂ PENTRU GIMNAZIU**, *Editura "Lumina"*, Chişinău, Republic of Moldova, 1993, 179 p.
16. **TEME ŞI PROBLEME PENTRU CERCURILE DE FIZICĂ**, *Editura "Hyperion XXI"*, Bucharest, 1993, 254 p.
17. **PROBLEME DE FIZICĂ DIN REVISTA "KVANT", VOL. I**, *Editura Didactică şi Pedagogică*, Bucharest, 1993, 182 p.
18. **PROBLEME DE FIZICĂ PENTRU LICEU**, *Editura "Ex Libris"*, Rm. Vâlcea, 1993, 378 p.
19. **PROBLEME DE FIZICĂ DIN REVISTA "KVANT", VOL. II**, *Editura Didactică şi Pedagogică*, Bucharest, 1994, 194 p.
20. **CULEGERE DE PROBLEME DE FIZICĂ, VOL. I**, *Editura "TipCim"*, Chişinău, Republic of Moldova, 1995, 338 p.

21. **CULEGERE DE PROBLEME DE FIZICĂ, VOL. II**, *Editura "TipCim"*, Chişinău, Republic of Moldova, 1995, 117 p.

22. **GHIDUL PROFESORULUI ŞI AL ELEVULUI PENTRU CERCURILE DE FIZICĂ, VOL. I**, *Editura "TipCim", Chişinău*, Republic of Moldova, 1995, 498 p.

23. **PROBLEME DE FIZICĂ PENTRU GIMNAZIU**, *Editura Didactică şi Pedagogică*, Bucharest, 1995, 202 p.

24. **GHIDUL PROFESORULUI ŞI AL ELEVULUI PENTRU CERCURILE DE FIZICĂ, VOL. II**, *Editura "TipCim", Chişinău*, Republic of Moldova, 1996, 400 p.

25. **PROBLEME DE FIZICĂ PENTRU GIMNAZIU**, *Editura "ALL"*, Bucharest, 1996, Ediţia I, 503 p.

26. **PROBLEME DE FIZICĂ DIN REVISTA "KVANT", VOL. III**, *Editura Didactică şi Pedagogică*, Bucharest, 1996, 208 p.

27. **PROBLEME DE FIZICĂ DIN REVISTA "KVANT", VOL. IV**, *Editura Didactică şi Pedagogică*, Bucharest, 1996, 229 p.

28. **PROBLEME DE FIZICĂ PENTRU GIMNAZIU**, *Editura "ALL"*, Bucharest, 1997, Ediţia a II-a, 503 p.

29. **PROBLEME DE FIZICĂ – CONCURSURI ŞI OLIMPIADE**, *Editura "Petrion"*, Bucharest, 1998, 335 p.

30. **PROBLEME DE FIZICĂ PENTRU GIMNAZIU**, *Editura "ALL"*, Bucharest, 1998, Ediţia a III-a, 503 p.

31. **MECANICĂ FIZICĂ** (university course), *Editura Didactică şi Pedagogică*, Bucharest, 2002, 462 p.

32. **MECANICĂ TEORETICĂ** (university course), *Editura Didactică şi Pedagogică*, Bucharest, 2002, 476 p.

33. **ASTRONOMIE** (university course), *Editura Didactică şi Pedagogică*, Bucharest, 2003, 400 p.

34. **FIZICĂ. ÎNVĂŢĂMÂNTUL LICEAL ŞI CERCETAREA ŞTIINŢIFICĂ. MONOGRAFIA JUDEŢULUI VÂLCEA**, *Editura Conphys*, Rm. Vâlcea, 2004, 406 p.

35. **IN MEMORIAM – PROFESORUL LIVIU TĂTAR**, *Editura Conphys*, Rm. Vâlcea, 2004.

36. **PROBLEME DE FIZICĂ PENTRU GIMNAZIU**, *Editura "ALL"*, Bucharest, 2005, Ediţia a IV-a, 416 p.

37. **TEORIA RELATIVITĂŢII** (university course), *Editura Didactică şi Pedagogică*, Bucharest, 2005, 341 p.

38. **EVRIKA! PROBLEME DE FIZICĂ**, *Editura Didactică şi Pedagogică*, Bucharest, 2005, 600 p.

39. **CONCURSUL DE SELECŢIE PENTRU OLIMPIADA INTERNAŢIONALĂ DE FIZICĂ – 2005**, coauthor, *Editura Conphys*, Rm. Vâlcea, 2006, 262 p.

40. **PROBLEME DE FIZICĂ PENTRU GIMNAZIU**, *Editura "ALL"*, Bucharest, 2007, Ediţia a V-a, 416 p.

41. **ACTIVITĂŢI OLIMPICE LA C.P.P.P. CĂLIMĂNEŞTI-CĂCIULATA, 2004 – 2005 – 2006, ASTRONOMIE ŞI ŞTIINŢE**, *Editura Conphys*, Rm. Vâlcea, 2007, 611 p.

42. **ACTIVITĂŢI OLIMPICE LA C.P.P.P. CĂLIMĂNEŞTI-CĂCIULATA, 2004 – 2005 – 2006, FIZICĂ**, *Editura Conphys*, Rm. Vâlcea, 2007, 530 p.

43. **TOP-FIZ, PROBLEME DE FIZICĂ**, *Editura Didactică şi Pedagogică*, Bucharest, 2009, 833 p.

44. **LUCRĂRI EXPERIMENTALE DE FIZICĂ**, *Editura Conphys*, Rm. Vâlcea, 2009, 156 p.

45. **ŞTIINŢE PENTRU JUNIORI. CHIMIE – FIZICĂ – BIOLOGIE**, coauthor, *Editura MISTRAL*, Bucharest, 2009, 358 p.

46. **CONCURSUL INTERJUDEŢEAN DE FIZICĂ "LIVIU TĂTAR"**, coauthor, *Editura Universitaria*, Craiova, 2011, 236 p.

47. **ŞTIINŢE PENTRU JUNIORI. CHIMIE – FIZICĂ – BIOLOGIE**, coauthor, *Editura MISTRAL*, Ediţia a 2 – a, Bucharest, 2011, 358 p.

48. **PROBLEME ŞI EXPERIMENTE DE FIZICĂ**, *Editura Didactică şi Pedagogică*, Bucharest, 2012, 820 p.

49. **INTERNATIONAL OLYMPIAD ON ASTRONOMY AND ASTROPHYSICS, PROBLEMS, 2007–2013, SOLUTIONS, COMMENTS, DETAILS, EXTENSIONS**, *Editura CYGNUS*, SUCEAVA, 2014, 600 p.

50. **OLIMPIADA INTERNAŢIONALĂ DE ASTRONOMIE Ş ASTROFIZICĂ, PROBLEME, VOLUME 1**, *Editura CYGNUS*, Suceava, 2015, 400 p.

51. **OLIMPIADA INTERNAŢIONALĂ DE ASTRONOMIE ŞI ASTROFIZICĂ, PROBLEME, VOLUME 2**, *Editura CYGNUS*, Suceava, 2015, 460 p.

52. **CONCURSUL INTERJUDEŢEAN DE FIZICĂ "LIVIU TĂTAR"**, coauthor, *Editura else*, Craiova, 2016, 280 p.

53. **INTERNATIONAL OLYMPIAD ON ASTRONOMY AND ASTROPHYSICS, PROBLEMS, VOL. I**, *Trisula Adisakti*, Jakarta, Indonesia; Amazon, USA, 2016, 500 p.

54. **INTERNATIONAL OLYMPIAD ON ASTRONOMY AND ASTROPHYSICS, PROBLEMS, VOL. II**, *Trisula Adisakti*, Jakarta, Indonesia; Amazon, USA, 450 p.

55. **ASTRONOMIE Ę ASTROFIZICĂ – EVENIMENTE OLIMPICE – 1996–2010, PROBLEME**, *Editura Didactică şi Pedagogică*, Bucharest, 2018, 972 p.

56. **EXPERIMENTE DE FIZICĂ**, *Editura Didactică şi Pedagogică*, Bucharest, 2018, 476 p.

57. **ASTRONOMIE ŞI ASTROFIZICĂ. TEME ŞI PROBLEME PENTRU OLIMPIADE Ş CONCURSURI**, *Editura Didactică şi Pedagogică*, Bucharest, 2019.

58. **ASTRONOMY AND ASTROPHYSICS. THEMES AND PROBLEMS FOR OLYMPIADS AND COMPETITIONS**, *Editura Didactică şi Pedagogică*, Bucharest, 2019.

59. **ASTRONOMIE ŞI ASTROFIZICĂ – EVENIMENTE OLIMPICE – 2011–2013, PROBLEME, VOL. II**, *Editura Didactică şi Pedagogică*, Bucharest, 2020, 500 p.

60. **ASTRONOMIE ŞI ASTROFIZICĂ – EVENIMENTE OLIMPICE – 2013–2015, PROBLEME, VOL. III**, *Editura Didactică şi Pedagogică*, Bucharest, 2020, 500 p.

61. **ASTRONOMIE ŞI ASTROFIZICĂ – EVENIMENTE OLIMPICE – 2016–2017, PROBLEME, VOL. IV**, *Editura Didactică şi Pedagogică*, Bucharest, 2020, 500 p.

62. **ASTRONOMIE ŞI ASTROFIZICĂ – EVENIMENTE OLIMPICE – 2017–2018, PROBLEME, VOL. V**, *Editura Didactică şi Pedagogică*, Bucharest, 2020, 500 p.

63. **ASTRONOMIE ŞI ASTROFIZICĂ – EVENIMENTE OLIMPICE – 2019, PROBLEME, VOL. VI**, *Editura Didactică şi Pedagogică*, Bucharest, 2020, 548 p.

64. **INTERNATIONAL ASTRONOMY OLYMPIAD, VOL. I**, *Editura CYGNUS,* Suceava, 2021, 464 p.

65. **INTERNATIONAL ASTRONOMY OLYMPIAD, VOL. II,** *Editura CYGNUS,* Suceava, Romania, 2021, 484 p.

66. **INTERNATIONAL OLYMPIAD ON ASTRONOMY AND ASTROPHYSICS, VOL. III,** *Editura CYGNUS,* Suceava, Romania, 2021, 589 p.

67. **ASTRONOMY AND ASTROPHYSICS. ALL MY PROBLEMS FOR INTERNATIONAL OLYMPIADS, VOL. I,** *Editura CYGNUS,* Suceava, Romania, 2021, 344 p.

68. **ASTRONOMY AND ASTROPHYSICS. ALL MY PROBLEMS for INTERNATIONAL OLYMPIADS, VOL. II,** *Editura CYGNUS,* Suceava, Romania, 2021, 314 p.

69. **"SUB CERUL BUCOVINEI", VOL. I, CONCURSUL INTERJUDEŢEAN DE FIZICĂ "CYGNUS", CONCURSUL NAŢIONAL DE FIZICĂ "MARIN DACIAN BICA", Clasele VI–IX, 2015–2019,** *Editura CYGNUS,* Suceava, 2021, 300 p.

70. **"SUB CERUL BUCOVINEI", Vol. II, CONCURSUL INTERJUDEŢEAN DE FIZICĂ "CYGNUS", CONCURSUL NAŢIONAL DE FIZICĂ "MARIN DACIAN BICA", CLASELE X–XII, 2015–2019,** *Editura CYGNUS,* Suceava, 2021, 326 p.

71. **"SUB CERUL BUCOVINEI", VOL. III, CONCURSUL NAŢIONAL DE ASTRONOMIE ŞI ASTROFIZICĂ "MARIN DACIAN BICA" FIZICĂ, 2015–2019, CONCURSUL INTERDISCIPLINAR "ŞTIINŢELE PĂMÂNTULUI", OLIMPIADA NAŢIONALĂ DE ASTRONOMIE ŞI ASTROFIZICĂ",** *Editura CYGNUS,* Suceava, 2021, 388 p.

72. **PROBLEME DE FIZICĂ, VOL. I, EVENIMENTE OLIMPICE, SELECŢII PENTRU IPhO 1995–2009**, *Editura Didactică şi Pedagogică,* Bucharest, 2021, 340 p.

73. **PROBLEME DE FIZICĂ, VOL. II, EVENIMENTE OLIMPICE, SELECŢII PENTRU IPhO 2010–2021**, *Editura Didactică şi Pedagogică,* Bucharest, 2021, 340 p.

74. **ASTRONOMIE ŞI ASTROFIZICĂ, EVENIMENTE OLIMPICE, 2020–2021, PROBLEME, VOL. VII,** *Editura Didactică şi Pedagogică,* Bucharest, 2022, 600 p.

75. PROBLEME DE PERFORMANŢĂ ÎN FIZICĂ, VOL. I, *Editura Didactică şi Pedagogică*, Bucureşti, 2023, 664 p.

76. ASTRONOMIE ŞI ASTROFIZICĂ, EVENIMENTE OLIMPICE, 2020–2022, PROBLEME, VOL. VIII, *Editura Didactică şi Pedagogică,* Bucharest, 2023, 595 p.

77. ASTRONOMY AND ASTROPHYSICS – MY NEW PROBLEMS, VOL. I (for IOAA 2023, Edition XVI, Poland), *Editura Didactică şi Pedagogică*, Bucureşti, 2023, 395 p.

78. ASTRONOMY AND ASTROPHYSICS – MY NEW PROBLEMS, VOL. II (for IOAA 2023, Edition XVI, Poland), *Editura Didactică şi Pedagogică*, Bucureşti, 2023, 460 p.

79. ASTRONOMY AND ASTROPHYSICS – MY NEW PROBLEMS, SECOND ED., VOL. I (for IOAA Juniors 2023, Edition II, Greece), *Editura Didactică şi Pedagogică*, Bucharest, 2023, 395 p.

80. ASTRONOMY AND ASTROPHYSICS – MY NEW PROBLEMS, SECOND ED., VOL. II (for IOAA Juniors 2023, Edition II, Greece), *Editura Didactică şi Pedagogică*, Bucharest, 2023, 460 p.

81. ASTRONOMY AND ASTROPHYSICS – MY NEW PROBLEMS, THIRD ED., VOL. I (for IAO 2023, Edition XXVII, China), *Editura Didactică şi Pedagogică*, Bucharest, 2023, 460 p.

82. ASTRONOMY AND ASTROPHYSICS – MY NEW PROBLEMS, THIRD ED., VOL. II (for IAO 2023, Edition XXVII, China), *Editura Didactică şi Pedagogică*, Bucharest, 2023, 460 p.

83. PROBLEME DE PERFORMANŢĂ ÎN FIZICĂ, VOL. II, *Editura Didactică şi Pedagogică,* Bucharest, 2023, 500 p.

84. PROBLEME DE PERFORMANŢĂ ÎN FIZICĂ, VOL. III, *Editura Didactică şi Pedagogică,* Bucharest, 2024, 500 p.

85. **INTERNATIONAL PRE-OLYMPIC CONTEST OF PHYSICS, ROMANIA, HUNGARY, MOLDOVA,** *Editura Didactică şi Pedagogică*, Bucharest, 2024, 350 p.

86. **ŞTIINŢE PENTRU JUNIORI ÎN ROMÂNIA 2004–2023, PROBLEMELE MELE DE FIZICĂ,** *Editura Didactică şi Pedagogică*, Bucharest, 2024, 480 p.

87. **SCIENCE FOR JUNIORS IN ROMANIA 2004–2023, MY PROBLEMS OF PHYSICS,** *Editura Didactică şi Pedagogică*, Bucharest, 2024, 480 p.

88. **ŞTIINŢE PENTRU JUNIORI ÎN ROMÂNIA, 2024, PROBLEMELE MELE DE FIZICĂ,** *Editura Didactică şi Pedagogică*, Bucharest, 2024, 200 p.

89. **SCIENCE FOR JUNIORS IN ROMANIA, 2024, MY PROBLEMS OF PHYSICS,** *Editura Didactică şi Pedagogică*, Bucharest, 2024, 200 p.

90. **CONCURSUL NAŢIONAL DE FIZICĂ ŞI CHIMIE "IMPULS PERPETUUM!" AL ELEVILOR DE GIMNAZIU DIN MEDIUL RURAL, PROBLEMELE MELE DE FIZICĂ, 2011, 2013–2020**, *Editura CONPHYS*, Rm. Vâlcea, 2025, 200 p.

91. **PROBLEMELE MELE DE FIZICĂ PENTRU EVENIMENTE OLIMPICE, VOL. I, 2022–2023**, *Editura Didactică şi Pedagogică*, Bucharest, 2025, 300 p.

92. **PROBLEMELE MELE DE FIZICĂ PENTRU EVENIMENTE OLIMPICE, VOL. II, 2023–2024**, *Editura Didactică şi Pedagogică*, Bucharest, 2025, 350 p.

93. **ASTRONOMIE ŞI ASTROFIZICĂ, PENTRU ELEVI OLIMPICI, STUDENŢI ŞI PROFESORI**, *Editura Didactică şi Pedagogică*, Bucharest, 2025, 450 p.

94. **ASTRONOMY AND ASTROPHYSICS OLYMPIAD: TOPICS, PROBLEMS AND SOLUTIONS, VOL. I,** *World Scientific,* London, 2025, 596 p.

95. ASTRONOMY AND ASTROPHYSICS: PROBLEMS AND SOLUTIONS, VOL. II, *World Scientific*, London, 2025, 432 p.

96. ASTRONOMY AND ASTROPHYSICS: PROBLEMS AND SOLUTIONS, VOL. III, *World Scientific,* London, 2025, 456 p.

97. PHYSICS OLYMPIAD: PROBLEMS AND SOLUTIONS, *World Scientific,* London, 2025, 396 p.